Computer Systems
Performance Evaluation

DOMENICO FERRARI

Computer Science Division
Department of Electrical Engineering
  and Computer Sciences
University of California, Berkeley

PRENTICE-HALL, INC., Englewood Cliffs, New Jersey 07632

Library of Congress Cataloging in Publication Data

Ferrari, Domenico (date)
    Computer systems performance evaluation.

    Bibliography: p.
    Includes index.
    1. Electronic digital computers—Evaluation.
I. Title.
QA76.9.E94F47   621.3819'58   77-15096
ISBN 0-13-165126-9

To Alessandra and Giuliarachele
for their love, patience and support

Printed in the United States of America

10 9 8 7 6 5 4 3

PRENTICE-HALL INTERNATIONAL, INC., *London*
PRENTICE-HALL OF AUSTRALIA PTY. LIMITED, *Sydney*
PRENTICE-HALL OF CANADA, LTD., *Toronto*
PRENTICE-HALL OF INDIA PRIVATE LIMITED, *New Delhi*
PRENTICE-HALL OF JAPAN, INC., *Tokyo*
PRENTICE-HALL OF SOUTHEAST ASIA PTE. LTD., *Singapore*
WHITEHALL BOOKS LIMITED, *Wellington, New Zealand*

Now it may be said of any kind of action that the action itself, as such, is neither good nor bad. Take, for example, what we are doing now. Neither drinking nor singing nor talking has any virtue in itself, for the outcome of each action depends upon how it is performed. If it is done rightly and finely, the action will be good; if it is done basely, bad.

PLATO, *Symposium*

CRESSIDA: *They say all lovers swear more performance than they are able, and yet reserve an ability that they never perform, vowing more than the perfection of ten and discharging less than the tenth part of one. They that have the voice of lions and the act of hares, are they not monsters?*

SHAKESPEARE, *Troilus and Cressida*

*Et l'école du monde, en l'air dont il faut vivre,
Instruit mieux, à mon gré, que ne fait aucun livre.*

MOLIÈRE, *L'Ecole des Maris*

Contents

7

Performance Evaluation in Improvement Problems   **332**

8

Performance Evaluation in Design Problems   **396**

9
The Evaluation of Program Performance   451

List of Examples

Chapter 8

Chapter 9

Preface

Computers are man-made machines. Thus, they belong to the realm of engineering. They are designed by engineers, according to certain cost-performance specifications, to satisfy the information-processing needs of individuals and organizations. The programs they execute are also designed by people who, when engaged in this endeavor, act as engineers.

An essential aspect of any engineering activity is the evaluation of the systems this activity is concerned with. Engineering systems are evaluated by their designers, manufacturers, buyers, managers, and users. One of the dimensions, and a very important one, along which systems are evaluated is the dimension of performance. This book deals with the evaluation of computer systems performance. Its subject is, or should be, of interest to the great majority of computer professionals. System designers, installation directors and staff members, data processing and corporate managers at all levels, systems analysts, program designers, and computer users all have daily to cope with problems whose solution may be made substantially easier and more satisfactory by some knowledge of performance evaluation methodologies, techniques, and tools.

All computer installations have to deal with problems which require a considerable involvement in performance-evaluation activities. Examples of such problems are procurement, configuration design, system tuning, upgrading, accounting and pricing, scheduling and operations management, and short- and long-term planning. Practically all organizations which make use of computer systems must take performance into account in some of their decision-making processes. A system which does not perform as expected, or whose cost/performance ratio can be decreased, causes a waste of resources which must be avoided or eliminated.

The recognition of its practical importance and scope and the fact that it may be seen as the application of the scientific method to the study of computer systems make performance evaluation an attractive subject for an increasing number of researchers and teachers. However, the very fact that performance evaluation is being studied as a discipline distinct from system design is a symptom of an unsatisfactory situation. In other more traditional branches of engineering there are very few cases in which, as quite frequently happens with computer systems, the performance of a system can be improved even by primitive techniques by a very large factor after the system has been designed and implemented. Very few engineers specialize in, or even talk about, the evaluation of the performance of cars, planes, bridges, industrial processes, and electric circuits, since this is an essential aspect of any type of engineering design.

Computer systems engineering is not mature enough yet. It cannot base itself on quantitative laws similar to those which constitute the scientific foundations of other types of engineering: the laws of mechanics, electromagnetism, thermodynamics, and so on. Thus, performance evaluation problems should be studied with the ultimate objective of incorporating the results into design, implementation, and usage methodologies, that is, of making such a separate study meaningless.

In the long run it is reasonable to expect that the quantitative approach will permeate the core courses of computer science and engineering curricula, thereby making the offering of specific courses on performance evaluation unnecessary. However, reaching this point will require extensive and successful research, and even more important and difficult to achieve, a radical change of mentality. The distance between the present state of affairs and the goal mentioned above is perhaps best exemplified by the almost completely qualitative and descriptive approach that is currently taken to the teaching of computer system organization. In this situation it seems indispensable to offer courses entirely dedicated to performance evaluation. These courses should provide students with a new and very important viewpoint on computer systems, and with a picture of this rapidly growing field, its main themes, its problems, and the known approaches and solutions to them.

This book was born from one of such courses, which has been offered several times to Berkeley students. The level of the course, and therefore also the one of the book, has been chosen so as to be appropriate for computer science seniors and first-year graduate students. As for taking the course, the prerequisites for understanding the book are some familiarity with the material usually covered in an undergraduate two-quarter course on computer systems organization and/or operating systems, as well as with the principles and the basic techniques of computer programming and some elementary background in discrete mathematics, statistics, and probability theory. Computer professionals will not have any problems with the first two prerequisites (computer systems and programming) and will find references in the bibliography to a few textbooks that adequately cover the mathematical and statistical material required to make good use of this book.

I have emphasized the conceptual aspects of performance evaluation techniques and problems that I believe should always be given maximum priority. However, I have not neglected those informative aspects that, in my opinion, significantly contribute to providing the reader with a comprehensive view of the state of the art both in research and in the commercial world. The resulting picture is, of course, profoundly subjective and biased. I have stressed those techniques, viewpoints, and approaches that I think will become more and more important in the near future, rather than trying to provide a faithful snapshot of the present situation. I have presented methodologies and tools borrowed from other fields as if they had been invented for evaluating computer systems, and discussed their characteristics only from this standpoint. I have committed a number of other major and minor sins which the hopefully forgiving reader will soon discover.

The unifying theme of the book is a very pragmatic one: the *evaluation study* seen as a set of procedures whose end goal is to gather information on the system being evaluated so as to be able to answer certain performance-related questions. Thus, the book is mostly concerned with the evaluation studies required to solve the main problems which arise in computer systems engineering and with the techniques to be used in these studies.

Chapter 1 introduces the subject of the book by describing the viewpoint from which computer systems will be regarded. It discusses the concept of performance, the most important performance indices, and the most popular classifications of evaluation problems and techniques.

The next three chapters are devoted to the major evaluation techniques and tools. Most of these techniques are well-known in other scientific and technical fields. Except for some minimal amount of background information, these chapters deal only with their applications to computer systems. Chapter 2 describes measurement studies, measurement tools, the design of experiments, and the application of empirical modeling methods to the problem of experimental results interpretation. Chapter 3 deals with the simulation of computer systems. Model formulation, construction, calibration and validation are discussed, as well as the design of simulation experiments and the interpretation of simulation results. Chapter 4 is devoted to analytic modeling. Both deterministic and probabilistic models of systems are treated, with a particular emphasis on the application of queuing network-modeling techniques to performance analysis.

Chapter 5 is concerned with a problem of crucial importance in any evaluation study, the one of work-load characterization. Our lack of knowledge in this area is probably the most serious obstacle to progress in performance evaluation. A separate chapter has been devoted to it since the basic problems in work-load characterization are conceptually the same for all techniques. These problems, together with the known approaches to work-load modeling, are explored in this chapter.

Having been exposed to the techniques which constitute an essential part of any evaluation study, the reader should be ready to apply them to various types of evaluation problems. Three broad classes of problems are examined in the next three chapters. Chapter 6 describes the technical aspects of computer selection and discusses the adequacy of the known techniques and tools with respect to this problem. Chapter 7 deals with performance improvement, the area in which the most striking successes have been obtained, but whose importance is hopefully going to decrease as better system and installation design methodologies become available. Chapter 8 discusses the role of performance evaluation in computer system design. The techniques exposed in the first part of the book are applied there to various design problems.

Finally, Chapter 9 contains a discussion of program performance evaluation. The indices, techniques, and problems related to the performance aspects of programs are briefly described following the organizational scheme of the rest of the book.

Needless to say, this book may be correctly characterized as an introduction to performance evaluation. The reader will easily realize that each chapter might be seen as the introductory chapter, or an extended summary, of an entire book that could be written on the same subject. Besides being usable as a textbook in courses on computer systems performance evaluation or as a reference in courses on computer organization, computer systems design, and operating systems, the book, possibly supplemented with readings from periodical literature and other books, can serve as a textbook in specialized courses or short courses on measurement, modeling of computer systems, computer selection techniques, tuning techniques, and software evaluation.

Many individuals and organizations gave me substantial help in the conception and preparation of this book. The necessary background was provided by all my teachers. Among the most effective of them, I must include my parents, who taught me their philosophy of life, and my students at Berkeley, whose motivation has been a constant source of inspiration and encouragement. A number of my colleagues in the Department of Electrical Engineering and Computer Sciences at Berkeley are also to be thanked for their scientific and moral support and for the continuous challenge of their example. Several people have stimulated my work with their research and their interest in the book. I am really indebted to all the authors listed in the bibliography and to many other workers in the performance evaluation area. My particular gratitude goes to all the individuals who gave me valuable advice on the manuscript or some of its parts, especially to the reviewers, Harold Heath and Daniel Siewiorek, and to Steve Kimbleton, Frank Palermo and Felix Lam. Karl Karlstrom's encouragement and editorial support were extremely helpful throughout my effort. The typing of the manuscript was done with great care, rare patience, and excellent results by Ruth Suzuki, Edith Purser, and Mary

Ann Ratch. Finally, I would like to thank the birds, the squirrels, the trees, and the flowers of my garden in Berkeley, in whose company most of this book has been written.

The Regents of the University of California supported the preparation of this book by granting me a sabbatical quarter and a Regent's Summer Fellowship. The Universities of Pisa and Genoa and the Polytechnic Institute of Milan are also to be credited for their support. Some of the work reported in Chapter 2 was sponsored by the Advanced Research Projects Agency under contract DAHC15-70-C-0274. Some of the material reported in Chapter 9 was supported by the Division of Computing Research of the National Science Foundation under grant DCR74-18375 and the Research Division of the IBM Corporation.

For all the errors and omissions, I am indebted to no one but myself.

DOMENICO FERRARI

1

The Performance
Evaluation Viewpoint

1.1 INTRODUCTION

The evaluation of performance is an essential activity in all branches of engineering. Any system which is being designed (e.g., a car, a building, a machine tool, an industrial plant) must satisfy certain preassigned *performance specifications*. Design methodologies and evaluation procedures are used by designers to obtain systems which meet these specifications. Evaluation techniques and tools can also be applied by the prospective or current users of a system when some decision about the system (for instance, purchase, rental, sale, modification) is to be made.

The nature of performance specifications usually varies depending on the type of system and on the viewpoint of the evaluator. Every system has a function or a set of functions to perform. Thus, the most important condition it has to satisfy is that it perform its function or functions correctly. Correctness is the prerequisite of all other requirements. Its verification is generally not a subjective endeavor; for most systems, reaching a consensus about whether they work or not is relatively easy. For example, a means of transportation must move, a bridge must not collapse, and an amplifier must amplify an electric signal.

Performance specifications, which must also be met by a system in order for it to be acceptable to its users, refer to *how well* the system performs its function. The choice of performance requirements is usually more subjective than that of correctness specifications. However, the former are often expressed in quantitative terms so that their verification is not conceptually more complicated than that of the latter. For example, the maximum speed of a car with a load of 1000 pounds is to be greater than 100 mph; the efficiency of an electric transformer must be greater than 90% within a given load range. What is especially subjective, and very much dependent on the evaluator's viewpoint, is the relative emphasis given to the various aspects of performance; for instance, the speed of a car often has secondary importance with respect to its reliability, lifetime, fuel consumption, comfort, and ease of driving.

The distinction between the correctness and performance aspects of a system is often not a very sharp one. In fact, correctness could be legitimately viewed as one of the aspects (actually, an essential aspect) of performance. However, in this book we shall use the term *performance* to indicate *how well* a system, assumed to perform correctly, works. The reader certainly realizes that correctness is very seldom sufficient to make a system acceptable. In other words, the fulfillment of performance requirements is very often as important as that of correctness specifications in determining whether or not a system will be usable for a certain application. For instance, a clock whose hands move but whose accuracy is too low with respect to its intended use will generally be worthless.

According to the above definition, performance may be interpreted as the technical equivalent of the economical notion of *value*. That is, performance is what makes a system valuable to its user. Like value, performance is only one of the two faces of reality in the economic world, the other side being *cost*. Decisions concerning systems, be they design, implementation, acquisition, or modification decisions, are almost always dictated by both performance and cost considerations.

The concept of performance is a subjective one. However, as will be seen in Section 1.4, it is often possible to translate subjective definitions of performance into purely technical terms, which can sometimes be quantified and therefore objectively evaluated. Thus, *performance evaluation* activities can (and in this book will) be regarded as those technical activities whose purpose is the assessment of performance. We shall not be directly and primarily concerned here with the cost aspects of the systems to be evaluated. However, the reader should always bear in mind that cost and performance can be separated only for pedagogic purposes and that performance evaluation should always be accompanied by some form of cost evaluation.

In this chapter we shall introduce the general concepts and the definitions to be used in the rest of the book, which describes in detail various aspects of performance evaluation activities in the computer systems field. These activities are collectively designated as *performance evaluation studies*. The types of systems whose performance we shall be interested in evaluating are discussed in Section 1.2. The phases an evaluation study should consist of are discussed in Section 1.3. In Section 1.4, which deals with performance criteria and performance indices, we shall introduce a definition of performance much more restricted than the one discussed above. In this book, we shall be mostly concerned with the evaluation of performance according to the definition given in Section 1.4.

In Section 1.5 we shall describe the classification we have adopted for evaluation problems; that section can be viewed as an introduction to Chapters 6, 7, and 8. Finally, the evaluation techniques and tools to be described in Chapters 2, 3, 4, and 5 are introduced in Section 1.6.

1.2   THE OBJECTS OF EVALUATION STUDIES

In computer engineering, performance evaluation is less developed but not less essential than in other, older branches of engineering. The products of computer engineering are all designed to perform certain functions related to the processing of information. How well these systems execute their tasks is a matter of tremendous technical, economical, and social importance. Their evaluation is, as will be seen in this book, a challenging and by no means easy endeavor, at least in the present state of our knowledge.

There are many types of systems in computer engineering, having many different functions and natures. For example, we have computer installations, computer systems, computer networks, system components, operating systems, programs, programming languages, and language translators. The performances of these systems have to be evaluated by their designers, manufacturers, managers, maintainers, and users. This book is concerned with the evaluation of the performance of computer systems and, in Chapter 9, of computer programs. The evaluation of other types of systems will be considered only in those of its aspects which relate directly to the evaluation of computer systems and programs. For example, evaluation methods for central processing units (CPU's) will not be covered as a separate topic but only when, where, and to the extent needed to attack and solve computer system or program evaluation problems.

A definition of *program* suitable for our purposes will be given in Section 9.1. We shall now introduce computer systems and discuss their features from a performance evaluation viewpoint.

A *computer system* (to be often called *system* for brevity) is an aggregation of hardware components (central and input–output processors, memories, peripheral devices, interfaces) and software components (the programs which constitute the operating system). These components are often called the *resources* of the system. Each component has its own attributes, which will be called *system parameters* even if they cannot be expressed by a single number; for example, they may be the algorithms according to which a component works. Since we assume that the reader is familiar with the functions and characteristics of at least the fundamental system components, we shall not describe them here. We should note, however, that the identification of components or resources in a system is not unique. Since this identification is to a large extent arbitrary, it will be dictated by convenience and therefore will generally differ from study to study even for a given system.

Some problems arise when we try to precisely specify the *boundaries* of a computer system. There should be no doubt about the inclusion of the operating system. However, an operating system may be defined as "a set of manual and automatic procedures that enable a group of people to share a computer installation efficiently" [Brinch Hansen (1973)]. Thus, the operators, who usually execute such manual procedures as starting the machine, mounting tapes and disk packs, and inputting card decks into a card reader, should also be included. The presence of human beings in a system to be quantitatively evaluated makes its evaluation more complicated, and one may be tempted to ignore it. Often, however, the performance of a computer system is so heavily influenced by the performance of its operators that their presence cannot be ignored.

Another problem is the one of public software (for example, compilers, editors, assemblers, debuggers) and public data bases: Should the programs and data which are accessible by all the users of a system be considered as a part of the computer system or as a part of its environment? The most reasonable solution to this and other boundary definition problems seems to be the one of not making any general a priori decisions. The precise definition of the boundaries should be influenced by the particular evaluation problem one is interested in solving and should therefore be left to the evaluator. For example, if the performance of a data base system is to be evaluated, the object of the study will not only include the hardware-operating-system complex but also the data bases and their supporting programs. The same programs and data will have to be considered as part of the input from the external world in studies focusing on the performance of the hardware-operating-system complex.

Thus, we shall for the moment leave some of the details at the boundary undefined in order to accommodate in our treatment a larger class of studies. One should never forget, however, to specify very clearly the system's boundaries, once the objectives of the study have been clarified.

The term *installation* will be used to refer to the complex consisting of a specific system and its environment. The *environment* of a system, though not precisely defined at the system's boundary for the reasons mentioned above, will always include the *user community*. This is the community of those people who use the system in order to satisfy their information-processing needs. There are several other persons who should be considered as part of either the environment of a system or of the system itself, for example, the installation's manager and staff members, the maintenance personnel, and the managers of the information-processing function within the organization. However, since in this book we shall concentrate on the technical aspects of performance evaluation, our considerations will in most cases focus on an environment which practically coincides with the community of the users. These people influence the performance of a system by producing inputs (programs, data, commands) that will be collectively designated by the term *work load*. The system will in turn influence its environment by producing outputs with a certain level of performance. The performance is part of the environment's input and therefore influences its behavior (*see* Fig. 1.1).

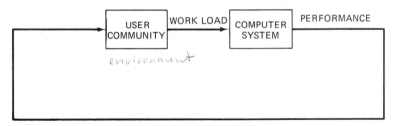

environment

Figure 1.1   Block diagram of a computer installation.

The attributes of the work load will be called *work-load parameters* even if they cannot be expressed by a single number. The parameters of a system and of its work load will be collectively termed *installation parameters.*

Any modification made to a system produces in principle a different system. However, if the change is a minor one, we shall often say that a new *configuration* or a new *version* of the same system has been obtained. Configuration usually refers to the set of a system's hardware components and to the way they are interconnected. Version, on the other hand, is a more software-oriented term.

The cost of performance evaluation studies makes them likely to be especially profitable when their object is a relatively large and expensive system or a cheap system to be mass-produced and marketed in very large amounts. The emphasis in this book will be on medium-large systems, but the principles and several of the techniques to be described are applicable also to smaller and less complicated systems such as minicomputers and microcomputers.

Central server module

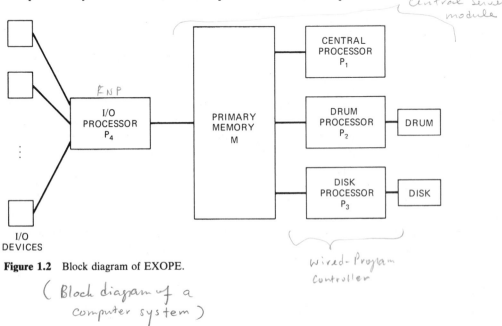

ƒ N P

Figure 1.2   Block diagram of EXOPE.

Wired-Program Controller

(Block diagram of a computer system)

A system with the configuration depicted in Fig. 1.2 offers a number of interesting evaluation problems, worth considering in practice, even though it consists of a very limited number of hardware components. In fact, the complexity of a system does not depend so much on its hardware configuration as on the way its resources are organized and managed by the operating system. Our examples in this book will be limited to very simple configurations and management schemes. Many of them will refer to the configuration in Fig. 1.2, which for convenience has been given the name *EXOPE* (Example Configuration for the Study Of Performance Evaluation).

Thus, the term *EXOPE system* will designate a system with the configuration reported in Fig. 1.2. Note that the nature of the input–output (I/O) devices controlled by processor P_4 is not specified; it will depend on the type of system being considered in each specific instance. The basic system organizations to be dealt with in this book are summarized in Table 1.1 and will now be briefly described referring to EXOPE.

Table 1.1

BASIC TYPES OF SYSTEM
ORGANIZATION TO BE
CONSIDERED

Processing mode
  Batch
  Interactive

Concurrency
  Uniprogramming
  Multiprogramming

Memory management
  Manual
  Automatic (virtual memory)

The typical I/O devices of a *batch-processing* EXOPE system are card readers, card punches, and printers. The users submit their *jobs* (programs and data) punched on cards. The cards are read by a card reader, and, after a code conversion, their contents are transferred into a buffer in primary memory M via P_4. When the buffer is full, its contents are transferred to disk via P_3. On disk, the jobs wait until their turn to be loaded into memory comes. Once a job is loaded via P_3, it can be processed by the CPU P_1. During its execution, a job will generally require information which resides on drum or disk. The operating system, which is at least partially stored in M, will take care of the transfers. A job will also generate output for the user, which will be accumulated on disk and printed out, via P_3, M, and P_4, at the end of the run. The users of a batch system specify their resource requirements to the operating system by *job control language* statements, to be submitted with the job's deck of cards. The execution of several job steps in sequence can usually be requested for the same job, that is, within the same deck. A *job step* is a phase in the processing of a job which is logically distinct from the others and is to be explicitly specified in a job control language statement. Typical job steps are compilation, execution of the compiled code, the copying of a file from disk to drum or vice versa, and the printing out of the contents of a file. When a job step terminates, the region of memory allocated to it is freed, and the next step of the same job is added to the list of those waiting to be loaded into M.

If all the processors in Fig. 1.2 in fact represent the same physical processor, say P^*, no concurrency is possible. While P^* is acting as P_4, it cannot act as P_1, or P_2, or P_3. In this case, jobs are executed in a strictly sequential order; it would be inconvenient to initiate a job before the previous one is completed. This organization in which no concurrency is allowed could be called *pure uniprogramming*.

Let now the processors in Fig. 1.2 be implemented by four independent physical processors. P_2, P_3, and P_4 may be wired-program *controllers* or stored-program processors, called *I/O channels*. In this case, the activities of the four processors may overlap in time. Thus, for example, while a transfer of information between card reader and disk, or between disk and printer, is taking place, P_1 might be processing a job. This is a *SPOOLing system* (SPOOL means Simultaneous Peripheral Operation On-Line). In such a system, CPU and I/O activities can be overlapped. However, only one executable user job is in memory at any given time. Thus, in spite of the independence of the processors, the CPU cannot be switched to other tasks during the I/O transfers requested by the running job and has to wait until they are completed. In a SPOOLing system, therefore, concurrency is restricted; for instance, no overlap is possible between the activities of P_1 and P_2 if the running job cannot continue its computation after issuing a drum request.

If more than one user job can be loaded in memory, the CPU can be switched to one of the others as soon as the running job needs an I/O transfer and the necessary arrangements for the transfer to take place have been made by the operating system. We shall call *active* the jobs which are in memory at any given time. Switching the CPU is possible only if at least one of the other active jobs is *ready* to run. An active job is not ready, or is *blocked*, if it is waiting for the completion of an I/O transfer it has requested. This is the type of system we shall refer to as a *multiprogramming system*. In such a system, the number of active jobs is usually called the *degree of multiprogramming*. The term *uniprogramming* will generally be applied also to SPOOLing systems, in spite of the several activities taking place concurrently in these systems, since the CPU is not switched to another job when the running job blocks itself due to an I/O request.

Both in a uniprogramming and in a multiprogramming system, a program may have to be completely loaded into memory in order for its execution to begin. A certain amount of memory space is given to each job. If its size exceeds this amount, the programmer must segment it into *overlays*, to be successively loaded by the operating system following directions explicitly provided by the user. This organization is called, for evident reasons, *manual memory manage-ment*.

However, it is possible (and especially convenient in multiprogramming systems) to build mechanisms which allow programs to be executed even if partially loaded, without the rigid constraints imposed by the overlaying technique and without the programmer's intervention. This can be obtained by *automatic memory management* schemes, which let the operating system decide what part of the program should be in memory at any given time. A reference made by the running program to an information item which is not in primary memory causes a *fault*. Faults are handled by the operating system, which fetches the missing item from a secondary memory device used for this purpose, for instance, from the drum. Thus, the *memory hierarchy* consisting of M and the drum is automatically managed by the operating system, which transfers information between M and the drum without any directions from the programmer. In fact, when dealing with these systems, programmers write their programs in an address space which does not coincide with the real-address space, that is, with the set of the addresses of M. This space is a *virtual-address space*, the set of the addresses of a *virtual memory*. The size of a job's virtual memory is usually much bigger than the size of M (or than the size of the region of M allotted to the job). Thus, only rarely does a programmer have to worry about fitting jobs into the available space. The mapping of the virtual addresses into real addresses (of M or of the drum) is performed dynamically reference by reference by a special hardware mechanism.

The typical I/O devices of an *interactive* EXOPE system are teletypewriter terminals or display consoles. The users input *commands*, instead of job control language statements, and *data* for the user or systems programs they are interacting with. These programs must exist in the system before they are invoked by user-issued commands. Each *message* input by a user, consisting of a command or of data or of both, is assembled character by character by P_4 into a buffer in M. When an end-of-message character is received, the operating system interprets the message and "wakes up" the process with which the user wants to interact. This process usually has most of its information on drum or on disk. Waking it up means, in this case, adding it to the queue of the processes which are waiting to be loaded into memory. At some point, the process's information (programs and data) is loaded partially or completely into M, and as soon as the CPU is allocated to it, its execution is started.

A user who inputs a "light" command requiring a small amount of system resources expects the system to respond quickly. For instance, a command to edit a line of text should be executed in at most a few seconds. Otherwise, the user's attention will wander, and interacting with the system will be painful and inefficient.

However, some of the commands to be serviced at any given time may well be "heavy" commands; for instance, some users may request a compilation, or the execution of a long program, or the manipulation of a large file, while others are simply editing, or asking for the time of the day, or using the system as a desk calculator. To prevent the heavy requests from intolerably affecting the responsiveness of the system to light requests, the *time-sharing* technique is normally used. This technique consists of limiting the time which the CPU can devote to any single process without being switched to other ready processes. Obviously, the CPU is switched only if other ready processes exist. The maximum CPU time that can be given to a process each time it is scheduled to run is called *time quantum* or *time slice*. If a process's execution is not completed when a quantum expires, the process is suspended and inserted into the ready queue. When its turn comes, the process will receive another quantum, and so on until its completion. Note that completion in an interactive system usually means that the process requires a new command or additional input data from the user.

An interactive system may be uniprogrammed or multiprogrammed. In the former case, only one process at a time is in primary memory; when it terminates or its CPU time exceeds the quantum, the process is *swapped out* of memory and another process which is ready to run is *swapped in*. In the multiprogramming case, several processes may be in memory at any instant, and the CPU is switched to a ready process if the running process blocks itself for an I/O operation. When this is a terminal I/O operation (that is, when the process terminates), or when the quantum is exceeded, the process is usually (but not always) swapped out.

The memory hierarchy, even in an interactive system, may be managed manually or, at least in part, automatically. In the latter case, processes will not have to be either loaded entirely in memory or properly segmented into overlays in order to be executable. Thus, an interactive system, whether uniprogrammed or multiprogrammed, may provide a virtual memory to each one of its users.

The reader should notice that the three organizational dimensions listed in Table 1.1 are independent of each other. Any one of the eight combinations of policies is conceptually possible. Also, in some systems both of the policies listed in Table 1.1 along a certain organizational dimension coexist. For example, there are many operating systems which support the batch- as well as the interactive-processing mode. Also, part of a memory hierarchy may be automatically managed while the rest is to be managed manually.

It is worth noting that multiprogramming was introduced primarily to increase the amount of work done by the CPU—hence the productivity of the system— and that its presence is hidden from the user. On the other hand, the time-sharing technique was motivated by considerations of responsiveness to user commands. Moreover, the user sees a macroscopic difference between batch processing and interactive computing. The presence of virtual memory also affects the user but not so profoundly and immediately as the processing mode.

1.3 THE PHASES OF AN EVALUATION STUDY

It is useful to make a distinction between *performance evaluation studies* and *continuous-monitoring activities*. Although the durations of both types of effort are limited, since a system's lifetime is finite, continuous monitoring is usually performed for a substantial portion of the lifetime of an existing, running system. Its objective is to keep the system's performance under observation in order to detect performance problems as soon as they arise. An evaluation study is generally much more limited in time, does not always require the system to exist, and is usually triggered by the identification of a performance problem or the suspicion of its presence. In this book we shall concentrate on evaluation studies, but the measurement techniques and tools described in Chapter 2 include also those applied in continuous monitoring.

The activities which constitute an evaluation study can be grouped into five phases, pictorially represented by the block diagram in Fig. 1.3.

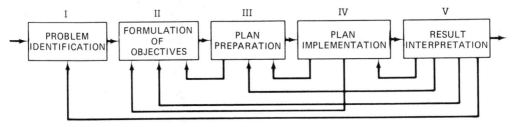

Figure 1.3   Phases of a performance evaluation study.

Phase I.   The need for a study arises.
Phase II.   The objectives of the study are formulated.
Phase III.   A plan of the study is prepared.
Phase IV.   The plan is implemented.
Phase V.   The results are interpreted.

Figure 1.3 also shows some of the possible paths which may have to be followed during an evaluation study.

A few general observations are to be made on the phases listed above. First of all, phases II and III should include a careful estimation of the costs involved and of the possible benefits of the study. Each decision which is made about the objectives and about the resources to be invested in the study should take the cost-benefit criterion into account. Carefully planned evaluation studies often pay off, but they must be planned very carefully. Predicting with some degree of confidence the benefits that may result from a study is usually very hard, much harder than predicting its cost. Questions about the improvements which may be obtained by a certain study, for example, are relatively easy to answer at the end of the study; at the beginning, without knowing the outcomes of the study, answering them reliably is almost impossible. Thus, the evaluators will have to resort to their previous experience in similar cases, to worst-case and best-case estimates, to rules of thumb, and to their good luck. However, serious attempts should always be made and the cost-benefit trade-offs always kept in mind.

Another perhaps obvious but important remark is that it is essential to specify as clearly as possible the objectives and the scope of the study before

anything else is done. Thus, this specification has to be done in phase II. These objectives, and possibly those emerging during the study, have to guide the evaluators in all phases and iterations of the study. In other words, a practical evaluation study (as opposed to a performance evaluation research project) must be as goal-oriented as possible. During phase II, a suitable set of performance indices will also have to be chosen (*see* Section 1.4).

Phases III, IV, and V might be viewed as the components of the iterative procedure which is the basis of the scientific method: A hypothesis is formulated, tested, and if the test is unsuccessful, modified. In performance evaluation, as will be seen in the sequel, hypotheses are not always tested experimentally. However, experimental verification remains the ultimate criterion for certainty. It should also be noted that evaluators can formulate hypotheses with much higher chances of success if they know the internal organization and behavior of the system. There is no real substitute for knowledge, and the black-box approach is not usually very cost-effective. The deeper the knowledge about the system, the faster and less expensive an evaluation study generally is. Sometimes, a system expert can reliably answer questions which would require long and costly investigations to be answered by others.

The reader should also note that each one of the phases listed above will very often include activities aimed at the gathering of information about the system and its installation: reading system manuals; examining logic diagrams, flowcharts, and program listings; questioning operators and other installation staff members; interviewing users; measuring work-load parameters; collecting data about system usage; interpreting accounting data; and so on.

1.4 PERFORMANCE INDICES

In Section 1.1, an analogy has been drawn between the technical concept of performance and the economical concept of value. The remark has also been made that, like value, performance is a subjective concept. This means that different people tend to use different performance indices in assessing systems. A *performance index* is a descriptor which is used to represent a system's performance or some of its aspects.

If we ask several different persons to rank various computer systems in the same price range, it is likely that their rankings will differ. In evaluating the various alternatives, these persons will use their own individual, subjective performance indices. The ranking proposed by each person for each system will express in some way the value that person attributes to that system.

Since performance, according to our broad definition of Section 1.1, is equivalent to value, it could be measured in dollars (or some other monetary measure) and therefore reduced to a common quantitative basis for evaluation. However, this would neither make performance a more objective concept nor provide computer engineers with suggestions on how to design better systems or

improve the existing ones. We may instead try to translate the various subjective notions of performance in terms of more objective, possibly quantifiable, technical performance indices. These indices, if carefully defined, would be objective measures of some performance aspects of a system. Thus, the subjectivity of evaluation would mostly be confined to their choice and to the relative weights given to them. Weights will generally differ for different categories of people (manufacturers, installation managers, company executives, field engineers, systems programmers, operators, applications programmers) and sometimes from individual to individual.

However, a number of important performance indices are difficult or impossible to quantify, for example, the *ease of use* of a system, the *structuredness* of a program or of a language, and the *power* of an instruction set. In this book, we shall adopt a restricted definition of performance, which suggests easily quantifiable indices. Only the efficiency of a system, its speed in processing a given task or set of tasks, and its promptness in responding to external stimuli will be considered among the aspects of the broad definition of performance given in Section 1.1. Thus, we shall reserve the term *performance* for these aspects and shall call all the others (correctness, ease of use, structuredness, reliability, and so on) *functional aspects*.

The most popular classes of quantitative performance indices for computer systems are listed in Table 1.2. It should be evident from the general definitions given in the same table that the *indices of productivity* have the dimension volume × time^{-1}, the *indices of responsiveness* have the dimension of time, and the *indices of utilization* are dimensionless. There is at present no standardized, unique way to measure the *volume* or *quantity of information* processed by a system (some of the attempts at providing a universal measure will be mentioned in Section 5.2.3). Thus, various measures of volume are used depending on the system and its work load; among the most popular ones, we have the *job*, the *program*, the *process*, the *job step*, the *task*, the *transaction*, the *interaction*, and the *instruction*. Listing all the meanings these terms have assumed and assume in the computer system literature is probably impossible. Here, we shall note only that all of them are to some extent dependent on the nature of the work load, on the language used by the programmers to describe their algorithms to the machine, on the language of the machine itself, and on the way the system is organized. Thus, none of these measures is *work-load-independent* and *system-independent*, two properties necessary to establish a measure of information volume as a universal measure. We shall also defer the precise definition of the meaning we assign to most of the above terms, as well as to some of those in the second column of Table 1.2, to when they will be used. Evaluators should always specify unambiguously what a certain measure of volume means in the specific context of their study.

In the following example, we shall discuss the choice of performance indices for an interactive system.

Table 1.2

MAIN CLASSES OF QUANTITATIVE INDICES OF COMPUTER
SYSTEM PERFORMANCE

Index class	Examples of indices	General definition
Productivity	Throughput rate Production rate Capacity (maximum throughput rate) Instruction execution rate Data-processing rate	The volume of information processed by the system in the unit time
Responsiveness	Response time Turnaround time Reaction time	The time between the presentation of an input to the system and the appearance of the corresponding output
Utilization	Hardware module (CPU, memory, I/O channel, I/O device) utilization Operating system module utilization Public software module (e.g., compiler) utilization Data base utilization	The ratio between the time a specified part of the system is used (or used for some specified purposes) during a given interval of time and the duration of that interval

Example 1.1   The diagram in Fig. 1.4 is a characterization of an interactive installation as seen from the viewpoint of an individual user who is interacting with the system from a terminal. Note that the terminal portion of an *interaction* is often called *think time*, even though it also includes the input time as well as part of the output time. For a user, the most important aspect of performance (according to our restricted definition of this term) will be the responsiveness of the system. The diagram in Fig. 1.4 allows us to precisely define an index of responsiveness called *response time*. For instance, response time will be defined as the interval between the instant the user types in the last character of the input message and the instant the first character of the output message is typed out by the terminal. This is only one of the several possible definitions which can be proposed. In certain systems, it may even be ambiguous and have to be modified or, at least, clarified.

It is important to note that the relationship between the values of system performance indices and the value (in the economic sense) attributed to them by the persons involved is not necessarily linear. For instance, it is by no means true that a response time of 4 seconds to a given message is about half as desirable as a response time of 2 seconds to the same message. The shape of this relationship, which varies with the user and with the type of message, is likely to resemble the curve plotted in Fig. 1.5. Below a certain threshold, human users cannot even appreciate the differences among response times.

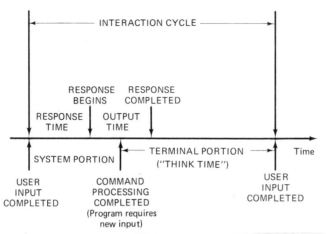

Figure 1.4   Definition of interaction and response time for an interactive system.

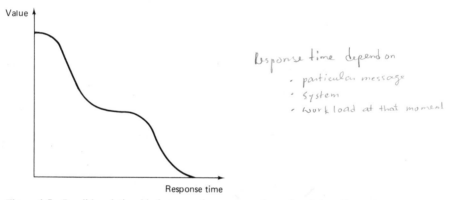

Figure 1.5   Possible relationship between the response time of an interactive system and its value to a user.

Beyond another threshold, the level of satisfaction drops sharply, and feeling of frustration and impotence prevail. The characteristics of human users should always be given a great deal of attention by system designers and evaluators.

What installation parameters influence the value of the response time? In general, the response time depends on the particular message, on the system, and on the rest of the work load that the system is processing at the time the message is typed in. To use the response time as a system performance index, we must specify the message and the rest of the work load. Its value would be meaningless if this additional information were not supplied. However, characterizing the work load in a sufficiently compact way is very difficult, as we shall see throughout the book and especially in Chapter 5. Furthermore, the messages of interest to the user community, or even to a single user, are very numerous and very different from each other in terms of resource demands. Therefore, we shall view response time as a random variable and consider as our system performance index its distribution over a specified period of time. If this period is sufficiently long, the effects of the individual messages and of the various load conditions existing when they are executed are not likely to appreciably influence the statistical distribution of response times. This distribution can then be used to represent the behavior of the system under the work load it processes during the specified period of time. The rationale of our decision will have to be very clearly kept in mind when measuring or estimating the response time of a system.

It is usually desirable to work with performance indices whose values can be represented by a single number or by a few numbers. Thus, instead of the response time distribution, we may use as index its first moment (the *mean response time* $\bar{t}$) or its first two moments (the mean $\bar{t}$ and the standard deviation σ_t).

Let us consider an interactive EXOPE system having six active users who enter six commands at approximately the same time. The system is multiprogrammed but not a virtual-memory system. We assume that the programs to be executed are completely loaded in memory when the commands are input and that no disk or drum request is issued by any one of them. No additional commands arrive during the processing of those being considered here. Four of these commands are of the editing type, and each is assumed to require 1 unit of CPU time for completion. The other two are compiling commands, and each requires 4 units of CPU time. The order in which the commands are executed coincides with the one of their arrival: one editing command (c_1) first, followed by the two compiling commands (c_2, c_3), followed in turn by the other three editing commands (c_4, c_5, and c_6). When the CPU time consumed by a process exceeds the quantum, which is equal to 2 time units, the process is suspended and joins the queue of the ready processes. The next process to be executed is taken from this queue according to the first-come-first-served rule. The switching of the CPU from one process to the next requires 0.2 units of CPU time. This is the only type of *overhead*, that is, of resource consumption which cannot be directly attributed to any user process, we take into account in this extremely simple example.

The processing of the six commands is depicted in the timing diagram in Fig. 1.6(*a*). The process completion times are circled on the time axis. Since all commands were input at the origin of times, these are also the response times, assuming that the output message is typed out at the very end of each process. The mean response time $\bar{t}$ is 8.16 time units, and its standard deviation σ_t is 9.55 time units.

Evidently, the editing users will be more interested in the system's responsiveness to editing commands and the compiling users to the responsiveness to compiling commands. Thus, we may take as performance indices the distributions of both the editing times and the compiling response times or their respective moments. In the case of Fig. 1.6(*a*), the mean response time to editing commands is 6.1 time units and to compiling commands is 12.3 time units.

The users' viewpoints cannot be completely espoused by the installation manager, who has to worry about the productivity of the system. Clearly, the minimum value of the mean response time would be achieved if each command were executed immediately upon its arrival. This would be the case if the system were entirely dedicated to a single user. In a multiuser system, this condition can be approached only if the system is always kept very lightly loaded. However, the CPU would tend to be idle during most of the terminal portion of each interaction (*see* Fig. 1.4). Thus, its productivity, which may be expressed by the number of interactions completed per unit time, would be very low. In Fig. 1.6(*a*), the think times of the users who typed in the commands completed first partially overlap with the processing of the other commands.

virtual-memory

Job came in all at once.

edit   1 unit
Compile   4 unit

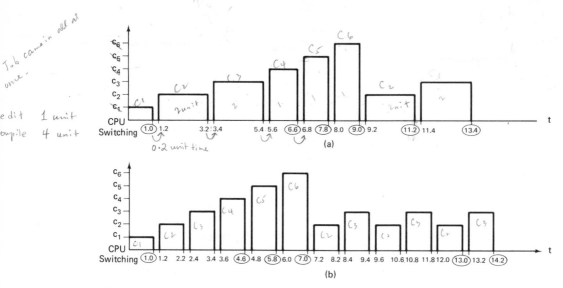

Figure 1.6   Timing diagrams for the executions of commands $c_1, \ldots, c_6$ in Example 1.1: (a) time quantum: 2 units; (b) time quantum: 1 unit. Command processing completion times are circled. Editing commands c_1, c_4, c_5, c_6 take 1 time unit, and compiling commands c_2, c_3 take 4 time units each.

The manager will therefore be interested not only in the quality of the service provided to the users but also in the *throughput rate*, defined as the number of interactions processed by the system per unit time. This rate is generally a function of time. It may be reduced to a single number by considering its time average (the *mean throughput rate* $\bar{T}$) as the primary index of productivity. In Fig. 1.6(a), six interactions are completed in 13.4 time units. This period does not include the terminal portions of the interactions but does include terminal activities belonging to some of the interactions which will follow. These "edge effects" are important here because of the very short duration of the period. However, applying the above definition of mean throughput rate, we have $\bar{T} = 6/13.4 = 0.447$ interactions/time unit.   ■

Different performance indices describe different aspects of the behavior of a system within an installation. Therefore, they are generally not independent of each other but, rather, somehow interrelated. Improving one index does not always improve other indices, as shown by the following example.

Example 1.2   In the interactive EXOPE system discussed in Example 1.1, let us decrease the time quantum from 2 time units to 1. The new timing diagram is depicted in Fig. 1.6(b). Adopting the same performance indices as in Example 1.1, we find that the mean response time decreases from 8.16 to 7.6 time units. However, its mean throughput rate also decreases, from 0.447 to 0.422 interactions/time unit. Note that the standard deviation of the response time increases from 9.55 to 11.35 time units. The mean response time to editing commands decreases from 6.1 to 4.6 time units, whereas the one to compiling commands increases from 12.3 to 13.6 time units.   ■

variance $\quad s^2 = \dfrac{\sum\limits_{i=1}^{N}(x_i^2 - \bar{x}^2)}{N}$

stand. Dev. $\sqrt{s^2}$

An evaluation study may consider *secondary* performance indices besides the *primary* ones. The primary indices are those which the evaluator is really interested in. A system's performance specifications are usually expressed in terms of the primary indices. Generally, the objective of a study on an existing system is to improve the primary indices. These indices vary with the type of system, with the evaluator, and with the problem. For instance, the primary index for the users is normally an index of responsiveness. On the other hand, installation managers are usually interested in productivity as well as responsiveness. Depending on the circumstances, a manager will emphasize one or the other, but both types of indices should always play a primary role in a manager's evaluation of a system. Thus, even in those studies whose objectives are stated in terms of one type of index, the other type should always be given adequate attention.

Secondary indices are usually suggested by the study itself. Their values may be useful in detecting symptoms of inefficiencies or in finding clues about the causes of these inefficiences. Examples of these indices are, in a number of studies, those of the utilization type (*see* Table 1.2).

In most studies, the values of primary and secondary performance indices have to be determined for given values of the installation parameters. This operation may be called *performance analysis*. Its converse, the determination of the parameters from given values of the indices, will be termed *performance synthesis*. Synthesis methods, if they were available, would find their natural application in system design. However, since this is not the case, performance analysis is widely applied also in design problems, as we shall see in Chapter 8. The evaluation techniques to be introduced in Section 1.6 are all essentially performance analysis techniques. The analysis of performance may be repeated for a number of different combinations of values of the installation parameters. By this method, we can explore the parameter space, that is, gather information on how the performance indices depend on the parameters and are related to each other. This exploration is essential to our understanding of a system's behavior.

1.5 A CLASSIFICATION OF EVALUATION STUDIES

The objectives of an evaluation study must be clearly and carefully stated at its beginning, during the phase which has been called phase II. Evaluation studies can be classified along several dimensions according to their objectives. Perhaps the most popular classification is the one which divides studies into the following three categories:

    a. selection studies,
    b. improvement studies,
    c. design studies.

This classification, in spite of the fuzziness of the boundaries between the classes it proposes, will be adopted in this book. We shall introduce these classes of studies in the rest of this section and discuss them in much greater detail in Chapters 6, 7, and 8.

Selection studies deal with the problems one encounters in installation design and in procurement. These problems include the selection of the processing mode; the choice of the system to be installed among those proposed by various vendors; and the selection of a computing service bureau, of a language to be used to write a certain program, and of a software package. In summary, selection studies can be defined as those undertaken to determine, among the various alternatives which are available, for example, on the market, the most convenient alternative for a given application. A selection study tries to achieve certain objectives by choosing an existing system which is the best according to some specified selection criteria.

Improvement studies are concerned with modifications made to an existing system in order to increase its performance or decrease its cost, or both. The *tuning* of a system, that is, the adjustment of its parameters to adapt it to the work load of an installation, falls into this category of studies. Also included are those studies resulting in the *upgrading* of a system, which consists of the replacement or addition of one or more hardware components. For example, a system may be upgraded by expanding its primary memory size, by adding a CPU, or by replacing its CPU by a faster one. Other types of changes, which will be considered as modifications of the tuning type, are the rearrangement of information within one of the storage devices, or among several of them, and the modification of the connections between I/O devices and I/O processors. The studies in this class could be called *optimization studies* if the term *optimization* did not have strong mathematical connotations, which would be misleading in this case.

Design studies are those aimed at answering the questions which arise in the design of computers, computer components, operating systems, programs, and languages. These studies are usually undertaken by the producers of a system rather than by its users. The parts of which the system is to be composed may preexist or not. In the latter case, they will have to be designed and implemented according to the specifications dictated by the system's designer. In a computer system design study, the applications of the system are often more broadly and vaguely stated than in a selection study. For example, a system may be designed for commercial applications with no further specifications. However, during a selection procedure, this system will have to undergo a scrutiny based on the knowledge (perhaps still vague but much more precise than the one its designers had) of the specific commercial applications of the installation for which the selection study is being performed.

The reader should note that a given evaluation problem may be classified differently depending on the context in which the problem is attacked. This is an aspect of the fuzziness of the class boundaries we mentioned above. For example, the determination of a satisfactory size for a system's primary memory may be seen as a selection problem if the alternative systems being considered differ from each other in their memory sizes; it is an improvement problem if memory space has been found to be the performance-limiting factor in an existing and working system; it is a design problem if operating system designers want to determine the minimum amount of memory needed to process a realistic work load with reasonable levels of performance.

However, it should also be noted that classifications are only convenient ways of organizing a certain body of knowledge into mental frameworks. The purpose of these frameworks usually is to emphasize the macroscopic differences among the classes in order to make a discipline easier to understand, learn, and remember. Thus, even though we recognize that the classification of evaluation studies described in this section is not completely satisfactory, we shall adopt it since we find it reasonably comprehensive and adequate for our purposes.

1.6   AN OVERVIEW OF EVALUATION TECHNIQUES

An evaluation study is always intended to answer questions about the performance of a given system. To do so, an evaluator has to gather performance information. Typically, this information consists of the values of the system's performance indices under a given work load and with specified values of the system's parameters. In other words, it is the information produced by performance analysis. The methods by which this information may be obtained will be called *evaluation techniques.* The known techniques can be classified in various ways. The most popular classification, which is adopted in this book, is introduced below.

The performance information required by a study may be obtained from the system itself (*measurement techniques*) or from a model of it (*modeling techniques*).

A *model* of a system is a representation of the system which consists of a certain amount of organized information about it and is built for the purpose of studying it. Since there are very many questions which may be asked about a system, a number of different models can be constructed. All of these models represent the same system but either look at it from different standpoints and have different purposes or contain different amounts of detail.

A model may be viewed as a system (note that here *system* is not an abbreviation of *computer system*). The various models of a system correspond to different ways of partitioning it into components, of representing the interactions among them and with the system's environment. The possibility and convenience of representing a system in many different ways should not surprise anybody; after all, our knowledge of the world is based on mental models of the "systems" around us (which include other human beings and ourselves), and scientific progress may be viewed as the creation of new, better models of the world. The descriptions of several types of EXOPE systems made in Section 1.2 can be considered as verbal and somewhat superficial models of a number of real systems. We shall term these models, which exist in the minds of evaluators, *conceptual models.*

Conceptual models of computer systems play a fundamental role in the evaluation of their performance. They consist of all the information an evaluator has about their structure and behavior. This information is necessary or at least very helpful in all phases of an evaluation study. The deeper our knowledge of a system, that is, the better our conceptual model of it, the easier and more successful the study is likely to be. System experts can often answer performance evaluation questions which would require somebody else to make a long and expensive evaluation effort; thus, sometimes, a suitable conceptual model is all that is needed in a study. Also, as will be shown in Chapters 2, 3, 4, and 5, conceptual models are the basis of measurement techniques and of the two types of modeling techniques, *simulation* and *analytic techniques*, to be covered in this book.

A very popular and convenient characterization of the behavior of a system (not only of a computer system) is the one based on the concepts of *state* and *state transition*. The state of a system at time t is defined as the set of values of the system parameters of interest at t. Any variation in these values may be viewed as a transition to another state. Evidently, a variety of characterizations of this type exist for any given system. The characterization indeed depends on the choice of the system parameters of interest.

If the model's behavior in the time domain reproduces the behavior of the system according to some conventions which establish a correspondence between various aspects of the model and of the system (in particular, between states and between transitions), we have a *simulation model.* A simulation model is dealt with "in the same way" as the system itself: Its behavior in time, under stimuli which represent the system's environment, is observed and its performance indices determined. Thus, there is a conceptual similarity between simulation and measurement. An important consequence of this similarity is that the problems which arise in designing measurement experiments are identical, or very similar, to those to be solved for simulation experiments. The solutions valid for one type of experiment can often be applied to the other type (*see* Chapters 2 and 3).

From a more mathematical viewpoint, a simulation model can be viewed as consisting of equations which are solved by following the evolution of their solutions over a period of time. Computer systems are usually seen as *discrete* (or *discrete-state*) *systems*, which evolve by predominantly discontinuous state transitions called *events*. Thus, their simulation models will include equations expressing the logical conditions under which these transitions occur. Solving the equations by a simulation technique means determining the chronological sequence of the interesting events occurring in the system and the corresponding sequence of system states. This method of solution is evidently a numerical one.

When the solution of the equations constituting a model is obtained by mathematical methods, we say that an *analytic technique* is used and that an *analytic model* has been constructed. The term *analytic* is slightly misleading here, since, in our classification, the category of analytic solution techniques also includes all numerical techniques except simulation. However, for lack of a more satisfactory term, we shall follow the tradition and use the term *analytic* to designate these models and techniques.

Example 1.3   In Example 1.1, we used an extremely simple simulation model, derived from a conceptual model of the interactive EXOPE system considered there. The values of our two performance indices $\bar{i}$ and $\bar{T}$ were computed by pencil-and-paper simulation of the processing of the six-command work load (*see* Fig. 1.6). The simulation model, shown in flowchart form in Fig. 1.7, can conceptually be treated like the system which it is supposed

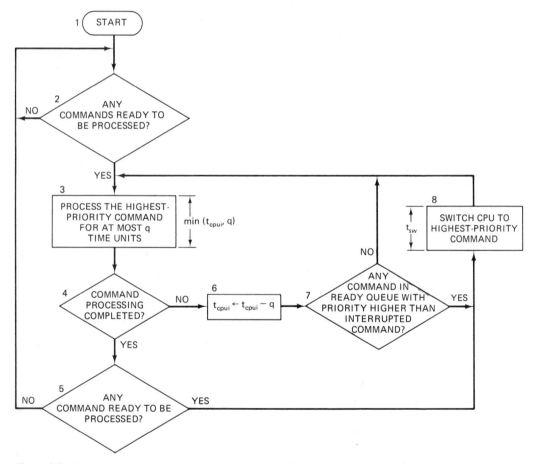

Figure 1.7   Flowchart representation of the simulation model used to construct the timing diagrams in Fig. 1.6. The only boxes in which an appreciable amount of time is spent are box 3 [$t = \min(t_{cpui}, q)$] and box 8 ($t = t_{sw}$).

to replace for the purposes of our study. This means that if we feed the model with a suitable representation of a work load, the model's responses will reproduce those of the real system. A suitable work-load model here consists of a sequence of processes, each characterized by its arrival time and its CPU time demand. Note that the reproduction of the system's behavior will depend on the accuracies of the system model and of the work-load model.

An analytic model of the same system consists of a set of mathematical relationships which may be used to calculate, by any method except simulation, the values of our performance indices from given values of system and work-load parameters. This model, like the simulation model discussed above, can replace the system for the purposes of our study. For instance, the following simple expression of the mean throughput rate, valid under the assumptions made in Example 1.1, can be immediately derived from Fig. 1.6:

$$\bar{T} = \frac{n}{\sum\limits_{i=1}^{n} t_{\text{cpu}_i} + n_{\text{sw}} t_{\text{sw}}}, \tag{1.1}$$

where n is the number of commands to be processed, t_{cpu_i} is the CPU time it takes to process the ith command, t_{sw} is the time required to switch the CPU from one process to another, and n_{sw} is the number of times the CPU is switched during the processing of the n commands being considered. Thus,

$$n_{\text{sw}} = \sum\limits_{i=1}^{n} \left\lceil \frac{t_{\text{cpu}_i}}{q} \right\rceil - 1, \tag{1.2}$$

where q is the time quantum and $\lfloor x \rfloor$ denotes the smallest integer larger than or equal to x. Writing equations which allow us to calculate the mean response time is much harder. We shall see in Chapter 4 how this can be done under more general and realistic assumptions. ∎

A problem which is common to all modeling techniques is the one of the model's accuracy, that is, its fidelity to the modeled system. Any analytic or simulation model must be validated before it can be used to produce the information needed for evaluation. Validation is often difficult, and sometimes impossible. It may be based on previous theoretical or simulation results, but if the modeled system exists, the ultimate foundations of a validation procedure must be empirical. Our confidence in a model may come from our certainty that its conceptual bases are sound and that a correct procedure was followed in its construction. However, there is no better way (probably, no other way) of confirming our confidence than by experimentation. Thus, in a sense, measurement is the most important evaluation technique, since it is needed also by the other techniques. However, it cannot be used when the system does not exist or is not available, for instance, at the beginning of a design project. In these cases, since the model's validity cannot be empirically tested, our faith in the model will have to rely on our confidence in the correctness of its conception and construction.

Often, more than one type of evaluation technique is used in an evaluation study. The different characteristics of the various techniques, to be discussed in

Chapters 2, 3, and 4, make each one of them more suitable than the others for different types of problems frequently encountered within the same study. Also, attacking a study with various approaches, techniques, and tools may give the evaluator a deeper insight.

A problem which is common to all types of computer system evaluation techniques is the one of *work-load characterization*. The work load of a computer system has been defined in Section 1.2 as the set of the inputs produced by its user community. As will be seen in Chapter 5, the work load is to be characterized both in modeling approaches and in measurement experiments. In measurements, the work load must be controlled to make experiments reproducible. This problem, as shown in Chapter 5, is conceptually similar to the one of constructing work-load models in modeling approaches. Because of its crucial role in performance evaluation, work-load characterization is one of the major themes of this book.

PROBLEMS

1.1. Assuming that the interactive EXOPE system described in Example 1.1 has only one user, who inputs sequentially the six commands $c_1, \ldots, c_6$ with a constant think time of 5 seconds, define and calculate $\bar{t}$ and $\bar{T}$ by
(a) drawing a timing diagram as in Fig. 1.6;
(b) writing analytic formulas and using them.
Does the length of the time quantum influence the performance of the system? Is a time quantum necessary in a one-user system? And in an interactive multiuser uniprogramming system?

1.2. Define a single performance index which combines the two indices introduced for the EXOPE system in Example 1.1. Determine, according to the new index, the optimum value of the time quantum q for the work load described in Fig. 1.6.

1.3. Define at least two indices you would choose to evaluate the performance of a program that you have recently written. Assuming that you have to design the program again, write its performance specifications in terms of the indices you have selected. Assign a relative weight to each index, and justify the choice of these weights.

1.4. Define the CPU utilization ρ_1 for the interactive EXOPE system described in Example 1.1 as the ratio between the time spent processing user commands and the total time needed to complete the processing of the whole work load. Write an analytic formula to calculate ρ_1 under the same assumptions made to obtain equations (1.1) and (1.2). Derive the relationship between ρ_1 and $\bar{T}$, and plot ρ_1 versus q.

1.5. List the various reasons why the CPU of the interactive EXOPE system described in Example 1.1 may be idle. Define the CPU utilization ρ_1 as the ratio between the time period during which the CPU is working (including overhead) and the total time necessary to process the n commands which constitute the system's work load. Derive from the definitions of ρ_1 and $\bar{T}$ (mean number of commands processed per unit time) the relationship between these two indices. Show, by referring to the relationship you have derived, how certain changes in the system may increase ρ_1 but decrease $\bar{T}$.

1.6. An index of system productivity which is sometimes used is the mean instruction execution rate, measured in instructions per second. This index (which will be denoted by $\bar{v}_{cpu}$) is not to be confused with the maximum instruction execution rate of the CPU, $v_{cpu\,max}$. What is the relationship, if any, between $\bar{v}_{cpu}$ and $v_{cpu\,max}$? What is the relationship, if any, among $\bar{v}_{cpu}$, $v_{cpu\,max}$, and the utilization of the CPU? Would you expect v_{cpu} to always increase if the CPU were replaced by one with the same instruction set and a higher $v_{cpu\,max}$?

1.7. A simple uniprogrammed batch-processing system is composed of a CPU, a primary memory, a card reader, a printer, and four tape drives. Two of the drives are used for input and two for output. While a batch is being read in and stored on one tape, the CPU may transfer jobs one at a time from the other input tape (which contains the previous batch) to memory. Also, while the results of a job are being printed out from one of the output tapes, the CPU may be writing the results of the next job onto the other output tape. A block diagram of the system and the transfer rates between the various units is shown in Fig. P1.1. Assume that jobs are all in machine language

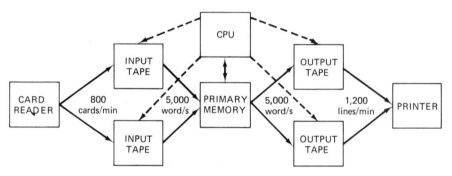

Figure P1.1 Batch-processing system studied in Problem 1.7.

form when they enter the system; that a batch is input every 30 minutes into the card reader; that the particular batch we consider consists of 60 jobs, 55 of type 1 and 5 of type 2 (*see* Table P1.1); and that the CPU is idle at the time our batch has been completely loaded on the input tape. Calculate the mean throughput rate (i.e., the mean number of jobs processed per unit time) over a period of time much longer than

TABLE P1.1

CHARACTERIZATION OF THE WORK LOAD FOR PROBLEM 1.7

Job parameter	Type 1 (55 jobs)	Type 2 (5 jobs)
Cards read	200	500
Size [words]	12,000	30,000
Execution time [s]	15	90
Words output	4,500	1,500
Lines printed	300	100

30 minutes. Calculate also the CPU utilization and the maximum turnaround time, defined as the longest possible interval between the instant the card deck is handed in to the operator and the instant the printout is received. Assuming that all the jobs of type 1 precede in the batch all those of type 2, calculate the mean system-residence time of a job, defined as the time between the instant the job's batch is read in from the card reader and the time the job's printout appears. Define now the *average job* as a job whose characteristics are the weighted means of those in Table P1.1, and consider a batch composed of 60 average jobs. Is the mean system-residence time for this batch the same as the one for the original batch? Why?

1.8. In a batch-processing EXOPE system (*see* Fig. 1.2), all jobs are identical. Each job consists of one job step. Loading the job in memory takes 0.5 s(seconds). The execution of the job consists of 10 CPU intervals, each 10 ms (milliseconds) long, separated by accesses to the drum, each taking 30 ms. At the end of the last CPU interval, the job's output data are transferred to disk in 0.2 s. A never-ending batch of jobs is assumed to be waiting on disk their turn to be loaded into memory. Calculate the mean throughput rate of the system over a long period of time (say, 1 day) for degrees of multiprogramming from 1 (uniprogramming system) through 5. Calculate also, under the same conditions, the mean memory-resistance time of a job, that is, the mean time between the instant a job is completely loaded into memory and the time all its output data are stored on disk. What is the cost associated with the increases in the throughput rate obtained when the degree of multiprogramming is increased?

2

Measurement Techniques

2.1 MEASUREMENT STUDIES

In the planning phase of an evaluation study, one of the decisions to be made is concerned with the evaluation technique (or techniques) to be used. If an empirical technique is selected, the most important objectives of the planning phase consist of

a. deciding what to measure,
b. selecting the measurement tool (or tools),
c. designing the experiments, and estimating their cost.

In the plan implementation phase, the experiments are performed, and the data are gathered and stored. Finally, the data are analyzed by the evaluators in the result interpretation phase. In Sections 2.2 to 2.5 we shall describe measurement tools and discuss tool selection and design criteria. The problems which arise in designing measurement experiments are partly covered in Section 2.6 and partly in Chapter 5, which discusses the work-load selection problem. Finally, in Section 2.7 we shall illustrate some data reduction and analysis techniques. In the rest of this section, the problem of determining what can and should be measured is briefly examined.

What do measurement instruments measure in computer systems? Their purpose is the one of measuring performance indices and installation parameters. Any measurement experiment may be viewed as being based on a conceptual input–output characterization of the system to be measured. This conceptual model is of the stimulus-response type. Considering it explicitly helps us design correct experiments.

    For example, suppose that in a batch-processing system we want to measure a performance index such as the mean throughput rate $\bar{T}$ and an installation parameter such as the mean disk seek time $\bar{t}_{seek}$. The mean throughput rate is an index of productivity usually defined as the number of jobs processed per unit time over a given interval. The seek time in a moveable-arm-disk operation is the time spent moving the arm to reach the requested cylinder. The mean $\bar{t}_{seek}$ will have to be computed over a number of seeks—in our case, those performed during the interval in which $\bar{T}$ is measured.

    Both $\bar{T}$ and $\bar{t}_{seek}$ depend on the work load which is processed by the system during the experiment. Thus, the situation is as depicted in Fig. 2.1(*a*). The conceptual model in this figure focuses our attention on the stimulus, to which the system "responds" with the values of $\bar{T}$ and $\bar{t}_{seek}$ we are going to measure. For the experiment to be correct and meaningful, this stimulus will have to be controlled or, at least, observed.

depend on workload

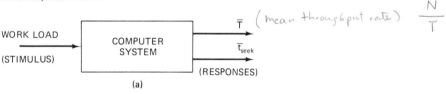

(a)

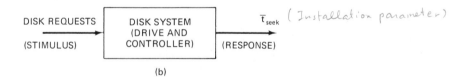

(b)

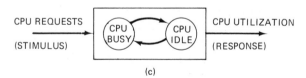

(c)

Figure 2.1   Conceptual models underlying some measurement experiments.

    Another conceptual model for the measurement of $\bar{t}_{seek}$ is presented in Fig. 2.1(*b*). The two-state model which underlies a measurement of CPU utilization is depicted in Fig. 2.1(*c*).

    Due to the discrete interpretation we usually give to computer system behavior, measurement tools generally measure indices and parameters by detecting *events*.

An event is any system or work-load change an evaluator is interested in. Within the context of an installation's characterization in terms of states, events correspond to state transitions.

In computer systems, changes have a wide spectrum of levels of detail and of time scales. For example, a transition of a voltage level from high to low or vice versa, the appearance of a pulse on a line, the execution of a prespecified instruction, the appearance of a certain bit pattern into a register, the end of a disk seek, the initiation of a job's execution, and the arrival of a command from a terminal may all be defined as events occurring within the same system.

In many cases, the measurement of performance indices and installation parameters is actually a calculation, performed at event-detection time or later, based on the collected data. Thus, many of the measurements are *indirect*, since their results are obtained through a *data reduction* process. For example, the mean throughput rate $\bar{T}$ of a batch-processing installation can be obtained by counting the number of jobs leaving the system during a specified time interval. The measurement tool needed in this case is one which can detect the departure of every job. The counting of these events can be performed at detection time or, if the occurrence of each event is recorded in some storage medium, later on. Note that those indices and parameters which are available and accessible by the tool at event-detection time can be measured directly.

A measurement tool which is to detect an event must be able to discriminate the corresponding change from all the others, at different levels as well as at the same level of detail. Real-time *selectivity* allows a tool to *filter* events, discarding nonneeded information at collection time instead of recording all changes and then selecting the relevant ones later.

With respect to the type of changes defined as events, one can distinguish measurements of *internal events* from those of *external events*. This classification implies that the boundaries of the system have been clearly defined. If we consider the whole installation as the object of our measurements, an external event can only be some action undertaken by us or the occurrence of a predetermined instant of time. Detection of external events is often used to *sample* the values of an installation's indices and parameters.

Once the performance indices and installation parameters of interest have been specified, it is generally easy to determine what events the tools should be able to detect and, on this basis, what types of tools should be used. A much harder problem to solve is the one of deciding what indices and parameters should be measured.

Some general considerations on the selection of performance indices have been made in Section 1.4. The parameters of interest depend on the type of installation and system as well as on the evaluation problem being dealt with. Several examples of problems to which measurement techniques can be applied are discussed in Chapters 6, 7, and 8. In general, evaluators are interested in measuring those parameters which might help them better understand the behavior of a system. For instance, the values of certain parameters may reveal the causes of a system's inadequate performance. In the example discussed above, a value of $\bar{t}_{seek}$ larger than expected would suggest that one of the reasons $\bar{T}$ is lower than expected might be the inefficient organization of the information stored on disk.

2.2   AN INTRODUCTION TO MEASUREMENT TOOLS

3 conceptual parts:—

Every instrument conceptually consists of three parts which perform three distinct functions (*see* Fig. 2.2): *a sensor*, whose task is to sense the magnitude of the quantity being measured; a *transformer*, which is able to perform the desired transformations of the information it receives from the sensor; and an *indicator*, which allows the experimenter to read the result of the measurement. For example, a yardstick senses (or allows its user to sense) the mark corresponding to the end of the object whose length is being measured and transforms it into a number which indicates, in a certain conventional scale, the object's length. Similarly, a thermometer senses the temperature of its environment and transforms it into an expansion or contraction of mercury, whose height in a graduated capillary tube indicates, in a conventional scale, the value of temperature.

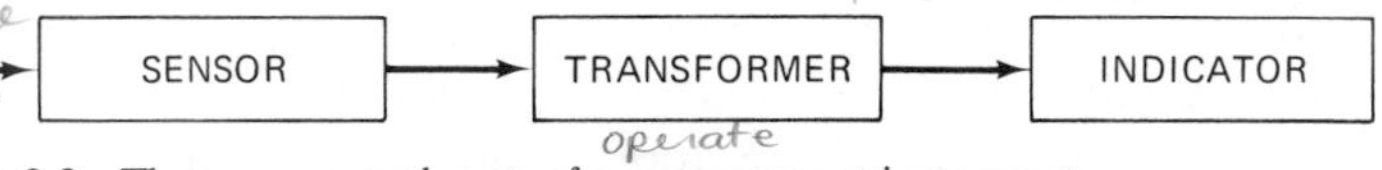

performed desired transformation of the info.

Sense the magnitude of the quantity being meas.

| SENSOR | → | TRANSFORMER | → | INDICATOR |

Report

operate

Figure 2.2   Three conceptual parts of a measurement instrument.

Instruments for computer system measurement often detect events at a much higher rate than a human being can read. Thus, the indicator will usually store the results of the measurements in a storage medium instead of presenting them visually to the experimenter in real time. This does not mean that measurement results can never be displayed in real time. It is possible to do so if the monitored events are relatively infrequent or if the collected data are periodically output during the experiment after suitable reduction. Note that the transformer may do nothing, in which case the events are recorded without any transformation. Or it may prereduce the result; for instance, it may increment by 1 the event count every time an event is detected. Sometimes, the transformer also performs other actions; for example, it reads the clock, or the contents of a register, or those of one or more memory locations, or any combination of these contents.

Characteristic

The most important characteristics of measurement tools, those upon which their design specifications and their selection are usually based, are listed (not in order of importance) in Table 2.1. We shall now briefly discuss these characteristics.

If a tool makes use of system resources, its operation may interfere with the operation of the system and have a nonnegligible influence on the quantities being measured. Thus, *interference* may cause both performance degradation and inaccuracies in measurement results. *Degradation* is any reduction of performance with respect to the level which could be achieved under the same user work load. The inaccuracies which may be due to interference are certainly of more serious concern, at least to an experimenter.

Table 2.1

MAIN CHARACTERISTICS
OF MEASUREMENT TOOLS

Interference
Accuracy
Resolution
Scope *relates to classes of events it can detect*
Prereduction capabilities *save storage space, I/o proc. time, but increase interfere*
Compatibility *Various aspect*   *decrease resolution*
Cost
Ease of installation
Ease of use

The *accuracy* of a tool can be represented by the error which affects the data collected by the tool. There are several sources of error which may cause the measured value of a quantity to differ from the true value of that quantity. The interference of the tool with the system is one of these sources. Other errors may be due to an improper installation or usage of the tool, to the incorrect operation, or to the limitations of its sensor (event detector) or transformer. One of these limitations is that of the number of digits used to represent the collected data. This is a constraint on the *precision* of the tool. Another limitation is related to the *resolution* of the tool, that is, the maximum frequency at which events can be detected and correctly recorded.

Measurement errors may also be due to the malfunction or the limited precision or accuracy of other tools, such as a clock, involved in the experiment. Additional errors may affect the data reduction, presentation, and interpretation phases. The analysis of experimental errors is a complicated and extremely important endeavour. In this chapter, we shall discuss several of its aspects, both in connection with some specific measurement tools (see Examples 2.1–2.4 and 2.6) and with the general problems of experimental design and result interpretation (Sections 2.6 and 2.7).

The *scope* of a tool relates to the classes of events it can detect. This characteristic may be interpreted in various ways: as describing, for instance, the flexibility of a tool, or the amplitude of its domain of application, or its transportability from system to system. It should be noted here that in a system there may be built-in tools, having a scope limited to one or a few types of events which cannot be changed by the experimenter. These will be called *fixed tools*. Since flexibility and generality are usually expensive, the majority of the tools used in continuous monitoring (*see* Section 1.3) are fixed.

The transformer part of a tool can manipulate the collected data. Hence, a first reduction, to be called *prereduction*, may be performed before storing them. This is, for instance, the case with *counting tools*, which count events. When there is no prereduction, we have a *tracing tool*. This is a tool which records a sequence of events in chronological order of occurrence. Such a sequence is called a *trace*.

A tracing tool is able to filter the events of interest and disregard all other changes. However, it does not manipulate the collected data.

Prereduction saves storage space, I/O processor time, and some of the computer time needed for the subsequent off-line reduction. On the other hand, it makes a tool more expensive, due to the additional hardware or software required. It also increases the interference or decreases the resolution, or both. Prereduction destroys some information which may turn out to be useful or necessary later, especially if the experiment has not been planned carefully enough. Thus, the choice of the proper amount of pre-reduction involves a trade-off, which will be examined in Section 2.4.1 for a particular case.

The *compatibility* property refers to various aspects of the system to be measured. A tool which is to detect voltage pulses must not be damaged by their amplitude and must properly react to their edges and durations. A tool consisting of a set of programs must be correctly interfaced to the operating system. Also, all tools should be compatible with the protection mechanisms of the system they measure. These issues are considered again later in this chapter.

The *cost* of a tool includes the price for its purchase, rental, or lease (or its design and implementation cost); the price of its installation and maintenance; the price of the training of its users; and its usage costs. The importance of the last two characteristics listed in Table 2.1 is evident and needs no additional comments. However, it may be useful to emphasize that the existence of clear, unambiguous, comprehensive documentation is, also for measurement tools, essential.

With respect to their nature, measurement tools are traditionally divided into the classes of *hardware tools*, *software tools*, and *firmware tools*. This distinction does not have anything to do with the nature of the quantities to be measured; in principle, the behavior of a program can be monitored by a hardware tool, and the performance of a hardware module can be measured by using a software tool. In fact, hardware tools consist of hardware which is added to a system for measurement purposes. Software tools are composed of instructions to be executed by the measured system. Firmware tools consist of microinstructions, also to be executed by the measured system, which is assumed to contain at least one microprogrammable processor. The fuzziness of the boundaries between hardware, software, and firmware makes this distinction a rather vague one, also because of the recent emergence of *hybrid tools*. These tools (*see* Section 2.4.1) require the addition of both extra hardware and extra software to the system to be measured. The use of general-purpose computers as measurement tools is increasing. We shall classify these as hardware tools, even though they are in reality hardware-software complexes.

Another important distinction to be mentioned is the one concerned with whether the events detected by a tool are internal or external. In the former case, the tool is said to be *internally driven*. In the latter, we have an *externally driven* tool, which is usually of the *sampling* type.

1. high-resolution
2. Scope - board
3. Low interference

2.3 HARDWARE TOOLS

2.3.1 Introduction

Hardware tools, especially the internally driven ones, detect events occurring at a relatively microscopic level, for example, the presence of an electric voltage pulse or of a pulse edge on a wire or the appearance of a certain bit pattern into a register. This makes them high-resolution tools, capable of detecting high-frequency, microscopic events. Their scope is potentially broad, since most of the interesting points in a system can usually be reached from the outside, in spite of the fact that the trend toward larger-scale integrated circuits has made an increasing number of signals inaccessible. The interesting points are accessible, especially if measurement requirements have been taken into account at system design time. Of course, the actual scope depends on the particular tool being considered. In general, detecting more macroscopic events and relating microscopic events to their causes (for example, to the jobs which generate them) are difficult problems to solve for most hardware tools.

The fact that these tools consist of additional hardware makes their interference very low or equal to zero. A nonzero interference is produced when the collected data are periodically stored into the measured system for immediate or delayed reduction or when the tool is allowed to access the primary memory of the measured computer. The interference may be higher when a substantial fraction of the measured system's resources (for instance, one processor, part of the primary and secondary memory) is used for measurement purposes.

The accuracy and prereduction capabilities vary from tool to tool; they will be discussed for specific types of instruments in the next sections. The spectrum of hardware tool costs is as broad as the one of their types and features. Their installation generally requires great expertise and thorough knowledge of the measured system, and their users have to be carefully trained.

Almost all hardware tools need the computational power of a computer, at least to reduce the collected data. Sometimes this power is provided by the measured system itself, either during the experiment, in which case the interference is often nonnegligible, or after the end of it. In other cases, data reduction is performed by an external computer, which may be directly interfaced to the tool and reduce the data in real time. If a computer is used only for data reduction and does not control the experiment, the tool is said to be a *wired-program tool.* It is a *stored-program tool* when its heart is a computer properly interfaced to the system to be measured and when the software of that computer controls event detection, data collection, manipulation, and storage.

These two types of hardware tools are described in Sections 2.3.3 and 2.3.4, respectively. The next section briefly discusses fixed hardware tools.

2.3.2   Fixed Hardware Tools

[handwritten margin note: Can be read but not be controlled limited scope.]

A fixed tool is an instrument which can be read but not controlled by its users. An aspect of this lack of controllability is that users can select neither the event (or the events) to be detected by the tool nor the actions it performs upon the detection of an event. Hence, the scope of a fixed tool is extremely limited.

Fixed hardware tools are usually incorporated into a system at design time. The addition of such a tool to a complete working system is generally not straightforward. There are *operator-readable* tools and *program-readable* tools. The former category includes the machine-room clock and those registers or counters, incorporated into the system for debugging and measurement purposes, whose contents are displayed on the operator's console. The latter category includes the program-readable system clock and those hardware counters, if any, which continuously count the occurrences of an event and can be read by special instructions. The two categories are not disjoint; for instance, the system clock can usually also be read by the operator.

Example 2.1   The total time t_{tot} needed by a system to process a batch of N jobs is to be measured. We may define the mean throughput rate of the system when processing these N jobs as

$$\bar{T} = \frac{N}{t_{tot}}. \tag{2.1}$$

Thus, the measurement of t_{tot} will allow us to indirectly measure $\bar{T}$ by applying (2.1). Once we have precisely defined the instants of initiation and termination of the batch's execution, we can read the machine-room clock, or the system clock, or our watch when these two events occur. The difference between their occurrence times will give us the value of t_{tot}. Also this measurement of t_{tot} is indirect. A direct measurement requires a stopwatch or a tool equivalent to it, for instance, a counter which is initialized to zero at the beginning of the experiment and read at the end.

Even the result of a simple measurement like this may be affected by several errors. Among them, we shall mention those due to the limited precision of the clock, to inaccurate clock readings, to mistakes in the computation of the difference between the two recorded times, and to an imprecise detection of event occurrences (for instance, the second reading of the clock may not have coincided with the completion of the batch's execution). It is useful to observe that systematic errors, which affect both readings in the same direction, influence the value of t_{tot} only by their difference.

Another, potentially more accurate, method for performing the same measurement exploits the program readability of the system clock. The operating system may be instructed to read this clock at the instant defined as the initiation of the batch's execution and at the instant of completion. Alternatively, each job can read the clock at its beginning and at its end and output the two readings. All of the sources of errors listed above may in principle also affect these measurements. In this case, however, the responsibility for the inaccurate clock readings and the lack of simultaneity is to be attributed to the clock-accessing procedure.

In many systems, reading the clock is a time-consuming operation, especially if this is done by a user job. Another source of inaccuracies is the interference caused by the clock readings and the outputting of the results. Corrections may often be introduced to partially or totally compensate for these errors. The modifications to be made to the operating system or to the user jobs in order to enable them to read the clock and output the result may be easily guessed by the reader; in any event, they are described in Section 2.4.2. Note that practically all operating systems perform these measurements routinely for accounting purposes. ■

Many contemporary systems are equipped with program-accessible tools which can generate external events. For instance, the IBM System/370, besides a 64-bit real-time clock which is incremented every microsecond, has a CPU timer and an interval timer. The CPU timer is a 64-bit register which can be loaded by a program and is decremented every microsecond. When its contents become negative, an external interrupt to the CPU is generated. The interval timer is a 32-bit fixed location in primary memory, whose contents can be loaded by a program and are decremented every 3.3 milliseconds. Again, when the contents become negative, an external interrupt is generated. These two timers can be used as clocks in the same way as the real-time clock. Another facility existing on the 370 and other systems is the clock comparator. In the 370, this is a 64-bit register in which a program can load a bit pattern which is interpreted as a value of real time. When the contents of the real-time clock match that value, an interrupt is generated. In measurement experiments, this tool may be used to start or stop a measurement session at a specified time of the day. Both the clock comparator and the timers (when used to produce a deferred interrupt) are sensors of external events. However, the timers may be considerd fixed tools when used as clocks.

2.3.3   Wired-Program Tools

The block diagram of a simple wired-program tool is presented in Fig. 2.3. The *probes* are high-impedance voltage-level detectors which are to be connected to the proper pins on the backplane of the system. High impedance is required to avoid perturbing the circuits they are attached to. The signals (voltage levels and pulses) collected by the probes are manipulated by the *event filter,* usually a set of logic elements whose interconnections can generally be selected and manually implemented by the user on a patch panel. These elements may include combina-

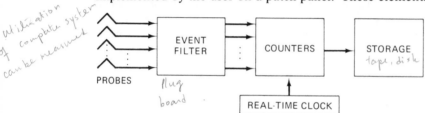

Figure 2.3   Simple wired-program tool.

tional and sequential circuits and are sometimes replaceable. Note that the filter may be implemented by a read-only memory. This memory must be loadable or easily replaceable if the tool is to be flexible. It must be fast in order not to be too serious a limitation for the tool's resolution.

The outputs of the filter are connected, together with those of the real-time clock, to an array of *counters*. Each counter can be used in two modes: In *count mode*, pulses coming from the logic elements are counted; in *time mode*, a signal coming from the filter gates clock pulses to the counter input (*see* Fig. 2.4).

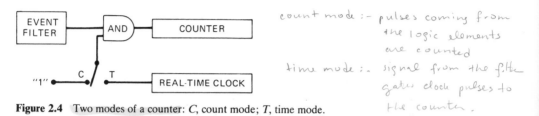

count mode :- pulses coming from the logic elements are counted

time mode :- signal from the filter gates clock pulses to the counter.

Figure 2.4   Two modes of a counter: *C*, count mode; *T*, time mode.

Counters in time mode can be used to measure pulse durations much longer than the clock period. The mechanism is illustrated in Fig. 2.5, which explains how the utilization of a computer system component can be measured by a tool like that in Fig. 2.3. If at the end of the measurement session the contents of the two counters A and B, which had been reset at the beginning of the session, are C_A and C_B, respectively, an estimate of the utilization factor of the measured unit is C_A/C_B.

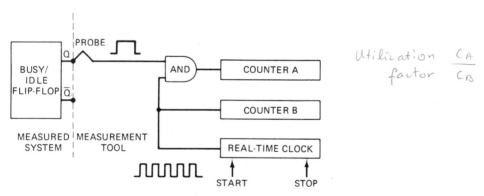

Utilization factor $\dfrac{C_A}{C_B}$

Figure 2.5   Measurement of a utilization factor by a hardware tool.

The contents of the counters and of the real-time clock are periodically dumped into the *storage*. The storage medium is in most cases a magnetic tape. The tape will be processed later by the measured machine or by another computer for data reduction and report generation. Some early tools had a visual display instead of the storage unit. A display is also useful in addition to the storage in order to monitor the experiment. The frequency of dumps to tape can usually be chosen by the experimenter within certain limits. The dump pulses are generated by the clock, which has several exits with different frequencies. In several tools, the clock may also be synchronized with an external pulse generator, for example, with the clock of the measured system.

Although wired-program tools had been used much earlier by some manufacturers [for example, the Program Monitor described by Apple (1965) and TS/SPAR described by Schulman (1967), both developed at IBM], they made their appearance on the market in 1968. Their evolution since then has been rapid and has brought them closer and closer to stored-program tools. Two major additions were those of a parallel input and of a random-access memory. *Parallel input* consists of a set of probes which may capture the contents of any accessible register of the measured system. These contents can be continuously compared with values loaded into the tool's registers by the user. The results of these comparisons may then be sent to the counters working in count or time mode.

A *random-access memory* (RAM) may replace the counters, provided that the inevitable decrease in counting speed can be tolerated. Together with parallel input, a RAM may be made to work in *distribution mode*, in which the histogram of a sequence of events belonging to several classes is incrementally constructed. This is done by addressing memory using properly encoded event tags or other suitable data collected at event occurrence time. A simple example is reported in Fig. 2.6, which shows an experimental setup to obtain the histogram of the types of instructions executed during a measurement session. The event to be detected occurs when the OPCODE STABLE line goes up. Every time a reference to the

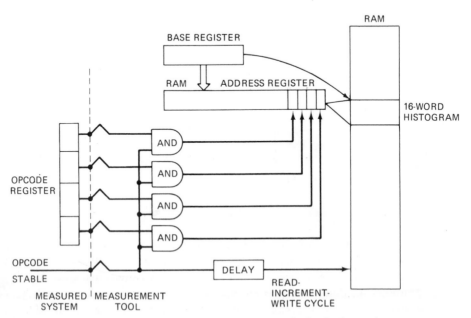

Figure 2.6   Use of parallel input and random-access memory in distribution mode.

RAM is made, the word fetched is incremented by 1 and restored. At any time, the vector of 16 adjacent words in memory whose starting address is the contents of the base register followed by four 0's contains the histogram of the opcode types executed until then. It should be noted that the read-increment-write cycle of the RAM must be shorter than the minimum interval between two consecutive instruction fetches; otherwise some information may be lost.

Another way of using parallel input and RAM is the *trace mode,* in which bit patterns entering the tool at the parallel input are stored into sequential RAM cells. Periodically, the trace accumulated in RAM will have to be dumped onto a secondary storage medium, unless the measurement session is a very short one. Thus, the RAM may be used as a buffer for the collected data.

Also in trace mode there is an obvious lower bound for the RAM's speed. This bound depends on the mean and maximum frequencies of the events to be detected. Traces generally require a big amount of storage space and hence are bound to be collectable only for short periods of time.

When prespecified sequences of events are to be detected, the need for collecting a trace may be eliminated by *sequence detectors.* These detectors are sequential circuits which recognize the occurrences of a sequence specified by the user. For instance, suppose that we want to measure the number of times two or more branch-type instructions are consecutively executed during a certain time interval. Assume, for simplicity, that all branch-type instructions have the same opcode. Thus, the problem is the one of recognizing in the instruction stream all appearances of two or more consecutive branch opcodes. A three-state sequential circuit may be used to solve the problem. The appearance of a branch opcode will cause a transition from state S_0 to state S_1. The next opcode, if it is of the branch type, will cause a transition to state S_2 and an output pulse which will increment a counter; if not, it will change the state back to S_0. In state S_2, a branch opcode will leave the sequence detector in state S_2, with no output being generated, whereas a nonbranch opcode will change the state to S_0.

Table 2.2 summarizes the main features of some commercial wired-program tools.

Perhaps the most typical application of wired-program tools is in the measurement of utilizations and overlap factors. A generalization of the setup illustrated in Fig. 2.5 is described in the following example.

Example 2.2   An EXOPE system (*see* Fig. 1.2) is to be measured. The evaluators are interested in, among other quantities, the activities of the CPU and of the drum processor (to be called, for brevity, *the channel*). Some of the basic questions are concerned with how the CPU and the channel spend their time and with the temporal relationships between their activities. For the purposes of this experiment, three CPU states and two channel states are defined. At any given instant, the CPU is either *busy* or *idle* and if busy, either in the *problem state* or in the *supervisor state.* The CPU is in the problem state when it is processing user jobs and in the supervisor state when it is executing the operating system. Similarly, the channel is at any instant either busy or idle. The states of the CPU-channel pair may be defined as the combinations of the states of the individual

Table 2.2   (out of date)

TECHNICAL CHARACTERISTICS OF SOME COMMERCIAL WIRED-
PROGRAM HARDWARE TOOLS

	Allied Computer Technology	Computer Synectics	Tesdata Systems	Tesdata Systems
Manufacturer				
Model	CPM-II	SUM	1010	1155
Probes				
Number	20, 40	20	20	32, 96
Min. pulse duration [ns]	50	50	20	30
Maximum rate [MHz]	5	10	20	15
Logic (plugboard)	450, 600 hubs	300 hubs	200 hubs	480, 960 hubs
Counters				
Number	16, 32	16, 32	8, 16	8, 32
Length	10 decimal digits	9 decimal digits	32 bits	32 bits
Maximum rate [MHz]	5	2	20	3.5
Comparators	1 (optional)	1, 5 (optional)	—	—
Sequence detectors	No	No	No	Yes
Distribution mode	No	No	No	Yes
Random-access memory	No	No	No	Yes
Word length [bits]	—	—	—	16
Size [bytes]	—	—	—	$4K, 8K$
Cycle time [μs]	—	—	—	1
Storage	1 9-track tape	1 7- or 9-track tape	1 cassette (optional)	1 7- or 9-track tape
Peripherals	Visual display	Visual display	CRT display Column printer (optional)	—
Software	MSR (summary report program)	SUMDAP (data analysis)	Batch analyzer	Batch analyzer

devices. If the CPU is thought of as having three states, there are six possible combinations. If only two states (busy and idle) are considered for the CPU, then the possible combinations are four.

We shall assume that the evaluators are primarily interested in these four states as well as in the breakdown of the time spent in the CPU-busy state into its problem and supervisor components. The duration of the CPU-busy/channel-busy state is a measure of the *CPU/channel overlap*. The CPU-busy/channel-idle and the CPU-idle/channel-busy states are designated by the terms *CPU only* and *channel only*, respectively. Finally the CPU-idle/channel-idle state is called the *idle state*.

   If the busy/idle flip-flops of the two devices and the problem/supervisor flip-flop of the CPU are accessible, three probes connected to their output pins will be sufficient to measure the durations of all the states defined above over a time interval to be called a *measurement session*. The experimental setup is illustrated in Fig. 2.7. The choice of the quantities to be directly measured presents many alternatives. Figure 2.7 shows how the first four quantities in Table 2.3 can be measured by a wired-program tool. How other quantities of interest can be derived from the first four is also shown in this table. The utilizations of the states of the CPU-channel pair, namely ρ_{12}, ρ_{10}, ρ_{20}, may be called *overlap factors*.

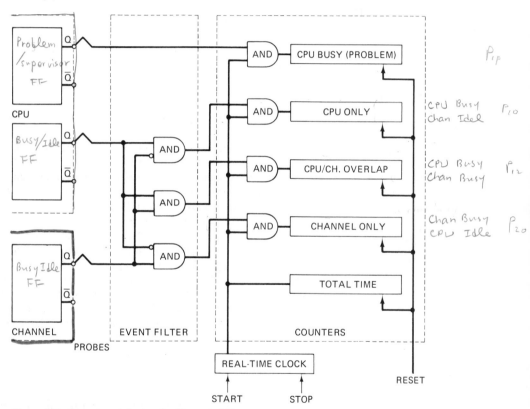

Figure 2.7   Experimental setup for Example 2.2.

   The main source of error which affects the results of this experiment is the sampling technique used to measure durations (*see* Fig. 2.5). This problem will be discussed in general in Section 2.4.3. Other common errors are those due to the fact that a probe may have been attached to the wrong pin or that the monitored signals have a meaning which differs from the one attributed to them by the experimenter. For instance, in setting up this experiment, it is extremely important to correctly answer questions such as, When is the problem/supervisor flip-flop set or reset by the CPU? What is its state when the CPU is

Table 2.3
RESULTS OF AN EXPERIMENT

Symbol	Measured quantity	Fraction of total time [%]
ρ_{10}	CPU only	13.03
ρ_{12}	CPU/channel overlap	47.88
ρ_{1p}	CPU busy (problem state)	54.60
ρ_{20}	Channel only	19.04
$\rho_1 = \rho_{10} + \rho_{12}$	CPU busy	60.91
$\rho_{1s} = \rho_1 - \rho_{1p}$	CPU busy (supervisor state)	6.31
$\rho_2 = \rho_{20} + \rho_{12}$	Channel busy	67.92
$\bar{\rho}_1 = 1 - \rho_1$	CPU idle	39.09

Source: Kolence and Kiviat (1973).

idle? We assume in this example that the CPU is always in the supervisor state when it is idle.

In the setup in Fig. 2.7, the collected data are prereduced quite drastically. If the duration of the measurement session is not too long, dumping the counters to the storage may not be necessary; in this case, some of the results of interest are immediately obtainable from the counters, both during the session and at its end. Extremely simple calculations will then yield the other quantities shown in Table 2.3.

A substantial loss of information is usually connected with a substantial prereduction. For instance, it is impossible to determine, from the collected data, the amount of overlap between the channel and the CPU in the problem state. Also, the durations of each individual burst of CPU activity and channel activity cannot be reconstructed due to the cumulative counting technique employed. At the opposite extreme, we have no prereduction at all. In this case, no prereduction would mean recording the three waveforms monitored by the probes. Any question about the behavior of the CPU-channel pair at the level of detail corresponding to the traced signals could be answered, but a large amount of processing would be required every time. ■

2.3.4   Stored-Program Tools

Wired-program tools have evolved from simple counting devices to such complex and sophisticated digital systems that the replacement of wired control logic by a set of microprograms or programs has become a straightforward and often convenient modification. Thus, stored-program tools, which once were used only by some manufacturers and in some research projects, are now commercially available from a number of companies in the computer measurement field. The existing families of minicomputer-based hardware tools offer prospective customers a wide choice of configurations, supervisory software systems, and hardware and software options.

There are obvious advantages of stored-program tools over wired-program tools. The main advantage is probably their much greater flexibility, which allows them to modify the setup during the experiment depending on various conditions. For example, a stored-program tool can be connected to a direct-memory-access port of the measured system and fetch any of the words from that system's memory; note that this is conceptually equivalent to having parallel probe connections to all memory locations and being able to select them at electronic speed. Also, the functions performed by the filter in the scheme in Fig. 2.3 can be changed during the measurement session depending on partial results or on the occurrence of particular events.

Another advantage of stored-program tools is their full data reduction capabilities, which eliminate the interference due to real-time or off-line reduction.

On the other hand, the resolution of these tools tends to be lower than the one of wired-program tools. This is generally due to the additional stage of interpretation required by software control. Sometimes, the resolution is actually limited by the I/O characteristics of both the measuring and the measured system. The bandwidth limitations of standard I/O communications in either system or in both may be overcome by providing the tool with an ad hoc interface, sometimes having characteristics very similar to those of wired-program tools. For example, both commercial stored-program tools described in Table 2.4 are equipped with probes. Also, care must be taken in exploiting their additional capabilities, since a nonnegligible amount of interference or some undesirable losses of information might be associated with their use.

It should be noted that the machines used as stored-program tools have characteristics very similar to those of process control computers; here the process is another computer, which is at present generally controlled in an open-loop fashion, even though some studies of closed-loop systems have been performed (*see* Section 2.5).

The interested reader may find descriptions and discussions of particular stored-program tools in Estrin et al. (1967), Greenbaum (1969), Roek and Emerson (1969), Aschenbrenner and Natarajan (1971), and Hughes and Cronshaw (1973).

Example 2.3   The utilizations of some software resources in an EXOPE system are to be measured. Suppose that the investigators want to determine the amount of time spent by the system during a certain session executing the operating system and executing a given compiler. One of the objectives of the study is to see whether the present partitioning of the operating system into a memory-resident part and a drum-resident part is adequate or could be improved. Thus, monitoring the state of the problem/supervisor flip-flop as described in Example 2.2 is not sufficient. The time spent in the supervisor state must at least be broken down into the times spent in the memory-resident part and in the drum-resident part of the operating system.

The memory-resident part is stored in a fixed and dedicated region of memory. Thus, every time the CPU is in the supervisor state and the program counter points to another

Table 2.4

TECHNICAL CHARACTERISTICS OF SOME COMMERCIAL STORED-
PROGRAM HARDWARE TOOLS

Manufacturer	COMRESS, Div. of Comten	Tesdata Systems Corp.
Model	Dynaprobe 8000/II	1200
Probes		
Number	48	144
Minimum pulse duration [ns]	30	30, 5
Maximum rate [MHz]	10	15, 40
Logic (plugboard)	600 hubs	1280 hubs
Counters		
Number	Variable	16, 4
Length	Variable	32 bits
Maximum rate [MHz]	10	20, 40
Word length [bits]	16	16
Memory size [bytes]	$64K$	$16K$
Memory cycle time [μs/word]	1	1
Secondary memory	7- or 9-track tape	1 or 2 7- or 9-track tape(s) 1 2.5- or $5M$-byte disk (optional)
Peripherals	Teletype Alphanumeric display (optional)	CRT display Column printer (optional)
Software	TSM summary software DYNAPAR/TSM data reduction software	Batch analyzer Real-time display Interactive analysis

region of memory, a module of the drum-resident part is being executed. A wired-program tool equipped with a parallel-input facility can be used, in an obvious way, to detect this condition and measure its duration. However, determining what drum-resident module is being executed, or measuring the utilization of the compiler (which, every time it is loaded into memory from the drum, may occupy a different region), is much more difficult, even with a very sophisticated wired-program tool. A stored-program tool, for instance, with the setup depicted in Fig. 2.8, greatly facilitates this task.

A serial-input probe is connected to the busy/idle flip-flop in the drum processor. Parallel-input probes are attached to the program counter in the CPU. The program running in the measuring computer knows the addresses of the operating system tables, which are memory-resident, and can read them by sending requests via its I/O bus to the memory of the EXOPE system.

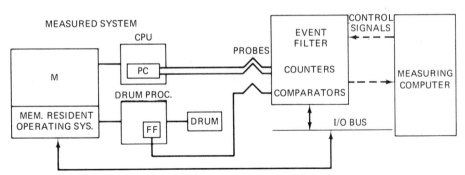

Figure 2.8   Experimental setup for Example 2.3. PC is the program counter of the measured system. FF is the busy/idle flip-flop of the drum processor.

Whenever an idle-to-busy transition of the drum processor is detected, the measuring computer is interrupted. From the operating system tables and from its map of the drum, this computer determines whether or not the transfer involves the drum-resident operating system or the compiler. If it does, the area of memory in which the information being transferred is to be loaded is also determined from the tables. The bounds of this area are transmitted to the comparators, so that whenever the program counter points to an address comprised between those bounds, the counter which accumulates the time spent executing the drum-resident part of the operating system or the one which performs the same task for the compiler is incremented.

Note that in this experiment at least three pairs of comparators are needed, all working on the contents of the program counter. One pair is for the memory-resident portion of the operating system, whose bounds never change. The other two pairs are to detect when modules from the drum-resident part of the operating system and, respectively, the compiler are executed. ∎

Those discussed so far could be called *external stored-program tools* since they consist of computers which monitor from the outside the system to be measured. In a multiprocessor system, one of the processors may be used as an *internal stored-program tool* to monitor the rest of the system. For example, the hardware tool which has been built for C.mmp, a multiprocessor system implemented at Carnegie–Mellon University, contains several registers which can be addressed by one of the processors in the system [*see* Fuller et al. (1973)]. Thus, this processor can set up and control experiments to be performed on another processor, besides being able to store and reduce the data collected by the tool.

It should be noted that an internal stored-program tool could be classified as a software tool, or more properly as a hybrid tool (*see* Section 2.1), since it always requires the addition to the system of a set of programs to be executed by the measuring processor.

A processor can be used as an internal tool only if it has access to the regions of primary memory, to the registers, or to the buses where the information to be collected is at event-detection time. Otherwise, the scope of such a tool is very limited, unless the measured subsystem is programmed to ship all necessary data to the measuring processor. In this case, the measuring processor could be seen as a reducer of data collected by a software tool. In PRIME, a multiprocessor system designed at the University of California at Berkeley, the partitioning of the hardware into completely separate subsystems, imposed by privacy requirements, made it impossible for a processor to access the memory and the registers of any other processor. This is an aspect of the conflict between protection and measurement. One of the design goals of the instrumentation system of PRIME was to comply with all the protection rules of the system [*see* Ferrari (1973)]. This decision required several sacrifices to be made, among which the one of not implementing an internal stored-program tool.

An internal tool detects events by continuously comparing the contents of registers or buses with prespecified bit patterns or by monitoring signals coming from the measured subsystem or from its own clock. Data may be gathered via the interprocessor communications channels. In this case, the bandwidth of these channels must tolerate the additional activity without excessively degrading the performance of the measured subsystem. The same considerations can be made when processors intercommunicate via primary memory instead of via data paths. Secondary storage units which are not being frequently accessed by the measured subsystem should be employed to store measurement results.

2.4 SOFTWARE AND FIRMWARE TOOLS

2.4.1. Introduction

In Section 2.2, *software tools* have been defined as those consisting of instructions which are added to a hardware-software system in order to gather data related to its performance. The fact that these additional instructions must be executed by the system being measured is bound to produce interference. The amount of interference produced depends on the frequency of the events to be detected and on the operations performed by the tool at the occurrence of each event. Two components of interference can usually be identified: the *time* component and the *space* component. Space and time may often be traded for each other. Space can be decreased (by increasing the amount of prereduction) at the expense of increased time, and vice versa.

For instance, if the mean and the standard deviation of a certain quantity are to be determined from a number of successive measurements of that quantity, the minimum interference in time will be obtained by storing the measured values and postponing the calculation of their mean and standard deviation to some later time. Alternatively, we could keep estimates of the mean and standard deviation during the experiment and update them every time a new value is measured [*see* (3.7) and (3.8) in Example 3.2]. Clearly, the latter solution would cause more interference in time than the former, due to the updating of the estimates. However, interference in space would be lower since only the space for the two estimates, for the new value of the quantity, and for the updating routine would be needed.

Sometimes, the inaccuracies due to interference can be totally or partially corrected. For example, the time spent during an experiment collecting and prereducing the data may be measured and subtracted from the durations of the time intervals which were affected by it. The effects of interference in space on the measured quantities are usually much harder to determine.

The resolution of software tools is generally lower than that of hardware tools. Software tools can detect only more macroscopic, less frequent events. Their scope is different from the one of hardware tools, even though there are several types of events which can be detected by both. When the same quantity can be measured by a hardware and a software tool, the values obtained by the hardware tool are usually to be considered more accurate because of the lower interference [*see*, for example, Carlson (1971) and Peterson (1974)]. Thus, hardware tools may be used to verify the accuracy of certain software tools.

A software tool may be more flexible than a hardware tool within its domain of application. The purchase price of commercial software tools has a much narrower spectrum, concentrated in the lower-price region of the corresponding spectrum for hardware tools. They are somewhat easier to install, but experienced personnel is often needed for this operation. Some training is also necessary for using them and for interpreting their outputs.

Firmware tools are similar in nature and in features to software tools, but their space-time interference trade-off has different characteristics. In general, space is a more limited resource for microprograms than for programs, and microinstruction execution time is shorter. However, time is in certain cases critical in firmware, while it is rarely so in software. Also, firmware tools have a higher resolution, but their prereduction capabilities are limited more drastically by interference. The scope of a firmware tool, in terms of the level of detectable events and measurable quantities, is in between those of hardware and software tools. Their flexibility depends also on how easily the contents of the control memory can be modified.

A set of firmware tools, implemented in a Standard Computer Corporation IC 7000 System with a writable control memory in both the CPU and the I/O processor, is described by Saal and Shustek (1972). Among other quantities, these tools can measure the usage of primary-memory areas by a given program and the utilization of CPU opcodes and opcode pairs. They can also trace the branches taken by a program. A dedicated buffer area in primary memory and a tape drive are required to use them. They considerably degrade the speed of execution, especially because of the very high frequency of data collection; of the use of tape as the storage medium; and of the conflicts between measurement I/O and normal I/O in the I/O processor.

There are software tools which are supported by firmware additions to the measured system. For example, in a microprogrammable processor, one or more measurement-oriented CPU instructions can be incorporated into the instruction set by storing the corresponding microprograms in the control memory. While it is not necessary that the machine be microprogrammable, since instructions intended for measurement purposes can be designed also in a processor with hardwired control, microprogramming may allow these instructions to be added later.

As a simple example of such an instruction, Fig. 2.9 presents the format of an event-recording instruction for a 32-bit machine with an 8-bit opcode, modeled after the RX format of the IBM System/360 and /370. The instruction reads the clock and stores its contents and the contents of the E field (an event identification tag) in the memory location whose address is $(B) + (X) + D$, where (B) denotes the contents of base register B, (X) the contents of index register X, and D is a displacement. Finally, the instruction increments the contents of X.

OPCODE	E	X	B	D
0	7 8	11 12	15 16 19 20	31

Figure 2.9 Format of a simple measurement-oriented instruction.

Another example, which could be more properly classified as a firmware tool since it consists of a single microinstruction, is the one of the Burroughs B1700 [Wilner (1972)]. In that machine, the "Monitor" microinstruction outputs a bit pattern specified by the programmer to pins accessible to the probes of a hardware tool. This is also an example of a *hybrid tool*. Hybrid tools consist of external hardware tools which receive data collected on their behalf by a software or firmware tool running in the system to be measured. Svobodova (1973) describes the design of a hybrid tool for an IBM System/370 Model 145. Other hybrid tools are described by Estrin et al. (1967) and Hughes and Cronshaw (1973).

Hardware, software, and firmware tools are in some sense complementary, since there are events and data which can only (or much more economically) be detected and accessed by one type of tool than by the others. This observation suggests that an integrated hardware-firmware-software approach to instrumentation could provide the most convenient solution. The coordination existing in a hybrid tool between an external hardware instrument and a software tool running internally is an example of this trend toward the integration of the various techniques. However, the simultaneous usage of cooperating tools of the same or different nature, their coordination, and the partitioning of their functions and jurisdictions create problems which are still open for research. Instead of instrumenting a system after designing and implementing it, a comprehensive set of measurement facilities should be incorporated into it during its design. The organizational relationships among these facilities, as well as those with the rest of the system, should be specified at system design time. This practice has not been very popular so far among computer manufacturers but has been adopted for some research machines such as Multics [Saltzer and Gintell (1970)] and PRIME

[Ferrari (1973)]. Some of the problems which arise in instrumentation system design are discussed in Section 2.5.

2.4.2 Internally Driven Tools
*{ to detect internal events
e.g. execution of an instruction.*

Software techniques allow us to detect internal events such as the following: A variable or a data structure is accessed; the value of a variable is modified; a variable takes on a given value; a specified instruction or instruction type is executed. Most of these events can be directly or indirectly detected by tools which can detect the execution of a given instruction. For instance, all accesses to a certain storage object can be detected by detecting the executions of all instructions which refer to that object.

In some cases, it would be more convenient to use other methods of detection. For example, when one is interested in counting all accesses made to a given data structure, it would be more natural to monitor the "entry point" of the data structure than the execution of all instructions which access it. However, this is not generally feasible, unless the data structure is accessed via a single descriptor or a subroutine in which a tool can be installed. A feasible but economically questionable solution would be to use one bit of each data or instruction word as a trap indicator. Whenever a memory word is accessed, a trap would be generated by the hardware or firmware of the CPU if this bit is 1. This feature could be used for measurement as well as for program debugging, an activity which has much in common with software measurements.

Thus, the only type of internal event which is really detected by internally driven software tools is the execution of an instruction. The sensor, called a *checkpoint* or *software probe*, is very similar to the breakpoint used in interactive debugging. However, after it has performed its task, a checkpoint does not return control to the user but to the program being measured. A checkpoint is an instruction which is inserted at the proper place into the code of a program. It either collects and stores the data by itself, as in the case of the instruction in Fig. 2.9, or calls a *measurement routine* for the same purpose.

The interference in time due to a checkpoint is equal to the execution time of the checkpoint and of the measurement routine, if any. This time can often be estimated with good accuracy; sometimes, if the system is equipped with a high-resolution clock and the overhead in reading the clock is not too big, it can be measured. In these cases, measurement errors due to time interference can be eliminated or substantially reduced by correcting the event times recorded. Evaluating the effects of interference in time on other types of data is usually more complicated. The effects of the interference in space, which is due to the space required by the additional code (the checkpoints and the measurement routines) and by the collected data, are also quite hard to determine. Note that the interference in time may be intolerable if software probes are inserted into time-critical portions of the operating system, such as those controlling synchronous devices such as disks or drums.

Example 2.4 In an interactive system, the distribution of the commands issued by the users is to be measured. The command interpreter is the operating system module invoked every time a command arrives from a terminal. This module interprets the command and transfers control to the appropriate section of its code which is to process it. Assuming that the relative frequency of each type of command is to be obtained, we can associate command types to the elements of a vector, say COMTYP, and keep in each element the number of times the corresponding command type has been issued. COMTYP will be reset to all zeroes at the beginning of a measurement session by some privileged command, and the experimenter will be allowed to read it at any time by another privileged command. The checkpoints shown in Table 2.5(a) perform the task of accumulating the histogram of command usage in COMTYP. The language used in the table is FORTRAN. Each section of code which processes a distinct command type begins with a checkpoint which increments the corresponding element of COMTYP.

If a command trace is to be collected, the instrumentation shown in Table 2.5(b) may be used. Each event record consists of the event tag (the command type) and the event time. The tags are collected in the vector EVTAG and the times in the vector EVTIME. STORE is a routine, not reported in Table 2.5, which is called when these two vectors in memory are full and which transfer their contents to a secondary storage medium. ITIME is a routine, also not shown in the table, which reads the real-time clock and returns its reading as an integer K.

It is evident that the solution in Table 2.5(b) causes considerably more interference than the one in Table 2.5(a), both in time and in space. However, the command trace contains much more information than the command histogram. Furthermore, the nature of the quantities being measured is such that these interferences do not affect the accuracy of the measurements in the case of Table 2.5(a), which consist of event counts. In the case of Table 2.5(b), the interference might cause the recorded command times to be slightly inaccurate with respect to those which would be measured by a hardware tool. However, the accuracy desired for command times is probably low enough so that these errors will be tolerable in all the conceivable applications of command times in a performance evaluation study.

If it were necessary, the time spent in executing the routine MEASUR could be measured and the command times automatically corrected as shown in Table 2.5(c). Note that the total error TOTERR is initialized to zero at the beginning of the session. Of course, the clock's resolution should be sufficiently high to make this time measurable with reasonable accuracy. For instance, a clock which is incremented at every microsecond will satisfy this condition, whereas one with a 1-millisecond resolution will not. ∎

Checkpoints can be used to implement both fixed and nonfixed software tools. A *fixed software tool* is any permanent checkpoint which collects data every time the flow of control reaches that location in the instrumented program. There are many examples of fixed tools in operating systems.

Extremely popular fixed tools are those used for accounting purposes. A typical accounting routine is invoked when a job leaves the system, reads various registers and tables, calculates from these readings the amounts of resources used by the job, and, by applying an installation-specified charging algorithm, produces the user's bill. The statistics collected by the accounting routine are usually accumulated in a log and periodically reduced to allow performance to be

Table 2.5

SOFTWARE TOOLS FOR THE PROBLEM IN EXAMPLE 2.4

(a)	(b)
C COMMAND INTERPRETER	C COMMAND INTERPRETER
⋮	⋮
C EDIT COMMAND PROCESSOR	C EDIT COMMAND PROCESSOR
100 COMTYP(1) = COMTYP(1) + 1	100 CALL MEASUR(1)
⋮	⋮
C COMPILE COMMAND PROCESSOR	C COMPILE COMMAND PROCESSOR
200 COMTYP(2) = COMTYP(2) + 1	200 CALL MEASUR(2)
⋮	⋮
C SAVE COMMAND PROCESSOR	C SAVE COMMAND PROCESSOR
300 COMTYP(3) = COMTYP(3) + 1	300 CALL MEASUR(3)
⋮	⋮

(b)

```
      SUBROUTINE MEASUR(COMD)
      COMMON NCOMD
      DIMENSION EVTAG(1000),
     EVTIME(1000)
      CALL ITIME(K)
      EVTAG(NCOMD) = COMD
      EVTIME(NCOMD) = K
      NCOMD = NCOMD + 1
      IF(NCOMD.LE.1000) RETURN
      CALL STORE
      NCOMD = 1
      RETURN
      END
```

(c)

```
      SUBROUTINE MEASUR(COMD)
      COMMON NCOMD,TOTERR
      DIMENSION EVTAG(1000),
     EVTIME(1000)
      CALL ITIME(K)
      EVTAG(NCOMD) = COMD
      EVTIME(NCOMD) = K - TOTERR
      NCOMD = NCOMD + 1
      IF(NCOMD.LE.1000) GO TO 10
      CALL STORE
      NCOMD = 1
10    CALL ITIME(K1)
      TOTERR = TOTERR + K1 - K
      RETURN
      END
```

minimize Interference

monitored, even though with a substantial delay, by the installation's personnel. This log is often a valuable source of performance data for evaluation studies. Some accounting routines, which have been designed with measurement objectives in mind, produce reports showing the values of performance indices such as throughput rates and device utilization factors.

Sometimes, other types of *logs* are kept in a system, for example, the log of all detected errors, failures, and down times of the various modules; the log of all threats to the privacy of user files; and logs of job characteristics at a much more detailed level than those recorded in the accounting log. A log generally requires a large amount of permanent storage and is usually stored on tape or disk.

The *software meter* is another useful type of fixed tool. It consists of a permanent checkpoint whose only function is to increment by 1 the contents of a memory location every time the checkpoint is executed. This location can be accessed by program whenever needed, and successive readings of its contents can provide event counts relevant to an evaluation study or to a continuous-monitoring activity. For example, meters counting the number of times each module of the operating system is executed are worth incorporating into a system. Another example is a meter which counts the number of interrupts received (or serviced) by the CPU. The designers of Multics have incorporated into their system a number of meters and other slightly more complicated fixed tools. These tools have been found to be very useful, especially because of the difficulty and the risk of inserting temporary tools into a large software system [*see* Saltzer and Gintell (1970)].

Duration time A more sophisticated type of fixed tool is to be used in order to measure the durations of intervals between two events. For instance, the CPU-time clock in a multiprogramming system reads the real-time clock when a process starts and when it stops receiving the attention of the CPU and accumulates the differences between consecutive readings.

The flexibility of *nonfixed software tools* presents wide variations. Some of them can only be turned on and turned off, but the events they detect cannot be modified. This is the case for a large part of the instruments incorporated in the Multics system. In other tools, such as the System Internal Performance Evaluation (SIPE) program [Deniston (1969)], which can be incorporated into the complex of resident operating system modules of TSS/360, the user can specify those subsets of the events monitored by the tool that are to be recorded. Others, such as the System Management Facility (SMF) of IBM [*see* Pomeroy (1972)], allow users to write their own measurement and reduction routines but impose restrictions on the checkpoint locations. SMF, in particular, collects information on the resources used by each job during each job step and provides several *control-program exits* which can be used to call optional installation-written routines. These exits correspond to important changes in a job's life within the system, which can be detected and recorded by the routines added by SMF users.

Two software tools which leave an almost complete freedom to their users are the Informer and the SMT. They can be used to instrument any program, and not only the operating system. Furthermore, they exploit the capabilities of interactive systems in the temporary instrumentation of programs, which is often an iterative, trial-and-error process.

The Informer [Deutsch and Grant (1971)] is a software package designed and implemented for the Xerox 940 time-sharing system. It automatically inserts checkpoints into a given program at user-specified locations. The checkpoints may call measurement routines submitted by the user and verified by the Informer against some acceptance criteria. These criteria are satisfied if a measurement routine, which is to be inserted in the address space of the program being measured, does not

    a. store or branch into the program,
    b. contain illegal or privileged instructions,
    c. run for an uncontrolled length of time,
    d. modify itself or other measurement routines,
    e. have the possibility of being reentered before being exited,
    f. read private sections of the code or of the data of the program.

To facilitate the verification of measurement routines, they must all have a standard structure, which consists of some distinct regions having different access characteristics. Also, the use of backward branches is forbidden, unless the branch closes a loop to be executed no more times than a known constant number. This restriction allows the Infomer to rapidly compute a worst-case estimate of a measurement routine's running time. Calls to the operating system are illegal for a measurement routine, except those related to certain I/O instructions having to do with the concurrent use of a hardware tool. To verify condition f above, the Informer is to be given a table of the program's private areas. Since there are some regions in the program's address space where checkpoints cannot be inserted (data areas, "execute" instructions, instruction areas whose execution time is critical), a table of these regions must be provided. The Informer also needs a table of the maximum tolerable interferences in time for each measurable region of the program and a table of the unused areas of the address space, where measurement routines can be stored.

    The Informer uses the *patching technique* illustrated in Fig. 2.10 to insert checkpoints. The call to the measurement routine (or routines) is made through a *software switch* housed in one of the regions of the measurement routine space. A switch, whose implementation in the Informer is shown in Fig. 2.10, can be turned

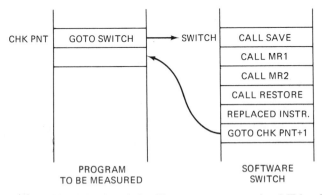

Figure 2.10   Software switch calling measurement routines MR1 and MR2 (the switch may be turned off by replacing CALL MR1 and CALL MR2 by no-operation instructions).

on to connect the checkpoint to the measurement routine or turned off to disconnect it. When certain measurement data are not to be collected, the corresponding switches may be turned off to reduce the performance degradation caused by the instrumentation.

The users can interact with their measurement routines, a feature especially useful in debugging these routines. Interactive communication is supported by part of the Informer, which resides in the address space of the measured program. This allows some checks which can be made only at run time to be performed but increases the interference of the tool. The primitives which constitute the interface between the Informer and its users are listed in Table 2.6.

Table 2.6
SET OF PRIMITIVE COMMANDS FOR THE INFORMER

Command	Function
NEW MEASUREMENT PROGRAM (⟨user-space address⟩)	Checks routine at user-space address and, if correct, copies it into the operating-system address space
ATTACH (⟨identifier⟩, ⟨op.sys.address⟩)	Inserts at specified address a checkpoint calling measurement routine with given identifier
DELETE MEASUREMENT ROUTINE (⟨identifier⟩)	Removes specified routine and disconnects all checkpoints calling it
DETACH CHECKPOINT (⟨op.sys.address⟩)	Disconnects specified checkpoint from its switch
SET SWITCH (⟨switch number⟩, ⟨identifier⟩)	Associates identified routine with specified switch
CLEAR SWITCH (⟨switch number⟩)	Detaches from specified switch all routines associated with it
BLOCK( )	Causes a pause in user program until one of its measurement routines wakes it up
EXECUTE IN CONTEXT (⟨instruction⟩)	Executes instruction as if it were part of a measurement routine
ACCESS MEASUREMENT SPACE (⟨user-space address⟩)	Places measurement space in the user's virtual space with read-only status
IS CHECKPOINT? (⟨op.sys.address⟩)	Tells the user whether there is a checkpoint at the specified address
IS CONNECTED? (⟨identifier⟩)	Returns list of checkpoints to which the specified measurement routine is connected

Source: Deutsch and Grant (1971).

The Software Measurement Tool (SMT) is a package, having the same scope as the Informer, designed for intraprocess measurements in the PRIME system [*see* Ferrari and Liu (1975)]. The three phases of the SMT are schematically represented in Fig. 2.11. The SMT was conceived as a general-purpose measurement facility for all users of PRIME. Since in PRIME, a highly secure system, users could not measure anything outside their jurisdiction, most of the restrictions imposed by the Informer on measurement routines and checkpoint locations were not necessary. Whatever users did in their jurisdictions had no effect on the rest of the system. The operating system was fully protected against nonauthorized users and could be measured only by a few authorized system programmers. These programmers were allowed to add to their copy of the SMT some automatic verifications of measurement routines to protect the operating system against their nonintentional mistakes.

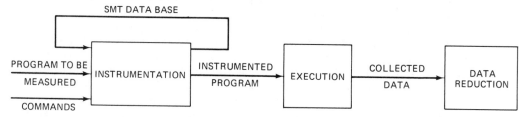

Figure 2.11   Three phases of SMT operation. [*Source:* Ferrari and Liu (1975), by permission of John Wiley & Sons Ltd.]

Besides accepting user-written routines, the SMT offers its users a number of standard measurement routines (see their types in Table 2.7). The standard

Table 2.7

TYPES OF STANDARD MEASUREMENT ROUTINES IN THE SMT

Measurement routine	Actions performed
CT(⟨counter number⟩)	Increments one of 16 counters
DP(⟨register names⟩)	Records the program counter contents and (optionally) those of the A and/or B and/or X registers
RV(⟨variable name⟩)	Records the value of a variable
RP(⟨variable name⟩)	Records the value of a variable and the program counter contents
TC(⟨limit⟩,⟨program term. flag⟩)	Stops data collection and turns checkpoints off when number of executions reaches limit; halts program if flag is on

Source: Ferrari and Liu (1975).

routines reduce the interference (since their execution characteristics have been carefully optimized) and facilitate the use of the tool.

Measurement routines can be written in any language for which there is a compiler running on PRIME. Also, each routine can be given several different names so that the user can selectively turn off, or completely eliminate, some calls to a routine while leaving the other calls untouched. Checkpoint locations may be referenced by symbolic addresses having the format used in the system's interactive debugger. The SMT has macrocommands, for example, to trace the flow of control in a program. Its design also includes a macrocommand definition facility, a program-sampling facility which calls a given standard or user-written measurement routine at every sampling instant, and an expandable library of standard data reduction routines.

Example 2.5 The use of the SMT in temporarily instrumenting a pseudo-random-number-generating routine (RAND) is illustrated in Tables 2.8 and 2.9. The SMT commands used in Table 2.9 are listed in Table 2.10. Table 2.8 shows the text of the routine to be instrumented. RAND is written in the assembly language of PRIME, which coincides with the one of the Xerox 940 System. A trace of the first 1000 numbers generated by RAND is to be collected. Table 2.9(a) presents the commands to be typed in for this purpose by the user (in uppercase letters) and the computer's responses (in lowercase letters). File /PROG contains RAND and the program which uses it; file /INSPROG is created to store the instrumented programs and the associated SMT data base. Two standard measurement routines (see Table 2.7) are loaded into RAND's address space by the SMT. One of them, called RANVAL by the user, is of the read variable (RV) type; it records VALUE and is invoked by one checkpoint, to be executed just before the return branch BRR RAND. The other measurement routine is of the terminate collection (TC) type and is called TCNT; it terminates the collection of the data, without stopping the program's execution, after having been invoked 1000 times. TCNT is

Table 2.8

PSEUDO-RANDOM NUMBER GENERATING ROUTINE TO
BE INSTRUMENTED IN EXAMPLE 2.5

RAND	BSS	1	return address is stored here
	LDA	VALUE	load A register with old value
	MUL	MFAC	multiply by MFAC; high order bits in A register, low order bits in B register
	CBA		copy B register to A register
	ADD	AFAC	add AFAC to A register
	STA	VALUE	store new value = (old value∗MFAC + AFAC)(mod 2^{24})
	BRR	RAND	return branch with new value in A register

Source: Ferrari and Liu (1975), by permission of John Wiley & Sons Ltd.

Table 2.9
SMT SESSION TO INSTRUMENT
THE PROGRAM IN TABLE 2.8

(a) @SMT.
    # LOAD. file: /PROG.
    # DEFINE. mrname: RANVAL
        type: RV
        loc: VALUE·
    # DEFINE. mrname: TCNT
        type: TC
        limit: 1000
        halt?: N
    # CHECKPOINT. mrname: RANVAL
        loc: RAND+6
    # CHECKPOINT. mrname: TCNT
        loc: RAND+6
    # SAVE. file: /INSPROG
        starting address: GO
    # FINISH.
    @GO TO /INSPROG.
    data file: /smtdt∅

(b) @SMT.
    # RELOAD. file: /INSPROG
    # ON. all?: Y
    # FORGET. all?: N
        c:
        m: RANVAL
    # DEFINE. mrname: CALLER
        type: RV
        loc: RAND
    # CHECKPOINT. mrname: CALLER
        loc: RAND+1
    # SAVE. file: /INSPROG
        starting address: GO
    # FINISH.
    @GO TO /INSPROG.
    data file: /smtdtl
    @

Source: Ferrari and Liu (1975), by permission
of John Wiley & Sons Ltd.

called from the same location as RANVAL and turns off all checkpoints when the
termination conditions are satisfied.

    After saving the instrumented program, the user exits from the instrumentation
phase of the SMT. The instrumented program is then executed. The measurement data
produced during execution are stored in file /SMTDT∅. The name of this file is chosen by
the SMT.

    Table 2.9(b) shows the commands to be input by the user in order to delete the
measurement routine RANVAL and consequently the checkpoint which calls it. Also,

TABLE 2.10

SMT COMMANDS USED IN TABLE 2.9 (*see* EXAMPLE 2.5)

Command	Arguments	Function
LOAD	⟨file name⟩	Loads and links binary file(s) containing program to be measured
RELOAD	⟨file name⟩	Loads a core-image file created in a previous instrumentation phase and its associated SMT data base
DEFINE	⟨meas. rout. name⟩	Assigns a name (and arguments) to a standard or user-written measurement routine
CHECKPOINT	⟨meas. route. name⟩, ⟨location⟩	Inserts a call to the specified routine at the designated location in the program
ON	⟨all flag⟩, ⟨location⟩, ⟨meas. rout. name⟩	Turns on the specified checkpoints
FORGET	⟨all flag⟩, ⟨location⟩, ⟨meas. rout. name⟩	Removes the specified checkpoints
SAVE	⟨file name⟩	Saves into designated file the core image of the instrumented program and its SMT data base
FINISH		Terminates the instrumentation phase

Source: Ferrari and Liu (1975).

another standard measurement routine, named CALLER, is added, with one checkpoint inserted between the first and the second location of RAND. CALLER is of the RV type, and, when invoked, records the return address. Thus, file /SMTDT1 will, after the subsequent execution of the instrumented program, contain the return addresses of the first 1000 calls to RAND issued by the program during its execution. The two data files will then be reduced so that the user of the SMT may readily understand and interpret the results of the two experiments. ■

Other examples of the use of checkpointing techniques in program measurement are given in Section 9.3.1.

2.4.3 Externally Driven (Sampling) Tools { time sampling

Sampling techniques allow one to substantially reduce the amount of data which are to be collected in order to estimate some quantities of interest. They may be based on the detection of internal events. For instance, data can be collected every time the contents of an event counter reach a certain value. This may be called *count sampling*. Examples of count-sampling tools are those which collect data when a given number of instructions have been executed or when a given number of memory references have been issued.

In most cases, however, sampling tools detect the occurrences of prespecified time instants, which have been termed *external events* in Section 2.2. This type of tool may be called a *time-sampling* tool. Externally driven tools are usually of the time-sampling type.

Sampling instants can be separated by intervals of constant durations (*periodic sampling*), or of randomly chosen durations (*random sampling*), or of durations obeying other laws of variation. When an event is detected, a sampling tool acts as an internally driven one, collecting, possibly manipulating, and storing the data which are relevant to the experiment. The data collected at the sampling instants are called *observations*.

Sampling techniques may be used in hardware tools. For instance, the measurement of utilization factors illustrated in Figs. 2.5 and 2.7 is based on the periodic sampling of electric signals. However, this sampling is performed within the tool, which receives continuously the signals to be monitored. Thus, the changes in the voltage levels of these signals may be used as in internally driven tools; for example, they may be counted. If we exclude this type of sampling from our consideration, we can say that sampling techniques are more popular in software tools than in hardware tools. This is the reason they are discussed here.

Suppose that the utilization of the CPU is to be measured. Then, as illustrated in Fig. 2.5, we can sample the state of the CPU, which varies in time as shown by the Boolean function $a(t)$ in Fig. 2.12. At each sampling instant t_i, we observe and record the value $a_i = a(t_i)$. The sequence $a_1, a_2, \ldots, a_i, \ldots$ may be modeled as a stochastic sequence, that is, as a discrete-time stochastic process.

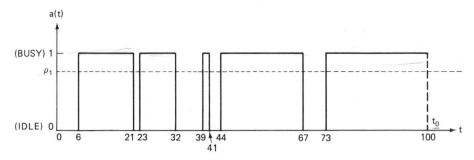

Figure 2.12 State of a CPU as a function of time.

A *stochastic process* $X(t)$ is a function of time t whose values are random variables. The value of $X(t)$ at time t^* represents the state of the stochastic process at t^*. If each random variable may take on only a finite or countable number of values, we have a *discrete-state* process or *chain*. Otherwise, we have a *continuous-state* stochastic process. The natural numbers may be used to identify the states of a chain $X(t)$. If $X(t)$ is in state S_j at time t, we say that $X(t) = j$, where j is a natural number. If the time instants at which state transitions may occur are finite or countable, then the process is a *discrete-time* one, or a stochastic sequence. These time instants can be replaced by the integral values of a time index i. Hence, a stochastic sequence can be denoted by X_i ($i = 1, 2, \ldots$). A finite stochastic sequence is also called a *time series.* If transitions may occur at any point on a continuous time axis, the process is *continuous-time.*

Returning to our problem, we see that if we are interested in the utilization ρ_1 of the CPU during an interval $(0, t_0)$, we should measure the time average $\bar{a}$ of $a(t)$ over that interval, since $\rho_1 = \bar{a}$. If n observations of $a(t)$ in $(0, t_0)$ are made, we obtain a discrete-state time series $a_1, \ldots, a_n$. An estimate of ρ_1 is the *sample mean*

$$\text{Sample mean} \quad \hat{\rho}_1 = \frac{1}{n} \sum_{i=1}^{n} a_i. \qquad \frac{(\hat{\rho}_1 - \rho_1)}{(\sigma/\sqrt{n})} \to \begin{array}{l}\text{stand.}\\\text{normal}\\\text{dist.}\\\text{if } n \to \infty\end{array} \quad (2.2)$$

Our time series is *independent* if the random variables $a_1, a_2, \ldots, a_n$ are statistically independent of each other. The validity of the sampling technique relies heavily on the assumption of independent observations.

Let us make this assumption and let σ_1 be the standard deviation of the distribution of the values of $a(t)$ in $(0, t_0)$. Then, by the central limit theorem [*see,* for example, Snedecor and Cochran (1967)], the distribution of $(\hat{\rho}_1 - \rho_1)/(\sigma_1/\sqrt{n})$ approaches the standard normal distribution as n tends toward infinity. The standard normal distribution is a normal distribution with mean 0 and variance 1. Thus, $\hat{\rho}_1$ tends to be normally distributed with mean ρ_1 and variance σ_1^2/n as n gets larger.

If the observations are correlated with each other, the mean of the distribution of $\hat{\rho}_1$ still tends toward ρ_1, but its variance differs from σ_1^2/n. A general expression of the variance of $\hat{\rho}_1$ about ρ_1 is given in Section 2.6.4.

If there is some functional relationship between the observations, then the sample mean $\hat{\rho}_1$ may be a biased estimate of ρ_1; that is, it may not tend to ρ_1 as n increases. Thus, collecting functionally related observations is to be avoided in order for the sample means to be unbiased estimators. For example, if $a(t)$ were sampled at every millionth instruction executed by the CPU, the CPU would always be found busy, and the erroneous result $\rho_1 \cong \hat{\rho}_1 = 1$ would be obtained.

Note that functionally unrelated observations need not be generated by random sampling intervals. Also periodic sampling can be used if care is taken not to choose a sampling frequency equal to an integral multiple or submultiple of a frequency component present in the quantities to be sampled. For instance, if the CPU is always periodically interrupted by the real-time clock, sampling its state with a frequency equal to an integral multiple of the clock's frequency may synchronize the observations with the clock. Since the CPU is always busy immediately after it has received an interrupt, this may lead to the erroneous conclusion $\rho_1 \cong \hat{\rho}_1 = 1$.

What is the minimum number of observations to be taken so that the error made estimating ρ_1 by $\hat{\rho}_1$ is tolerable? In probabilistic terms, this question is equivalent to asking what is the minimum value of n which satisfies the inequality

$$\text{Prob}\,(|\hat{\rho}_1 - \rho_1| < e) \geq K, \tag{2.3}$$

where K is called the *confidence level* and e the *confidence interval* of $\hat{\rho}_1$. Note that the size of the confidence interval is actually $2e$.

By the central limit theorem we have

$$N\!\left(\frac{e\sqrt{n}}{\sigma_1}\right) - N\!\left(\frac{-e\sqrt{n}}{\sigma_1}\right) \geq K, \tag{2.4}$$

where $N(x)$ denotes the value in x of the standard normal distribution function.

Let z be chosen so that the probability that a random variable with the standard normal distribution falls within $(-z, z)$ is K. Then we have

$$N(z) = \frac{1 + K}{2}, \qquad N(-z) = \frac{1 - K}{2}, \tag{2.5}$$

and, from (2.4),

e confidence interval

z relate to conf. level.

$$n \geq \left(\frac{\sigma_1 z}{e}\right)^2. \tag{2.6}$$

Relationship (2.6) shows that the minimum number of observations is proportional to the variance and inversely proportional to the square of the confidence interval. Since in general σ_1 is not known, it can be replaced in (2.6) by the *sample standard deviation*

$$\hat{\sigma}_1 = \sqrt{\frac{\sum\limits_{i=1}^{n} (a_i - \hat{\rho}_1)^2}{n - 1}}. \tag{2.7}$$

The random variable $(\hat{\rho}_1 - \rho_1)/(\hat{\sigma}_1/\sqrt{n})$ has the Student's t-distribution with $n - 1$ degrees of freedom. Given $h + 1$ random variables $x, y_1, \ldots, y_h$, all independent of each other and all having the standard normal distribution, the random variable

$$t_h = \frac{x}{\sqrt{(1/h)\sum\limits_{i=1}^{h} y_i^2}} \tag{2.8}$$

has the Student's t-distribution with h degrees of freedom. The t-distribution is symmetric about its mean, which equals zero, and has a variance equal to $h/(h - 2)$, with $h > 2$.

The t-distributions corresponding to different numbers of degrees of freedom differ from each other, even though they have several common properties. As this number increases, the t-distributions become closer to the normal distribution. The distribution of $(\hat{\rho}_1 - \rho_1)/(\hat{\sigma}_1/\sqrt{n})$ has $n - 1$ degrees of freedom since only $n - 1$ of the n differences $a_i - \hat{\rho}_1$ in (2.7) are independent. This is due to the fact that, by (2.2), they must satisfy the condition $\sum_{i=1}^{n} (a_i - \hat{\rho}_1) = 0$.

In applying (2.6) with σ_1 approximated by $\hat{\sigma}_1$, it is more appropriate to use, instead of z, the quantity z', which is for the t-distribution with $n - 1$ degrees of freedom what z is for the standard normal distribution. Thus, z' is defined by $t_{n-1}(z') = (1 + K)/2$ and $t_{n-1}(-z') = (1 - K)/2$.

The value of z defined in (2.5) may be found in the tables of the standard normal distribution function reported in most statistics textbooks. Similarly, the value of z' defined above may be read in the tables of the t-distribution.

Example 2.6   The state of a CPU is sampled periodically in order to estimate ρ_1. Let the (unknown) behavior of $a(t)$ be the one depicted in Fig. 2.12. To make the sampling periodic, the observations have to be taken at times which divide $(0, t_0)$ into equal intervals. Thus, if three observations are taken they will be those at $t = 25, 50, 75$, since $t_0 = 100$; if $n = 4$, the sampling instants will be $t = 20, 40, 60, 80$. Table 2.11 lists the values of $\hat{\rho}_1$ which would be obtained for various values of n. Note that the actual value of CPU utilization, which can be easily derived from Fig. 2.12, is 0.76. The actual variance of the distribution of a, which can be calculated as the mean of the squares of the deviations around the mean ρ_1, is $\sigma_1^2 = 0.182$. The standard deviation is $\sigma_1 = 0.427$.

Table 2.11 also reports the sample standard deviations $\hat{\sigma}_1$, computed by using (2.7), for the various values of n. We shall assume a confidence level $K = 0.95$. That is, we want to compute the width of a confidence interval of $\hat{\rho}_1$ such that the probability that ρ_1 falls outside that interval, centered around $\hat{\rho}_1$, is 5%. This computation may be done by taking the equal sign in (2.6) and solving for e. Since in practical cases only $\hat{\sigma}_1$ is known, z will have to be replaced in (2.6) by z'. The e column in Table 2.11 shows these confidence intervals for the various values of n. For instance, when 50 observations are taken, the value of ρ_1 falls within the interval 0.76 ± 0.12, that is, $(0.64, 0.88)$, with probability 0.95.

Table 2.11

RESULTS OF PERIODIC-SAMPLING EXPERIMENTS
PERFORMED ON THE CPU STATE DEPICTED IN FIG. 2.12
(*see* EXAMPLE 2.6)

Number of observations, n	Sample mean, $\hat{\rho}_1$	Sample standard deviation, $\hat{\sigma}_1$	Confidence interval for $K = 0.95$, $e = \hat{\sigma}_1 z'/\sqrt{n}$
3	1.0	0.0	±0.0
4	1.0	0.0	±0.0
5	0.8	0.447	±0.55
6	0.666	0.516	±0.54
7	0.857	0.377	±0.35
8	0.75	0.462	±0.38
9	0.888	0.333	±0.25
15	0.733	0.457	±0.25
31	0.741	0.444	±0.16
50	0.76	0.431	±0.12

The minimum number of observations needed to reduce the confidence interval to ± 0.02, so that $\hat{\rho}_1 - 0.02 \leq \rho_1 \leq \hat{\rho}_1 + 0.02$ with probability 0.95, can be computed from (2.6). Using the best estimate of σ_1 in Table 2.11 ($\hat{\sigma}_1 = 0.431$) and the value of z (since z' tends toward z as n increases), we obtain $n \geq 1784$. If e is to be ± 0.01, then $n \geq 7136$. If $K = 0.99$ and $e = \pm 0.01$, then $n \geq 12,324$.   ∎

If the utilization of the CPU and other quantities are to be measured during a time period whose duration is fixed, the minimum sampling frequency is determined by the minimum value of n given by (2.6). If there are no constraints on the duration of the measurement session, the sampling frequency can be chosen freely, provided that it does not coincide with an integral multiple or submultiple of a periodic component of quantities to be measured. In fact, for a given confidence level, the accuracy of the estimates depends only on the number of observations n. However, the reader should note that this is true only if the distributions of the quantities being observed do not depend on time – in other words, if the sequence of observations can be modeled as a stationary sequence. A stochastic sequence X_i ($i = 1, 2, \ldots$) is said to be *stationary* if the joint probability distribution functions $F_{X_j X_{j+1} \ldots X_{j+h}}(x_j, x_{j+1}, \ldots, x_{j+h}) = \text{Prob}$ $(X_j \leq x_j, X_{j+1} \leq x_{j+1}, \ldots, X_{j+h} \leq x_{j+h})$ are equal for all $j = 1, 2, \ldots$ and for all $h = 1, 2, \ldots$. This is equivalent to requiring that all the joint probability distribution functions be invariant with respect to shifts in the time index.

The sequences of observations of work-load parameters are very often assumed to be modelable as stationary time series. In computing centers or computing utilities, this may not be the case. Consider a very simple work-load parameter, the number of jobs submitted per unit time to a batch-processing installation. If we plot the job arrival rate versus time, the resulting curve is likely to display relatively high-frequency fluctuations over intervals of, say, 1 hour. Periodic or quasi-periodic variations with longer periods (1 day, 1 week, 1 month, 1 quarter) will also be found to exist in many installations. Finally, an even slower, aperiodic drift, generally toward higher arrival rates, will probably be observed. Over time intervals which are either very short or very long with respect to the periodic variations mentioned above, the work load (and hence also the system) is probably far from exhibiting a stationary behavior. The situation may be closer to a stationary one over medium-duration intervals, selected taking the periodic variations into account. For example, we may expect this to be the case if we consider the same 1-hour interval for a few consecutive weekdays or the same day of the week for a few consecutive weeks. However, we should always try to check the validity of the stationary-behavior assumption by experimental means.

Sampling techniques were introduced in the field of software instrumentation by Kolence in 1968 [*see* Kolence (1971)]. One of the sampling tools produced since then by Boole and Babbage, Inc. is the Configuration Utilization Evaluator (CUE).

CUE consists of two parts: the extractor and the analyzer. During a measurement session, the extractor is periodically called by the system's interval timer and collects data from the operating system's tables to which it has access. The maximum sampling frequency is equal to the frequency of the interval timer. A submultiple of this frequency can be selected by the user in order to reduce the interference. The collected data are stored by the extractor in secondary storage and later reduced by the analyzer. These data include the states of the CPU and of the I/O processors and devices, the names of the disk units which are performing seek operations, and those of the non-memory-resident modules of the operating system which are in memory at the time the system is sampled.

Table 2.12 presents excerpts from a report prepared by the analyzer. The data in the table were obtained during two 1-hour measurement sessions. The times of the two sessions were chosen so as to coincide with the daily peak period. Samples were collected at 33.33-millisecond intervals. Since the total measurement time was 2 hours, 216,000 observations were made for each one of the data collected at sampling instants. Subreport a displays the values of the same utilization and overlap factors whose measurement by wired-program hardware tools has been described in Example 2.2 (*see* Table 2.3).

Table 2.12

EXAMPLE OF CUE OUTPUT

(a) *Equipment usage subreport*

Equipment sampled	Amount of time [s]	Percentage of total time
CPU busy	2679.84	37.22
CPU busy in supervisor mode	303.84	4.22
Any channel busy	3060.72	57.46
CPU busy and any channel busy	1514.16	21.03
CPU busy and no channel busy	1355.94	18.82
CPU wait and any channel busy	2622.96	36.43
CPU wait and only channel 1 busy	1779.84	24.71
Channel 1 and channel 2 busy	181.44	2.52
⋮	⋮	⋮

(b) *Concurrent I/O request subreport*

Number of I/O requests	Percentage of time in use	Cumulative percentage of time in use
0	3.51	3.51
1–6	7.32	10.83
7–12	19.87	30.70
13–18	54.92	85.62
19–24	7.43	93.05
25–30	6.95	100.00

Table 2.12—cont.

(c) *Head movement subreport*
   Device 131

Number of cylinders	Number of movements which traveled this number of cylinders	Head movement time [ms]	Percentage of total time
1	845	21125	2.08
⋮	⋮	⋮	⋮
60	700	50400	4.96
⋮	⋮	⋮	⋮
141	1944	204120	20.09
142	579	61374	6.04
⋮	⋮	⋮	⋮

Cylinder addresses	Number of movements between these two addresses	Head movement time [ms]	Percentage of total time
37 178	1119	117495	11.56
124 184	700	50400	4.96
36 177	527	55335	5.45
41 183	446	47276	4.65
124 125	338	8450	0.83
38 179	298	31290	3.08
⋮ ⋮	⋮	⋮	⋮

(d) *SVC subreport*

SVC ID	Number of loads	Percent of total loads	Cumulative percentage
IGC0007B	61	20.40	20.40
IGG01910	41	13.71	34.11
IGG0191B	19	6.35	40.46
⋮	⋮	⋮	⋮
IGC0003D	1	0.33	100.00

Source: Holtwick (1971).

A comparison between CUE measurements and those obtained during the session with a hardware tool [*see* Peterson (1974)] showed that, for the measured installation, CUE produced accurate results for almost all the I/O channels. However, the values of ρ_1 reported by CUE were on the average about 7% lower than those reported by the hardware tool, the values of ρ_{1p} (*see* Table 2.3 for the symbology) were on the average about 14% higher, and the values of ρ_{1s} about 21% lower. These errors can be explained by considering the fact that in some cases, when the CPU is busy in the supervisor state, interrupts are disabled. Thus, CUE cannot take samples, and the probability that CUE finds the CPU in the problem state, or idle, is higher than it would be if the CPU were interruptable at all times. This is an example of the inaccuracies caused by nonrandom, functionally related observations.

The relative frequencies of the system states characterized by different numbers of I/O requests pending or being serviced are given in subreport b. For each movable-arm disk, subreport c yields a histogram of the number of cylinders traversed during a seek and a list of the numbers of seeks performed between the various pairs of cylinders. Finally, the number of times each SVC (supervisor call), that is, each nonresident module of the operating system, is loaded into memory is provided by subreport d.

Another sampling tool produced by Boole and Babbage, Inc. is the Problem Program Evaluator (PPE). This tool will be briefly discussed in Section 9.3.1.

2.5 INSTRUMENTATION SYSTEMS

Usually, measurement tools are designed for existing systems, to which they are then applied. A result of this approach is that tool designers and users frequently encounter serious problems due to the constraints imposed on the tools by the organization and implementation of the system to be measured. For example, events of interest may not be practically accessible, interference may be excessive, or the validity of the collected data may not be verifiable. On the other hand, modifying a system in order to make it more suitable for measurements is generally a difficult, risky, and expensive task.

Most of these problems would disappear, or be mitigated, if provisions for measurement tools were made at system design time—even better, if the system and its instrumentation were designed and implemented together. The latter approach would also allow the measurement tools to be used in the final phases of the design of the system (*see* Chapter 8). Several research projects have investigated the problem and gathered some experience. The instrumentation systems of Multics [*see* Saltzer and Gintell (1970)] and of PRIME [*see* Ferrari (1973)] have already been mentioned in previous sections. In these designs, one of the main problems was to predict, at a time when the system was not even fully specified, what events and quantities would have to be observed in the future. The solutions adopted in these two projects can be described as different mixtures of ad hoc fixed tools and (especially in PRIME) general-purpose tools. The fixed tools were incorporated to detect events whose future importance was clear since the beginning. On the other hand, the more flexible tools were to take care of the other events, in particular those to be detected in evaluation studies requiring temporary measurements.

When measurement tools are designed together with the system, the requirements of instrumentation may exert some influence on the design of the system. For example, special instructions like the one in Fig. 2.9 may be added to the instruction set of the machine. Special registers, counters, buses, and memory ports may be incorporated into the system. The structure of the operating system and the layout of the backplanes may also be affected to some extent by measurement considerations.

When instrumentation is added to an existing system, influences are in one direction only. That is, the architecture of the system affects the tools, often imposing restrictions on their capabilities, but not vice versa.

In some cases, serious restrictions to instrumentation design may come from the protection mechanisms of the system. Protection and measurement, as was observed in Section 2.3.4, have conflicting needs. Experimenters would often like to gather information which, by its own nature, cannot be made accessible to them without destroying the privacy of the users' information or weakening the protection system which is to enforce the technical aspects of the privacy requirements. The instrumentation system of PRIME, a machine for which high interprocess privacy was one of the major design objectives, offers an example of the restrictions caused by the protection rules, which it was decided not to modify for measurement purposes. For example, in PRIME no process can monitor another process, since their domains (or jurisdictions) are completely disjoint.

Design-time concern for instrumentation facilitates measurements during the testing, tuning, and working phases of a system's life, thereby improving our understanding of the system and making it more suitable for our needs. Furthermore, this concern may become necessary if the current trend toward incorporating more sophisticated control mechanisms into operating systems continues. Taking real-time measurements of performance indices and work-load parameters and feeding them into these mechanisms are essential to the implementation of a closed-loop control system. An appropriate analogy, already applied to stored-program tools in Section 2.3.4, is the one with industrial process control. When an information-handling process is to be controlled, a module of the operating system acts as the controller. This module tries to optimize the performance of the system by modifying system parameters (in particular, resource management policies) and sometimes certain aspects of the work load. For instance, the number of users of an interactive system may be reduced in a situation of congestion by not accepting any new log-ons and by automatically logging off some of the current users. The choice of the quantities to be measured and of those to be modified in a closed-loop performance control system is discussed from a general viewpoint in Section 7.4.2.

All operating systems contain some fixed software tools on whose readings their resource allocation decisions are based. For example, the scheduling policy of many batch-processing systems orders the jobs to be executed according to the priorities and to the maximum resource requirements (CPU time, memory space, number of tapes to be mounted) indicated by the programmer on a job control card. However, those systems which incorporate closed-loop dynamic control algorithms need a much more extensive instrumentation system of the continuous-monitoring type. The stability problems which may arise with this approach are still very little known. Indeed, the methods and results of control theory might be applicable to operating system design if suitable system and work-load models could be formulated.

2.6   THE DESIGN OF MEASUREMENT EXPERIMENTS

2.6.1. Problem Definition

In Section 2.1, we saw that one of the essential steps of the planning phase of an empirical evaluation study is the design of the experiments. An *experiment* consists of the set of empirical (or simulation) tests performed to obtain answers to questions which arise in an evaluation study. A study may require many experiments, and an experiment consists of a number of *sessions* or *runs*. The term *session* is often used when measurement techniques are applied, whereas *run* is more frequently employed in the case of simulation techniques. During a session or run, data are gathered on the behavior of the system and possibly of its work load. Since the work load naturally fluctuates, a number of observations must be collected for each quantity of interest, so that the distributions of these quantities and their moments can be estimated with sufficient accuracy. Thus, the duration of a session will depend on the number of observations to be made. The problem of determining the duration of a session and the time of its execution will be examined in Section 2.6.4.

The performance indices of a system depend on a number of installation parameters. Adopting the terminology used in the statistical design of experiments, we shall call *factors* the parameters which influence appreciably the value of a given performance index. Some of the factors are *quantitative*, such as the CPU time demand of the jobs which constitute a certain work load. However, also *nonquantitative* factors such as the CPU scheduling policy must usually be considered. Thus, the "values" of a factor are called *levels*, a term which applies also to nonquantitative factors.

A session is normally defined by a particular combination of levels for the factors. If there are three factors A, B, and C, whose levels are denoted by $A1$, $A2, \ldots, B1, B2, \ldots, C1, C2, \ldots$, the triple (Ai, Bj, Ck) defines a session, during which the level of A is Ai, the level of B is Bj, and the level of C is Ck.

Single-session experiments are sufficient for an evaluation study when only one configuration of the system and one type of work load need to be considered. This may be the case, for instance, when a computer system is being measured to determine whether its performance under a given work load is satisfactory, that is, whether it meets certain minimum requirements.

Multiple-session experiments are necessary if the influences of the factors on the performance of a system are to be determined or if the system is to be iteratively optimized. In designing these experiments, the main problems are

    a. the identification of the factors,
    b. the choice of their levels for each session to be performed.

These problems will be discussed in Sections 2.6.2 and 2.6.3, respectively.

No experiment is valid if it is not reproducible. In computer performance measurement, it is very difficult to design a reproducible experiment. This problem will be discussed in Chapter 5, since the reproducibility of experiments on computer systems is strictly related to the selection and control of the work load. Note that the fluctuations of the work load in time do not necessarily imply that the levels of the factors which characterize the work load vary. For example, if the work-load parameters can be described as stationary random variables, their time-invariant distributions can be considered as the levels of the corresponding factors. Thus, a different session would have to be defined only if at least one of these distributions were modified.

2.6.2 The Identification of the Factors

The first step in the design of a multiple-session experiment is to identify the factors. This is in general a very difficult task. Often, the quantification of the influence of certain factors on a performance index is in itself a problem requiring an evaluation study for its solution. As we shall see in Section 2.7, the discovery, after an experiment, that an index does not appreciably depend on a certain parameter leads us to conclude that this parameter is not a factor. However, when the experiment is being designed, we must often choose the parameters which are likely to be important factors without knowing their actual weight.

In this identification task, investigators have to rely on their past experience, on their knowledge of the system, and on their intuition. The number of parameters which can a priori be expected to influence a performance index may be very large. On the other hand, as will be seen in Section 2.6.3, the cost of an experiment increases rather sharply with the number of factors being considered. Thus, a selection must be made, and must be made carefully. Unfortunately, this selection is complicated by the intricate interdependencies among parameters, which are often only superficially known or suspected.

A useful classification of the factors selected for an experiment is the one into *primary* and *secondary* factors. Primary factors are those parameters whose influence on performance the experimenter is directly interested in studying. Secondary factors must be taken into account since their influence is likely to be nonnegligible. However, the quantification of this influence is not among the objectives of the study; rather, the experimenter often tries to eliminate or reduce this influence by a careful design of the experiment, so that the effects of the primary factors may be neatly seen and interpreted.

Two additional definitions of interest are those of *controllable* factor and *observable* factor. A controllable factor is a factor whose levels can be chosen by the experimenter. An observable factor is a factor whose levels can be measured during the experiment. If a system during a measurement session is driven by its normal *production work load*, very little control can be exerted on the work-load parameters. In this case, the factors which characterize the work load can only be observed. These factors would be controllable if the users were excluded and the system were completely dedicated to the experiment and driven by an *artificial work load*. We shall see in Chapter 3 that all the factors in simulation experiments can be controlled and observed, even though the degree of controllability of the work-load parameters depends on the type of model used to represent the work load.

Example 2.7   The identification of the factors in the design of a paging experiment will now be discussed, following Tsao et al. (1972).

Paging is one of the techniques by which a virtual memory (*see* Section 1.2) can be implemented. In its simplest version, a paged virtual-address space is an ordered set of n locations, or information containers, which may be indexed by the consecutive natural numbers from 0 to $n - 1$. These numbers are the virtual addresses of the information items stored in the corresponding locations. The set is partitioned into fixed-size subsets containing consecutive virtual addresses, called *virtual page frames*.   When a program is loaded into this virtual space, the set of its words is partitioned into subsets corresponding to virtual page frames. All the words stored in a virtual page frame constitute a *page* of the program. The *paging device* is a secondary-memory device where the whole program can be assumed to be stored while it is being processed. Information is transferred in pages between the paging device and the primary memory. The primary memory is divided into *real page frames*, having the same size as their virtual counterparts. Each page, when loaded into memory, occupies a real page frame.

As we saw in Section 1.2, in virtual-memory systems only part of a program is usually loaded into primary memory. When the program references a piece of information which is not in memory, we have a fault. In a paged system, this is called a *page fault*, since it causes the whole page containing the referenced word to be brought into memory. If there is no room for the incoming page, one of the pages currently in memory is to be pushed out. The selection of this page is made by the operating system according to a *replacement algorithm*.

Let us consider a large program, say a compiler, running alone on a paged machine whose available memory is smaller than the program. The turnaround time of the program will be strongly influenced by the number of page faults generated during its execution, since the time needed to transfer a page from a rotating paging device, say a drum, to the primary memory is about four orders of magnitude longer than this memory's access time. Thus, the number of page faults is an important performance index for the program. We now want to design an experiment to determine what system and program parameters have the strongest impact on the number of page faults. How can we identify the parameters among which the factors should be chosen? How can we choose the factors?

The number of page faults generated during an execution depends on the behavior of the program being executed and on the policy followed by the system in managing the memory hierarchy. In the uniprogramming case we are considering, the amount of space allotted to the program in primary memory is constant and coincides with the size of the available memory. The policies for managing this space may be viewed as combinations of a *loading policy* and a *replacement policy*. The two main types of loading policies are *demand loading* and *preloading*. Under demand loading, a page is loaded into memory only when one of its words is referenced. Preloading policies, on the other hand, try to predict the future needs of the running program and may load pages before they are referenced. Mixtures of these two types of policies are also used; for instance, the allotted region of memory can be filled at the beginning of an execution (a typical preloading, or swapping, approach) and subsequently managed by demand loading. Replacement policies have been briefly introduced above.

Therefore, we can expect the number of page faults to depend on the amount of memory, on the loading policy, and on the replacement policy.

Parameters which may affect the behavior of a given program are its input data and the order in which its parts (for example, its routines) are stored in the virtual-address space. The influence of the latter parameter is due to the fact that different orderings generally cause the page contents to differ. Thus, different parts of the program are loaded into memory when a page fault occurs, and the contents of memory at the times the same reference is issued with the two orderings usually differ from each other.

Among the parameters we have identified, the factors of the experiment have now to be chosen. There are several criteria for this choice. Some of the parameters may be discarded because of their likely irrelevance or because their impact on the performance index is already well known. The experimenters may also exclude the parameters which they are not interested in and which can be fully controlled. For instance, we shall assume that we are not interested in studying the effects of the loading policy on the number of page faults. Thus, this policy will have to be chosen and kept constant throughout the experiment. We shall choose demand loading.

The four factors selected for the paging experiment are listed in Table 2.13. Note that all of them are primary and controllable factors.   ∎

2.6.3   The Selection of the Levels for Each Session

Having identified the factors to be controlled, their levels must then be selected. The levels of a factor should adequately cover the range of variability of that factor. On the other hand, the total number of levels should be minimized for economic reasons. Thus, a compromise is usually to be made between the two conflicting requirements. Sometimes, the number of levels to be considered for a factor is limited by the objective of the experiment. For example, if this objective is to compare the effects of two different policies, then the corresponding factor will naturally have only two levels.

Once the levels of each factor have been specified, the combinations of these levels which are worth experimenting with should be selected. Recalling the symbology introduced in Section 2.6.1, this problem may be stated, for an n-factor experiment, as the one of choosing the n-tuples $(Ai, Bj, Ck, \ldots)$ of levels corresponding to each session. If $l_A, l_B, l_C, \ldots$ are the numbers of levels selected for factors $A, B, C \ldots$, respectively, then we have $1 \leq i \leq l_A$, $1 \leq j \leq l_B$, $1 \leq k \leq l_C$. Since a different session corresponds to each n-tuple we choose, the cost of the experiment will in general increase linearly with the number of n-tuples. A *factorial design*, which includes all the distinct combinations of levels, often

Table 2.13

FACTORS AND LEVELS SELECTED FOR A PAGING EXPERIMENT

Program: a FORTRAN compiler
Loading policy: demand loading

Factors		Levels	
Name	Symbol	Name	Description
Memory size	*M*	LARGE	24 page frames
		MEDIUM	20 page frames
		SMALL	16 page frames
Replacement algorithm	*R*	LRU	Least recently used
		FIFO	First in, first out
		RAND	Random
Input data (length of program to be compiled)	*I*	SMALL	55 statements, 3.88 s (CPU time)
		MEDIUM	215 statements, 18.05 s (CPU time)
		LARGE	595 statements, 149.55 s (CPU time)
Subroutine ordering in virtual memory	*S*	GROUP	Based on frequency of interroutine calls
		FREQY	Based on intensity of paging activity
		ALPHA	Based on alphabetical ordering

Source: Tsao et al. (1972).

involves a prohibitive number of sessions and should be avoided whenever possible. This number is equal to the product $l_A l_B l_C \ldots$; if all the n factors have the same number of levels l, the product is l^n. For instance, if each of the four factors identified in Example 2.7 has three levels, $3^4 = 81$ sessions are required by a factorial design.

Unfortunately, as will be seen in Section 2.7, factorial experiments are the only ones which allow the experimenter to estimate the effects of the interactions among factors. Thus, when interactions are to be analyzed, the numbers of factors and levels to be included in the experiment must be chosen with an even greater care than in other cases. Indeed, the impact of these numbers on the cost of the experiment is much bigger than when the effects of interactions are not to be studied. When interactions can be assumed either not to exist or to have much smaller effects than each individual factor, a *fractional factorial*, or *incomplete factorial*, *design* may be selected to reduce the cost of the experiment.

If the combination of levels for each session is chosen at random, we have a *completely randomized design*. Using this type of design implies that the set of parameters not included in the experiment is assumed to be constant. If this assumption cannot be made, as is often the case in the study of computer systems, the parameters which do not remain constant during the experiment ought to be included as secondary factors in the design. Their variations may often be controlled to some extent by a careful selection of the combinations of the controllable factors' levels and of the conditions under which the sessions take place. The purpose of this selection is, as will be seen more in detail in Section 2.7, to separate the effects on the performance index of the following *sources of variation*: the primary factors, the secondary factors, and the experimental errors.

Suppose that there is one secondary factor, such as, for example, the time of the day at which the system, processing its normal work load, is observed. Then observations can be grouped into *blocks*, characterized by a greater homogeneity of experimental conditions than that of the whole experiment. For instance, if the effects of some scheduling algorithms on the mean response time in an interactive system are to be studied, and observations are gathered during several days, blocks might contain those observations collected between the same times every day. Within each block, the levels of the primary factors are generally arranged in random order so as to reduce possible systematic variations from one session to another. This arrangement is called *randomized block design*. An example of such a design is given in Table 2.14 for the experiment we have just mentioned.

Table 2.14
RANDOMIZED BLOCK DESIGN

	Time of day		
Day	10 a.m.	1 p.m.	4 p.m.
1	FCFS	RR	SJF
2	RR	FCFS	LJF
3	SJF	LJF	RR

FCFS: First come, first served.
 RR: Round robin.
SJF: Shortest job first.
LJF: Longest job first.

When there are two secondary factors, blocks can be made to correspond to those combinations of their levels which produce more homogeneous experimental conditions in each session. A *Latin square design* for an experiment with one primary factor A having l_A levels is obtained by choosing l_A levels for each of the two secondary factors B and C, arranging the l_A^2 blocks corresponding to the combinations of the levels of B and C in a square matrix, and assigning the levels of A to the blocks so that any given level of A appears only once in each row and once in each column. This assignment is not unique, and there are some degrees of freedom in choosing it. A Latin square design for the experiment described in the previous paragraph is illustrated in Table 2.15. Note that this experiment consists of 16 sessions, whereas the corresponding factorial design would require $4^3 = 64$ sessions.

At the opposite extreme with respect to factorial designs, we have *one-factor-at-a-time experiments*. This approach, which presents itself naturally to an investigator's mind, consists of varying one factor at a time while all other $n - 1$

Table 2.15
LATIN SQUARE DESIGN

Day of week	Time of day			
	9 a.m.	11 a.m.	1 p.m.	3 p.m.
Monday	FCFS	RR	SJF	LJF
Wednesday	RR	SJF	LJF	FCFS
Friday	SJF	LJF	FCFS	RR
Saturday	LJF	FCFS	RR	SJF

factors are kept constant. Thus, the experiment is broken down into n distinct experiments, each having as its objective the study of the effects of one factor. With factors A, B, C, ..., the total number of sessions will be $l_A + l_B + l_C + \cdots$. For instance, the experiment to which Table 2.15 refers, having 3 factors and 4 levels for each factor, would require 12 sessions if designed following the one-factor-at-a-time approach. Note that the information this method provides is incomplete for most practical purposes, since the effect of A when the other factors are at levels different from those selected for the experiment in which only A is varied cannot generally be predicted. Therefore, the one-factor-at-a-time approach can be used only when it is known that there are no interactions among the factors—in other words, when the effect of a factor does not depend on the others. Otherwise, the conclusions drawn from the experiment may be erroneous.

As pointed out by Grenander and Tsao (1972), nonfactorial experiments seem to be more suited to investigations whose objective is to compare different systems, algorithms, or policies. On the other hand, those design and performance optimization problems in which the analysis of the possible interactions is very desirable, or mandatory, require the execution of factorial experiments.

Example 2.8   In Example 2.7, the parameters to be considered in a paging experiment were identified and the factors selected (*see* Table 2.13). The program to be experimented on is a FORTRAN compiler. The selection of the levels for the factors is to be made taking into account the nature of the program we have chosen, the region of the parameter space that we want to cover with the results of our experiments, and the inevitable physical and economical limitations.

To eliminate most of the sources of variation external to the program, the measurement sessions will take place on a dedicated system. This decision, of course, makes the experiment much more accurate but also much more expensive. Another aspect which contributes to the cost of the experiment is our desire to analyze the interactions among factors, since this requires a factorial design. Having two levels per factor would yield $2^4 = 16$ sessions. However, two levels would not adequately cover the region we want to explore. Three levels per factor would require 81 sessions, and four levels, 256 sessions. We assume that 81 is still a number of sessions compatible with our budget and choose the three levels of each factor so that they correspond to *light paging*, *medium paging*, and *heavy paging*, respectively. These levels are listed in Table 2.13 in the order of presumably increasing number of page faults.

Note that M is a quantitative factor, whereas the other three are qualitative. The choice of the levels of a factor such as I, the input data, is usually very hard to justify. In this case, all the characteristics of the programs to be compiled are ignored except their length. Thus, a short, medium, and long program from the FORTRAN work load of the installation have been selected as the three levels of I, and I has in some sense become a quantitative factor.

Of the levels of factor S, GROUP is expected to generate the least number of page faults, since it is obtained by grouping together the routines which call each other most frequently. The second level, FREQY, corresponds to ordering the routines by decreasing frequency of the page faults generated in a previous execution of the compiler. The third level, ALPHA, is a version of the compiler in which routines are loaded in virtual memory in alphabetical order.

The reader should note that the selection of the levels has a strong influence on the cost of the experiment. In a factorial design, each level of a factor is used in combination with all the levels of the others; in this example, each level is used in 27 sessions. Thus, a level which causes excessive paging activity will undesirably affect the duration of one third of the sessions in the experiment.

Note also that the nature of our performance index is such that only one session per combination of levels is sufficient. If the measurement tool which counts the page faults works correctly, no experimental error should be present. However, if the index were a statistical descriptor such as the mean of a distribution, we might have to repeat each session several times in order to reduce the experimental errors. This additional burden should of course be considered when choosing factors and levels.   ∎

2.6.4   The Time and Duration of a Session

Due to the variability of the work load, each individual measurement of a performance index or of an installation parameter is very often useless. In general, the purpose of a measurement session is to evaluate time integrals (for example, event counts) or to estimate the distributions of the interesting quantities and their moments.

How long should a session last? When should a session be performed?

The latter question is relevant only if the system is observed while processing its production work load. In this case, the answer depends on the problem at hand, on the usage characteristics of the installation, and also on the answer which is given to the former question. For example, it is obvious that if the performance of the system under heavy load is to be studied, the measurements have to be taken when the usage intensity peaks are likely to be reached. However, if each session is going to last a whole day, then the starting-time problem is to be replaced by the one of choosing the days for the sessions. As was seen in Section 2.6.3 (Tables 2.14 and 2.15), the time of a session may in some experiments be dictated by the design selected.

The question about session duration is generally more difficult to answer. In a number of experiments, this duration is itself one of the performance indices to be measured or is directly related to an index. This occurs, for instance, when an artificial work load consisting of N jobs is to drive the system, especially if the mean throughput rate is among the performance indices to be estimated (*see* Example 1.1). In these cases, the problem of selecting a suitable session duration does not exist, but an analogous, equally important question arises: How large should N be, and what should be the composition of the artificial work load? This question is discussed in detail in Chapter 5.

In this section, we shall restrict our attention to the experiments in which the investigator has direct control over the duration of measurement sessions. The data collected in these experiments may be viewed as time series consisting of observations of certain quantities. The series of observations of a quantity u may be regarded as a sample drawn from a stochastic sequence. If this sequence is stationary, its mean $\bar{u}$ is independent of time. An estimator of $\bar{u}$ is the mean $\bar{u}_n$ of the time series $u_1, \ldots, u_n$. If the accuracy of this estimator increases with n, the sequence is said to be *ergodic*. We shall assume that the sequences we deal with are ergodic. Thus, given the maximum tolerable error which may affect the estimate (the confidence interval) and the minimum probability that the true mean $\bar{u}$ lies within that interval around the sample mean $\bar{u}_n$ (the confidence level of the estimate), there is a minimum sample size to be examined (*see* Section 2.4.3). This size corresponds to the minimum duration of the session.

It should be noted that there are exploratory studies, even of the type we are considering here, in which determining the minimum session duration is not important. For instance, if an experiment consists of one or very few sessions, estimating the minimum acceptable duration might be more expensive than selecting one so long that the probability of not meeting the accuracy requirements is very low. In other cases, in particular when the expected number of sessions is large or when the adequacy of the work load used to drive the system and the validity of the conclusions drawn from an experiment have to be certified, it is necessary, or at least very desirable, to calculate the minimum acceptable session duration.

As shown in Section 2.4.3, if the observations made during a measurement session were not correlated, the variance of the sample mean around the true mean would be σ^2/n, σ^2 being the true variance of the distribution and n the sample size. Thus, the minimum duration of the session could be derived from inequality (2.6). If we consider only the equal sign, (2.6) expresses the minimum value of n, say n_{min}, as a function of σ^2, of the confidence interval e, and of the confidence level. Even under these assumptions, the duration of the session is very sensitive to the size of the confidence interval, since n_{min} is inversely proportional to the square of this size. For example, to halve the confidence interval, the duration would have to be quadruplicated.

However, mainly because of the scarcity of nonshareable resources for which jobs compete, observations in computer systems are often autocorrelated. For example, the waiting time of a job in a queue is strongly correlated to the waiting times of the higher-priority jobs in the same queue. Thus, the variance of the sample mean usually differs from σ^2/n. If, however, the distribution of $\bar{u}_n$ is normal, inequality (2.4) can still be applied, provided that σ_1^2/n be replaced by

Var $(\bar{u}_n)$. Thus, n_{min} will be the minimum value of n which satisfies the inequality [analogous to (2.6)]

$$\text{Var}(\bar{u}_n) \leq \left(\frac{e}{z}\right)^2, \tag{2.9}$$

where e is the confidence interval and z is related to the confidence level as shown in (2.5).

Unfortunately, the distribution of $\bar{u}_n$ is generally unknown. If the only assumption we can make about it is that $\bar{u}_n$ has finite mean and finite variance, then Chebyshev's inequality [*see*, for example, Feller (1968)] can be written as

$$\text{Prob}(|\bar{u}_n - \bar{u}| < e) \geq 1 - \frac{\text{Var}(\bar{u}_n)}{e^2} \qquad (e > 0). \tag{2.10}$$

This inequality, compared with (2.3), yields the condition

$$\text{Var}(\bar{u}_n) \leq e^2(1 - K), \tag{2.11}$$

where K is the confidence level of $\bar{u}_n$. The value of n_{min} given by (2.11) is usually much larger than the one resulting from (2.9) for the same values of e and K. If additional assumptions are made about the distribution of $\bar{u}_n$, the value of n_{min} can be reduced. When these assumptions are weaker than the one of normality, the resulting value of n_{min} is comprised between those given by (2.9) and (2.11).

How can we estimate Var $(\bar{u}_n)$? Recalling the definitions of variance, Var $(x) = E[(x - \bar{x})^2]$, and of covariance of two random variables x and y, Cov $(x, y) = E[(x - \bar{x})(y - \bar{y})]$, where $E(w)$ denotes the mean (or expectation) of w, the reader will easily verify that if $u_1, \ldots, u_n$ are a series of observations drawn from a stationary stochastic sequence with mean $\bar{u}$ and $\bar{u}_n$ is the mean of the n observations, the variance of $\bar{u}_n$ and $\bar{u}$ is

$$\text{Var}(\bar{u}_n) = \frac{1}{n^2}\left[\sum_{i=1}^{n}\text{Var}(u_i) + \sum_{\substack{i,j=1 \\ i \neq j}}^{n}\text{Cov}(u_i, u_j)\right]. \tag{2.12}$$

If $u_1, \ldots, u_n$ are independent and identically distributed with mean $\bar{u}$ and variance σ^2, (2.12) becomes

$$\text{Var}(\bar{u}_n) = \frac{n\sigma^2}{n^2} = \frac{\sigma^2}{n}, \tag{2.13}$$

since Cov $(u_i, u_j) = 0$ for all i, j with $i \neq j$. However, if the observations are correlated, (2.13) cannot be applied, as stated above.

There are several methods for *variance estimation*, besides the obvious one of using (2.12). We shall briefly describe the methods of autocovariances, independent replications, and subsamples.

The method of *autocovariances* is based on an equation which can be directly derived from (2.12). An assumption we have to make is that $u_1, \ldots, u_n$

are identically distributed with mean $\bar{u}$ and variance σ^2. Also, in the series of observations being considered, the covariance between any two observations should be finite and a function only of their distance τ in time:

$$R_\tau = \text{Cov}\,(u_i, u_{i+\tau}) = \text{Cov}\,(u_i, u_{i-\tau}) \qquad (2.14)$$

for all i $(1 \le i \le n)$ and all $\tau = 1, \ldots, n - 1$. If these assumptions are satisfied, then (2.12), which contains all autocovariances, may be written as

$$\text{Var}\,(\bar{u}_n) = \frac{\sigma^2}{n} + \frac{2}{n} \sum_{\tau=1}^{n-1} \left(1 - \frac{\tau}{n}\right) R_\tau. \qquad (2.15)$$

Since the autocovariances R_τ tend to become smaller and smaller as τ increases, the number m of autocovariances to be estimated can often be made much lower than n. A real-time estimate of the R_τ's $(\tau = 1, \ldots, m - 1)$ can be kept during a measurement session by remembering only the single observations collected within a backward window containing m observations. $\text{Var}\,(\bar{u}_n)$ can therefore be estimated dynamically and the session terminated when its value satisfies the condition selected [for example, (2.11)]. Since a software tool would be likely to cause an intolerable interference, this approach only looks really applicable when a stored-program hardware tool is used.

Another method for estimating $\text{Var}\,(\bar{u}_n)$ is the method of *independent replications*. It tries to recreate the conditions under which (2.13) holds. Each measurement session is replaced by h independent subsessions, during each one of which q observations $u_{j1}, \ldots, u_{jq}$ $(j = 1, \ldots, h)$ are collected. Thus, the total number of observations is $n = hq$. Because of the independence assumption, the h means

$$\bar{u}_{q(j)} = \frac{1}{q} \sum_{i=1}^{q} u_{ji} \qquad (j = 1, \ldots, h) \qquad (2.16)$$

are independent random variables, and therefore, by the central limit theorem, their distribution around $\bar{u}$ tends to become normal as h increases. Also, the mean of the sample defined in (2.16),

$$E(\bar{u}_{q(j)}) = \frac{1}{h} \sum_{j=1}^{h} \bar{u}_{q(j)} = \bar{u}_n, \qquad (2.17)$$

tends to $\bar{u}$ as q increases. Thus, for h and q sufficiently large, we have, from (2.13),

$$\text{Var}\,(\bar{u}_n) = \frac{1}{h} \text{Var}\,(\bar{u}_{q(j)}). \qquad (2.18)$$

The values of $\text{Var}\,(\bar{u}_{q(j)})$ may be estimated by the sample variance as in (2.7):

$$\widehat{\text{Var}}\,(\bar{u}_{q(j)}) = \frac{1}{h - 1} \sum_{j=1}^{h} (\bar{u}_{q(j)} - \bar{u}_n)^2. \qquad (2.19)$$

A method very similar to the one of independent replications is the method of *subsamples*. It consists of subdividing a long, continuous session into h subsessions and collecting q observations in each one of them. The means of the observations gathered during each subsession are not independent but, if q is large enough, can be assumed to have small covariances. If this assumption, which should be verified by estimating the covariances from the data, is satisfied, then (2.18) can be used to estimate Var $(\bar{u}_n)$.

Real-time estimation of confidence intervals is possible also with this and the previous method. A convenient strategy for selecting q, applicable to both methods, is to collect means and variances for subsamples with a small q; then q should be gradually increased, considering double-, triple-, and quadruple-size subsessions, until the desired accuracy is obtained. In doing this, one must remember that q in the independent-replication method is to be large in order to make $\bar{u}_n$ an unbiased estimator of $\bar{u}$. In the method of subsamples, q is also to be large in order to make the covariance between the means of adjacent subsessions sufficiently small.

To calculate the confidence interval in real time without introducing too much interference, a stored-program hardware tool should be used. With such an arrangement, the sessions may be terminated when the value of the interval becomes acceptably small. The reader should note, however, that the methods for variance estimation described above ought to be applied with care in measurement experiments. One of the difficulties is that the real-time estimation of confidence intervals may be made unreliable by the presence of a nonstationary work load. Most of the problems which arise in the measurement of systems driven by their production work load are certainly less severe in simulation experiments (*see* Chapter 3), which are easier to control, or in measurement experiments in which the system is driven by an artificial work load. In fact, the above methods for estimating confidence intervals, and others, are much more widely used in simulation than in measurement.

Example 2.9 The performances of four scheduling algorithms for an interactive system have to be evaluated and compared to each other. The algorithms are those listed in Table 2.14. The primary performance index is the mean response time of the system. Since the investigators are mainly interested in how highly interactive tasks are treated by the various scheduling algorithms under different loads, a script consisting of a sequence of editing commands has been prepared. This script is to be input into the system by an external driver. The driver is a hardware tool which simulates a single user, reproducing also the user's think times and typing speed. In addition, the tool is capable of measuring the response times to the commands in the script and of storing their values for later reduction.

To somehow separate the effects of the production work load from those of the scheduling algorithms, we introduce the two secondary factors "time of day" and "day of week" and use the Latin square design in Table 2.15. How long should the 16 sessions be? In other words, how many observations of response time should we take in each session?

It is important to note that these questions implicitly assume that the stochastic process to be measured is stationary. Otherwise, expressing the mean of the response time distribution as a single number, and estimating its confidence interval, would be meaningless. On the other hand, very little is known about this aspect of the processes which characterize the behavior of computer systems. Extensive statistical tests should be performed on the system to be measured in order to determine to what extent the stationary-process assumption is valid. This assumption will be made, as customary, in our discussion.

The fact that the experiment consists of 16 sessions justifies our concern with the problem of reducing session duration to the minimum which still provides the desired accuracy in the estimation of the performance index. The nature of our study is such that a confidence interval of ±5% for the mean response time, at a 95% confidence level, is sufficient. In other words, we shall not consider significant a difference of less than 10% between the performances of two scheduling algorithms.

To determine the duration of each session, the method of subsamples will be used. The assumption will be made that a duration found to be sufficient for one of the sessions is going to suffice (possibly when multiplied by a safety coefficient larger than 1) for all sessions. This is, of course, a rather strong assumption, since different sessions take place under work loads of different characteristics. An alternative would be to make this assumption only for the sessions to be performed at the same time of the day. In this case, a separately determined duration would be associated to each column in Table 2.15. Another, better, alternative would be the one of estimating the variance in real time during each session and terminating the session when the desired accuracy is obtained.

One of the sessions is therefore to be selected for the purpose of estimating the variance, for instance, the one which uses the FCFS algorithm at 9 a.m. on Monday. The script we use consists of 15 editing commands. The driver may be instructed to input the script repeatedly without intermissions, so that the first command follows the fifteenth as if it were the sixteenth. Each script takes on the average 2.5 minutes of real time. Thus, in a 2-hour session the driver is expected to be able to input 48 consecutive replicas of the script.

Let the 48 means of the response times to the 15 commands in each one of the 48 replicas be those listed in chronological order in Table 2.16. The overall mean, $\bar{t}_n$, is 1.756 seconds. To see whether the 15 observations collected for each replica of the script can be taken as a subsample, we calculate the autocorrelation coefficient between the means $\bar{t}_j$ and $\bar{t}_{j+1}$ ($j = 1, \ldots, 47$) of consecutive replicas. This coefficient is defined as the ratio $\mathrm{Cov}\,(\bar{t}_j, \bar{t}_{j+1})/\mathrm{Var}\,(\bar{t}_j)$. Note that for brevity we replace $\bar{t}_{15(j)}$ with the shorter symbol $\bar{t}_j$. An estimate of $\mathrm{Var}\,(\bar{t}_j)$, obtained from (2.19), is about 0.074. $\mathrm{Cov}\,(\bar{t}_j, \bar{t}_{j+1})$ can be estimated by applying its definition. Since this estimate is about 0.048, the resulting autocorrelation coefficient approximately equals 0.65.

The autocorrelation coefficient is by definition comprised between -1 and $+1$. If the means of adjacent replicas were independent, the coefficient would be equal to 0. A coefficient of 0.65 indicates that a rather strong autocorrelation exists between consecutive means. To reduce it, larger subsamples have to be selected. If we repeat the above calculations for the means of subsamples composed of pairs of adjacent replicas of the script, we obtain an autocorrelation coefficient of 0.56. This is still too large. Thus, we keep grouping together consecutive replicas. When each subsample encompasses four replicas, the autocorrelation coefficient for the 12 subsample means is 0.08. In the context of our limited accuracy requirements, this degree of autocorrelation may be considered so low as to be negligible. Thus, our subsample will consist of four consecutive replicas of the script, or, equivalently, of a sequence of 60 commands.

How many subsamples should a session contain? From (2.18) and (2.9), we obtain the inequality

$$h \geq \text{Var}\,(\bar{t}_j)\left(\frac{z}{e}\right)^2, \qquad (2.20)$$

which is analogous to (2.6). $\text{Var}\,(\bar{t}_j)$, according to an estimate based on the means of the 12 quadruples (see Table 2.16), is about 0.052, e is $0.05\bar{t}_n = 0.087$, and z' is 2.201 for $K = 95\%$ and $n = 12$. Therefore, (2.20) yields $h \geq 33.7$. If we choose $h = 36$, the corresponding session duration will be about 6 hours. Even devoting the entire 2 hours between 9 and 11 a.m. on Mondays to the collection of FCFS subsamples, 3 weeks would be needed to gather 36 subsamples, and the experiment would take about 3 months. To reduce this time, variance reduction techniques could be applied (*see* Section 3.4.2). In addition, or alternatively, we could redesign the experiment so as to exploit also Tuesdays and Thursdays, and the evenings, to be grouped together with Saturdays.

Note that if the total session duration were restricted to 2 hours (that is, 12 subsamples), the confidence interval of the mean response time corresponding to a 95% confidence level would be about ±8.3%. For a confidence level of 90%, the interval would be ±6.7%. ■

Table 2.16
MEAN RESPONSE TIMES IN SECONDS FOR EACH SCRIPT
REPLICA, PAIR, AND QUADRUPLE OF
REPLICAS IN THE EXPERIMENT OF EXAMPLE 2.9

Single script	Pair	Quadruple	Single script	Pair	Quadruple
1.21	1.44		2.27	2.1	
1.67		1.53	1.93		2.1075
1.71	1.62		2.19	2.115	
1.53			2.04		
2.03	2.09		1.92	1.945	
2.15		2.02	1.97		1.8125
1.88	1.95		1.65	1.68	
2.02			1.71		
1.75	1.795		1.89	1.795	
1.84		1.6375	1.70		1.6725
1.61	1.48		1.62	1.55	
1.35			1.48		
1.43	1.535		1.55	1.47	
1.64		1.5075	1.39		1.515
1.52	1.48		1.45	1.56	
1.44			1.67		
1.17	1.295		1.62	1.695	
1.42		1.5225	1.77		1.7725
1.64	1.75		1.88	1.85	
1.86			1.82		
1.68	1.795		1.93	2.01	
1.91		1.875	2.09		2.105
1.73	1.955		2.24	2.2	
2.18			2.16		

2.7 THE INTERPRETATION OF MEASUREMENT RESULTS

2.7.1 Data Reduction and Presentation Techniques

In our discussion of measurement tools, we have seen that when measurement results do not have to be presented or utilized in real time it may be convenient to store the raw data and reduce them later, after the end of the session. This is especially advisable when prereduction would cause excessive interference in time. Also, when the objectives of the study are not completely specified at the outset or when the probability that new, unforeseen questions will arise during the study or as a result of it is nonnegligible, raw data can generally provide many more answers than data that have been reduced at collection time with considerable loss of information.

In any case, the data collected during a session almost always require some transformation before they can be presented to the experimenter. Measurement tools are generally equipped with data reduction and report-generating programs, which compute statistics of performance indices and other installation parameters and present them in tabular or graphic form.

Often, these reduction and presentation facilities offer the experimenter a choice among several output formats, quantities, and statistics to be presented. A convenient and flexible organization for the collected data may be achieved by storing them into a data base and providing the users with a query language by which they can interrogate the data base and interact with it. An example of how powerful such an arrangement may be is given by Cooperman et al. (1972), whose Statistics Gathering Package (SGP) incorporates a PL/I-like query language allowing users to define subsets of the data base to be created and to request summaries, as well as more detailed statistics, by user, program, and other job and system attributes.

It is interesting to note the operational differences between this and the interactive measurement approach exemplified by the Informer and the SMT (*see* Section 2.4.2). The former implies that data as detailed as possible be collected in raw form and used to answer a large number of questions. On the other hand, the latter allows an experimenter to rapidly and safely set up a measurement session whenever the need for it arises and to measure just the quantities of interest at that time.

The form in which results are presented can greatly facilitate (or confuse) their interpretation. One of the important problems in this area is the usually large number of quantities to be simultaneously considered in interpreting results, which makes it hard to work with two-dimensional tables and diagrams. Since the existence of relationships, patterns, and trends may easily be masked and go unnoticed unless the results are arranged or plotted in a suitable fashion, chances often are that only relationships expected to exist will be discovered. Among the types of graphic presentation which have been proposed to help the experimenter interpret measurement results, Gantt charts and Kiviat graphs will be briefly

80

introduced here. Their applications in evaluation studies are described in Chapter 7.

Gantt charts may be used to summarize graphically the utilization characteristics of a system's components. In this case, they are often called *system
utilization profiles*. A simple profile for a system including one CPU and one I/O
channel, whose measurement has produced the data displayed in Table 2.3, is
represented in Fig. 2.13. The reader will realize that the human mind can
understand the time interrelationships among the quantities involved more easily
from the profile in Fig. 2.13 than from the numbers in Table 2.3. This is even
more the case when the installation contains several channels and devices. The
system utilization profile gives the experimenter a summary representation in
graphic form of the states of activity of the units in an installation and of their

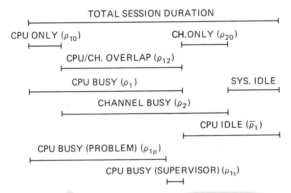

Figure 2.13   Gantt chart (system utilization profile) corresponding to the data in
Table 2.3.

overlaps in time. It is a presentation technique especially oriented toward
multiprogramming systems, which try to exploit the mutual independence of
various system components in order to obtain higher throughput rates.

The data in Table 2.3 can be plotted in a circular graph whose radii are used
as axes for the quantities to be presented (*see* Fig. 2.14). This synoptic form of
presentation has been called a *Kiviat graph*. It exploits the experimenter's ability
to recognize patterns, and hence to immediately detect the presence of some
problem or of plausible causes for it which would otherwise be hard to discover.
The choice of the quantities to be reported on the axes is completely arbitrary. A
popular approach, which has been followed also in Fig. 2.14, is the one of
choosing a number of quantities considered to be "good" and an equal number of
"bad" quantities and to plot them on alternate axes. The larger a "good"
quantity and the smaller a "bad" quantity, the better. Thus, the Kiviat graph of a
good system will be a star-like picture, and our eye can easily perceive the
"distance" between any pattern and a perfect star.

Very little can be said in general about the interpretation of results. It is
mostly an art, which can be learned by practicing it and observing others practice

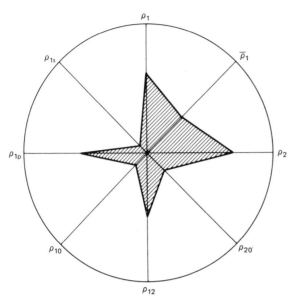

Figure 2.14   Kiviat graph corresponding to the data in Table 2.3.

it. Successful interpretation relies heavily on both intuition and deep knowledge of system structure and organization. Several examples of interpretation in specific cases will be given in Chapters 6, 7, and 8. In the two following sections, some methodologies which can be used to interpret the results of statistically designed experiments will be introduced by describing examples of their applications to performance evaluation problems.

2.7.2   The Analysis of Variance

The term *analysis of variance* designates those data analysis methods which can be used to estimate the relative influence of different sources of variation on the values of a performance index. These methods decompose the total variation of the index into components which correspond to the sources of variation being considered. When all the factors in an experiment are quantitative, *regression analysis* techniques can be applied. An example of regression analysis is discussed in Section 2.7.3. In this section, we shall describe the application of analysis-of-variance methods to a case in which not all factors are quantitative.

Example 2.10   Let us consider the paging experiment described in Examples 2.7 and 2.8, assuming that throughout the experiment the replacement algorithm R and the input data I are kept constant at, say, their respective levels LRU and SMALL (see Table 2.13). The $3^2 = 9$ results (each being the logarithm base 10 of the total number of page faults generated in the corresponding session) are displayed in Table 2.17. The logarithm was taken since the factors were found to have multiplicative effects on the number of page faults (see below).

Table 2.17

RESULTS OF A TWO-FACTOR FACTORIAL EXPERIMENT

		S		Row means $(\bar{F}_{i.})$	Main effects of M (M_i)
	GROUP	FREQY	ALPHA		
M LARGE	1.51	1.72	1.77	1.666	−0.629
MEDIUM	1.68	2.39	2.73	2.266	−0.029
SMALL	2.73	3.00	3.13	2.953	+0.658
Column means $(\bar{F}_{.j})$	1.973	2.370	2.543	2.295	Grand mean $(\bar{F}_{..})$
Main effects of S (S_j)	−0.322	+0.075	+0.248		

Source: Tsao et al. (1972).

     In general, factor M has l_M levels, and factor S has l_S levels; in our case, $l_M = l_S = 3$. Also, $F_{ij}(i = 1, \ldots, l_M; j = 1, \ldots, l_S)$ is the value of the performance index (i.e., the logarithm of the number of page faults) for the session corresponding to level i of factor M and level j of factor S. The *row means* are given by

$$\bar{F}_{i.} = \frac{\sum_{j=1}^{l_S} F_{ij}}{l_S}, \tag{2.21}$$

the *column means* by

$$\bar{F}_{.j} = \frac{\sum_{i=1}^{l_M} F_{ij}}{l_M}, \tag{2.22}$$

and the mean of all observations, also called the *grand mean*, by

$$\bar{F}_{..} = \frac{\sum_{i=1}^{l_M} \sum_{j=1}^{l_S} F_{ij}}{l_M l_S}. \tag{2.23}$$

     The *main effect* of row i (i.e., of factor M at level i) is defined as

$$M_i = \bar{F}_{i.} - \bar{F}_{..}, \tag{2.24}$$

and the one of column j (i.e., of factor S at level j) as

$$S_j = \bar{F}_{.j} - \bar{F}_{..}. \tag{2.25}$$

Note that the grand mean defined in (2.23) may be viewed as the mean of the row means as well as the mean of the column means. The sums of the deviations of these means from the grand mean are zero, as can be verified in Table 2.17:

$$\sum_{i=1}^{l_M} M_i = \sum_{j=1}^{l_S} S_j = 0. \tag{2.26}$$

The deviation of F_{ij} from the grand mean can be written as

$$F_{ij} - \bar{F}_{..} = (\bar{F}_{i.} - \bar{F}_{..}) + (\bar{F}_{.j} - \bar{F}_{..}) + (F_{ij} - \bar{F}_{i.} - \bar{F}_{.j} + \bar{F}_{..}). \tag{2.27}$$

Identity (2.27) expresses the deviation as a sum of the main effects M_i and S_j of the two factors at their respective levels i and j and of another term. This term represents the combined effects of the interaction between M and S and of the experimental errors. When only one observation is made in each session, as is the case in our study, this term cannot be decomposed into its two components. Thus, we refer to it as the *interaction effect* MS_{ij}, thereby assuming that the contribution of the experimental error to it is zero or very small. In our experiment, this assumption is likely to be satisfied, since the performance index is an event count. In general, the two components can be separated only if each session provides h values of the performance index, as will be seen below in this section.

Thus, (2.27) can be written as

$$F_{ij} - \bar{F}_{..} = M_i + S_j + MS_{ij}, \tag{2.28}$$

and it is easy to see from (2.27), (2.21), and (2.22) that

$$\sum_{i=1}^{l_M} MS_{ij} = \sum_{j=1}^{l_S} MS_{ij} = 0. \tag{2.29}$$

It should be noted that *interaction* is not synonymous to "dependence between factors." The interaction effect defined in (2.27) may be nonzero even if the factors are independent. Suppose, for instance, that there is a multiplicative functional relationship between the performance index F^* and the two factors, both of which, for simplicity, are assumed to be quantitative:

$$F_{ij}^* = H \cdot Mi \cdot Sj, \tag{2.30}$$

where Mi and Sj are the ith and jth (quantitative) levels of M and S, respectively. It is easy to see that F_{ij}^* cannot be expressed as the sum of only the two main effects. Therefore, the presence of interaction may be due to dependence or to lack of additivity, or to both. A lack of additivity may in some cases be removed by appropriate transformations of the data. For instance, in the case of a multiplicative relationship such as (2.30), one may take the logarithms of both sides:

$$\log F_{ij}^* = \log H + \log Mi + \log Sj. \tag{2.31}$$

If there are dependencies among the factors, no data transformations can eliminate them.

The variance of the observations around the grand mean is proportional to

$$\sum_{i=1}^{l_M} \sum_{j=1}^{l_S} (F_{ij} - \bar{F}_{..})^2. \tag{2.32}$$

By identity (2.28), (2.32) can be written as

$$\sum_{i=1}^{l_M} \sum_{j=1}^{l_S} M_i^2 + \sum_{i=1}^{l_M} \sum_{j=1}^{l_S} S_j^2 + \sum_{i=1}^{l_M} \sum_{j=1}^{l_S} MS_{ij}^2 + 2 \sum_{i=1}^{l_M} \sum_{j=1}^{l_S} M_i S_j + 2 \sum_{i=1}^{l_M} \sum_{j=1}^{l_S} M_i MS_{ij} + 2 \sum_{i=1}^{l_M} \sum_{j=1}^{l_S} S_j MS_{ij}$$

$$= l_S \sum_{i=1}^{l_M} M_i^2 + l_M \sum_{j=1}^{l_S} S_j^2 + \sum_{i=1}^{l_M} \sum_{j=1}^{l_S} MS_{ij}^2. \quad (2.33)$$

Note that the simplification in (2.33) is possible since the three cross-products are equal to zero [*see* (2.26) and (2.29)]. The three nonzero terms in (2.33) are, respectively, called the *sum of squares* for factor M (denoted by *SSM*), for factor S (denoted by *SSS*), and for the interaction (denoted by *SSI*). The total sum of squares in (2.32), denoted by *SST*, has therefore been partitioned into three components:

$$SST = SSM + SSS + SSI, \quad (2.34)$$

which represent the relative importances of the three sources of variation being considered.

The ratios SSM/SST, SSS/SST, and SSI/SST are usually interpreted as the fractions of the total variation "explained" by factor M, factor S, and their interaction MS, respectively. These fractions may be represented graphically in the form of a *pie chart* such as the one in Fig. 2.15. Since the three sources of variation we have considered explain completely the total variation, equation (2.28) can be interpreted as an *empirical model* of F_{ij}:

$$F_{ij} = \bar{F}_{..} + M_i + S_j + MS_{ij}. \quad (2.35)$$

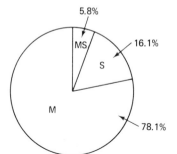

5.8%

MS

16.1%

S

M

78.1%

Figure 2.15 Pie chart representing the effects of memory size M, subroutine ordering S, and their interaction MS on the variations of the logarithm of the number of page faults in the experiment described in Example 2.10.

The values of the model's parameters, derived from the results in Table 2.17, are reported in Table 2.18. The value of the performance index corresponding to a given combination of levels can be obtained from (2.35). For instance, the logarithm base 10 of the number of page faults for a memory size of 20 page frames and alphabetically ordered subroutines is $F_{23} = \bar{F}_{..} + M_2 + S_3 + MS_{23} = 2.73$. Thus, we have 536 page faults.

The pie chart in Fig. 2.15 shows that the size of the primary memory allotted to the FORTRAN compiler has by far the heaviest influence on the amount of paging. The effects of the subroutine ordering are certainly less important but not at all negligible. The interaction MS explains about 6% of the total variation. Because of its relatively small size, we can say that the two factors contribute almost additively to the logarithm of the number of page faults. This is equivalent to stating that their variations affect the number

Table 2.18

PARAMETERS OF THE EMPIRICAL
MODEL OF F_{ij} IN (2.35)

$\bar{F}_{..} = 2.295$	$MS_{11} = 0.166$
$M_1 = -0.629$	$MS_{12} = -0.021$
$M_2 = -0.029$	$MS_{13} = -0.144$
$M_3 = 0.658$	$MS_{21} = -0.264$
$S_1 = -0.322$	$MS_{22} = 0.049$
$S_2 = 0.075$	$MS_{23} = 0.216$
$S_3 = 0.248$	$MS_{31} = 0.099$
	$MS_{32} = -0.028$
	$MS_{33} = -0.071$

of page faults almost multiplicatively. The model (2.35) represents a decomposition of the logarithm of the performance index into the contributions of the sources of variation. If we ignore the interaction term, we can express the performance index, which is the antilogarithm of F_{ij}, as the product of the antilogarithms of the other terms in (2.35). Thus, a change in the level of a factor will affect the number of page faults in an approximately proportional way (this observation obviously applies to quantitative factors only).

When the contribution of a source of variation is neglected on the grounds that its sum of squares is very small with respect to SST, the remaining sources cannot explain completely the total variation anymore. For example, Tsao and Margolin (1972) in the four-factor factorial experiment described in Examples 2.7 and 2.8 were able to explain 98% of the total variation by considering only the four main effects and one first-order interaction effect (MS):

$$F_{ijhk} = \bar{F}_{....} + M_i + R_j + I_h + S_k + MS_{ik} + E_{ijhk},\tag{2.36}$$

where E_{ijhk} is the term representing the missing interaction effects. This term is also called the *residual* for entry $ijhk$ and is the error made when estimating F_{ijhk} by

$$\hat{F}_{ijhk} = \bar{F}_{....} + M_i + R_j + I_h + S_k + MS_{ik}.\tag{2.37}$$

The examination of the residuals is useful to measure the goodness of fit of the empirical model to the data. Their values may point to *outliers*, that is, aberrant observations. Also, their signs may help discover systematic errors, for instance, the omission of an important interaction effect.   ■

At the end of Example 2.10, we have seen that the total variation cannot be fully explained when some of the effects are ignored. This is also the case when there are experimental errors. Let us consider a factorial experiment with two factors A and B, and let the performance index be a quantity to be estimated with some uncertainty. For example, the index might be the mean response time of an interactive system. If we replicate each session h times, as described in Section 2.6.4, each entry ij in the table of the results ($i = 1, \ldots, l_A; j = 1, \ldots, l_B$) contains h observations $\bar{t}_{ijv} (v = 1, \ldots, h)$.

Thus, we can construct the empirical model

$$\bar{t}_{ijv} = \bar{t}_{...} + A_i + B_j + AB_{ij} + E_{ijv},\tag{2.38}$$

and (2.34) becomes

$$SST = SSA + SSB + SSI + SSE. \tag{2.39}$$

Using the notations introduced in Example 2.10, the sums of squares on the right-hand side of (2.39) may be expressed as

$$SSA = hl_B \sum_{i=1}^{l_A} (\bar{t}_{i..} - \bar{t}_{...})^2,$$

$$SSB = hl_A \sum_{j=1}^{l_B} (\bar{t}_{.j.} - \bar{t}_{...})^2,$$

$$SSI = h \sum_{i=1}^{l_A} \sum_{j=1}^{l_B} (\bar{t}_{ij.} - \bar{t}_{i..} - \bar{t}_{.j.} + \bar{t}_{...})^2,$$

$$SSE = \sum_{i=1}^{l_A} \sum_{j=1}^{l_B} \sum_{v=1}^{h} (\bar{t}_{ijv} - \bar{t}_{ij.})^2. \tag{2.40}$$

Note that the ratio SSE/SST represents that part of the total variation explained by the experimental errors.

Among the effects A_i, B_j, AB_{ij} which appear in the empirical model (2.38), relationships analogous to (2.26) and (2.29) hold. Thus, only $l_A - 1$ of the l_A main effects of factor A are independent: If the values of $l_A - 1$ A_i's are known, the value of the remaining A_i is given by the equivalent of (2.26). Thus, SSA is said to have $l_A - 1$ *degrees of freedom*. Similarly, the degrees of freedom of SSB are $l_B - 1$, and, because of relationships analogous to (2.29), those of SSI are $(l_A - 1)(l_B - 1)$. For instance, it is easy to verify that all of the MS_{ij}'s in Table 2.18 can be derived from the knowledge of four of them.

From the definition of grand mean in (2.23) and the expression of SST in (2.32), we obtain that SST has $hl_Al_B - 1$ degrees of freedom. Equation (2.39) tells us that degrees of freedom are additive. Thus, the number of degrees of freedom of SSE is

$$hl_Al_B - 1 - (l_A - 1) - (l_B - 1) - (l_A - 1)(l_B - 1) = (h - 1)l_Al_B. \tag{2.41}$$

This result confirms the statement, made in the discussion of Example 2.10, that the effects of experimental errors cannot be separated from the ones of interactions if there is only one observation per session ($h = 1$).

The ratio between each sum of squares and the corresponding number of degrees of freedom is called the *mean square*. For instance, $MSA = SSA/(l_A - 1)$. The mean squares are useful in testing the significance of analysis-of-variance results. Because of the experimental errors, the effect on the performance index of a factor or an interaction, which appears to be nonzero, might in fact be nonsignificant (that is, smaller than the effect of the errors). In statistical-inference terms, we should test the following hypothesis first:

$$H_0': \quad AB_{ij} = 0 \quad (i = 1, \dots, l_A; j = 1, \dots, l_B). \tag{2.42}$$

When testing a hypothesis, a *level of significance* α must be selected. The level of significance is the probability that the hypothesis is rejected when it is true. Clearly, the smaller α, the greater the confidence in the results of a test.

If H_0' is rejected at the selected level of significance, the probability that the interaction between A and B exists is high. Thus, the main effects of the two factors will also be significant. If, on the contrary, H_0' cannot be rejected, then we should conclude that A and B do not appreciably interact, and it is possible that the effects of either or both are nonsignificant. To determine whether this is statistically true or not, we should test the two hypotheses

$$H_0'': A_i = 0 \quad (i = 1, \ldots, l_A) \qquad \text{and} \qquad H_0''': B_j = 0 \quad (j = 1, \ldots, l_B). \quad (2.43)$$

Let us now make the following assumptions:

a. The $\bar{i}_{ijv}$'s are normally distributed random variables;
b. the E_{ijv}'s are mutually independent and normally distributed random variables with mean 0 and variance σ_E^2 for all i, j, and v.

If these assumptions are satisfied and if H_0' is true, it can be shown that the ratio MSI/MSE is a random variable having an F-distribution with $(l_A - 1)$ $(l_B - 1)$ and $(h - 1)l_A l_B$ degrees of freedom. Given n_1 independent random variables x_i having the standard normal distribution and given n_2 random variables y_j of the same type, the random variable

$$F_{n_1,n_2} = \frac{(1/n_1) \sum\limits_{i=1}^{n_1} x_i^2}{(1/n_2) \sum\limits_{j=1}^{n_2} y_j^2} \quad (2.44)$$

has an F-distribution with n_1 and n_2 degrees of freedom. Most statistics textbooks report tables of the F-distribution. Usually, the entry in those tables corresponding to α, n_1, and n_2, which we denote by $F_{\alpha;n_1,n_2}$, is such that

$$\text{Prob} \, (F_{n_1, n_2} > F_{\alpha;n_1,n_2}) = \alpha. \quad (2.45)$$

Let H_0' be true. Then the probability of its rejection must be less than or equal to α. By (2.45), H_0' is rejected at the α level of significance if

$$\frac{MSI}{MSE} > F_{\alpha;(l_A-1)(l_B-1),(h-1)l_A l_B}. \quad (2.46)$$

Similarly, H_0'' and H_0''' are rejected at the α level of significance if

$$\frac{MSA}{MSE} > F_{\alpha;(l_A-1),(h-1)l_A l_B} \quad \text{and} \quad \frac{MSB}{MSE} > F_{\alpha;(l_B-1),(h-1)l_A l_B}.$$

The quantities which permit the testing of the significance of an analysis of variance are usually organized as in Table 2.19. The test described above is called the *F-test*. In Section 2.7.3, the *F-test* is applied to the problem of determining the significance of a regression equation.

Table 2.19
ANALYSIS-OF-VARIANCE TABLE FOR A TWO-FACTOR
FACTORIAL EXPERIMENT WITH h OBSERVATIONS PER
COMBINATION OF LEVELS

Source of variation	Sum of squares	Degrees of freedom	Mean square	Calculated F value
Factor A	SSA	$l_A - 1$	$MSA = SSA/(l_A - 1)$	MSA/MSE
Factor B	SSB	$l_B - 1$	$MSB = SSB/(l_B - 1)$	MSB/MSE
Interaction AB	SSI	$(l_A - 1)(l_B - 1)$	$MSI = SSI/[(l_A - 1)(l_B - 1)]$	MSI/MSE
Errors E	SSE	$(h - 1)l_A l_B$	$MSE = SSE/[(h - 1)l_A l_B]$	
Total T	SST	$h l_A l_B - 1$		

Assumptions a and b above are often likely not to be valid in experiments on computer systems. Assumption a has been empirically found not to seriously affect the outcome of the test if it is not satisfied. This is also the case of the equal-variance part of assumption b if the differences among variances are not too large. In any event, the validity of the assumptions should be tested by using the available statistical techniques [*see* Snedecor and Cochran (1967)].

2.7.3   Regression Analysis

When the factors in an experiment are all quantitative, an empirical model can be constructed which estimates the performance index not in terms of the components of its total variation but as a function of the levels of the factors. For instance, in the paging experiment described in Examples 2.7 and 2.8, let us consider only factors M and I, which can be quantified, and choose a fixed level for the replacement algorithm and for the subroutine ordering. We may want to express the number of page faults produced by the FORTRAN compiler as a function of the primary-memory space and of the length of the program to be compiled. Such a model, called a *regression model*, may be used (with caution) as a predictive tool to estimate the number of page faults which would correspond to levels of M and I not considered in the experiment.

Our discussion of the application of regression analysis techniques to computer system evaluation is based on a study described by Waldbaum (1973).

Example 2.11   The effects of certain modifications on the performance of the APL interactive operating system running under OS/MVT in an IBM System/360 Model 91 installation have to be determined. The following changes are under consideration:

a. an increase of the maximum size of an APL *work space* (i.e., of an APL process) from 36,000 bytes (5 disk tracks) to 48K bytes (7 disk tracks);
b. a reduction from 3 to 2 of the maximum number of work spaces which can simultaneously be in primary memory; this reduction is necessary to avoid increasing the size of the APL region in primary memory, thereby affecting the non-APL users of the system.

The performance index selected is the *system reaction time,* defined as the duration of the interval between the time a character which ends an input line is detected by the system and the time the corresponding process first receives the attention of the CPU. In the installation under study, most of the commands are processed in less than one time quantum, which is generally very short with respect to the reaction time. Thus, this performance index, which may be used to evaluate the efficiency of the scheduler, differs very little from the response time.

Table 2.20 lists the factors selected for the experiment. Each one of the two primary factors X_1 and X_2 has the two levels mentioned in a and b above. The experiment is to be performed under production work loads. Thus, some secondary factors, uncontrolled but observed, have to be introduced to characterize the work load, whose variability can be reduced by collecting data always at the same time every day. Waldbaum selected the six secondary factors listed in Table 2.20. A one-factor-at-a-time design is adopted, with several observations per combination of the levels of X_1 and X_2. The numbers of observations made by Waldbaum for each combination are reported in Table 2.21. In each session, we observe the distribution of the system reaction time Y, which is characterized for the purposes of the study by the coordinates of the nine points $Y_1, \ldots, Y_9$ listed in Table 2.20, and the corresponding values of the six work-load factors.

Since all factors are quantitative, regression techniques can be applied to build an empirical model. This is usually done in three phases, to be cyclically repeated until the model obtained fits satisfactorily the experimental data:

  a. A mathematical form is selected to express the relationships between the dependent variables (performance indices) and the independent variables (factors);
  b. the *regression parameters* appearing in the model proposed in phase a are calculated from the data;
  c. the goodness of fit of the model to the experimental data is evaluated.

A regression model is a set of equations, each relating one dependent variable to the v independent variables and to $r + 1$ regression parameters, to be determined in phase b. For instance, the model for Y_g $(g = 1, \ldots, 9)$ in this experiment has the general form

$$Y_g = Y_g(X_1, \ldots, X_v; \beta_{g0}, \beta_{g1}, \ldots, \beta_{gr}) + E_g, \tag{2.48}$$

where $v = 8$ and E_g is the regression error. An observation of Y_g is a $(v + 1)$-tuple of values of $(Y_g, X_1, \ldots, X_v)$. Let n be the total number of observations (in our example, $n = 36$). Then the model in (2.48) will have to be applicable to each one of them:

$$Y_{gk} = Y_g(X_{1k}, \ldots, X_{vk}; \beta_{g0}, \beta_{g1}, \ldots, \beta_{gr}) + E_{gk} \qquad (k = 1, \ldots, n). \tag{2.49}$$

The choice of the model may be dictated by a priori knowledge of the mathematical form of the relationships or by an educated guess about it. Very often, a *linear model* is initially assumed, since linear regression is simpler and much better known than nonlinear regression. Linearity in regression refers to the relationship between the dependent variable and the parameters. Therefore, a linear model is a polynomial form in the independent variables. In particular, a *first-order* linear model for Y_g in our example is

$$Y_g = \beta_{g0} + \sum_{i=1}^{v} \beta_{gi} X_i + E_g. \tag{2.50}$$

Note that in a first-order linear model we have $r = v$.

Table 2.20

FACTORS AND PERFORMANCE INDICES IN THE
EXPERIMENT DISCUSSED IN EXAMPLE 2.11

Primary factors

X_1 = number of work spaces in primary memory
(two levels: 2, 3)

X_2 = maximum number of disk tracks
per work space
(two levels: 5, 7)

Secondary factors

X_3 = number of conversational
inputs/hr

X_4 = CPU utilization for requests with
CPU time ≤ 2 s

X_5 = CPU utilization for requests with
CPU time > 2 s

X_6 = number of requests/hr with CPU
time > 2 s

X_7 = number of commands/hr requiring two work spaces in primary
memory simultaneously

X_8 = number of log-ons/hr

Indices (points of the distribution
of system reaction time t_r)

Y_1 = fraction of inputs with $t_r \leq 0.5$ s

Y_2 = fraction of inputs with $t_r \leq 1.0$ s

Y_3 = fraction of inputs with $t_r \leq 1.5$ s

Y_4 = fraction of inputs with $t_r \leq 2.0$ s

Y_5 = fraction of inputs with $t_r \leq 3.0$ s

Y_6 = fraction of inputs with $t_r \leq 4.0$ s

Y_7 = 50th percentile of t_r (median)

Y_8 = 90th percentile of t_r

Y_9 = 95th percentile of t_r

Source; Waldbaum (1973).

Table 2.21

LAYOUT OF THE EXPERIMENT IN EXAMPLE 2.11

		X_2	
		5 tracks (36,000 bytes)	7 tracks (48K bytes)
X_1	2	9 days	8 days
	3	19 days	—

Source: Waldbaum (1973).

There are various methods to estimate the regression parameters. The one univer-
sally used in linear regression is the *method of least squares*, which, by Gauss' theorem [*see*
Draper and Smith (1966)], provides for each parameter an unbiased estimate having the
minimum variance among all possible estimates which are linear functions of the observations $Y_{g1}, \ldots, Y_{gn}$. The least-squares estimator is the one which minimizes the sum of
squares of the errors:

$$\sum_{k=1}^{n} E_{gk}^2 = \sum_{k=1}^{n} \left(Y_{gk} - \beta_{g0} - \sum_{k=1}^{v} \beta_{gi} X_{ik} \right)^2. \tag{2.51}$$

Parameters $\beta_{g0}, \ldots, \beta_{gv}$ are estimated by differentiating (2.51) with respect to each one of them, setting the derivatives equal to zero, and solving the resulting $v + 1$ algebraic equations. To indicate that the values obtained in this way are estimates of the regression parameters, they will be denoted by $b_{g0}, \ldots, b_{gv}$, with $b_{gi} = \hat{\beta}_{gi}$ ($i = 1, \ldots, v$). The *regression equation*, or *fitted model*, of Y_g will be written as

$$\hat{Y}_g = b_{g0} + \sum_{i=1}^{v} b_{gi} X_i, \tag{2.52}$$

from which we have

$$\hat{Y}_{gk} = b_{g0} + \sum_{i=1}^{v} b_{gi} X_{ik} \qquad (k = 1, \ldots, n). \tag{2.53}$$

The goodness of fit of this model can be estimated in various ways. For instance, the analysis of variance can be used to decompose the total variation of the observations of Y_g into a term explained by the fitted model and a residual term due to the variations of the observations with respect to the fitted model, that is, due to the errors:

$$\sum_{k=1}^{n} (Y_{gk} - \bar{Y}_{g.})^2 = \sum_{k=1}^{n} (\hat{Y}_{gk} - \bar{Y}_{g.})^2 + \sum_{k=1}^{n} (Y_{gk} - \hat{Y}_{gk})^2, \tag{2.54}$$

where $\bar{Y}_{g.}$ is the mean of all observations of Y_g (the grand mean).

The analysis-of-variance table corresponding to the sums of squares in (2.54) is given in Table 2.22. The significance of the regression may be tested by using the F-test described in Section 2.7.2, provided that the errors are mutually independent, normally distributed random variables with zero mean and equal variances σ_E^2. Then the hypothesis

$$H_0: \quad \beta_{g1} = \beta_{g2} = \cdots = \beta_{gv} = 0 \tag{2.55}$$

is rejected at the α level of significance if

$$\frac{MSR}{MSE} > F_{\alpha; r, n-r-1}. \tag{2.56}$$

Table 2.22
ANALYSIS OF VARIANCE OF Y_g IN EXAMPLE 2.11

Source of variation	Sum of squares	Degrees of freedom	Mean square
Regression R	$SSR = \sum_{k=1}^{n} (\hat{Y}_{gk} - \bar{Y}_{g.})^2$	r	$MSR = SSR/r$
Error E	$SSE = \sum_{k=1}^{n} (Y_{gk} - \hat{Y}_{gk})^2$	$n - r - 1$	$MSE = SSE/(n - r - 1)$
Total T	$SST = \sum_{k=1}^{n} (Y_{gk} - \bar{Y}_{g.})^2$	$n - 1$	

If H_0 is rejected, the regression is significant at the α level. This means that the portion of the total variation explained by a regression equation such as (2.52) is greater than would be expected in the $100(1 - \alpha)\%$ of similar observations with the same value of n.

However, the rejection of H_0 does not mean that all the terms in the model are significant. Let us consider a first-order model such as (2.52). To test the significance of an individual factor X_i, a *partial F-test* for parameter β_{gi} may be performed. The parameters of another fitted model, identical to the one being considered except for the fact that the term in X_i is absent, are calculated. The sum of squares of regression for this model, SSR', has $r - 1$ degrees of freedom. The difference $SSR_i = SSR - SSR'$ has one degree of freedom, and its mean square is $MSR_i = SSR_i$. Thus, hypothesis $H_0^i: \beta_{gi} = 0$ is rejected at the α level of significance if

$$\frac{MSR_i}{MSE} > F_{\alpha;1,n-r-1}. \tag{2.57}$$

When H_0^i cannot be rejected, the term in X_i may be eliminated.

The partial F-test tests the significance of a term as if this term were the last to be added to the model. If a fitted model is conceived of as being incrementally built by successive additions of terms, then the significance of each term may be tested by a *sequential F-test*, which is based on the procedure described above for partial F-tests.

Another measure of the goodness of fit of a regression equation is the square of the *multiple correlation coefficient*, $R^2 = SSR/SST$. As we saw in Section 2.7.2, this ratio represents the proportion of the total variation about the mean explained by the fitted model. When $R^2 = 1$, the regression equation is able to perfectly predict the data ($SSE = 0$). When $R^2 = 0$, we have $SSR = 0$. Then, by (2.54), it is $\hat{Y}_{gk} = \bar{Y}_{g.}$ for all k, and, by (2.52), we have $\hat{Y}_g = \bar{Y}_{g.} = b_{g0}$, $b_{gi} = 0$ ($i = 1, \ldots, v$). Thus, R^2 is a measure of the usefulness of the terms containing the factors in the model: The closer R^2 to 1, the better the fit.

The values of the regression parameters in (2.52) and the corresponding values of R^2 found by Waldbaum (1973) are reported in Table 2.23. Since the values of R^2 for the nine regression equations are not close enough to 1, the accuracy of the model must be increased. Waldbaum repeated the analysis for the *second-order* or *quadratic linear model*

$$Y_g = \beta_{g0} + \sum_{i=1}^{v} \beta_{gi}X_i + \sum_{i=1}^{v}\sum_{j=1}^{v} \beta_{gij}X_iX_j + E_g. \tag{2.58}$$

For a regression model, the higher the number of terms in the equations, the better the fit will be. However, the costs involved in gathering and handling data on a large number v of factors when the regression equations are to be used for predictive purposes suggest that v should be minimized. A compromise is therefore to be reached, which consists of including in the model only those terms which have a significant influence on the performance index. There are various iterative procedures to identify these terms, besides the exhaustive approach, which considers all possible regression equations and chooses the one representing the best compromise between the two conflicting requirements of economy and goodness of fit [*see*, for example, Draper and Smith (1966)].

The *backward elimination* procedure tests by a partial F-test the significance of each term in the complete regression equation, the one containing all the terms, such as (2.58). The least significant term among those which did not pass the test is eliminated. Every time a term is eliminated, a new fitted model is to be computed, and the procedure stops when all terms pass the partial F-test.

Table 2.23

LEAST-SQUARES ESTIMATES OF REGRESSION PARAMETERS AND
SQUARED MULTIPLE CORRELATION COEFFICIENT FOR THE FIRST-
ORDER MODEL IN (2.52)

Index	b_{g0}	b_{g1}	b_{g2}	b_{g3}	b_{g4}	b_{g5}	b_{g6}	b_{g7}	b_{g8}	R^2
Y_1	135.7	1.076	−6.349	0.00471	8.512	−0.5827	−0.1668	−0.1469	−0.8859	0.70
Y_2	115.5	0.309	−2.602	0.00382	3.349	−0.2329	−0.0604	−0.1036	−0.1683	0.67
Y_3	106.4	0.036	−1.292	0.00288	1.227	−0.0830	−0.0358	−0.0579	−0.0703	0.63
Y_4	102.6	0.018	−0.718	0.00218	0.477	−0.0330	−0.0287	−0.0328	−0.0674	0.60
Y_5	100.1	−0.016	−0.337	0.00161	0.121	−0.0111	−0.0156	−0.0183	−0.0464	0.52
Y_6	99.1	0.017	−0.202	0.00139	0.042	−0.0044	−0.0119	−0.0135	−0.0345	0.47
Y_7	−0.0770	−0.0183	0.0435	−0.00002	−0.051	0.0033	0.0008	0.0009	0.0056	0.74
Y_8	−0.9581	−0.0136	0.2029	−0.00026	−0.264	0.0178	0.0039	0.0072	0.0146	0.68
Y_9	−1.660	−0.0346	0.3242	−0.00066	−0.292	0.0242	0.0082	0.0123	0.0387	0.61

Source: Waldbaum (1973).

The *forward selection* procedure starts from the simplest equation, $Y_g = Y_g(X_i)$, where X_i is the variable most correlated with Y_g. Terms are then added in the order dictated by the values of the partial correlation coefficient between each term and Y_g until a satisfactory regression equation is found. A method to calculate partial correlation coefficients is described in Draper and Smith (1966).

The *stepwise regression* procedure is a modification of the forward selection procedure. Every time the addition of a term is made, the significance of all terms previously added to the model is tested, and those terms whose contribution is found to be nonsignificant are eliminated. The procedure stops when no more terms are inserted and no more terms are removed.

Other procedures may also be used, some of which are mixtures of the ones outlined above. For example, Waldbaum employed a combination of backward and stepwise regression. All but the following six terms were eliminated from the quadratic model in (2.58):

$$\hat{Y}_g = b_{g0} + b_{g33}X_3^2 + b_{g77}X_7^2 + b_{g24}X_2X_4 + b_{g27}X_2X_7 + b_{g47}X_4X_7$$
$$+ b_{g58}X_5X_8 \qquad (g = 1, \ldots, 9). \qquad (2.59)$$

The values of the parameters and of R^2 for the model in (2.59) are displayed in Table 2.24. R^2 is consistently much higher in this than in the first-order model, which includes eight terms instead of six. The equations of $\hat{Y}_5$ and $\hat{Y}_6$ were found to be significant at the 5% level, and the other regression equations, at the 1% level.

The knowledge of the parameters in Tables 2.23 or 2.24 allows one to predict the distribution of the system reaction time for a given work load and given levels of the primary factors. For instance, consider the work load characterized by the means of the 6 secondary factors over the 36 sessions performed: $X_3 = 1505$ conversational inputs per hour; $X_4 = 1.48\%$ $X_5 = 12.87\%$; $X_6 = 18.9$ large CPU requests per hour; $X_7 = 120$ commands per hour, requiring two work spaces in memory; $X_8 = 19.7$ log-ons per hour.

Table 2.24

LEAST-SQUARES ESTIMATES OF REGRESSION PARAMETERS AND
SQUARED MULTIPLE CORRELATION COEFFICIENT FOR THE
SECOND-ORDER MODEL IN (2.59)

Index	b_{g0}	$10^7 \times$ b_{g33}	$10^4 \times$ b_{g77}	b_{g24}	b_{g27}	b_{g47}	b_{g58}	R^2
Y_1	107.2	13.2	39.9	7.155	−0.1441	−0.2568	−0.0341	0.82
Y_2	105.8	12.8	18.6	3.622	−0.0686	−0.1348	−0.0135	0.83
Y_3	101.6	9.5	9.34	1.851	−0.0346	−0.0722	−0.00531	0.81
Y_4	99.7	6.88	5.28	1.030	−0.0193	−0.0418	−0.00255	0.74
Y_5	98.6	4.91	2.54	0.528	−0.00959	−0.0222	−0.00115	0.60
Y_6	98.4	4.28	1.69	0.3667	−0.00653	−0.0156	−0.00068	0.52
Y_7	0.089	−0.046	−0.23	−0.0387	0.000884	0.00134	0.000179	0.82
Y_8	−0.172	−0.873	−1.40	−0.2686	0.00513	0.00984	0.00103	0.86
Y_9	−0.257	−2.06	−2.53	−0.4876	0.00891	0.01942	0.00151	0.81

Source: Waldbaum (1973).

Using the first-order model in (2.52) and the parameters in Table 2.23, the estimates of the median reaction time Y_7 are

    a. for $X_1 = 2$ work spaces, $X_2 = 5$ tracks; $\hat{Y}_7 = 0.2742$ second;
    b. for $X_1 = 2$ work spaces, $X_2 = 7$ tracks; $\hat{Y}_7 = 0.3612$ second;
    c. for $X_1 = 3$ work spaces, $X_2 = 5$ tracks; $\hat{Y}_7 = 0.2559$ second;
    d. for $X_1 = 3$ work spaces, $X_2 = 7$ tracks; $\hat{Y}_7 = 0.3429$ second.

    Thus, the value of X_1 is seen to make little difference, whereas the value of X_2 has a rather large impact on Y_7. An increase in work-space size causes the median reaction time to increase appreciably. For the work load selected, the contributions of the terms in X_7 and X_8 are the largest ones after that of the term in X_2. The physical interpretation of these and other findings, as is frequently the case with regression models, is quite difficult. These models are in fact useful to analyze data but have no relationships with the internal structure and the operation of the system under study. Therefore, justifying the results of regression analysis in system terms is often not an easy task.

    If we use the quadratic model in (2.59) and the parameters in Table 2.24, we obtain

    a. for $X_2 = 5$ tracks: $\hat{Y}_7 = 0.2747$ second;
    b. for $X_2 = 7$ tracks: $\hat{Y}_7 = 0.3723$ second.

    The most influential terms, in order of decreasing impact on the value of $\hat{Y}_7$, are those in $X_2 X_7$, $X_2 X_4$, X_7^2, $X_4 X_7$. Those in $X_2 X_4$ and X_7^2 are negative. The sensitivity of $\hat{Y}_7$ to the various factors may be evaluated by computing the derivative of (2.59) with respect to that factor. This calculation is straightforward if the factors are assumed to be mutually independent.

    The two most remarkable aspects of the quadratic model (2.59) are the absence of first-order terms and the fact that X_1, one of the two primary factors, does not appear in the regression equation. We have already observed above that not even in the first-order model did changes in X_1 have any major effect on $\hat{Y}_7$.

    Some of the predictions obtained by using the quadratic model were compared by Waldbaum with measurement data collected later, and the agreement was quite satisfactory.

PROBLEMS

2.1. Design two fixed hardware instruments which produce at their output an electric signal proportional to the quantity being measured. Both tools are to be used in an interactive system. One is to measure the utilization of the CPU and the other one the mean throughput rate, in interactions per second, over a short backward window in time starting from the present instant. Assume that a pulse appears on an accessible line when a new output message is transmitted to a terminal. The signal produced by the tools may, but need not, be a dc (direct-current) voltage level. It is to be used for visual (mechanical or optical) indicators of the two quantities, to be read by the machine operators.

2.2. Modify the experimental setup in Fig. 2.7 to measure, in the EXOPE system considered in Example 2.2, the following quantities:
(a) system idle,
(b) CPU busy (problem)/channel overlap,
(c) CPU idle,
(d) channel busy.
Are the values of these four quantities sufficient to derive those of the other quantities in Table 2.3?

2.3. In a computer system used for real-time applications, it is important to determine the delay with which the CPU services certain interrupts. For these interrupts, we want to measure the time which elaspses between their arrival and the beginning of the execution of their service routine. Assume that the CPU has a microprogrammed control unit. Which ones of the following types of measurement tools can be used: hardware, firmware, software? Which type of tool would you use? Why? How? Can a sampling tool be used? How?

2.4. The maximum bandwidth of a random-access memory is the maximum number of words which can be read from or written into it in the unit time. For simplicity, we assume that the maximum read bandwidth is equal to the maximum write bandwidth. The actual bandwidth of the same memory is the number of words which are actually transferred into or out of it in the unit time. The maximum bandwidth is a design objective and, for a given memory, a known and constant upper bound for the actual bandwidth. On the contrary, the actual bandwidth is generally unknown and time-variant, since it depends, among other things, on the rate of the requests coming from the various units of the system. The actual-bandwidth/maximum-bandwidth ratio is an index of memory bandwidth utilization. How would you measure the actual bandwidth of the primary memory in a running system? After making appropriate assumptions about the structure of the memory and the signals which are accessible, design an experimental setup of the type shown in Fig. 2.7 to illustrate how a wired-program hardware tool could be used. Also, design a fixed hardware tool for the same purpose, specifying how the measurement results would be presented to the experimenter. Can a software tool be used? If so, what type and how?

2.5. The utilization of the primary-memory space in a computer system is to be measured. For this purpose, the $128K$-word memory is divided into 128 regions, each containing $1K$ words. The time of the experiment is divided into intervals of duration τ. Typically, τ will range between 1 ms and 1 s. A Boolean variable $a_j(t)$ is used to describe the behavior in time of region j ($j = 0, 1, \ldots, 127$). At time t_i, which is the end of interval (t_{i-1}, t_i), with $t_{i-1} = t_i - \tau$, we set $a_j(t_i) = 1$ if region j has been referenced at least once during (t_{i-1}, t_i). Otherwise, we set $a_j(t_i) = 0$. Determine whether and how a stored-program tool could be used to collect and store the sequences of values of the a_j's. Specify how references to each region can be detected and what connections are to be established between the measured computer and the tool (*see*, for example, Fig. 2.8). Could a wired-program tool be used? If so, what features would be needed?

2.6. A computer system contains a movable-head disk having 400 cylinders and a seek characteristic which can be approximated by the equation $t_{\text{seek}} = 25 + 0.3(n_c - 1)$, where t_{seek} is in milliseconds and n_c is the number of cylinders to be traversed. A tool and an experimental setup are needed, which allow the histogram of n_c over relatively long periods of time to be collected and stored. The operating system maintains a directory, which gives the disk addresses (cylinder, track, sector) of all the files stored on the disk and of all the empty regions of it. When a disk access is to be made, the directory provides the number of the cylinder over which the arm is to be positioned. The cylinder number is then sent by the CPU to the disk controller, which controls the seek. Using the style of Table 2.5, specify an internally driven software tool which performs the task described above. Can a stored-program hardware tool be employed for the same purpose? If so, what would be its advantages and its disadvantages with respect to the software approach?

2.7. Can a sampling tool be used to measure the histogram of n_c in Problem 2.6? Why?

2.8. Continue the SMT session in Table 2.9, turning on the checkpoints inserted in part (b) of the table and adding another checkpoint to measure the number of times the pseudo-random number generator is called. The checkpoint which calls measurement routine TCNT, inserted in part (a) of the table, is to be turned off. Analyze the interferences in time and in space produced by the instrumentation existing in the program after the modifications described above have been made. State how these interferences could be reduced, if necessary, or at least accounted for.

2.9. Are the opcode types executed by a CPU statistically independent of each other, in your opinion? Design a measurement tool to measure any autocorrelation which may exist in the sequence of opcodes, assuming that the opcode bits of the instruction register are accessible as in Fig. 2.6. Specify the speeds of the circuits you need, knowing that the shortest instruction cycle time of the CPU is 800 ns.

2.10. To measure the utilizations of the opcode types executed by a CPU, is periodic sampling of the opcode bits in the instruction register a correct solution? Why? If your answer to the first question is no, state in what way the results of this sampling experiment would be inaccurate and what corrections could be introduced to improve their accuracy.

2.11. For an interactive system, the curve which relates the mean response time $\bar{t}$ to the CPU time demand of an interaction is to be constructed. Interactions are classified, according to the values of their CPU time demands, into 10 categories. The desired curve will be obtained by interpolation of 10 experimental points. The ranges of CPU time demand corresponding to these categories have been chosen so that the relative frequencies of interactions in each category are approximately equal. The estimated mean rate of interactions over the period of interest is 20 interactions/min. Assuming that the sample means are normally distributed about the true mean of each category and that the standard deviation σ_t of response times in each category is known, determine the minimum durations of the measurement session in the following cases:

$$
\begin{array}{lcccc}
\sigma_t/\bar{t} & 50\% & 100\% & 50\% & 200\% \\
e/\bar{t} & 1\% & 1\% & 3\% & 5\% \\
K & 99\% & 95\% & 90\% & 90\%
\end{array}
$$

Is the normal-distribution assumption realistic?

2.12. Describe how you would estimate the variance of the sample means about the true means in the experiments referred to in Problem 2.11. Apply the method of independent replications.

2.13. Table P2.1 displays some of the results obtained by Schwetman and Browne (1972) in their one-factor-at-a-time experiments on a CDC 6600 computer system. Design an experiment to determine the effect of the interaction between the maximum degree of multiprogramming and the size of primary memory. Would you expect a large or a small interaction effect if the levels were chosen within the ranges in Table P2.1? What levels would you choose for your experiment? Knowing that the average job size during the experiments was $21K$ words, can you explain why the effect of decreasing primary-memory size was much less than one would have expected?

Table P2.1

RESULTS OF TWO SINGLE-FACTOR EXPERIMENTS

	CPU utilization [%]	Mean throughput rate [jobs/hr]
Factor: Maximum degree of multiprogramming		
5 (normal)	96	429
4	92	392
3	91	393
2	76	328
1	60	262
Factor: Primary memory size [K words]		
128 (normal)	97	426
120	96	417
112	93	406
104	93	406
96	93	403
88	91	400

Source: Schwetman and Browne (1972).

2.14. In an interactive multiprogramming system, jobs are given sets of contiguous locations in primary memory in which they have to fit completely. When a job has to wait for the completion of a terminal I/O operation, it is swapped out. When it is again ready to run and the memory space it requires is free, the job is swapped in. If the job is relocatable, it can be loaded into any set of contiguous free locations in memory. Otherwise, the job may be swapped in only when the region for which it was programmed becomes free. In general, the space assigned to a job is only partially used. Thus, before a job is swapped out, the operating system may try to eliminate the unused portions of the space, thereby decreasing the amount of information to be moved in and out of memory and increasing the probability of finding room for the job when it will be swapped in again. This operation, which requires some computing resources and therefore increases the overhead, has been called *krunching* by Nielsen (1971), who describes a simulation experiment similar to the one dealt with here. Design an experiment to determine the effects of relocation, of krunching, and of their interaction on the performance of the system.
(a) Choose the performance index (or indices).
(b) Identify the factors (primary and secondary), and choose their levels.
(c) Prepare the layout of the experiment.
(d) Describe the techniques you would use to interpret the results. Remember that the questions to be answered are, How beneficial is relocation? Is krunching useful? How do they interact?

2.15. Construct a pie chart of Y_1 (the fraction of interactions with a system reaction time not greater than 0.5 s) from Waldbaum's experiment discussed in Example 2.11, assuming the model in (2.59) and Table 2.24. The pie chart is to show the fraction of the total variation explained by the regression equation and the one to be attributed to the errors. With the data you have, can you break the variation explained by the regression into such components as primary (X_1, X_2) and secondary $(X_3, \ldots, X_8)$ factors? If your answer is yes, refine your pie chart accordingly. If it is no, state what data you would need. Independently of your answer to the preceding question, can you calculate the weight of each factor on performance index Y_1 (not on its variation)? If so, determine these weights for a given load and for all four combinations of the two levels of X_1 and X_2 considered in Example 2.11, and construct the four pie charts corresponding to these combinations. Can you draw from these results any conclusions related to the evaluation problem for which the experiment was designed?

2.16. Each session of a measurement study consists of driving a dedicated multiprogramming batch system by a fixed set of jobs and of measuring the total time the system takes to process the jobs in the set. The system's configuration includes one CPU and two I/O channels, one of which controls one movable-head disk drive and the other one a number of low-speed peripherals (card reader, printer, tape drive, and so on). Suppose that two sessions with the same work load and the same system (both hardware and software) have durations which differ by 15%.
(a) What hypotheses would you make about possible sources for such variation?
(b) How would you check the validity of these hypotheses?
(c) Assuming that one of your hypotheses turns out to be valid, what would you do to eliminate the effects of this source of variation on the results of the sessions of your experiment?

3

Simulation Techniques

3.1 SIMULATION STUDIES

Simulation has been defined in Section 1.6 as an evaluation technique which represents by a model the behavior of a system in the time domain. The observation of the behavior in time of the system's model, under stimuli generated by a model of the system's inputs, produces numerical results which may be used in evaluation studies. A model suitable for this purpose is called a *simulation model* or *simulator*.

An essential condition for the applicability of any model is its credibility. The results obtained by experimenting with a model cannot be trusted if the model is not sufficiently accurate. In the context of an evaluation study the *accuracy* of a model is to be defined with respect to the performance index, or indices, selected for the study. The values of the indices resulting from simulation experiments must be sufficiently close to those the simulated system would produce under the same inputs.

Figure 3.1 illustrates this definition in a simple case. The system being considered is a batch-processing system; its work load is a stream of N jobs. If the performance index we are interested in is the total time t_{tot} needed by the system to proceed the N jobs, the model will be said to be accurate if $|t_{tot} - t'_{tot}| <$ e, where e is a given maximum error and t'_{tot} is the simulation result. Of course, this definition assumes that t_{tot} can be measured, and with satisfactory accuracy.

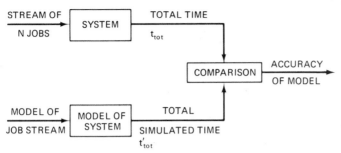

Figure 3.1   Illustration of the concept of model accuracy.

Note that sometimes the simulator does not produce t'_{tot} but a value which can be transformed into t'_{tot} by proper manipulation, for instance, its multiplication by a constant.

A simulator is to be viewed as a system, especially when it reproduces not only the time behavior of the modeled system, but also its structure and organization. This reproduction follows some *rules of similitude* which are very much dependent on the nature of the model. When these rules are applied, most of the mathematical relationships existing among the variables which can be used to describe the system may remain buried in implicit form in the model as they are in the system.

Some other times, the model consists of mathematical equations which describe the system's dynamic behavior. In this case, the technique used can be called simulation only if the equations are solved by a numerical method which follows the evolution of their solutions in the time domain. Thus, the simulator includes both the equations and the algorithm for their solution. In the terminology introduced in Section 1.6, a mathematical model is analytic if it is solved by any method except simulation, and it becomes a simulator if coupled with a simulation technique for its solution.

The above distinction between the two types of simulator should not be overemphasized. In fact, the mathematical structure explicitly stated in a model consisting of equations is simply hidden, but present, in a model which reproduces the behavior of the components of a system and their interactions according to certain rules of similitude. It should also be noted that both types of models may coexist within the same simulator. For instance, some parts or levels of the system may be modeled by explicit mathematical equations and others by using rules of similitude. Also, in all cases, the *simulated time*, to which the observations of the model's behavior are related during the simulation, does not coincide with the *real time*, during which the simulation process takes place. Even the flowing of time is modeled after the time of the system being simulated according to one of several possible rules of similitude.

In this chapter, we refer, unless explicitly stated otherwise, to simulators whose structure resembles the one of the system to be evaluated. These simulators, which include those simulating the mathematical models presented in

Chapter 4, are much more popular than those consisting of equations in the field of computer systems performance studies. In them, it is possible to identify *internal parameters* corresponding to system parameters, *input parameters* corresponding to work-load parameters, and *output parameters* corresponding to the primary and secondary performance indices of interest to the evaluators. Since simulators of computer systems are generally implemented as programs, these parameters will in fact be represented by variables (more generally, data structures) or, if they are nonnumerical, by subroutines. Exploiting the flexibility of programs, we can design parametric simulators, whose input variables include representations not only of work-load parameters but also of system parameters, so that the values of these parameters can be easily modified to simulate changes in the system as well as in its work load.

Computer systems are usually modeled as discrete systems, characterized by discrete states and by state transitions (*events*) occurring at discrete time instants. The hidden mathematical structure of these models can often be viewed as consisting of algebraic relationships and of logical relationships. To illustrate this statement, as well as the concepts introduced so far in this section, we shall discuss a simple example (*see also* Example 1.3).

Example 3.1   The execution time of a given program running alone on an EXOPE system (*see* Fig. 1.2) is to be determined. Assume that during execution the program accesses the drum and the disk but no peripheral device. A conceptual model which would underlie a measurement approach to the problem is depicted in Fig. 3.2(*a*). A conceptual model which describes the simulation approach is represented in Fig. 3.2(b). The diagram in Fig.

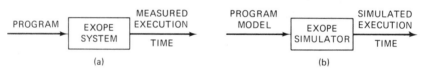

Figure **3.2**   Conceptual models of (*a*) the measurement approach and (*b*) the simulation approach to the problem considered in Example 3.1.

3.3(*a*) can be used as a basis for designing a suitable simulator for this problem. When the program is completely loaded into memory, it immediately gets the attention of the (previously idle) CPU, which starts executing it. Execution is suspended when the program references the drum or disk and resumes when the request has been satisfied. We define the program's execution time to be the interval between the beginning of the execution and the termination of the program. A very simple discrete model of the system is the one which considers the three entities in Fig. 3.3(*a*) as being at any given time in one of two states: either *busy* or *idle*. If the state of the CPU is represented by Boolean variable a_1, the one of the drum by a_2, and the one of the disk by a_3, the state S of the system will be defined by the triple (a_1, a_2, a_3). Only four of the eight possible states will be of interest to us, as shown in Table 3.1 and in the diagram of Fig. 3.3(*b*). The model of the program, to be discussed in detail in Example 3.3, has to contain information allowing the simulator to determine the times at which the program issues drum or disk requests and the time at which the program terminates. Of course, these times will have to be relative to the beginning of the program's execution. The beginning of execution, disk, and drum

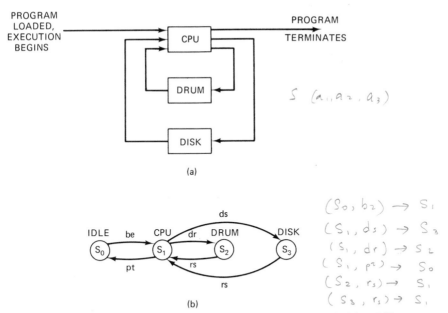

$$S (a_1, a_2, a_3)$$

$$(S_0, b_2) \rightarrow S_1$$
$$(S_1, ds) \rightarrow S_3$$
$$(S_1, dr) \rightarrow S_2$$
$$(S_1, pt) \rightarrow S_0$$
$$(S_2, rs) \rightarrow S_1$$
$$(S_3, rs) \rightarrow S_1$$

Figure 3.3 (a) Simple block diagram of an EXOPE system for Example 3.1 and (b) the corresponding state diagram.

requests, completions of disk and drum service, and termination are the input events which cause the system to move from a state to another. The following logical conditions can be derived from the state diagram in Fig. 3.3(b) using the symbols and notations explained in Table 3.1:

$$(S_0, be) \rightarrow S_1 \qquad (S_2, rs) \rightarrow S_1$$
$$(S_1, dr) \rightarrow S_2 \qquad (S_3, rs) \rightarrow S_1 \qquad (3.1)$$
$$(S_1, ds) \rightarrow S_3 \qquad (S_1, pt) \rightarrow S_0.$$

The program's execution time coincides with the total time spent by the system in states S_1, S_2, and S_3. This time can be calculated by constructing suitable representations of the system and of the program, as well as an algorithm which operates on these two models to reproduce the path of the program through the system. The logical conditions in (3.1) are used to determine the next step in this path. The program's execution time is calculated incrementally by adding to the current value of the simulated time the duration of the system's stay in its next state. This is equivalent to advancing the simulated-time clock to the time of the next event. The calculation of execution time is an example of the role of algebraic relationships in a simulator. In Section 3.2 we shall describe how a simulator can be constructed. ∎

In computer engineering, simulation techniques are used not only to evaluate the performance of various systems but also to verify their correctness. Logic simulators, for example, allow hardware designers to test the correctness of digital system designs or to study the effects of various failures on the functions

Table 3.1

SYMBOLS AND NOTATIONS USED IN EXAMPLE 3.1 AND FIG. 3.3(*b*)

Symbol	Description
(a) State variables	
a_1	CPU state (1: busy; 0: idle)
a_2	Drum state (1: busy; 0: idle)
a_3	Disk state (1: busy; 0: idle)

(b) System states	a_1	a_2	a_3	
S_0	0	0	0	System idle
S_1	1	0	0	CPU busy
S_2	0	1	0	Drum busy
S_3	0	0	1	Disk busy

(c) Input events	
be	Beginning of execution
dr	Drum request
ds	Disk request
rs	Request satisfied
pt	Program termination

(d) Conditional expression	
$(X, ev) \rightarrow Y$	If system is in state X and input event *ev* occurs, then system's state becomes Y

performed by a logic network and the effectiveness of fault-detection or fault-masking mechanisms. Although many of our considerations will also be applicable to simulators built for these purposes, we shall concentrate on the simulation approach to computer system performance evaluation.

When a simulation technique is selected for an evaluation study, phase III (plan preparation) includes the *formulation* and *construction* of the simulator, to be discussed in Section 3.2; its *calibration* and *validation*, to be dealt with in Section 3.3; and the *design of simulation experiments*, which is the subject of Section 3.4. The *interpretation of simulation results*, briefly discussed in Section 3.5, will be performed in phase V of the study. A careful estimation of the costs involved (programming time, debugging time, computer costs) is especially necessary in studies using simulation, which often tend to become prohibitively expensive.

It should be noted that the formulation and construction of the simulator can be avoided by making use of one of the existing commercial simulation packages. Two examples of these computer system simulators are SCERT (Systems and Computers Evaluation and Review Technique) and CASE (Computer-Aided System Evaluation). Some of the important features of these two products are summarized in Table 3.2. Their schematic block diagrams are presented in Figs. 3.4 and 3.5. The use of commercial simulators is not straightforward. The preparation of their input data and the interpretation of their results require a trained analyst working for a rather long time, often of the order of several days. These simulators generally accept work-load descriptions with a variety of degrees of detail, to accommodate a wide spectrum of studies characterized by

Table 3.2

CHARACTERISTCS OF TWO COMMERCIAL COMPUTER SYSTEM SIMULATORS

	Simulator	
	SCERT	CASE
Vendor	COMPRESS, Div. of Comten	Tesdata Systems Corp.
First version delivery date	1962	1969
Minimum memory requirements	$110K$ bytes (primary)	$256K$ bytes (primary) $1M$ byte (secondary)
Library contents	Cost performance specifications of all hardware and software products of ASI, Burroughs, CDC, Datasaab, DEC, Honeywell, IBM, ICL, NCR, Philips, Siemens, Univac, Xerox, plus selected products of other manufacturers; library is updated monthly	Hardware and software (language processors, sort routines, operating systems) parameters of about all major systems, plus those of selected terminals, displays, modems; library is updated monthly or quarterly
Input data	Data definition (description of each file), procedures (description of each program), configuration (descriptions of equipment and system software), environment (description of the available staff)	File specifications, run specifications (files and operations involved in each run), configuration specifications (hardware and software descriptions)
Output reports	25, in 4 categories: general (13), multiprogramming (3), real time (7), time sharing (2); areas of report usage: management evaluation and review (6), system design and implementation (17), performance analysis (19)	About 45, in 3 categories: sequential processing, multiprogramming, real time; summaries and detailed reports (on various aspects of system performance) are provided

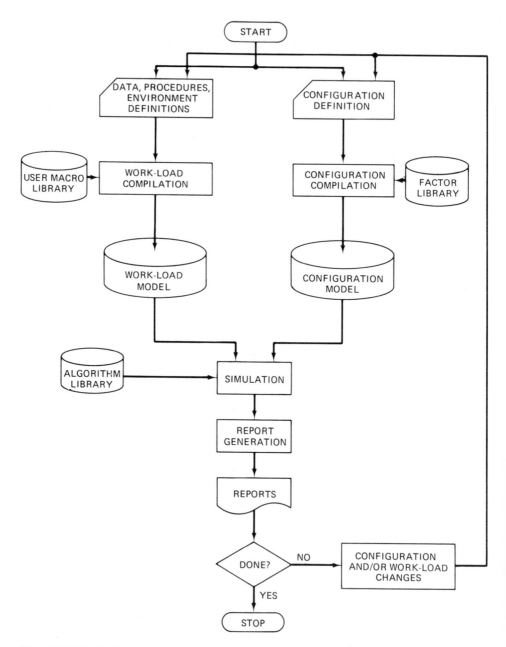

Figure 3.4 Block diagram of an iterative evaluation study based on SCERT.

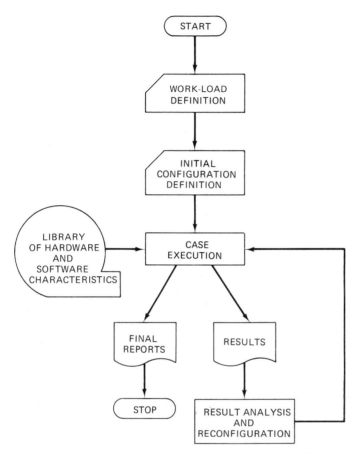

Figure 3.5   Block diagram of a study performed by using CASE.

different amounts of knowledge of the application. This spectrum usually includes comparisons for selection; analyses for improvement; feasibility, design, and implementation studies; and performance projection. The accuracy of the results is generally unknown, unless comparisons are made with those obtained by different techniques of known accuracy. For example, SCERT's manufacturers state that its typical accuracy is within 5% if the work load is specified in sufficient detail and within 10% for individual runs. CASE's results are estimated by its manufacturers to be typically within 10%, with those of individual runs being occasionally far from the actual ones by as much as 50%. Of course, the confidence in the results produced by the simulators decreases as the work-load specifications get less accurate and less detailed. Thus, commercial simulators seem to be better suited to studies aimed at obtaining relative (i.e., comparative) results than to those requiring absolute evaluations of performance indices.

3.2 MODEL FORMULATION AND CONSTRUCTION

3.2.1 The Basic Problems

The formulation of a simulation model for a computer system evaluation study requires a number of decisions to be made. These decisions have an enormous impact on the chances of success of the study. Most of them should be dictated or influenced by the objectives of the study. Here we see an important reason why the objectives should be specified first, and why the more detailed and precise they are, the higher the probability of success. It is usually very risky and very expensive to design a simulator, capable of answering all possible questions which may be asked about a computer system's behavior. Many failures of simulation projects, apparently due to this too ambitious goal (which is practically equivalent to having no objective at all), have been reported.

Computer systems for which a major evaluation effort is worth considering are generally too complex to be simulated with the degree of detail which would be necessary if the simulator were to answer all possible questions or a very broad spectrum of questions. In designing a simulator, its scope should ideally be defined by taking inspiration from the initial objectives of the study and from additional goals or subgoals which may be suggested by a preliminary analysis of the problem. Unfortunately, it is often very difficult or impossible to reliably predict the developments of a study. Thus, the scope of a simulator is frequently made broader than required by its stated purposes, so that it may encompass some unexpected areas of investigation.

Some of the specific issues to be considered in formulating the simulation model of a computer system will now be briefly discussed.

a. *Degree of detail.* The choice of the degree of detail is, as suggested by the above remarks on the influence of the objectives, perhaps the most important problem to be solved. A more detailed simulator is likely to be more accurate and to have a broader field of application than a less detailed one. However, it certainly is more expensive to design, to implement, to test, to document, and to use. In iterative procedures, working with it is often painful and inefficient, since its execution times tend to make interactive or nearly interactive usage impossible. Thus, in choosing the degree of detail of a simulation model, the designers will have to seek a delicate and difficult balance between the requirements of the study and the cost of the simulator.

How can one characterize the degree of detail? A widely accepted index of detail is the *real-to-simulated-time ratio*. This is the ratio between the execution time of the simulator with a given set of input data and the time the simulated system would take to process the work load modeled by those input data. For instance, if 1 minute of real computer time is needed to simulate 3 minutes of the simulated system's time, the ratio which characterizes the simulator is 1:3. Given two simulators of the same system, running on the same computer with ratios 1:3

and $1:10$, respectively, the former is likely to have a higher degree of detail than the latter. However, its lower speed might be partially or totally due to lower efficiency.

Another, perhaps more meaningful, index is the simulator's *resolution*. The resolution in time may be defined as the shortest interval of simulated time between two consecutive events being considered. The resolution in space is the smallest identifiable piece of information dealt with by the simulator, for instance, a word, a page, a routine, or a job. Other indices are the numbers of states and event types considered by the simulator.

The degree of detail need not be uniform throughout the model. It is often made higher in those parts whose accuracy is supposed, or known, to influence the most the accuracy of the results. Thus, also the distribution of the detail over the various sections of the simulator is usually to be considered.

The relationships among the degree of detail, the accuracy, and the cost of a simulator have already been briefly discussed. Two important observations are to be added. First, the robustness of a simulator, defined as its ability to accurately simulate the system with configurations or work loads not experimented with, and sometimes not even anticipated, during its design, usually increases as its degree of detail becomes higher. This point will be discussed in Section 3.3. Second, the accuracy required is a function of the objectives of the study, for example, of whether the evaluator is interested in absolute or relative values of performance indices.

b. *Flexibility*. Building a flexible simulator is the only convenient way to handle the problem, briefly referred to above, of the unpredictability of a study's developments. The other alternative is to build a simulator so detailed that it can take care of all the questions which may arise. However, we have seen that this approach should in general be discarded. Of course, flexibility also has its own design-time and run-time costs and is to be introduced with care. In any event, a simulator should always be able to easily accommodate the changes required by the calibration process (*see* Section 3.3) as well as those reflecting the system and work-load modifications likely to be considered during the study of the class of studies for which the simulator is being designed.

c. *Language*. The choice of the language to be used to implement the simulator has a big influence on its cost, since it affects its programming and debugging time, its running time, its maintainability, its readability, and its transportability. This problem is discussed in Section 3.2.5.

d. *Model structure*. There are various types of models for a computer system and for its input. The choice of the system's model influences the work load's model and vice versa. These choices are often affected by, or sometimes determine, the choice of the language. Some of the existing types of models are described in Sections 3.2.2, 3.2.3, and 3.2.4.

e. *Variables*. The output variables of a simulator will correspond to the primary and secondary performance indices selected for the study. The input variables and the internal variables will be selected according to the degrees of detail of the various sections of the simulator, the modifications expected to be made, and the available data.

f. *Experiments*. The requirements of the experiments expected to be run with the simulator should be given proper attention at the time the model is being built. In particular, the simulator has to be instrumented in order to be allowed to collect the necessary data during simulation runs. The tools used for this purpose can generally be described as internally driven or sampling software tools. Even though they require computing resources from the system on which the simulator runs, the simulator can be built so as to eliminate all interference in simulated time and in simulated space. Another consideration to be made relates to whether the simulator will be used within an iterative evaluation procedure, in which case it should be designed for minimum execution time. The required data reduction functions to be incorporated into the simulator should be considered. The techniques the experimenters will want to use in order to design their experiments and, in particular, to determine the duration of simulation runs may also have an influence on the design of a simulator (*see* Section 3.4).

3.2.2   The Structure of a Simulator

In this section we shall show by an example how a simple simulator of a computer system can be structured. Our discussion has been inspired by the one in MacDougall (1970). Some alternative simulator organizations are presented in Section 3.2.3.

Example 3.2   A simple simulator for a batch-processing EXOPE system (*see* Fig. 1.2) is to be built. The main objective of the study is to predict the effects of hardware performance changes on the system's mean throughput rate and mean job turnaround time.

The peripheral devices being considered are a card reader CR and a line printer LP. Both devices are controlled by the I/O processor P_4, which is assumed not to create any conflicts between them. In other words, the situation is as if CR and LP had two separate, independent controllers. A job consists of several *job steps*: compilation, execution, deck listing, and so on. A job's program and data are read in by CR and, via an input buffer in memory M, stored on disk. When enough memory space is available, the information needed by the first job step is entirely brought into M and waits for the CPU. When its turn comes, it is processed until it issues either a disk or a drum request. While the job waits for its request to be satisfied, the CPU processes other jobs which are ready to run, if any. When a drum request is satisfied, the job starts waiting again for the CPU in the CPU queue. When a disk request is satisfied, the job goes back to the CPU queue, unless its current job step is completed. In the latter case, the job is swapped out and, if there is a next step, joins the memory queue. Note that jobs are never swapped out during a job step. Their outputs are stored on disk and eventually go to LP via a reserved output buffer in M. Also, the space occupied by them in M is released only when the job step terminates. The disk is used for programs, their input data, and job step outputs. The drum contains the nonresident part of the operating system, the library of public programs and routines, and private files. The compiler is assumed to reside in primary memory all the time. To simplify our discussion, and since we feel that the resulting errors are likely to be tolerable, we shall initially neglect the effects of memory interference and operating system overhead on the system's performance indices. Indications will be given later on how these aspects of system behavior could be simulated.

A change in the performance of a hardware component affects the amount of time a job spends in activities related to that component. We shall consider the hardware components as the system's resources. Some resources, for example, P_1, P_2, P_3, CR, and LP, cannot be shared. They can be used only by one job at a time. Others can be shared by more than one job. For instance, P_4 can be shared by a job being read in and by the results of another job being printed. Also, the space in M can be used by a number of jobs at the same time. A job may (or must) use more than one resource at a time, for example, CPU and primary memory.

Since the card reader, the printer, the drum, and the disk can satisfy only one request at a time, we can eliminate any distinction between them and their channel controllers. Thus, the resources listed above can be reduced to those appearing in Fig. 3.6. Since the input and output buffers may be incorporated into CR and LP, respectively, our simulator will explicitly deal with the following six resources: CPU, M, DRUM, DISK, CR, and LP.

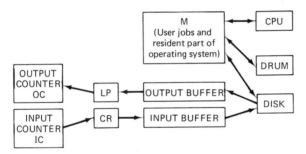

Figure 3.6   Resources and job paths in the batch-processing EXOPE system of Example 3.2.

For each job-resource pair, we are interested in determining how long job J makes use of resource R. In other words, we want the interval between the instant J is *allocated* R and the instant J *releases* R. However, R, in order to be allocated, must be *requested* by J, which will generally have to wait in a *queue* before its request is granted. Thus, we have the situation depicted in Fig. 3.7(*a*), where the three event classes we have introduced (request, allocate, release) are represented by boxes and the flow of jobs through them by arcs. The arc labels refer to the activities performed by the jobs between the source event and the destination event. The possible wait for the resource is visualized by inserting into the appropriate arc the symbol of a queue.

A simulator for the system can be organized around the following two principles:

    a. A chronologically ordered list of events (the *event list*) is constructed and continuously updated;

    b. there is an *event routine* for each type of event; this routine is called whenever an event of that type is the next one which is to occur according to the event list.

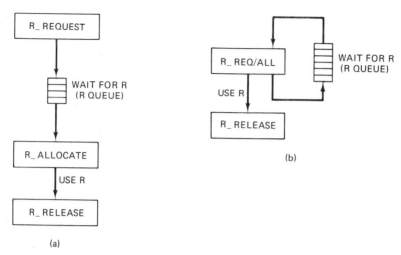

Figure 3.7   Types of job events and activities related to resource R.

Thus, for each resource R in the system, there will be three event routines: R_REQUEST, R_ALLOCATE, R_RELEASE. These routines have a job name J as their argument and may be given the following tasks to accomplish:

R_REQUEST (J): If R can be immediately allocated to J, then schedule the *allocate R to J* event and update the state of R; otherwise, insert the J respect into the R queue;

R_ALLOCATE (J): Schedule the next event for J (which is not necessarily the *release R* event);

R_RELEASE (J): Update the state of R; schedule the next event for J; if R can be immediately allocated to a job K in the R queue, then schedule the *allocate R to K* event and eliminate K from the R queue; otherwise, do nothing.

Note that all of the event routines have the ability to update the event list by creating new events and scheduling them for some future simulated-time instant.

It is easy to see that the R_ALLOCATE (J) routine can be merged with the R_REQUEST (J) routine, as shown in Fig. 3.7(*b*), provided that the basic operations of the routines specified above are modified, for example, as follows:

R_REQ/ALL (J): If R can be immediately allocated to J, then update the state of R and schedule the next event for J; otherwise, insert the J request into the R queue;

R_RELEASE (J): Update the state of R; schedule the next event for J; if the R queue is nonempty, then select a request (say, by job K) in the R queue, schedule the *request/allocate R by/to K* event and eliminate K from the R queue; otherwise, do nothing.

The reader should note that in this scheme additions to the R queue are made by the R_REQ/ALL (J) routine and deletions by the R_RELEASE (J) routine. Futhermore, the scheduling and allocation policies for resource R are implemented by the R_RELEASE (J) routine. When this routine selects a job to be immediately allocated the resource R, it must guarantee that R_REQ/ALL will not add it to the R queue again. This may be obtained, for instance, by marking in a special way the job name (K) which is passed to R_REQ/ALL.

How do the two event routines described above determine the next event for job J? To answer this question, we have to specify in more detail the path followed by a job through our system. Two event types need to be added to those in Fig. 3.7(*b*) for this purpose: the *arrival* event and the *departure* event. The arrival and departure processes differ from the request/allocate and release processes mainly because of the fact that there are no direct relationships between arrivals and departures. If we consider the whole system, including the input counter of the computer center, as a single resource, we see that this resource is immediately allocated to any incoming job, independently of job departures. (Note that this is not the case of a purely interactive system; see, for instance, Problem 3.7). Thus, the ARRIVAL routine has to schedule the next job arrival, and the DEPARTURE routine is much simpler than a RELEASE routine:

ARRIVAL (J): Prepare characterization of job J; schedule next event for J; schedule arrival of next job, say K;
DEPARTURE (J): Delete characterization of J.

We are now ready to construct what we call the *event chart* of our system. This chart, which is shown in Fig. 3.8, represents the history of a job through the system we want to simulate. Some of the assumptions made about the behavior of the system have not been explicitly mentioned above but can be easily derived from the chart, which the reader should carefully study in all of its details.

In the event chart in Fig. 3.8 there are 20 event boxes, 14 of which (two for each one of the six resources in Fig. 3.6, plus the arrival and departure events) correspond to distinct event types. The simulator is essentially based on the 14 routines which deal with these event types and may be organized as shown in Fig. 3.9. The *initialization routine* simply builds the data structures of the simulator and puts it into its initial state. The *simulation control routine* (SCR) has two basic tasks:

a. to choose the next event and call the appropriate event routine;
b. to advance the simulation clock, which measures the simulated time.

Both tasks can be accomplished by examining the top entry of the event list. Each entry in the list contains the type of event, which is used to call the corresponding event routine (for example, CPU_RELEASE); the name of the job, to be passed to the event routine as its argument; and the time of the event, to be loaded into the simulated-time clock by the SCR. The occurrence time of an event is determined by the event routine which generates it. For example, the CPU_REQ/ALL (J) routine in some cases calculates the simulated-time instant at which J will stop computing due to a drum or disk request (remember that job step termination causes a disk request to be issued). This calculation is based on the current value of simulated time and on the duration of the next compute interval for job J, which may be derived from the job's description (*see* Section 3.2.4).

What happens if CPU scheduling is *preemptive*, that is, if a job having higher priority than the one currently running, say J, is allowed to immediately get control of the CPU as soon as it enters the CPU queue, thereby causing an unforseen suspension of J? The *CPU release* event for J, scheduled to occur at a certain time, will have to be removed from the event list by the CPU_REQ/ALL routine, which allocates the CPU to the higher-priority job. Job J, whose remaining CPU time demand is to be updated, must be reinserted by the same routine into the CPU queue. Of course, the R_REQ/ALL routine needed in the preemptive case is more complex than the one described above. Note that the same technique may be used to account for the CPU time required to handle interrupts.

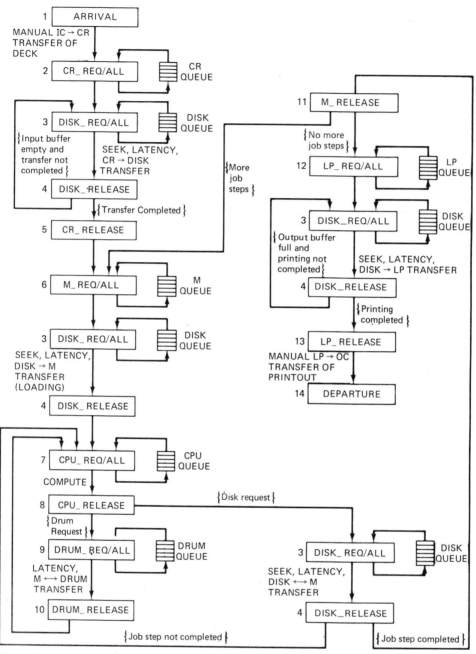

Figure 3.8 Event chart for the EXOPE system dealt with in Example 3.2. Arc labels describe activities. Labels in curly brackets express the conditions under which the arc is taken.

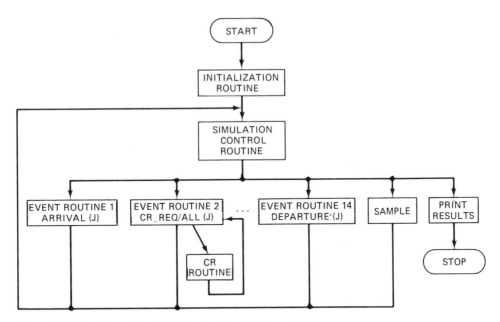

Figure 3.9   Flowchart of the simulator described in Example 3.2.

The mechanisms we have described so far in this example are illustrated in Table 3.3. This table presents the contents of the event list and of three of the six resource queues immediately after each one of seven consecutive simulation steps. The state of this part of the simulator just before the simulated-time clock reaches instant 1713 is shown first. The top element of each queue is the number of the job which is using the corresponding resource. Job 5 is initially running on the CPU and is scheduled to release it at time 1756. Job 9 is in memory, waiting for the CPU. The drum is servicing a request from job 11, while job 7 is waiting for it. The disk is idle. The next event, the one on the top of the event list, is a CPU request from job 3. The CPU_REQ/ALL routine finds the CPU busy and adds 3 to the CPU queue. The next event is caused by job 11, which releases the drum at time 1754. Since there are no events between instants 1713 and 1754, the clock is advanced immediately to 1754. The DRUM_RELEASE routine is called with argument 11. It schedules the next event for job 11, which has to request the CPU immediately (*see* Fig. 3.8). It also finds job 7 waiting in the drum queue and schedules an immediate allocation of the drum to it. In the event-list entry created by this routine for job 7, a special mark (represented by an asterisk in Table 3.3) will tell the DRUM_REQ/ALL routine that 7 is to be allocated the drum even if there are other jobs waiting for the drum. Finally, the DRUM_RELEASE routine erases job 7 from the drum queue and returns.

The CPU is then released by job 5 at time 1756. The CPU_RELEASE routine assigns the CPU to job 9 and schedules an immediate disk request for job 5. Since the disk is idle, it is immediately allocated to job 5, while the CPU starts processing job 9.

The time calculation required to schedule the next event can be performed with different degrees of detail and therefore with different accuracies. For instance, the drum or disk request following a CPU release event may be scheduled to occur immediately without CPU intervention, as has been done in Table 3.3. Alternatively, system overhead (directory searching, disk or drum address calculation, bookkeeping operations) may be taken into account with varying amounts of detail. Another example is the model of the disk used by the DISK_REQ/ALL routine to calculate the total time t_{ds} a request will keep control of the disk. This may be a very simple and crude analytic model such as one of the following:

$$t_{ds} = \bar{t}_{ds},\tag{3.2}$$

$$t_{ds} = \alpha,\tag{3.3}$$

$$t_{ds} = \bar{t}_{ads} + t_{wds}r_{ds},\tag{3.4}$$

$$t_{ds} = \bar{t}_{seek} + \beta R_{ds} + t_{wds}r_{ds}.\tag{3.5}$$

In equations (3.2)–(3.5), α is a random variable with a given distribution, β is a random variable uniformly distributed between 0 and 1, t_{wds} is the (constant) word transfer time, r_{ds} is the length in words of the record requested, R_{ds} is the (constant) disk revolution time, and the means are constant values supposedly derived from measured data or from manufacturer specifications.

However, the model may be a more sophisticated analytic model [see, for example, Chapter 5 of Coffman and Denning (1973)], or an even more accurate simulation model which keeps track of the identity and locations of the records as well as of the instantaneous positions of the disk and of the arm. The event chart of one of the many possible models of the latter type is presented in Fig. 3.10(b). Figure 3.10(a) shows the corresponding part of the global event chart in Fig. 3.8. We have assumed that the disk is controlled by a dedicated, non-stored-program controller. When the disk is allocated to a job, the CPU sends the controller a seek command. The seek time is calculated by the ARM_REQ/ALL event routine from the seek characteristic, which is the curve relating t_{seek} to the number of cylinders to be traversed. When the seek is completed, the CPU is interrupted. Since interrupts from the disk controller may be masked or have a priority lower than the one of the running program at that time, we have to introduce an interrupt queue. The CPU_REQ/ALL routine, which is immediately scheduled by any interrupt request, will have to decide whether or not the interrupt can be serviced or is to join the interrupt queue. When the interrupt is processed, the CPU sends a transfer command which specifies the direction of the transfer, the amount of information to be transferred, and the disk and memory addresses between which the transfer is to take place. Before we may transfer, the latency time must elapse. This time is computed by the RECORD_REQ/ALL routine from the knowledge of the current angular position of the disk and of the disk address for the transfer. The same routine calculates the transfer time and schedules a call to the RECORD_RELEASE routine after a time equal to the sum of the latency and transfer times. Finally, the RECORD_RELEASE routine schedules an immediate interrupt to the CPU. When the interrupt is serviced, the CPU_RELEASE routine schedules the *disk release* event, which terminates the servicing of the disk request.

A wide spectrum of accuracies, programming and running costs, characterizes the various models which may be devised for each system component. Also the data to be supplied by the user for each job and to be stored in the data structures of the simulator vary substantially from model to model. This is evident if one compares the model in (3.2) with the one in Fig. 3.10(b). The choice of the models to be used for the various resources should ideally be dictated by the criterion of minimum complexity for the required accuracy. This, however, is by no means an easy criterion to follow. A factor which usually

Table 3.3

SUCCESSIVE CONTENTS OF THE EVENT LIST AND THE RESOURCE
QUEUES DURING A SIMULATION RUN (*see* EXAMPLE 3.2)

Event list			CPU queue	DRUM queue	DISK queue
Event type	Job number	Event time	Job number	Job number	Job number
CPU_REQ/ALL	3	1713	5	11	Ø
DRUM_RELEASE	11	1754	—	—	—
CPU_RELEASE	5	1756	9	7	Ø
DRUM_RELEASE	11	1754	5	11	Ø
CPU_RELEASE	5	1756	—	—	—
			9	7	Ø
			3		
CPU_REQ/ALL	11	1754	5	Ø	Ø
DRUM_REQ/ALL	7*	1754	—	—	—
CPU_RELEASE	5	1756	9	Ø	Ø
			3		
DRUM_REQ/ALL	7*	1754	5	Ø	Ø
CPU_RELEASE	5	1756	—	—	—
			9	Ø	Ø
			3		
			11		
CPU_RELEASE	5	1756	5	7	Ø
			—	—	—
DRUM_RELEASE	7	1792	9	Ø	Ø
			3		
			11		
DISK_REQ/ALL	5	1756	Ø	7	Ø
CPU_REQ/ALL	9*	1756	—	—	—
			3	Ø	Ø
DRUM_RELEASE	7	1792	11		
CPU_REQ/ALL	9*	1756	Ø	7	5
			—	—	—
DRUM_RELEASE	7	1792	3	Ø	Ø
DISK_RELEASE	5	1815	11		
			9	7	5
			—	—	—
CPU_RELEASE	9	1783	3	Ø	Ø
			11		
DRUM_RELEASE	7	1792			
DISK_RELEASE	5	1815			

* Job to be immediately allocated the resource.

117

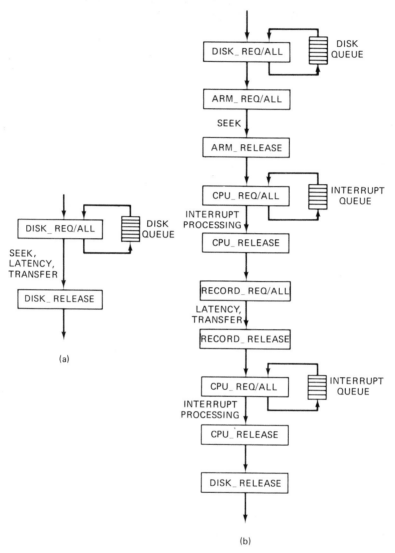

Figure 3.10   Two event charts for disk requests: (a) the chart used in Fig. 3.8; (b) the chart corresponding to a more detailed model of the disk.

cooperates with this criterion in keeping the complexity of these models low is the lack of adequate input information. It would indeed be meaningless to construct complex models requiring the knowledge of job characteristics that are unavailable from experimentation, and must inevitably be invented.

Our simulator is to be used to analyze the performance of various EXOPE system configurations differing from each other in the performances of the hardware components. Therefore, the parameters which represent these performances [for example, $\bar{t}_{seek}$, R_{ds}, and t_{wds} in the disk model (3.5)] should be among the arguments of the routines implementing the models of those components and among the input variables of the simulator. The model selected for the disk can be incorporated into the DISK_REQ/ALL routine, which is the only routine making use of it. However, having a separate disk routine to be called by DISK_REQ/ALL is usually more convenient, especially when the evaluator expects the model of the disk to require modifications (either to increase or decrease its degree of detail) during the calibration or the productive life of the simulator.

The event chart in Fig. 3.8 contains several event boxes having two next events. These next events are mutually exclusive and are to be selected by the appropriate event routine according to the characteristics of the job being dealt with. Note also that some event routines have several next events. For example, the DISK_RELEASE routine, whenever invoked, will have to schedule one of the following events for job J: *disk request/allocate, CR release, CPU request/allocate, M release,* or *LP release.* The *CPU request/allocate* event is scheduled if job J has just been loaded in primary memory or if a disk request issued by J has just been satisfied and the computation for the current job step has not been completed. Thus, the information about the characteristics and the state of each job in the system, which is necessary to make these decisions, is to be kept within the simulator and continuously updated by the event routines.

The instrumentation required to measure the values of the output variables during the simulation can be easily simulated. For instance, to obtain the mean throughput rate $\bar{T}$, defined as the mean number of jobs processed per unit time, we can simply count the number of job departures by inserting a meter into the DEPARTURE routine. Ignoring the problem of initial bias and the tail effect, both to be discussed in Section 3.4.2, we find that the mean throughput rate over the total duration of the run is given by the ratio between the final reading of the meter and the final value of simulated time. Of course, we assume that both the meter and the simulation clock were initialized to zero.

Often, either the total time or the total number of jobs to be processed is selected by the experimenter and used as a termination criterion. In this case, only the other quantity is to be measured.

The value of $\bar{T}$ as a function of time, that is, the throughput rate averaged over the interval between the beginning of the run and the current simulated-time instant, can be obtained by tracing and storing the job departure times $t_{d1}, t_{d2}, \ldots, t_{dn}$. The mean throughput rate at time t, with $t_{d,i} \leq t < t_{d,i+1}$, is i/t. Note, however, that this rate can be computed at any instant during the simulation by simply taking the ratio of the readings of the meter and the clock, without any need to trace and store all departure times.

The mean turnaround time $\bar{t}$ is obtained, according to the definition of mean, from the values of the turnaround times of each individual job. The turnaround time of a job is computed by the DEPARTURE routine as the difference between its departure time and its arrival time. Instead of storing all values of the turnaround times, the DEPARTURE routine may keep a running estimate of $\bar{t}$, which at any instant is the value of $\bar{t}$ up to that instant. If by $\bar{t}_i$ we denote the turnaround time averaged over the first i jobs completely processed by the simulator and by t_j the turnaround time of the jth job processed, we have

$$\bar{t}_i = \frac{1}{i} \sum_{j=1}^{i} t_j. \tag{3.6}$$

Writing (3.6) for $\bar{t}_{i+1}$ and substituting (3.6) into it, we obtain

$$\bar{t}_{i+1} = \frac{i}{i+1} \bar{t}_i + \frac{1}{i+1} t_{i+1}. \tag{3.7}$$

Thus, to compute $\bar{t}_{i+1}$, we do not need the values of $t_1, t_2, \ldots, t_i$. It is sufficient to know $\bar{t}_i$ (the previous value of the index), i, and t_{i+1} (the turnaround time of the job which has just left the system).

Also the variance σ_i^2 of the successive observations about their current mean $\bar{t}_i$ can be kept and updated during the simulation without having to store all the individual turnaround times. Applying the definition of variance and assuming that σ_i^2 is known, a few algebraic manipulations yield

$$\sigma_{i+1}^2 = \frac{i}{i+1}\sigma_i^2 + \frac{i}{(i+1)^2}(t_{i+1} - \bar{t}_i)^2. \tag{3.8}$$

Since $\sigma_1^2 = 0$, (3.8) allows us to recursively compute all successive values of the variance. This computation requires only the knowledge of i, σ_i^2, t_{i+1}, and $\bar{t}_i$.

Sometimes, to reduce the amount of data to be stored and the amount of real time spent in collecting and reducing the data, it is desirable to simulate a sampling tool rather than an internally driven one, which records all events of interest. Sampling can be performed by adding to the simulator an event routine (the SAMPLE routine in Fig. 3.9) which, whenever invoked, collects all the data it needs from the data structures of the simulator. Like the ARRIVAL routine, SAMPLE schedules its next call before returning control to the SCR. Some of the problems which arise in the measurement and interpretation of simulation data are discussed in Sections 2.6.4, 2.7, 3.4.2, and 3.5.   ■

3.2.3   Alternative Organizations

The approach taken in Section 3.2.2 to build a simulator for a batch EXOPE system has been based on the concepts of *event list* and *event routine*. The simulation control routine uses the event list to advance the simulated-time clock to the time of the next event. The technique of advancing the clock by variable steps skipping the intervals containing no events is known as the *next event technique*. The emphasis, in this kind of simulator, is clearly on the events. To each event type there corresponds a routine, which is called when an event of that type occurs, and which in turn creates one or more events and schedules their occurrences. Thus, a simulator like the one we developed in Section 3.2.2 is said to be based on the *event-scheduling approach*. The reader has certainly noticed how elegantly such a simple device as the event list reproduces the behavior of concurrent processes.

A simulator with a substantially different structure results when its designers focus their attention on the activities or on the processes (that is, on the sequences of events each job goes through) rather than on the individual events.

When the emphasis is on activities, no events are scheduled, but simulated time is advanced by constant intervals. At each step, all of the current activities are checked by the simulation control routine to determine whether the conditions for starting or terminating any one of them are satisfied. This method for advancing the clock is called the *fixed-step technique*, and the approach is usually known as the *activity-scanning approach*. A simple way of structuring a simulator based on this approach is to have the simulation control routine call an *activity routine* whenever the checking of conditions shows that the corresponding activity may be started or stopped at that time. An activity routine, besides doing other things, determines the conditions under which the activity will have to be stopped or resumed. This may be viewed as the scheduling of conditional events, which will take place only when the specified conditions are satisfied. For instance, an idle resource whose queue is empty will become busy again when, at some unpredictable time instant in the future, there is a new request for it. In programming language terms, instead of using unconditional statements such as **wait**⟨*time*⟩ as in an event-scheduling simulator, this approach uses conditional statements such as **wait until**⟨*conditions*⟩.

In computer system simulation, fixed-step activity scanning is usually less convenient than event scheduling since events tend to be very unevenly distributed in time. Also, their exact chronological ordering is generally too important to be ignored by choosing relatively long time steps. In addition, there are many activities whose duration may be precisely calculated at their beginning.

The simulation can be speeded up by applying the technique of variable time increments, that is, by combining event scheduling with activity scanning. Conceptually, a possible organization for this combination may be described as follows. The simulation control routine will advance the value of simulated time to the one of the next scheduled (unconditional) event and execute all events scheduled to occur at that time. Then it will scan the conditional-event list and execute all events whose conditions are satisfied. This scan will have to be repeated until no conditional events can be executed anymore. Finally, time will be advanced again to the instant of the next scheduled event. If the philosophy of the simulator is still activity-oriented, this may be termed the *variable-step activity-scanning approach*. The interested reader will find some more details in Section 3.3.3 of Fishman (1973).

A more popular philosophy which makes use of a combination of conditional and unconditional events is the one adopted in the *process interaction approach*. Here, the focus is on the history of each job through the system and on the interactions of the parallel, partially overlapping, and interacting histories of the jobs which happen to be within the system at the same time.

One way of structuring a simulator based on the process interaction approach is depicted in Fig. 3.11. The process routine describes the path (or paths) that jobs follow within the system. This description is similar to the one given in Fig. 3.8 for Example 3.2. When the next event for the job whose history is being simulated at some point in time can be scheduled unconditionally, the process routine does so by adding the appropriate entry to the unconditional-event list. If this is not possible, for example, due to an interaction with other jobs which keep the demanded resource busy, the request is added to the conditional-event list. Then control is returned to the simulation control routine, which will reenter the process routine at the entry point immediately following the **wait until** operation when the job will be selected for service at that resource. Thus, the process routine has a number of entry (or *reactivation*) points and of

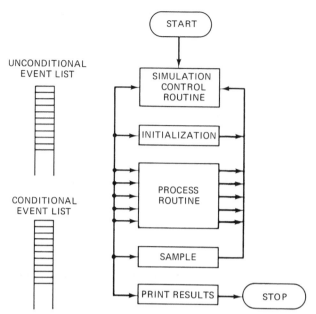

Figure 3.11 Possible structure for a simulator based on the process interaction approach.

exit (or *interaction*) points. When a return occurs to the simulation control routine, this routine scans the lists of conditional and unconditional events, as described above, to determine its next actions.

Figure 3.12 shows a flowchart of a portion of the process routine for a simulator of the system considered in Example 3.2. The portion shown deals with CPU requests and CPU allocation to a job. The reader should note that the performance of the CPU (for example, its speed) is taken into account in the block labeled "determine CPU time demand of job." In a simulator built for the study described at the beginning of example 3.2, CPU speed must be among the input parameters. This block will have to be modified or replaced if the model of the CPU is to be changed for some reason. Periodic gathering of data in this type of simulator can be effected by using the same mechanism described in Section 3.2.2 for the event-scheduling approach (*see* the data collection routine in Fig. 3.11). The considerations made in that section about the simulation of interrupts and preemptive scheduling also apply here.

With respect to resource scheduling and allocation, the reader may have noticed that the scheme of Fig. 3.12 implicitly assumed that these tasks are performed by the simulation control routine instead of by the process routine. It would be unnatural, although possible, to modify the scheme so that these tasks would be executed by the process routine, which represents the histories of the jobs. In fact, resources are seen as passive objects, and their behavior is not explicitly modeled by this version (which we shall call *version 1*) of the process interaction approach.

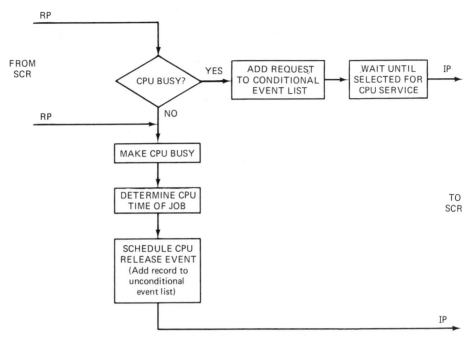

Figure 3.12   Flowchart of the portion of the process routine (see Fig. 3.11) representing CPU request by and allocation to a job (version 1 of the process interaction approach). RP: reactivation point; IP: interaction point.

Another version (*version 2*) of the same approach models resource behavior as well as job behavior. An example for the CPU request/allocation portion in this version of our simulator is given in Fig. 3.13. A comparison of this figure with Fig. 3.12 will enable the reader to understand the conceptual similarities and differences between the two versions. In particular, it is easy to see that scheduling policies are implemented in version 2 by the block called "select next job for CPU service."

3.2.4 The Simulation of the Work Load

A model for the work load, which is to drive the computer system's model during simulation runs, must be formulated at the same time as the system's model. In this section we shall describe the types of models which can be used to simulate an installation's work load.

A first useful distinction, which applies also to system models, is the one between *deterministic* and *stochastic* models. In a deterministic model, all variables are deterministic. If at least one of the variables is random, the model is said to be stochastic. For example, the models of a disk expressed by (3.3) or (3.5) are stochastic, whereas those represented by (3.2) and (3.4) are deterministic. However, in characterizing the work load, the record length r_{ds} in (3.4) may

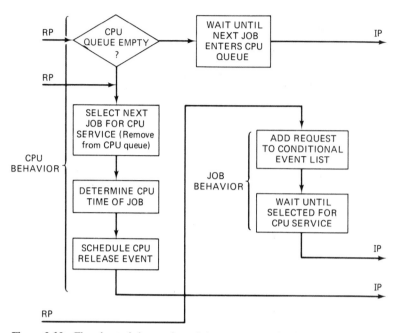

Figure 3.13 Flowchart of the portion of the process routine (see Fig. 3.11) representing CPU request by and allocation to a job (version 2 of the process interaction
approach). RP: reactivation point; IP: interaction point.

be considered as a random variable. This means that we may assign the
distribution of r_{ds} instead of the length of each individual record involved in the
simulation. In this case, since the work-load model contains the random variable
r_{ds}, the model and the whole simulator are said to be stochastic.

It should be evident from the very simple examples just discussed that the
amount of information required to adequately represent the many work-load
parameters and their fluctuations can be drastically reduced only by adopting a
stochastic model for the work load. This does not mean that deterministic
work-load models are not used. On the contrary, two types of such models have
been and are being successfuly employed: those consisting of a *trace* of input
events, generally recorded during a measurement session, and those which
describe the work load in *program* form, possibly using a specialized language.
Thus, depending on the type of work-load model, we have three types of
computer system simulators:

 a. *trace-driven simulators*,
 b. *program-driven simulators*,
 c. *distribution-driven simulators*.

In category c we include all simulators which are driven by stochastic models
of the work load.

The reader should note that a simulator does not necessarily fit exactly into one of the categories. All combinations of the three work-load modeling techniques are feasible and some of them have, in fact, been implemented in real simulators.

To illustrate the concepts we have introduced, we shall now describe in detail their applications to the simulators dealt with in Examples 3.1 and 3.2.

Example 3.3 The work load for the EXOPE system of Example 3.1 consists of a single program. The parameters of the program which are relevant to the simulation are those which determine the state transitions depicted in Fig. 3.3(*b*). These transitions coincide with the input events listed in Table 3.1. A trace-driven simulator could be designed so that it would accept the trace in Fig. 3.14(*a*). Each entry in the trace contains the resource tag and the time spent by the program using that resource.

Figure 3.14(*b*) presents a model of the program which could be input into a program-driven simulator. The model is specified in a self-explanatory FORTRAN-like language oriented toward this special application. The program in Fig. 3.14(*b*) generates the trace in Fig. 3.14(*a*) incrementally during the simulation. The COMPUTE and TRANSFER routines may be thought of as containing calls to the simulator of the system, which in this case is extremely simple.

It is easy to realize that this model is more compact but imposes more restrictions than the one in Fig. 3.14(*a*). Both models characterize the program by the durations of the uninterrupted intervals spent in each one of the three states S_1, S_2, and S_3 and by the exact order in which the resources corresponding to these states are requested.

If the program causes a very large number of state transitions or if we are interested in studying the behavior of a class of programs rather than determining the execution time of a specific program, we may characterize it by the distributions of state durations and by the probabilities of each transition that may occur when the system's stay in state S_1 terminates. A program model of this type is schematically represented in Fig. 3.14(*c*), where $f(x)$ denotes the probability density function of random variable x. Every time the simulator needs to know the duration of the state which has just been entered, it samples the corresponding distribution.

How can we generate the values of a random variable having the same probability distribution function $F_X(x)$ as a given random variable X? Let the diagram in Fig. 3.15 represent $F_X(x)$. We have assumed for simplicity, but with no loss of generality, that X may take only nonnegative values. This is, for instance, the case of state durations. $F_X(x)$, by definition the probability that the value of the random variable X is less than or equal to the given x, is a monotonically nondecreasing function going from 0 to 1. The usual procedure to sample $F_X(x)$ consists of the following steps (*see* Fig. 3.15):

    a. A random number is generated by sampling a random variable Y uniformly distributed on the interval $(0, 1)$; let y^* be its value;
    b. x^*, the value of x such that $F_X(x^*) = y^*$, is determined.

What is the distribution of the random variable X^* whose values are obtained by applying the above procedure? We have

$$\text{Prob}\,(X^* \le x) = \text{Prob}\,[Y \le y = F_X(x)]; \tag{3.9}$$

hence

$$F_{X^*}(x) = F_Y(F_X(x)). \tag{3.10}$$

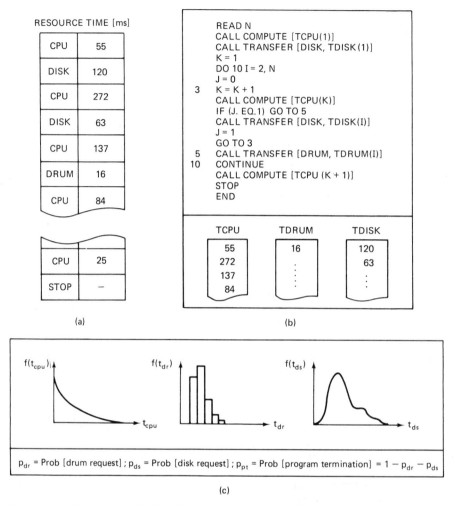

Figure 3.14 Program models for Example 3.3: (*a*) a model for a trace-driven simulator; (*b*) a model for a program-driven simulator; (*c*) a model for a distribution-driven simulator.

Differentiating both sides of (3.10) with respect to *x*, we obtain the following equation among probability density functions:

$$f_{X^*}(x) = f_Y(y) \cdot f_X(x). \tag{3.11}$$

Since *Y* is uniformly distributed on (0, 1), in the corresponding range of *x* we have $f_Y(y) = 1$. Thus, (3.11) becomes

$$f_{X^*}(x) = f_X(x), \tag{3.12}$$

which shows that the distribution of *X** coincides with the distribution of *X*.

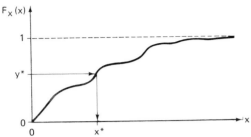

Figure 3.15   Procedure to generate the values of a random variable $X \geq 0$ which has a given distribution function $F_X(x)$. Note that Y must be a random variable uniformly distributed between 0 and 1.

The first step of the procedure which generates a sequence of independent and identically distributed random variables requires the existence of a mechanism for producing uniformly distributed random numbers. Various algorithms for generating pseudo-random numbers are available. The routine in Table 2.8, for instance, is a *linear congruential generator*, which is based on the recursive formula

$$r_i = (mr_{i-1} + a) \bmod 2^n \qquad (i = 1, 2, \dots). \tag{3.13}$$

In (3.13), r_{i-1} is the last pseudo-random number generated; r_i is the one to be produced; a, m, and n are constants; and r_0 is the initial number of the sequence, called *seed*. The seed is to be specified by the user and determines all the numbers in the sequence. Since $0 \leq r_i \leq 2^n - 1$, to obtain a number y_i between 0 and 1 we have to divide r_i by 2^n.

If the sequences of numbers used in a stochastic simulator for the purposes described above do not have sufficient degrees of *independence* and of *uniformity*, simulation results may lead to gross mistakes. Several statistical tests of independence and uniformity may (and should) be applied to the sequences to be used in simulation runs [*see* Knuth (1969)].

The second step of the procedure requires the equation $y^* = F_X(x^*)$ to be solved. If $F_X(x)$ is given in *empirical form* as a table of pairs $(x, F_X(x))$, the values of x^* may be obtained by interpolation. However, $F_X(x)$ may be given in an *analytic form*, resulting from the fitting of a measured distribution or from simplifying assumptions made by the investigators. If an analytic form exists also for the inverse function $x = F_X^{-1}(y)$, the mapping of the pseudo-random number onto the horizontal axis can be performed analytically instead of by interpolation. For example, if X is exponentially distributed, we have

$$y = F_X(x) = 1 - e^{-x/\bar{X}} \tag{3.14}$$

and

$$x = F_X^{-1}(y) = -\bar{X} \ln (1 - y). \tag{3.15}$$

Thus, for any given y^*, equation (3.15) yields the corresponding value of x^*.

A similar approach may be used to sample a given discrete distribution. Let X be a random variable which can take only one of two values: x_1 with probability p_1, and x_2 with probability $p_2 = 1 - p_1$. Replace step b of the above procedure with the following rule:

$$x^* = x_1 \quad \text{if } 0 \leq y^* < p_1,$$
$$x^* = x_2 \quad \text{if } p_1 \leq y^* < 1. \tag{3.16}$$

The distribution of random variable X^* defined by (3.16) is derived by observing that

$$\text{Prob} (X^* = x_1) = \text{Prob} (0 \leq y^* < p_1) = p_1$$

$$\text{Prob} (X^* = x_2) = \text{Prob} (p_1 \leq y^* < 1) = 1 - p_1 = p_2. \tag{3.17}$$

Thus, X^* has the same distribution as X. This mechanism may, for instance, be used to determine the next state when the system considered in this example leaves S_1, the only state which has more than one next state. The interval $(0, 1)$ is divided into subintervals whose lengths are equal to the probabilities p_{dr}, p_{ds}, and p_{pt}. A pseudo-random number y^* is generated and the next state is selected depending on what subinterval contains y^*:

$$\text{if } 0 \leq y^* < p_{dr}, \quad \text{then } S_1 \to S_2;$$

$$\text{if } p_{dr} \leq y < (p_{dr} + p_{ds}), \quad \text{then } S_1 \to S_3; \tag{3.18}$$

$$\text{if } (p_{dr} + p_{ds}) \leq y < 1, \quad \text{then } S_1 \to S_0.$$

Thus, the transitions from state S_1 to states S_2, S_3, and S_0 will occur with probabilities p_{dr}, p_{ds}, and $p_{pt} = 1 - p_{dr} - p_{ds}$, respectively.

More generally, the same approach can be applied to the simulation of *discrete-state stochastic models*. A discrete-state stochastic model (also called a *chain*) is a stochastic process whose states are finite or countable. In our example [*see* Fig. 3.3(b)], we have modeled the program as a process which is at any given time in one of four states. If we assign the distributions of the durations of these states—the probabilities of going, at the time of a transition, from the current state to each of the other states—and the initial state, we completely specify a stochastic model of the program (see Table 3.4). As explained in Section 4.3.1, this is a *continuous-time semi-Markov model*.

The mechanism by which the model in Table 3.4 may be simulated should convince the reader of its general applicability. We start by putting the model in its initial state, for instance, S_0. Then the distribution of t_{idle} is sampled to obtain a duration for S_0. When this interval expires, a transition must take place. The row of the transition-probability matrix in Table 3.4(a) corresponding to the current state is the discrete distribution to be sampled. Since in this case the first row contains a 1 in the S_1 column and all the other entries are 0, the transition must be made to S_1. We then sample the distribution of t_{cpu} to determine the duration of S_1. Again, when the CPU interval expires, we sample the S_1 row of the matrix to select the next state among the three possible candidates, and so on.   ■

A simulator may be designed so that the modifications needed to enable it to accept a work-load description in any of the three forms introduced above, or in any of their combinations, are minor and local. Of course, any changes in the characterization of the work load generally require much more profound and global modifications of the overall structure of a simulator as well as of several of its parts. A very flexible organization, which tends to minimize these modifications, is presented in Section 8.4. In this section, we are concerned only with the representation of a work-load model, a topic which can be discussed independently of the treatment of system models. The choice of the work-load model, which is intimately related to the simulator's structure and degree of detail, is dealt with in Chapter 5.

Table 3.4

SEMI-MARKOV PROGRAM MODEL FOR EXAMPLE 3.3

(a) *Transition-probability matrix*

		To state			
		S_0	S_1	S_2	S_3
	S_0	0	1	0	0
From	S_1	$p_{pt} = 1 - p_{dr} - p_{ds}$	0	p_{dr}	p_{ds}
state	S_2	0	1	0	0
	S_3	0	1	0	0

(b) *Distributions of state durations*

State	Duration (random variable)
S_0	t_{idle}
S_1	t_{cpu}
S_2	t_{dr}
S_3	t_{ds}

(c) *Initial state*

S_0

Example 3.4 The model of the work load for the simulator described in Example 3.2 must contain all of the information required for the numerous decisions that the simulator has to make in order to reproduce the progress of each job through the event chart in Fig. 3.8. Let the resource demands of the jobs be computed as shown in Table 3.5. Then the simulator has to be given, or to determine, the values of the quantities listed in Table 3.6.

Note that this table includes the job arrival time t_{arr}. Also, the manual transfer times which appear in the event chart in Fig. 3.8 are assumed to be system parameters rather than work-load parameters. This assumption is consistent with our discussion of the boundaries of a computer system in Section 1.2.

We assume that the simulator will estimate from the job parameters c and l the numbers of times each job is to use the input and output buffer, respectively. The values of n_{cpu}, n_{dr}, and n_{ds} are not independent, since they must satisfy the constraint $n_{dr} + n_{ds} = n_{cpu} + 1$. Additional work-load parameters may be required by the allocation policies adopted by the various resources, for example, job priorities, user-estimated job time, and memory size limits.

Thus, the simulator must be given the values of the quantities listed in Table 3.6 or data from which those values can be derived. This is to occur, at the latest, when each information item is needed. A possible way to implement this function in a simulator is to have all of the data which characterize a job read in or generated at the time of the job's arrival. These data are then stored in the appropriate cells of the simulator's data base, where the routines of the simulator can find them when necessary, and are deleted only when the job leaves the system. Note that this organization, which was assumed when the tasks of event routines ARRIVAL(J) and DEPARTURE(J) were specified in Example 3.2, allows the same simulator to be driven by different types of work-load representations. Of

Table 3.5

FORMULAS USED BY THE SIMULATOR OF EXAMPLE 3.2 TO
CALCULATE RESOURCE DEMANDS

$$t_{cr} = c/v_{cr} \qquad\qquad t_{cpu} = t_{cpu}$$

$$t_{ds} = \bar{i}_{ads} + t_{wds}r_{ds} \qquad t_{lp} = l/v_{lp}$$

$$t_{dr} = \bar{i}_{adr} + t_{wdr}r_{dr} \qquad m = m$$

Symbol	Unit	Definition
c	cards	Number of cards to be read
l	lines	Number of lines to be printed
m	words	Memory space requested
r_{dr}	words	Number of words in drum record requested
r_{ds}	words	Number of words in disk record requested
$\bar{i}_{adr}$	ms	Mean access time to drum
$\bar{i}_{ads}$	ms	Mean access time to disk
t_{cpu}	ms	Uninterrupted CPU time requested
t_{cr}	min	Card reader time requested
t_{dr}	ms	Drum time requested
t_{ds}	ms	Disk time requested
t_{lp}	min	Line printer time requested
t_{wdr}	ms/word	Drum transfer time
t_{wds}	ms/word	Disk transfer time
v_{cr}	cards/min	Card reader reading rate
v_{lp}	lines/min	Line printer printing rate

Table 3.6

WORK-LOAD INFORMATION NEEDED BY THE SIMULATOR OF EXAMPLE 3.2

	Symbol	Definition
For each job	t_{arr}	Job arrival time
	c	Number of cards to be read
	l	Number of lines to be printed
	n	Number of job steps
For each job step	m	Memory space requested
	n_{cpu}	Number of uninterrupted CPU time intervals
	n_{dr}	Number of drum requests
	n_{ds}	Number of disk requests
For each resource request	t_{cpu}	Uninterrupted CPU time requested
	B	Binary function which determines whether the drum or the disk is to be requested at the end of each CPU interval
	r_{dr}	Number of words transferred to/from drum
	r_{ds}	Number of words transferred to/from disk

course, it is only one of the several possible organizations. In another arrangement, job step descriptions could be generated at the time a job step is initiated.

The reader certainly realizes that any of the work-load representations described at the beginning of this section can provide the simulator with the required information.

A trace representation will contain the values of the parameters listed in Table 3.6, except possibly those of n, n_{cpu}, n_{dr}, n_{ds}, and B, which will be deducible from the trace itself and from the ordering of the requests. This ordering will allow the simulator to determine the chronological sequence in which the various resources are requested by each job. Usually, a system trace consists of a series of event records related to a variety of jobs and contains a mixture of work-load and system information. Such a trace has to be preprocessed in order to be usable as an input to a trace-driven simulator. Also, the degree of detail with which the system's behavior was traced must be sufficient for the information requirements of the simulator.

A representation of the work load in program form will typically consist of a limited number of programs intended to produce on the system's model a load similar to the one caused by the work load on the real system. Thus, this representation suggests by its very nature the use of work-load models conceptually analogous to those employed in controlled measurement experiments. These models, on which executable artificial work loads are based, are described in Sections 5.3.4 and 5.3.5. The programs in the work-load model may be utilized by the ARRIVAL routine to generate the job description of Table 3.6.

If the simulator is to be distribution-driven, several options, characterized by various degrees of detail, exist. For instance, each job could have its own set of distributions for the job step and request parameters, while the job parameters t_{arr}, c, l, and n would be identically distributed. The simplest and coarsest solution is the one of assigning to the simulator the global distributions of the following parameters: t_{int} (job interarrival time), c, l, n, m, n_{cpu}, t_{cpu}, r_{dr}, and r_{ds}. The value of b_{dr}, the probability of requesting the drum at the end of a CPU time interval, will also have to be assigned. When the n_{cpu}th CPU interval of a job step terminates, the disk is requested, and, at the completion of this request, the memory space allocated to the job step is released. These distributions will be utilized by the simulator as described in Example 3.3. The pseudo-random numbers needed to sample the given distributions may be drawn by the ARRIVAL routine when a job arrives so as to generate the complete description of the job. Alternatively, they might be drawn by any event routine which needs some currently unavailable value of a job parameter.   ■

What type of representation should be adopted for the work-load model in a computer system simulation study? The distribution-driven solution is generally the one which requires the most compact description of the workload. However, compact descriptions are often not very accurate. For instance, the correlations among job parameters, which do exist, are usually neglected when this solution is adopted, since the distributions are assumed to be independent. Taking correlations into account would be feasible but would also drastically increase the amount of information required.

A problem which can never be overlooked is the one of the availability of the data. Not only are correlations usually unavailable and difficult to measure, but also the shapes and parameters of the distributions, even those of such fundamental quantities as t_{int}, m, and t_{cpu}, are hard to find in the literature. Even if they exist, published distributions are seldom applicable to installations different from those in which they have been measured. Thus, very often, the only viable solution is the measurement of the necessary distributions in the real installation, if its exists.

Some of the above problems are not present in a trace-driven simulator. As an example, correlations are implicitly contained in a trace. Therefore, they do not have to be measured or simulated explicitly. Two disadvantages of traces, which in some cases may be very serious, are their large volume and their unmodifiability. A trace representation of the work load makes it very inconvenient to model changes in the work load which did not occur during the actual tracing, whereas modifying distributions in a distribution-driven simulator is quite easy.

The program-driven solution presents the problems one encounters in designing artificial work loads. It is usually more compact and more flexible than the trace-driven solution but is certainly less accurate. In particular, the variety of sequences of state durations that program-driven solutions produce is usually quite limited, unless straight-line programs are used. However, in this case, they very closely resemble traces and share their lack of compactness. With respect to the distribution-driven solution, the program-form representation tends to be less flexible and less compact. Its accuracy may be better, but only if the programs have been designed very carefully.

Examples of trace-driven computer system simulators are described in Cheng (1969), Beilner and Waldbaum (1972), Noe and Nutt (1972), and Sherman et al. (1972). Program-driven solutions have been used by Nielsen (1967) and Seaman and Soucy (1969). The paper by MacDougall (1970) describes one of the many examples of distribution-driven simulators.

3.2.5   The Implementation of a Simulator

The choice of the programming language for implementing the simulator is, as mentioned in Section 3.2.1, one of the basic decisions to be made when planning a simulation study. The eligible languages fall into one of the following categories:

   a. simulation languages;
   b. general languages, those which have not been purposely designed for simulation applications;
   c. simulation-oriented extensions of general languages.

Category a includes such languages as GPSS [see Gordon (1975)], SIMSCRIPT [see Kiviat et al. (1969)], and SIMULA [see Dahl and Nygaard (1966)]. Category b includes assembly languages, FORTRAN, ALGOL, and PL/I. Category c includes GASP [see Pritsker (1974)], which is an extension of FORTRAN. Often, as is the case of GASP, the extension of a general language which produces a language in category c consists of a subroutine package added to the library of an existing compiler.

Simulation languages are intended not only to help programmers in the coding of a simulator but also to provide them with a framework in which they can more easily formulate their models. This is the so-called *world view* of simulation languages, which their users have to adopt if they want to use them. The world view of a language deeply influences the organization of the simulators implemented in that language. SIMSCRIPT is based on the event-scheduling approach (*see* Example 2.2). GPSS and SIMULA adopt the process interaction approach. More precisely, GPSS structures its simulators according to what was called in Section 3.2.2 version 1 of this approach, and SIMULA according to version 2.

A simulation language generally contains features which facilitate

    a. the static description of the system to be modeled (statements for the creation and deletion of entities and the specification of their attributes and interrelationships);
    b. the dynamic description of the system (for instance, the automatic updating of the simulated-time clock, the definition and scheduling of events);
    c. the representation of stochastic phenomena (pseudo-random number generation, generation of samples from distributions given in analytic or empiric form);
    d. the collection, reduction, and presentation of data (that is, all the tasks related to the instrumentation of the simulator).

Other useful features, which can be found in some languages, include mechanisms to monitor the simulation, to debug the simulator (a particularly difficult task if the simulator is stochastic), and to put it into the desired initial state (*see* Section 3.4.2).

The presence in a simulation language of entities and constructs which represent the central concepts of simulation is certainly very useful, especially for the novice. However, these entities and constructs may be felt as a constraint by some investigators. In certain languages, for instance, it may be difficult to implement a non-distribution-driven simulator or some unusual queue management scheme. In general, it is reasonable to expect that the use of a simulation language will decrease the amount of programming time required to code and debug a simulator. Also, simulation languages provide a much better system-description vehicle than other languages. This makes them more effective as communication tools and the simulators implemented by using them easier to debug. However, these simulators are often less efficient at run time, since object-code efficiency is usually not among the primary objectives of simulation language design. Other often-heard complaints about most of the existing simulation languages refer to their debugging aids, their documentation, and their transportability. Most of these seem to be historical rather than intrinsic shortcomings and should not be used to discredit simulation languages in general. However, they can explain why so far these languages have not been so popular as they could have been.

The *extensions of general languages* represent an intermediate solution. They can be rapidly learned by programmers familiar with the general language they are embedded in. They provide a world view and a set of features (data structures, simulation control mechanisms, stochastic routines, instrumentation options) analogous to those listed above for simulation languages. Also, they generally produce more efficient code than simulation languages and simulators which, in principle, are more transportable. However, the syntactic restrictions and the idiosyncrasies of the general language on which they are based may make a model less readable and understandable than when a simulation language is used.

How should the language for implementing a computer system simulator be chosen? In many practical situations, there are no alternatives. The availability of a language is in practice the most important criterion, and the number of installations having a simulation language processor (or a simulation-oriented extension of a general language compiler) is increasing but still relatively low. This is certainly one of the main reasons a large fraction of the computer system simulators built so far used a general rather than a specialized language.

Another important reason is the better run-time efficiency usually provided by general languages, which is especially important when a large number of simulation runs is expected to be required by the study being undertaken.

A third reason may be found in the reluctance of certain programmers to learn a new language when they feel that a language they are already familiar with can be fruitfully used for a given task. However, guidance in model formulation, ease of implementation, debugging, and maintenance, which also have an important influence on the cost and the effectiveness of a simulator, tend to support the choice of a simulation language, or, at least, the one of a general language extension. There have, in fact, been cases in which a simulator was implemented, debugged, and calibrated in a simulation language, and then its production version was recoded in a general (assembly or higher-level) language. Extensions of general languages are sometimes, as observed above, a good compromise between the advantages and disadvantages of the other two types.

A discussion of the philosophies, specific features, and relative merits of the existing simulation languages goes beyond the scope of this book. We refer the interested reader to the surveys and comparative studies which have been published [for example, Teichroew and Lubin (1966), Section IX.3.1 of Sammet (1969), Kiviat (1971), and Chapters 4 and 5 of Fishman (1973)]. The use of FORTRAN in the implementation of a computer system simulator is illustrated, for instance, in MacDougall (1970).

3.3   MODEL CALIBRATION AND VALIDATION

3.3.1   Problem Definition

A fundamental question which arises when a modeling technique is used is how well does a model represent the modeled system. Only a satisfactory answer to this question can give the results of a study based on modeling techniques the necessary credibility. A model whose behavior is too dissimilar from the one of the modeled system is practically useless. But how much "dissimilarity" can we accept?

As mentioned at the beginning of Section 3.1, we may define the *accuracy* of a model in terms of the performance indices we have selected for the evaluation of the system. A model is sufficiently accurate if the values of the indices it produces differ from those which would be produced by the modeled system by less than some given maximum errors. Thus, model accuracy is measured by the differences between system performance and model performance. To simplify our discussion, we shall assume that the measurements of an existing system's performance indices to be compared with those of a model are not affected by errors. However, we know from Chapter 2 that this is generally not the case.

This definition of accuracy is schematically illustrated in Fig. 3.16. System $\mathscr{S}$ under work load W produces performance $\mathscr{P}$. The performance indices whose values are collectively denoted by $\mathscr{P}$ may be scalars, scalar functions of installation parameters, distributions or sequences of values of quantities viewed as random variables, and distribution descriptors such as means and variances. $\mathscr{S}'$ is a model of $\mathscr{S}$. Stimulated by W', which is a model of W, $\mathscr{S}'$ produces performance $\mathscr{P}'$. The comparison between the values the same indices take in $\mathscr{P}$ and in $\mathscr{P}'$ provides a measure of the accuracy of $\mathscr{S}'$ and W'. Consider, as an example, the model of an APL interactive system expressed by the regression equation (2.52). A measure of its accuracy is the sum of squares of the errors, denoted by *SSE* in Table 2.22. The smaller the ratio of *SSE* to the total sum of squares *SST* (or, equivalently, the greater the multiple correlation coefficient R^2), the higher the accuracy of the model.

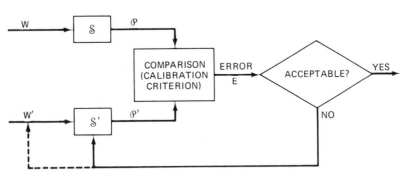

Figure 3.16 Block diagram of an iterative calibration procedure.

A difficulty arises when the system to be modeled does not physically exist or is not available for experimentation. This is the case when modeling techniques are applied to design problems. Philosophically, this obstacle can be overcome by recognizing that the system to be modeled is in fact a conceptual model of the system being designed. Thus, the model to be used in the study is to represent this conceptual model, which exists in the minds of the designers and in their written specifications. From a practical viewpoint, making sure that a conceptual model has been correctly translated into a simulator, or an analytic model, may not be an easy task. The problem is in principle very similar to the one of program correctness verification and can be approached by the same techniques. In particular, we can select a number of test cases, use the model to obtain values of the performance indices, and make reasonableness and pencil-and-paper checks on the results.

When the accuracy of a model is not satisfactory, the model must be modified and the verification process repeated. This operation is called *calibration*. An iterative calibration procedure is schematically shown in Fig. 3.16. The procedure terminates only when the accuracy of the model is found to be satisfactory by the investigators.

Having assumed that $\mathcal{P}$ in Fig. 3.16 is not affected by errors, all of the inaccuracies revealed by the comparison of $\mathcal{P}$ and $\mathcal{P}'$ are to be attributed to the model. There are three major classes of errors which can effect $\mathcal{P}'$:

    a. *formulation inaccuracies*, caused by an erroneous or incomplete or insufficiently detailed model;
    b. *solution inaccuracies*, due to an incorrect or too drastically simplified method of solution of the model;
    c. *parameter inaccuracies*, caused by the use of wrong parameter values.

The objective of calibration is to eliminate or reduce formulation inaccuracies. However, an accurate model may produce wrong results, also during its calibration, if the solution method, or the values of its parameters, or both are inaccurate. Thus, a model builder or user should avoid the mistake of attributing to the behavior of the model errors due to inaccurate solution methods or parameter values. And, of course, the solution method and the parameter values should not be held responsible for errors which are instead caused by an incorrect design of the model.

The main solution inaccuracies which may affect the results produced by a simulation model are discussed in Section 3.4. Parameter estimation from measured data and the inaccuracies which may affect its results are covered in various parts of this book and especially in Sections 2.4.3, 2.6, and 2.7. In our discussions of calibration and validation, we shall for simplicity assume that the only nonnegligible errors which affect the values of $\mathcal{P}'$ are formulation inaccuracies.

The implementation of the simple scheme illustrated in Fig. 3.16 poses a number of important problems. One of them is how to verify that the model of the work load faithfully represents the actual work load. This essential and difficult question is discussed in Chapter 5. Another problem, to be considered in Section 3.3.3, is concerned with the criteria for comparing the performances of the model and of the system. This may be difficult when the performance indices are represented by distributions of random variables instead of by a few scalar quantities. Statistical comparison methods are discussed in Section 6.3.1.

The choice of the indices and the values of the maximum tolerable errors depend on the type of study being performed. In studies which involve comparisons between different systems or between different versions of the same system, what usually matters is not the exact values of performance indices but their sensitivity to the types of changes being considered. Let $\mathscr{S}^*$ be the system to be compared with $\mathscr{S}$, and let $\mathscr{P}^*$ be the performance produced by $\mathscr{S}^*$ under work load W. Assume, for simplicity, that $\mathscr{S}^*$ is a modified version of $\mathscr{S}$ and that we are interested in a single, scalar performance index. Changing the model $\mathscr{S}'$ to reflect the differences between $\mathscr{S}$ and $\mathscr{S}^*$, we obtain the model $\mathscr{S}^{*\prime}$, which produces performance $\mathscr{P}^{*\prime}$. Clearly, the important comparison in this case will be the one between $\mathscr{P}^* - \mathscr{P}$ and $\mathscr{P}^{*\prime} - \mathscr{P}'$. Having models which also accurately reproduce the values of the index is certainly sufficient but by no means necessary in this type of study.

Yet another problem comes from the obvious fact that comparisons cannot be exhaustive. A model cannot be calibrated for all the experimental conditions in which it will have to be used. This is impractical due to the generally large number of such conditions and to their unpredictability. Furthermore, if an exhaustive calibration with measurement data were done, the model would be useless, since there would be no need to predict system performance anymore. A model is typically employed under conditions in which its accuracy has not been, and often cannot be, verified. Thus, calibration will generally be restricted to a few combinations of the work-load and system parameters. If the system exists and is measurable, these combinations are to be selected so that the measurement experiments are feasible and as easy as possible. The model during the calibration procedure will be fed input variables representing the selected combinations of system and work-load parameters.

Given certain accuracy requirements in terms of the maximum acceptable errors, we say that a model is *valid* for some input condition if it satisfies the requirements when its input variables correspond to that condition. The *domain of validity* of a model is the set of input conditions in which the model is valid. Of course, the size of this domain depends on how strict the accuracy requirements are. In calibrating a model, we make it valid in those input conditions we have selected for the calibration procedure. How can we determine whether the model will be valid also in the input conditions it will experience during its productive life? Is there a way to estimate the *robustness* of a model, defined as the degree of insensitivity of its accuracy with respect to variations of the input conditions?

Answering these questions would be possible if a generally applicable *validation* procedure were known. Unfortunately, this is not the case. Thus, model builders have to resort to ad hoc methods, partial tests, and, above all, common sense. Some feeling for the robustness of a model can be obtained by performing, after its calibration, a few additional, carefully selected comparisons of the type illustrated in Fig. 3.16 using new experimental data. If the available data cannot be supplemented with new data, evaluators can try to increase their confidence in a model by using part of the data for its calibration and the rest for its partial validation. Also a posteriori validation is often useful. It consists of comparing, after a certain change suggested by a modeling study has been made to an installation, the model predictions and the measurement results. If the model turns out to have been acceptably accurate, the confidence of the users in its robustness will justifiably grow.

Another, even more important problem is the one of how models can be designed which are sufficiently robust. In general, the principle may be stated that the closer the structure of the model to that of the system and the higher its degree of detail, the larger the model's domain of validity. Unfortunately, a very detailed model is quite expensive.

The robustness of a model can also be enhanced by careful calibration. In particular, we may choose a stronger calibration criterion than the one which would be strictly required. Suppose, for example, that the performance index we are interested in is the mean job turnaround time. If as the *calibration criterion* we choose some measure of the difference between the distribution of turnaround times produced by the model and the one produced by the system, rather than the difference between their means, the simulator we obtain is likely to have a wider domain of validity. The model's robustness should be expected to be even better if the calibration criterion is based on the turnaround time of each individual job or perhaps on its job step intervals rather than on the distribution of this time over all jobs. The definitions of error corresponding to the three criteria just outlined may be expressed as in Table 3.7. These criteria will be discussed again in Section 3.3.3.

Table 3.7

CALIBRATION CRITERIA FOR A SIMULATOR (PERFORMANCE INDEX: JOB TURNAROUND TIME)

Criterion based on	Error E
Mean job turnaround time	$\dfrac{1}{N} \sum\limits_{j=1}^{N} (t_j - t_j')$
Individual job turnaround time	$\sum\limits_{j=1}^{N} (t_j - t_j')^2$
Individual job step time	$\sum\limits_{j=1}^{N} \sum\limits_{i=1}^{n_j} (t_{ji} - t_{ji}')^2$

Symbol	Definition
t_j	Turnaround time of job j produced by the system
t_j'	Turnaround time of job j produced by the model
t_{ji}	Time to process job step i of job j by the system
t_{ji}'	Time to process job step i of job j by the model
N	Total number of jobs
n_j	Number of job steps in job j

In general, we should expect that increasing the degree of detail will not worsen the robustness of a simulator. There is sometimes, however, a point in the calibration process beyond which the robustness may get worse due to an excessive *tuning* of the model to the particular input conditions used in calibrating it. Unfortunately, determining when this point is reached is extremely hard.

Calibration can be regarded as an iterative optimization process, in which a figure of merit (the accuracy of the model) is to be maximized. Iterative calibration is economically feasible if the cost of using the model is not too high. For instance, in the case of a simulation model, the running time of the simulator must not be too long. In other words, the simulator should not be too detailed. Note that this type of simulator usually happens to be just the one requiring the most careful calibration. The speed of convergence to a calibrated simulator, another important aspect of the iterative procedure, depends on the "distance" of the initial simulator from a calibrated one and on the method used to determine the next change to be performed during the procedure. A simulator must be flexible enough to allow the modifications suggested by the calibration procedure to be made with relative ease. These modifications are discussed in the next section. Further considerations on calibration criteria and on the selection of the changes to be made at each iteration can be found in Section 3.3.3.

3.3.2   The Calibration of a Simulator

Three types of modifications may be made to a simulator in order to calibrate it:

a. global changes (for instance, addition of event routines, modifications of the events scheduled by certain routines);
b. local changes (for instance, replacement of models of components with externally equivalent but more accurate models);
c. changes of some special parameters, called *calibration parameters*.

These types of changes are illustrated in the following example.

Example 3.5   We assume here that the simulator of a batch EXOPE system we have designed in Examples 3.2 and 3.4 has been implemented and debugged. Before the simulator can be used, we must verify its accuracy and, if necessary, improve it. In formulating the simulator, we made a number of simplifying assumptions. We decided, for instance, to ignore memory access conflicts and operating system overhead, and we represented the disk and the drum by very crude analytic models (*see* Table 3.5). Are these assumptions reasonable in the context of our study? Is their effect on the accuracy of the results tolerable? What is the impact of having omitted a number of system and work-load details besides those mentioned above?

If the first calibration runs reveal some nonnegligible discrepancies between simulation results and the available measurement data, we shall naturally be led to conjecture that these discrepancies are caused by some of our crudest approximations. We may, for instance, formulate the hypothesis that the lack of accuracy of the simulator is mostly due to the fact that the overhead has not been taken into account. Experimental data on the amount of overhead, if available, can give this hypothesis effective support or seriously impair its credibility. Modifying the simulator to account for the overhead requires a number of global and local changes. Thus, it would be useful to gather some more information on the likelihood that the conjecture is correct before undertaking the cumbersome modification process. Approximations which seem very crude to us may in fact have no significant impact on the simulator's accuracy.

In our case, we could modify the work-load description in various ways to roughly determine the order of magnitude of the overhead's impact on the system's mean throughput rate. For instance, assuming that the simulator is distribution-driven, we may increase by a reasonable amount the mean of the CPU time distribution, and see what the effect of this increase is on the output of the simulator. We may choose the increment conservatively so that it is likely to be bigger than the actual increment in CPU activity caused by overhead. If the corresponding variation in the mean throughput rate is not significant at a reasonable confidence level, we shall conclude that our conjecture is wrong and that overhead can in fact be safely ignored. This conclusion, however, would be based on the results of a one-factor-at-a-time experiment. Thus, it might be incorrect under different input conditions.

Even the interactions among approximations might make our conclusions invalid. In principle, it is possible that two simplifications do not appreciably decrease the accuracy of a simulator when considered separately, whereas their combination does. The verifications of our hypotheses should be carefully designed so as to minimize the probability that their results lead us to wrong conclusions. In particular, one-factor-at-a-time experiments, which generally produce useful, easy-to-interpret information, should be followed by more complex experiments in which the effects of combinations of approximations may be determined.

The approaches which can be used to decide whether and how the degree of detail of a simulator should be increased may also be applied to the problem of simplifying a calibrated simulator's structure in order to reduce its execution time. The experiments mentioned above may in fact be run to determine the effects of a proposed simplification. However, it is often advisable to keep a simulator slightly overdetailed with respect to its objectives in order not to excessively restrict its domain of validity.

Most of the above remarks apply also to changes in the local degree of detail of a simulator. A typical modification of this kind is the replacement of, say, the disk routine by one with a different degree of detail. For instance, the routine which computes t_{ds} as in Table 3.5 could be replaced by one based on the model in (3.5). How can we determine the routines to be modified in order to improve a model's accuracy? The techniques described above for evaluating the effects of global changes may be used also for local modifications. In particular, one-factor-at-a-time experimentation can be used, with the same warnings and limitations discussed above.

The amount of detail to be added should normally be determined by successive approximations, unless a factorial experiment is performed to take interactions into account. For economic reasons, this experiment should involve a very small number of routines as possible candidates for modification.

Designing a simulator so as to facilitate local changes is certainly easier than obtaining the same flexibility with respect to global changes. Modularization with a careful choice and neat definition of the interfaces between modules allows most of the local changes to require only the replacement or modification of one module, plus sometimes a minor modification of the common data base of the simulator.

An even easier and faster way of modifying a simulator for calibration purposes is to change the values of its calibration parameters. The parameters to be assigned this task should be selected at simulator design time. They should also be made easily accessible, that is, included in the set of the simulator's input variables. Often, calibration parameters take the form of correction coefficients in analytic expressions used by the simulator. For instance, in our simulator we could introduce a coefficient k in the formula for the calculation of t_{ds} in Table 3.5 as follows:

$$t_{ds} = k\bar{t}_{ads} + t_{wds}r_{ds}. \qquad (3.19)$$

The calibration parameter k may be interpreted as a correction factor intended to partially offset the errors produced by the use of the mean $\bar{t}_{ads}$ in the calculation of t_{ds} when the distribution of t_{ads} is (as we expect it to be) appreciably skewed. In this case, the distribution would not be symmetric with respect to the mean, and the most probable values of t_{ads} would differ substantially from $\bar{t}_{ads}$. The value of k is to be determined during the calibration process.   ∎

Varying calibration parameters is the simplest and least expensive way to improve the local degree of detail of a simulator. One might think that structural changes, being the hardest and most expensive ones, should be considered last, only after all attempts at calibrating a simulator by parameter or local modifications have failed. This, however, is a very dangerous strategy. In fact, it may fail to reveal structural inadequacies or an insufficient degree of detail which could cause, without letting the modelers realize it, the simulator's domain of validity to be very small. The opposite strategy, which gives global modifications the precedence over local and calibration-parameter changes, is certainly safer. This strategy is adopted also in the statistical calibration methodology described in the next section.

3.3.3 A Calibration Methodology

The iterative calibration procedure outlined in this section is patterned after the one proposed by Beilner and Waldbaum (1972) and is summarized in Fig. 3.17. Each one of the three steps in Fig. 3.17 is iterative in nature. It involves a number of changes to the simulator, each change being followed by a test to determine whether the step is completed or should be continued.

The methodology is statistical but does not apply only to stochastic simulators. In fact, Beilner and Waldbaum used it to calibrate a purely deterministic, trace-driven simulator called SOUL. As will be seen below, the only requirement is that the model's accuracy be defined as a function of variables

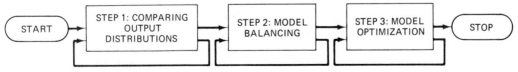

Figure 3.17 Block diagram of Beilner and Waldbaum's calibration methodology.

which, when the simulator is modified, behave like stochastic variables. In our description, we shall assume for simplicity that a single index has been selected to characterize the performance of the system. To satisfy the above requirement, such an index will reflect the behavior of the system in the processing of each individual job. An index of this type is, for instance, the job turnaround time t.

Step 1. Comparing output distributions. A possible definition of the error E to be minimized in the calibration process coincides with the difference between the means of the job turnaround times produced by the system and by the simulator. Assuming that our comparison is based on the processing of a set of N jobs by the system and of the set of their N models by the simulator, we have

$$E_1 = \frac{1}{N} \sum_{j=1}^{N} (t_j - t_j'),\qquad(3.20)$$

where, as specified in Table 3.7, t_j is the turnaround time of job j in the system and t_j' the turnaround time of its model in the simulator.

A more satisfactory definition of the error refers to the distributions of t and t' over the N jobs being considered. Let $F_t(\tau)$ and $F_{t'}(\tau)$ be the distribution functions of the turnaround times produced by the system and by the simulator, respectively. Remember that $F_t(\tau) = \text{Prob}\,(t \leq \tau)$ and $F_{t'}(\tau) = \text{Prob}\,(t' \leq \tau)$, with $0 \leq \tau \leq +\infty$. Then, we define

$$E_2 = \int_0^{+\infty} |F_t(\tau) - F_{t'}(\tau)|\, d\tau.\qquad(3.21)$$

E_2 is better than E_1 since it compares locally, point by point, the two distribution functions and sums the absolute values of their differences in order to avoid partial error compensation due to opposite signs. Consider, for instance, the job turnaround times in Table 3.8(a). Their means are $\bar{t} = 14.15$ seconds and $\bar{t}' = 14.14375$ seconds. The difference between these means is $E_1 = 0.00625$, that is, less than the 0.5% of $\bar{t}$. However, the distributions of t_j and t_j' differ, as can be seen in Table 3.8(b). The value of E_2 given by (3.21) is 0.13125. With respect to the integral of $F_t(\tau)$ between 0 and 25.2 seconds (the maximum value of t_j for all j), E_2 is quite small, though much larger than E_1. Since that integral is about 12.3, E_2 is only slightly greater than the 1% of it.

Thus, even the calibration criterion based on E_2 may be interpreted as leading to the conclusion that our simulator is calibrated. However, a simple inspection of the raw data in Table 3.8(a), which is possible in this case since only 16 jobs are considered, is sufficient to convince us that further calibration is needed. In fact, for some jobs, the difference between real and simulated turnaround time exceeds 20%.

The values of E_1 or E_2, or simply a visual comparison of plots of the two distributions, may often provide suggestions on how the simulator should be modified. They can also help us determine whether a certain modification has produced a true improvement or not. This step will mostly suggest macroscopic changes, for instance, structural modifications or replacements of major routines.

Table 3.8

JOB TURNAROUND TIMES PRODUCED BY A SYSTEM AND BY A
SIMULATOR

Job number j	(a) Turnaround times		(b) Distribution functions of turnaround times		
	$t_j[s]$	$t'_j[s]$	$\tau[s]$	$F_t(\tau)$	$F_{t'}(\tau)$
1	12.2	14.7	4	0.0	0.0
2	8.1	7.9	5	0.0625	0.0625
3	10.2	12.3	8	0.0625	0.125
4	14.9	13.4	9	0.125	0.125
5	25.2	25.5	10	0.1875	0.1875
6	12.9	11.3	11	0.25	0.25
7	18.3	18.2	12	0.3125	0.3125
8	9.5	10.2	13	0.4375	0.375
9	13.3	13.9	14	0.5	0.5625
10	21.0	20.8	15	0.6875	0.6875
11	16.2	16.1	17	0.75	0.75
12	14.6	13.1	19	0.8125	0.8125
13	11.2	9.4	20	0.8125	0.875
14	14.1	14.9	21	0.9325	0.9325
15	20.1	19.9	26	1.0	1.0
16	4.6	4.7			

The reader should realize that obtaining simulation results whose distributions are identical or very close to the real ones is a necessary but not sufficient condition for a simulator to be accurate in a reasonably large domain. It is perfectly conceivable that a simulator's treatment of certain jobs will be substantially different from the simulated system's treatment of the same jobs even if the simulator produces, under one or a few input conditions, the same output distributions as the system. Thus, using E_1 or E_2 as the calibration criterion does not guarantee that the simulator will work correctly under input conditions not considered during the calibration process.

Step 2. Model balancing. A calibration criterion more suitable than E_1 or E_2 for comparing real and simulated turnaround times is one related to the distribution of their difference for each job. A possible criterion of this type is the mean of the squared differences:

$$E_3 = \frac{1}{N} \sum_{j=1}^{N} (t_j - t'_j)^2. \tag{3.22}$$

The value of E_3 for the results in Table 3.8(a), for instance, is 1.418. Its square root is 8.4% of $\bar{t}$. Thus, this calibration criterion produces a result in better agreement with what we observe in Table 3.8(a) than those based on E_1 or E_2.

As the calibration procedure becomes more sophisticated and the most macroscopic discrepancies are removed, the difficulty of determining what changes should be made increases. A job-by-job performance comparison like the one which is the basis for E_3 might reveal, for example, that the simulator processes certain jobs more rapidly and certain jobs more slowly than the system. But what parts of the simulator are responsible for these distortions?

To answer this question, we must analyze the dependence of E_3 on the various characteristics of the jobs. For instance discovering that the simulator speeds up jobs with large memory requirements and slows down jobs with small memory requirements would immediately suggest that we look into the CPU scheduling and memory allocation policies of the simulator.

Definitions of the error such as E_2 and E_3 exhibit random-like variations when plotted against job parameters even when the simulator is completely deterministic. Usually, these variations can be decomposed into a functional component (the *trend*) and a random component (the *noise*). Thus, a statistical method such as regression analysis (*see* Section 2.7.3) seems appropriate to the study of the sensitivity of E_3 to job parameter changes. In the case of the simulator designed in Examples 3.2 and 3.4, the parameters in Table 3.6, with the exception of t_{arr}, the n_{cpu}'s, and the B's, should be considered as the independent variables in a regression equation to be written for E_3. The data needed to compute the regression coefficients can be obtained in one run of the simulator.

The significance tests described in Section 2.7.3 are then performed on each coefficient (partial F-test) and on the regression equation (F-test). If the regression equation is found to be significant at the specified confidence level, the job parameters whose coefficients are significant indirectly point to the changes which should be made to reduce the coefficient's significance. Note that these changes may still be of the global type, but in most cases local changes should suffice. The goal of the procedure, which has been called the *method of good balance*, is to obtain a nonsignificant regression. This corresponds to a situation in which the differences between the outputs of the simulator and those of the system do not significantly depend on job characteristics. In such a *well-balanced model*, the simulator treats all jobs the same way as the system does. To reach this point, regression analysis is only to provide indications, and a linear form of regression equation is expected to be sufficient. Note, however, that the choice of the significance levels must be made very conservatively since the assumptions under which the F-test is valid (*see* Section 2.7.2) are not generally satisfied.

Step 3. Model optimization. In a well-balanced simulator the value of E_3 is not necessarily zero or very small. The last step of the calibration procedure uses a statistical optimization technique to minimize E_3. The approach adopted by Beilner and Waldbaum (1972) is a statistical version of the steepest-descent method.

Only changes in the calibration parameters are considered in this step. Several runs of the simulator with different calibration parameter values are performed. Let **H** denote the vector of calibration parameters, and let $\mathbf{H}_b$ be the "best" value of **H** among those used for the various runs of the simulator. That is, $\mathbf{H}_b$ is the vector which produced the minimum value of E_3. A linear regression between the calibration parameters and E_3 is performed, based only on the data collected during runs corresponding to values of **H** sufficiently near to $\mathbf{H}_b$. For instance, we may consider only the points inside a hypercube centered on $\mathbf{H}_b$ in the space of calibration parameters. If the regression is significant, the regression equation, containing only those terms whose coefficients are significant, may be viewed as a local linear approximation of the function $E_3(\mathbf{H})$ after the elimination of the noise component. The direction of the vector of regression parameters **B** is close to the direction of steepest ascent of this function. Thus, the next "best" value of **H** is

$$\mathbf{H}_{bn} = \mathbf{H}_b - c\mathbf{B} \qquad (c > 0). \tag{3.23}$$

A simulation run is performed with $\mathbf{H} = \mathbf{H}_{bn}$. The resulting E_3 is compared to the one given by $\mathbf{H}_b$. Since E_3 has a random-like behavior, a comparison between two of its values is generally not sufficient to determine whether the modified simulator is significantly better than the one with $\mathbf{H} = \mathbf{H}_b$. Appropriate statistical tests [*see*, for instance, Snedecor and Cochran (1967)] are therefore performed on the sequence of paired observations consisting of the squares of the differences $(t_j - t_j')$ for each job j. If these tests show that the modified simulator is significantly better than the preceding one, a new local regression is performed around $\mathbf{H}_{bn}$, and the next value of **H** is computed by using (3.23). Otherwise, this step and the entire calibration procedure terminate.

The speed of convergence of the iterative methods used in the three steps of the procedure strongly depends on how well the simulator has been designed. It is also likely to be influenced by the choice of the changes to be made and by their extent. Since each iteration is usually quite expensive, the speed of convergence is very important. Beilner and Waldbaum were able to calibrate the SOUL simulator with very few iterations per step. An essential requirement for the simulator being calibrated is a very low real-time-to-simulated-time ratio, so that each run will be relatively fast and inexpensive. An approach to simulator design not incompatible with this requirement is the one which starts with a skeletal and coarse simulator and uses the calibration procedure to progressively refine it until it reaches the desired accuracy.

3.4   THE DESIGN OF SIMULATION EXPERIMENTS

3.4.1   Experimental Design in Simulation

The problems one encounters in designing simulation experiments are conceptually very similar to those discussed in Chapter 2 for measurement experiments. This similarity often allows us to attack them by the same techniques. For instance, what was said in Sections 2.6.2 and 2.6.3 on the application of statistical experimental design methods to measurement studies can be repeated for simulation studies.

The input variables of a simulator are often defined as stochastic variables so as to effectively reproduce the variability of the corresponding installation parameters. All of the variables of a simulator are observable, and all the input variables are controllable even if they are stochastic. Of course, installation parameters which are not represented in a simulator because of the limitations imposed by the simulator's designer on its degree of detail cannot be selected as factors or indices in any experiments based on that simulator. Performance indices and factors have to be selected at the time a simulator is designed. Since simulation runs are generally expensive, the number of factors and their numbers of levels should be kept at a minimum compatible with the goals of the experiment.

In Section 2.6.2, we saw that work-load-characterizing secondary factors are sometimes to be introduced in measurement experiments in which the system is driven by its production work load. These factors may be observed but cannot be effectively controlled. Thus, as described in Section 2.6.3, their effects have to be blocked by proper experimental design. This problem does not exist in simulation experiments. In a simulator, the work load is represented by input variables. Hence, it is always controllable and exactly reproducible.

Simulation experiments are characterized by a much easier reproducibility than that of measurement experiments. It is straightforward to initialize the simulator in exactly the same state and to drive it by exactly the same input for as many runs as needed. When the levels of each factor are selected, the experimenters should ideally try to make the simulator valid in all conditions corresponding to the combinations of levels selected for the runs.

Example 3.6 An experiment designed to be performed with the simulator described in Examples 3.2 and 3.4 is summarized in Tables 3.9 and 3.10. The study of which the

Table 3.9

FACTORS AND LEVELS FOR THE SIMULATION EXPERIMENT OF EXAMPLE 3.6

Factors			Levels		
Name	Symbol	Name	Symbol		Description
Memory	M	SMALL	$M1$		$32K$ words
size		MEDIUM	$M2$		$64K$ words
		LARGE	$M3$		$96K$ words
Drum	R	SLOW	$R1$		$\bar{t}_{adr} = 8$ ms, $t_{wdr} = 7\ \mu s$
speed		FAST	$R2$		$\bar{t}_{adr} = 5$ ms, $t_{wdr} = 4\ \mu s$
Disk	S	SLOW	$S1$		$\bar{t}_{ads} = 50$ ms, $t_{wds} = 12\ \mu s$
speed		FAST	$S2$		$\bar{t}_{ads} = 30$ ms, $t_{wds} = 8\ \mu s$

Table 3.10
LAYOUT OF A FACTORIAL EXPERIMENT WITH THE SIMULATOR OF
EXAMPLE 3.2

		R, S			
		$R1, S1$	$R1, S2$	$R2, S1$	$R2, S2$
M	$M1$	$\bar{T}_{111}, \bar{t}_{111}$	$\bar{T}_{112}, \bar{t}_{112}$	$\bar{T}_{121}, \bar{t}_{121}$	$\bar{T}_{122}, \bar{t}_{122}$
	$M2$	$\bar{T}_{211}, \bar{t}_{211}$	$\bar{T}_{212}, \bar{t}_{212}$	$\bar{T}_{221}, \bar{t}_{221}$	$\bar{T}_{222}, \bar{t}_{222}$
	$M3$	$\bar{T}_{311}, \bar{t}_{311}$	$\bar{T}_{312}, \bar{t}_{312}$	$\bar{T}_{321}, \bar{t}_{321}$	$\bar{T}_{322}, \bar{t}_{322}$

experiment is a part has the objective of designing a batch-processing installation. The simulator is intended to provide information about the performance expected to result from various possible choices of the size of primary memory and of the drum and disk speeds. Three memory sizes, two different drums, and two different disks are being considered. The factorial layout, requiring 12 runs, is represented in Table 3.10. In each run, with $M = Mi$, $R = Rj$, and $S = Sk$, the mean throughput rate $\bar{T}_{ijk}$ and the mean job turnaround time $\bar{t}_{ijk}$ are to be measured. The 12 pairs of values of these two performance indices will be among the technical bases for selecting the drum, the disk, and the primary memory size. ∎

The computer systems simulation literature contains a large number of papers describing multiple-run experiments performed for various purposes, such as computer selection and configuration design [*see*, for example, Nielsen (1967)], system design [*see*, for example, Nielsen (1971) and Sherman et al. (1972)], and performance improvement [*see*, for example, Nielsen (1967)]. A paper which presents statistically designed simulation experiments is Goel and Liu (1973).

3.4.2   The Duration of Simulation Runs

The problem of determining the duration of a simulation run is conceptually analogous to the one of deciding the duration of a measurement session. Thus, what was said in Section 2.6.4 about this problem and its solutions for measurements is valid also for simulation experiments. We can summarize the main point made in Section 2.6.4 as follows. Often, our observations of a simulator's behavior cannot be considered as independent and identically distributed. Therefore, we cannot apply the central limit theorem, as we did in Section 2.4.3, to estimate the variances of the estimators based on our observations. These variances about the unknown true means are needed to calculate the accuracies of the estimates of our performance indices. When all the estimates reach their desired accuracies, the run can be stopped. The variance estimation methods introduced in Section 2.6.4 (those of autocovariances, independent replications, and subsamples) can all be applied to simulation. In fact, they have been, and still are, much more widely used in simulation than in measurement experiments. On-line variance estimation, which in measurement requires a sufficiently fast and powerful external stored-program tool, is easier to perform during simulation runs. We saw in Example 3.2 that avoiding any interference in simulated time and in simulated space is straightforward, even though the instrumentation of a simulator consumes real resources.

The variance of an estimator is not only easier to estimate during a simulation run than during a measurement session but can also be reduced by applying one of the several existing *variance reduction methods*. The most popular methods operate on the streams of pseudo-random numbers which are input into a simulator. Thus, they are applicable only to stochastic simulation.

As mentioned also in Section 5.3.5, there are artificial work loads, usable in measurement experiments, which have the characteristics of the work load models suitable for distribution-driven simulators. It has been suggested [*see* Ferrari et al. (1975)] that when a system is driven by artificial work loads of that type, these variance reduction techniques could be effectively applied to shorten the duration of measurement sessions or to increase the accuracy of the estimators.

A stochastic simulator draws one or more sequences of pseudo-random numbers during each one of its runs. Multiple sequences may be produced by different generators or by a single generator initialized with different seeds. To simplify our discussion, we shall concentrate on a single sequence, which is either the only one or one among those used by the simulator in a certain run. Let us denote the sequence by $Z = z_1, z_2, \ldots$ ($0 \le z_i < 1$ for all $i = 1, 2, \ldots$), and let z_0 be its seed.

During the run, we collect observations of a quantity u. These observations are to be employed to estimate a performance index. For instance, the u's might be turnaround times, response times, or queue lengths. We denote the sequence $u_1, u_2, \ldots$ of our observations by $U(Z)$, to emphasize the fact that the sequence has been obtained when the simulator was driven by, among others, the pseudo-random-number stream Z.

The mean of the first n observations in $U(Z)$, $\bar{u}_n$, is an estimator of the true mean $\bar{u}$, which is the performance index we want to determine by the simulation. If we initialize the pseudo-random-number generator with another seed $z_0' \ne z_i$ for all $z_i \in Z$, we obtain a new stream Z', and the simulator produces a new sequence of observations $U'(Z') = u_1', u_2', \ldots$. The mean of the first n observations in U', $\bar{u}_n'$, is another estimator of the unknown true mean $\bar{u}$.

If both $\bar{u}_n$ and $\bar{u}_n'$ are unbiased estimators of $\bar{u}$, we can consider them as random variables having the same mean $\bar{u}$. Thus, the random variable

$$\bar{u}_{2n}^* = a\bar{u}_n + (1 - a)\bar{u}_n' \qquad (0 < a < 1) \tag{3.24}$$

has mean $\bar{u}$ and variance

$$\text{Var}\,(\bar{u}_{2n}^*) = a^2\,\text{Var}\,(\bar{u}_n) + (1 - a)^2\,\text{Var}\,(\bar{u}_n') + 2a(1 - a)\,\text{Cov}\,(\bar{u}_n, \bar{u}_n'). \tag{3.25}$$

Note that $\bar{u}_{2n}^*$ is an estimator of $\bar{u}$ based on $2n$ samples. In general, when n increases, we can expect the variance of $\bar{u}_n$ to decrease less than it would in the case of independent observations (*see* Section 2.6.4). Thus,

$$\text{Var}\,(\bar{u}_{2n}) \geq \frac{\sigma^2}{2n}, \tag{3.26}$$

where σ^2 is the variance of the random variables $u_1, u_2, \ldots$, assumed to be identically distributed. For the same reason, we also expect

$$\text{Var}\,(\bar{u}_n) \geq \frac{\sigma^2}{n}, \qquad \text{Var}\,(\bar{u}'_n) \geq \frac{\sigma^2}{n}. \tag{3.27}$$

For simplicity, assume that the left-hand sides in the inequalities (3.27) are equal to k_n times the corresponding right-hand sides, with $k_n \geq 1$. Similarly, (3.26) may be written as an equality introducing the coefficient $k_{2n} \geq 1$. Substituting in (3.25), we have

$$\text{Var}\,(\bar{u}_{2n}^*) = \frac{2k_n}{k_{2n}}(2a^2 - 2a + 1)\,\text{Var}\,(\bar{u}_{2n}) + 2a(1 - a)\,\text{Cov}\,(\bar{u}_n, \bar{u}'_n). \tag{3.28}$$

This equation shows that, under certain conditions, the variance of an estimator based on $2n$ samples such as $\bar{u}_{2n}$ can be reduced by considering two estimators $\bar{u}_n$ and $\bar{u}'_n$, each based on n samples. If the assumptions made above are satisfied, the condition for variance reduction [$\text{Var}\,(\bar{u}_{2n}^*) < \text{Var}\,(\bar{u}_{2n})$] is

$$\text{Cov}\,(\bar{u}_n, \bar{u}'_n) < \frac{1 - 2k_n(2a^2 - 2a + 1)/k_{2n}}{2a(1 - a)}\text{Var}\,(\bar{u}_{2n}). \tag{3.29}$$

For $k_{2n} = k_n$ and $a = \frac{1}{2}$ condition (3.29) reduces to

$$\text{Cov}\,(\bar{u}_n, \bar{u}'_n) < 0. \tag{3.30}$$

One method which tries to obtain negatively correlated estimators is the *method of antithetic variables*. After running the simulator with the *regular stream* Z and calculating $\bar{u}_n$, we run it with the *antithetic stream* $Z' = 1 - Z = 1 - z_1, 1 - z_2, \ldots$, and we calculate $\bar{u}'_n$. The estimator $\bar{u}_{2n}^*$ of the performance index $\bar{u}$ is given by (3.24). Of course, this technique is applicable to the estimation of any number of performance indices.

The method of antithetic variables is based on the hope that the negative correlation created between the inputs will somehow propagate to the outputs of the simulator. This is more likely to occur if the order of the events inside the simulator is not drastically different under different input streams and if the magnitudes of the outputs are in some way monotonically related to the values of the pseudo-random numbers in the input stream. For example, if these conditions are satisfied, the turnaround time of a job whose CPU time was determined by a small random number z_i will probably be shorter than the one of a job whose CPU time was computed from $1 - z_i$. Unfortunately, there is little evidence that these conditions are satisfied in simulators of multiprogrammed computer systems. Intuitition, on the contrary, suggests that they are unlikely to hold.

Since (3.28) shows that Var $(\bar{u}_{2n}^*)$ might even be greater than Var $(\bar{u}_{2n})$, we can always estimate both variances and select the estimator with the lower one. However, if $\bar{u}_{2n}$ is consistently better than $\bar{u}_{2n}^*$, the additional burden due to the use of the antithetic stream is not compensated for by any advantages whatsoever, and one should either avoid using this method or try to modify, if possible, the simulator.

The same remarks can be repeated for the *method of stratified sampling*, whose strategy to obtain negative correlation between the outputs consists of making $Z' = (Z + d) \bmod 1$, with $0 < d < 1$. Descriptions and assessments of other variance reduction methods can be found in the simulation literature [*see*, for example, Gordon (1969), Naylor (1971), and Fishman (1973)].

A problem always present in the design of simulation experiments, as well as in that of some measurement experiments which make use of artificial work loads, is the one of *initial conditions*. We are usually interested in the steady-state distributions or mean values of performance indices. However, our observations are generally affected by the initial transient, whose characteristics depend on the initial state of the simulator (or, in measurement experiments, on the initial state of the system). In our discussion so far, for the sake of simplicity, we have assumed sample means to be unbiased estimators of the mean values of performance indices. In fact, these estimators are often biased because of the initial transient.

Figure 3.18, based on data published by Rechtschaffen (1972), shows the very beginning of the transients of the sample mean waiting time $\bar{t}_{wn}$ produced by a distribution-driven simulator of an initially empty and idle single-server queuing system with exponential interarrival times (mean: 100 time units) and exponential service times (mean: 80 time units). The true mean waiting time $\bar{t}_w$ is known from queuing theory (*see* Section 4.3.2) to be 320 time units. Figure 3.18(*a*) displays $\bar{t}_{wn}$ as a function of n, the number of jobs processed by the system. Figure 3.18(*b*) presents the same transient as a function of simulated elapsed time. The broken curve in Fig. 3.18(*a*) is the initial part of the transient corresponding to another stream of random numbers input into the same simulator. The reader will notice the striking difference between the two behaviors in this very first part of the transient (the transient usually takes many more than 50 observations). An initial bias is generally present not only in distribution-driven simulators but in all types of simulators, as well as in certain types of measurement experiments.

There are basically three methods to reduce the error due to the initial conditions. The first consists of making the duration of simulation runs sufficiently long. As the number of observations and simulated time grow, the effects of the initial bias on an estimator tend toward zero. If we stop the simulation after collecting n observations of the quantity u, we can write

$$\bar{u}_n = \bar{u} + (\bar{u}_n^0 - \bar{u}) + (\bar{u}_n - \bar{u}_n^0), \tag{3.31}$$

where $\bar{u}_n^0$ is the value of the estimator we would compute if there were no initial

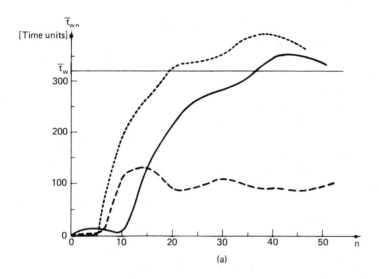

(a)

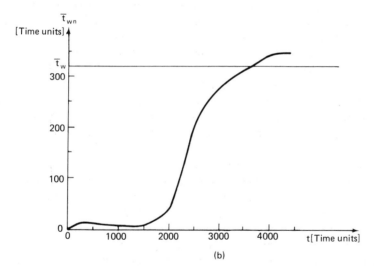

(b)

Figure 3.18 Initial parts of the transients in simulations of an exponential-interarrival-time, exponential-service-time singler-server queuing system. Performance index: mean job waiting time $\bar{t}_w$. The sample mean $\bar{t}_{wn}$ is plotted as a function of (a) the number n of jobs processed and (b) the simulated time since the beginning of the run. [*Source*: Rechtschaffen (1972).]

bias. Moving $\bar{u}$ (the symbol of the unknown true mean) to the left-hand side of (3.31) and squaring and taking the expectations of both sides, we obtain the mean square error of the estimator $\bar{u}_n$:

$$MSE = E[(\bar{u}_n - \bar{u})^2] = E[(\bar{u}_n^0 - \bar{u})^2] + E[(\bar{u}_n - \bar{u}_n^0)^2]. \tag{3.32}$$

Note that the term $E[2(\bar{u}_n^0 - \bar{u})(\bar{u}_n - \bar{u}_n^0)]$ does not appear on the right-hand side of (3.32) since we assume that the two random variables $(\bar{u}_n^0 - \bar{u})$ and $(\bar{u}_n - \bar{u}_n^0)$ are independent and that therefore their covariance is zero. Thus, the mean square error of the estimator $\bar{u}_n$ has two components. The first is its variance about the true mean $\bar{u}$ and often varies with n as $1/n$. The second is the mean square bias, and since the bias usually decreases with n as $1/n$, it may be considered of order $1/n^2$. This means that the effects of the bias vanish more rapidly than those of variance as the duration of a simulation run increases.

What is the minimum duration which is guaranteed to make the effect of the bias smaller than a given value? To answer this question, we should know the dependence of the bias on the number of observations. A feel for the speed at which the influence of the initial bias is decreasing can be obtained during a run by counting the number of times the series of observations $u_1, u_2, \ldots$ crosses the sample mean. This is the number of times $u_i < \bar{u}_i$ and $u_{i+1} > \bar{u}_i$, or $u_i > \bar{u}_i$ and $u_{i+1} < \bar{u}_i$. The larger this number, the farther the simulation has gone in reducing the effects of the initial conditions [see Fishman (1973)].

The second method to reduce the error due to the initial bias is the one of initializing the simulator in a purposely selected state. This state could be one in which the simulator was at the end or somewhere in the middle of a previous run. This method requires storing a suitable state, or the information sufficient to reconstruct it, during a run and having the initialization routine (see Fig. 3.9) reproduce it at the beginning of another run.

The third method consists of starting the collection of the observations after a certain simulated-time interval or after a certain number of job arrivals, instead of starting it immediately at the beginning of a simulation. The dynamic behavior of an estimator such as a sample mean during the initial transient may be quite sensitive to the point at which data collection is started.

For example, the dotted curve in Fig. 3.18(a) represents the mean waiting time when the first five observations are excluded. Note that no other conclusion can be drawn from the figure, which shows just the very beginning of the transient. If observations were taken starting after the arrival of the tenth job, or later, the $\bar{l}_{wn}$ curve of the example would go up very rapidly and remain definitely above $\bar{l}_w$ for the whole interval displayed in Fig. 3.18.

Ordinarily, the number of observations n_0 which should be excluded is much greater than 5, and even greater than 50. A possible way to determine it is to run the simulator for several short periods of time with different inputs and the same initial state and to plot the observations made. One may then choose as n_0 the first value of n in which none of the time series plotted has a maximum or a minimum [see Conway (1963)].

The exclusion of the first n_0 observations (or, equivalently, the initialization of the simulator in a nonempty state) reduces the initial bias but usually increases the variance term in (3.32). Thus, the experimenter is often confronted with the problem of choosing between exclusion and no exclusion. The undesirable effects of the former on the variance may require the runs to be longer than those needed to obtain the same accuracy without trying to reduce the bias. On the other hand, the latter solution (no exclusion) is in some cases worse because of the particularly strong initial bias.

When, for variance estimation purposes, we use the method of independent replications, each run is replaced by h independent subruns, each of which has its own initial transient. Thus, the duration of each subrun is to be so long that the error due to the initial bias is negligible, while h must be large to reduce the variance component of the error. With the method of subsamples, we have only one initial transient per run. However, the number h of subsamples must be large in order to reduce the variance component, and the number q of observations per subsample is to be large to make the estimation of the variance sufficiently accurate.

The reader should also note that the conditions for the termination of a run, which Fishman (1973) calls the *final conditions*, may introduce a bias in some estimators. This is, for instance, the case of the sample mean of the length of a queue when the termination condition is the completion of the nth job, with given n. The bias is due to the fact that the simulated-time interval needed to process n jobs is a random variable, and so is the number of samples periodically collected to determine the mean queue length. A final bias also affects the estimate of the mean throughput rate in simulation or measurement experiments which consist of inputting n jobs into a system or into a simulator and measuring the total elapsed time until the completion of the last job. If the job mix contains some jobs whose processing times are much longer than those of the others, the order in which the n jobs are submitted may have an appreciable influence on the total elapsed time. When a very long job is the last to be processed, the system (or its simulator) runs for a relatively long time in uniprogramming mode, with practically no overlap between CPU and I/O activities, and this has an obvious and undesired effect on the total elapsed time. This is often called the *tail effect* or the *end effect*. To eliminate or reduce it, the order in which jobs enter the system and the order in which they are processed should be carefully examined and, to the maximum possible extent, controlled. Truncating the experiment before the completion of service to all jobs would require defining the truncation time unambiguously. This is an extremely difficult task, since the truncation time should be uniquely defined for any ordering of the jobs and should be relatively independent of the order of arrival while being sufficiently sensitive to the system changes considered in the study. The implications of the tail effect on the design of executable artificial work loads are discussed at the end of Section 5.3.5.

We shall now summarize the topics introduced in this section by continuing the discussion of the experiment outlined in Example 3.6.

Example 3.7   After having laid out the experiment we want to perform, as described in Example 3.6, we must select the number of jobs to be processed during each one of the 12 runs required. Our primary performance indices to be estimated in each run are the two means $\bar{T}_{ijk}$ and $\bar{i}_{ijk}$. In principle, the minimum value of n needed to satisfy the same accuracy requirements may well differ from run to run. However, we shall aim at determining a value of n which is acceptable for all runs. This decision allows us to drive the simulator using exactly the same work-load model in all of the runs.

We are initially interested in the values of the performance indices for each configuration, since we want to consider only those of the 12 configurations whose performances are likely to be acceptable to the users of the installation. Then, for the eligible configurations, it is more important to obtain accurate relative values of the indices. Our goal is in fact to obtain a comprehensive picture of the differences in performance corresponding to the different configuration costs. These considerations help us specify the accuracy needed in the estimation of the performance indices. The accuracy may be expressed in terms of confidence intervals and confidence levels as illustrated in Section 2.6.4.

To calculate the minimum value of n required to achieve the desired accuracy, a method for estimating the variances of the estimators of $\bar{T}$ and $\bar{\imath}$ is to be chosen. We shall choose the method of subsamples (*see* Section 2.6.4). To each combination of levels in Table 3.10, there will correspond a relatively long simulation run, which will be divided, from the viewpoint of data collection, into h subruns.

As pointed out earlier in this section, the method of subsamples is attractive since the long duration of the run reduces the importance of the initial-bias problem. However, the number of observations in each subsample has a lower bound dictated by the need for an accurate estimation of the variance (*see* Section 2.6.4). To select appropriate values for q and for h, we shall use the technique, described in Example 2.9, of collecting the values of $\bar{T}$ and $\bar{\imath}$ for relatively short subruns during one or two long exploratory runs and combining them until a satisfactory level of accuracy is obtained. Since we do not know which one of the 12 configurations produces the largest variance for each estimator, our exploratory run could be performed for a medium-performance configuration such as the one corresponding to levels $M2$, $R2$, $S2$ (*see* Table 3.9). Then the minimum value of n obtained this way could be increased by a safety factor.

Alternatively, we could make two exploratory runs, one with levels $M1$, $R1$, $S1$ and the other one with levels $M3$, $R2$, $S2$. These two runs would explore the performances of the two extreme configurations. However, there is no evidence that the variances behave like the means. We do not know whether the minimum values of n corresponding to the other 10 configurations will all be bounded by the two values of n obtained from the exploratory runs. Thus, a safety factor should probably also be introduced in this case.

The problems of initial and final bias are to be considered before performing the exploratory runs. The initial conditions should be expected to affect in particular the means of the first subsamples. To reduce their effects to tolerable limits, we shall exclude the first n_0 observations of each run. Different runs may have different minimum values n_0 for a given maximum error due to the initial bias. Using the method suggested earlier in this section, we can determine n_0 for the exploratory run (or runs). We then multiply its value (or the greater of the two values) by a safety factor and adopt the result as the number of jobs whose contributions to $\bar{T}$ and $\bar{\imath}$ will be disregarded in all the runs, including the exploratory ones. If this number is denoted by n_0^*, each run will in fact process a total of $n_0^* + hq$ jobs. The simulated-time interval over which the mean throughput rate will be calculated is the one between the arrival of the $(n_0^* + 1)$st job and the departure of the $(n_0^* + hq)$th job.

The problem of the tail effect will be taken care of by simulating the normal activities of the system, including new arrivals and the processing of jobs, until the departure of the $(n_0^* + hq)$th job. This decision may cause the work-load models for the various runs to be slightly different, even if the simulator is trace-driven or program-driven. In fact, because of multiprogramming and because of the different configurations, the last job to be completed in one run might be only partially processed or be completed before the last in another. However, this is likely to be a minor distortion, less important than the one which would be produced by the tail effect if we did not simulate any arrivals after the $(n_0^* + hq)$th job has arrived.

Another question to be answered when designing the experiment is whether or not a variance reduction method should be used. To make a decision, we should compare the expected benefits and the expected cost of the method. Assuming that the simulator is distribution-driven, a rough indication of the expected benefits could be obtained by repeating half of an exploratory run with an antithetic or stratified stream of pseudo-random numbers. By combining the observations made with those of the first half of the original exploratory run, we could determine whether and to what extent the variance would be reduced. The improvement must be substantial in order to justify the use of a variance reduction technique in an experiment with only 12 runs. If the results are definitely successful for both indices, then we should consider having $h'/2$ antithetic, or stratified, subruns after the first regular $h'/2$ subruns in each run. Of course, the given accuracy requirements will be satisfied for a value of h' smaller than h. The antithetic or stratified streams would start with the same seed as the regular one.

A more orthodox application of these methods would consist of restarting the second half of each run from the same initial state as that of the first half. In this case, the experiment would require 24 runs, each processing $n_0^* + h'q/2$ jobs.

Another way of reducing the total duration of each run would be to reduce the variance of the subsample means by applying a variance reduction method within each subsample. This would entail switching to the antithetic or stratified stream for events regarding the last $q/2$ jobs of each subsample and back to the regular stream at the beginning of the next subsample. However, this arrangement is more cumbersome than the previous one and better suited to experiments in which the variance is estimated by the method of independent replications.   ∎

3.5 THE INTERPRETATION OF SIMULATION RESULTS

The methods used to interpret measurement results which have been described in Section 2.7 can be applied with no modifications to the results of simulation experiments.

Off-line data reduction is often not 'needed in simulation since most simulators reduce the data at the time these are collected, or at the end of the run when the output desired by the investigator is produced, or at both times. Graphical techniques to display many performance indices corresponding to the same system on a single chart are as useful in studies based on simulation as they are in measurement studies. Deriving empirical models from the data produced by a simulator is often very helpful in the process of obtaining the information relevant to the questions and problems by which the study was originated.

Not only with measurement but also (perhaps even more) with simulation, one should never forget that errors are possible and indeed frequent. In a simulation experiment, the most common sources of errors are the inaccuracies introduced in the formulation of the system model or of the work-load model; the incorrect logic or the presence of programming errors in the simulator; and the insufficient accuracy of the results due to flaws in the design of the experiments, to wrong statistical assumptions, to bad pseudo-random-number generators, to errors in the design or implementation of the simulator's instrumentation, and to the initial or final bias or both. It is so easy to overlook some, even essential, details when dealing with such complex problems as those which arise in the simulation of a computer system that an evaluator should *never* blindly accept the results produced by a simulator and base important decisions on them. A cautious, suspicious attitude with respect to the data obtained from a simulation run or from a measurement session is always advisable. Reasonableness checks by system experts, alternative techniques for obtaining the same data, comparisons with results of previous studies of the same type, and statistical analyses of the data should be attempted whenever possible to increase the confidence of the decision makers. This is especially desirable when the study is to provide the technical information needed for an important decision.

PROBLEMS

3.1. Draw the event chart for a simulator of the EXOPE system described in Example 3.1. Draw the flowcharts of the simulation control program and of all the event routines appearing in the event chart.

3.2. Suppose that, to provide fast turnaround to short jobs, the EXOPE system described in Example 3.2 assigns to each job a CPU time quantum. Whenever the uninterrupted CPU time consumption of a job reaches the value of the quantum, the job's execution is suspended, unless there are no jobs in the CPU queue, in which case the job is given another quantum. A suspended job is not swapped out but simply joins the CPU queue again. Modify the event chart in Fig. 3.8 to reflect this modification to the system, and draw the flowcharts of the event routines which are affected by the change, if any.

3.3. Repeat the step-by-step simulation reported in Table 3.3 assuming that initially the event list also contains the following events:

Event type	Job number	Event time
CR_RELEASE	2	1723
DISK_RELEASE	8	1739
(job step completed)		

Specify at each step the contents of the event list, of the three queues in Table 3.3, and of the memory queue. Initially, jobs 3, 5, 7, 8, 9, and 11 are in memory, and job 4 is waiting in the M queue.

3.4. If the simulator designed in Example 3.2 had been based on the three-routines-per-resource approach illustrated in Fig. 3.7(*a*) instead of on the two-routines-per-resource approach in Fig. 3.7(*b*), how would the contents of Table 3.3 differ from the present ones?

3.5. Design the detailed flowchart of the CPU_REQ/ALL routine for a simulator of a system in which CPU scheduling is preemptive. Each job has an externally assigned priority. Whenever a job whose priority is higher than the currently running one enters the CPU queue, the running job is suspended and goes back to the CPU queue, and the higher-priority job starts being processed.

3.6. Modify the simulator designed in Example 3.2 so that the effects of the interrupts generated by the completion of each drum or disk transfer on CPU performance can be taken into account. Describe the changes, if any, to be made to the event chart in Fig. 3.8, to the event routines, to the formulas in Table 3.5, and to the work-load parameters in Table 3.6. If at design time you had suspected that this modification might have become desirable, would you have structured the simulator in a different way? If so, how?

3.7. Design the ARRIVAL and DEPARTURE routines for an event-scheduling simulator of an interactive system, and show in what respects they differ from those described in Example 3.2 for a batch-processing system. In this problem, you are not required to choose and describe a specific representation of the system's work load, but you have to assume that a description of user behavior, for instance, in terms of the distribution or of a trace of user think times, is given.

3.8. Repeat Problem 3.1 assuming that the simulator is trace-driven and that the trace contains the drum addresses, specified as (track-number, sector-number) pairs, and the number of words to be transferred at each drum access, instead of containing simply the drum request times.

3.9. Design the structure of a simulator of the EXOPE system described in Example 3.1, basing it on
a. the activity scanning approach,
b. the process interaction approach (in the version you prefer).
In both cases, you should draw a flowchart of the whole simulator and detail as much as you can of the structure of its data and program parts.

3.10. Is the model of the work load affected by the particular approach (event scheduling, activity scanning, process interaction) chosen to design the model of the system? For example, do you expect that the work-load characterizations needed by the two simulators of the same system described in Problem 3.9 will have to differ from each other or that the two simulators can be driven by exactly the same work-load model? Why?

3.11. Design a simulator for the interactive EXOPE system described in Example 1.1 (*see* Fig. 1.6). Draw the event chart, and design the work-load model, choosing one of the three types of representations discussed in Section 3.2.4. Specify also the organization of the work-load and system data, including the queues and the event list, and express in flowchart form the actions of each event routine.

3.12. The work-load parameters listed in Table 3.6 are not the only set of parameters which can be used to represent the given work-load model. Propose one or two alternative sets of parameters. A set is to be considered an alternative representation even if it differs from the given set in only one parameter.

3.13. Devise a scheme for measuring the mean length of the memory queue over the entire duration of a run for the simulator designed in Example 3.2. Describe the changes you would make to the simulator in order to incorporate your scheme and the tests you would use to see whether your scheme is correct and has been properly implemented.

3.14. Design a work-load representation for a simulator so that it can be described as partially program-driven and partially distribution-driven. Justify your choice of the representation by showing that it can be more convenient than pure representations in program form or in distribution form in some evaluation study.

3.15. Draw an event chart for a simulator of the system studied in Problem 1.7, and list a set of work-load parameters that such a simulator would need.

3.16. An analytic model of a drum allows us to express, under certain assumptions and for the shortest-access-time-first drum-scheduling policy, the mean total time for servicing a drum request as [*see* Coffman and Denning (1973), p. 209]

$$\bar{t}_{dr} = \frac{2N + s - 1}{2} \frac{R_{dr}}{s},$$

where N is the total number of requests in the drum system, R_{dr} the drum revolution time, and s the number of sectors. Note that $\bar{t}_{dr}$ also includes the waiting time of a request in the appropriate sector queue. Also, we may consider N, assumed to be constant in the derivation of the formula, as the number of requests in the drum at the instant the request of interest arrives. If the simulator of Example 3.2 had to be designed with this model for the drum, what changes should be made to the design? What changes should be made to Table 3.6?

3.17. Examine Table 3.5 carefully, and say what calibration parameters you would introduce in the formulas of resource demands. Try to justify your choices by rational arguments.

3.18. Design a simulator of an interactive system in which each user may input three classes of commands. Each class is characterized by its distributions of input-message lengths, CPU times, output-message lengths, and think times following each output message. The transitions between command classes for each user are governed by a given 4 × 4 transition probability matrix. The fourth state of a user is the dormant (logged-off) state. A distribution of dormant-state durations is also given. All users have statistically identical behavior. The three command classes are edit commands, compile commands, and file manipulation commands. The system configuration consists of a CPU, a primary memory, and a disk. The editor and the compiler are permanently resident in primary memory. Draw the event chart of the simulator and the detailed flowcharts of the ARRIVAL and CPU_REQ/ALL routines. Assuming that the simulator is to model an existing installation for performance improvement purposes, state how you would debug and test it, and define a calibration criterion for it.

3.19. Design an experiment for the simulator formulated in Problem 3.18. The experiment should determine the dependence of the system's mean response time on the number of user terminals and on the length of the time quantum. Determine a layout for the experiment, and state how you would choose the durations of the required simulation runs.

4

Analytic Techniques

4.1 ANALYTIC STUDIES

According to the definition given in Section 1.6, a modeling approach to the evaluation of computer system performance is said to be *analytic* if the model is solved by a technique which differs from simulation.

The planning phase of an analytic study consists of the following three main operations:

    a. model formulation,
    b. model solution,
    c. model calibration and validation.

These operations are analogous to those which are performed in a simulation study. A model of the system and of its work load is to be designed and constructed first. Then, while a simulation model must be run, an analytic model is to be solved, either in symbolic or in numeric form, in order to obtain the desired results.

Sometimes one may be able to use an existing model, whose symbolic or graphical solutions are known. In this case, as when a commerical simulator is chosen for a simulation study, the results can be obtained by simply introducing into the model the values of the input parameters which characterize the installation being considered.

160

① Accuracy
② Valid
③ Domain of validity
④ Calibration

Characteristics of a model :-

For the results of a modeling study to be credible and reliable, the accuracy of the model must be verified and, if necessary, made acceptable by calibration and validation.

The accuracy of a simulation model has been defined in Sections 3.1 and 3.3.1. The same definition, illustrated in Fig. 3.1, can be applied also to analytic models. A model is *accurate* for a specified input condition if it produces values of the performance indices sufficiently close to those produced by the system under the same input condition.

Once the maximum tolerable errors in the performance indices have been defined, we can say that a model is *valid* under a certain input condition if the accuracy requirements expressed in terms of those errors are met. The *domain of validity* of a model is the set of all input conditions in which the model is valid.

Calibration is the verification of the validity of a model under a limited number of input conditions, followed, if necessary, by the model's modification so as to make its accuracy acceptable. If possible, this verification is made by comparing the outputs of the model with measured data. The calibration operation should always be performed before using the model in an evaluation study.

Since a model is generally used under input conditions which do not coincide with those for which it was calibrated, it is very important to verify that its accuracy is not appreciably affected by variations in the input conditions. A model whose accuracy is relatively insensitive to input conditions, or, in other words, whose domain of validity is large, is said to be *robust*. In general, the *robustness* of a model depends on its intrinsic accuracy and on how it has been calibrated. This is why robustness cannot be specified independently of the input conditions and of the accuracy requirements used in calibrating the model. Verifying the robustness of a model and trying to improve it if necessary are the tasks of a *validation* procedure.

As for a simulator, the accuracy of an analytic model depends on the degree of detail with which it is formulated, on the way it is solved, and on the accuracy of the parameter values introduced. In a simulator, some errors due to the "solution" of the model, that is, to the variance of the estimators of performance indices or to the initial or final bias, are almost always present. On the contrary, exact solutions exist for certain analytic models, the simplest ones from a mathematical viewpoint. This remark does not authorize us to consider these models as more reliable than those which are solvable only by approximate methods. In fact, their mathematical simplicity usually stems from a rather low degree of detail, which tends to make them relatively inaccurate.

The distinction between deterministic and probabilistic models is an important one. *Deterministic models* are useful in many areas of computer science and engineering. Turing machines, automata of various kinds, graph models of programs, and Petri nets fall into this category. Even though some of these models can be of substantial help in understanding a computer system or component and in constructing a simulation model of it, their applications as analytic models for system performance evaluation have been very limited so far.

One of the major obstacles to the use of deterministic models in evaluation studies is their relative inability to represent the variability of the work load found in most computer installations. Characterizing the behavior of a job by a few deterministic parameters requires some very crude approximations to be made. Thus, a work load can be modeled by the set of deterministic parameters which characterize its jobs only in those studies, or those installations, in which these approximations are acceptable. We must often make the additional assumption that jobs arrive all at the same time or with a constant frequency.

Another case in which a deterministic model of a work load is manageable is when the work load can be assumed to consist of a few jobs which are periodically resubmitted. Then the behaviors of these jobs can be characterized with greater detail than if the work load were not periodic. A particular case in which deterministic models are usually easy to handle is the one of a periodic work load composed of identical jobs. This work-load model is not too far from the reality of certain special-purpose installations.

In summary, deterministic models may only be used, at least at the present time, to estimate the order of magnitude or the bounds of certain performance indices, to study some resource allocation problems, or to design and evaluate certain systems whose work load may be not too inconveniently characterized in a deterministic way.

The case of *probabilistic models* is different, since they are naturally suited to the representation of certain aspects of work-load variability. Unfortunately, other aspects, such as the order of job arrivals and the correlations between the random variables characterizing the work load, are either impossible to represent within the context of a probabilistic model or make its solution very difficult. Therefore, these aspects are usually ignored.

Probabilistic models based on queuing theory are especially suitable for the study of computer systems in which several processes compete for each resource in a situation of congestion. The available mathematical techniques allow an investigator to solve a model only when the model is simple enough. Several simplifying assumptions must usually be made in order to obtain a solvable model, and these assumptions may cause the model's accuracy to become unacceptably low.

Very little is known in general about the sensitivity of performance indices with respect to certain simplifications adopted in an analytic model. A few studies in which the results obtained by analytic techniques were compared with measured values of performance indices showed a surprising agreement between the actual system's performance and that predicted by relatively simple and crude models. Two examples of these studies are discussed in Sections 4.4 [*see* Scherr (1967)], 7.4.1, and 7.4.3 [*see* Hughes and Moe (1973)].

An analytic model is solvable in *closed form* with respect to a performance index if its solution allows that index to be expressed symbolically as an explicit function of the model's parameters. The existence of a closed-form solution for an index does not imply that other indices can be expressed in closed form.

The reader should note that a model which is not solvable in closed form with respect to an index is not necessarily unsolvable with respect to that index. The class of models for which closed-form solutions are known is substantially smaller than the one of solvable models. Even though solvability is what really matters in most cases, closed-form solutions are more desirable than numerical solutions since they allow the values of a performance index of interest to be computed much more rapidly and economically. Also, these solutions provide better insight into the dependencies of performance indices on system and work-load parameters.

Some models admit what might be characterized as *partially closed-form* solutions. This happens when the mathematical structure of the formula which expresses the index of interest depends on the value of one or more of the model's parameters. Thus, we have a number of closed-form formulas for the index, one of which is to be selected in each instance depending on the values of certain parameters. Two examples of partially closed-form solution are given in Section 4.3.5.

Another useful distinction is the one between *exact* and *approximate* solutions. When an exact solution of a model cannot be found, an approximate one is certainly acceptable if the errors it introduces into the results are tolerable. An approximate closed-form solution may sometimes be preferable to an exact solution which requires a numerical approximation method to be used since it cannot be expressed in closed form. For probabilistic models, only a few approximation methods are available, but rapid progress is expected to take place in this area. The two main types of methods applicable to queuing models are *diffusion approximations* and *decomposition*. The fundamental concepts on which these methods are based are briefly summarized at the end of Section 4.3.4.

The use of analytic models in performance evaluation studies has been so far restricted by the difficulty of solving realistic models and by the lack of confidence in simpler, solvable models on the part of most evaluators. This lack of confidence is not always justified. However, analytic techniques have been applied much more frequently to the study of system components and of scheduling policies for allocating their services than to the evaluation of whole computer systems. This situation, which in part reflects a correct assessment of the state of the art but is also in part due to obstacles of a psychological nature, may well change in the near future, as both the state of the art and the understanding of analytic techniques will improve.

4.2 DETERMINISTIC MODELS

4.2.1 Introduction

Computer systems and their work loads are very often too complex to be accurately representable by manageable deterministic models. The work load of a computer installation can be characterized by a reasonably small number of deterministic parameters only in a study in which a very rough approximation is acceptable or which is concerned with a particular type of installation. Some real-time installations, used, for instance, for reservation, information retrieval, or process control applications, have work loads whose deterministic representations may be made both manageable and reasonably accurate.

Even in those applications in which the jobs constituting the work load have identical or very similar resource demand characteristics, their pattern of arrivals is often more accurately modeled as if it were produced by a stochastic process rather than by a simple deterministic process such as a periodic one.

Deterministic approaches have been used to determine and prove properties of some subsystems or resource management algorithms. The models in this category will not be dealt with in this book. Two important applications of deterministic models in these areas are the study of optimal schedules for multiprocessor systems [see, for example, Conway et al. (1967) and Chapter 3 of Coffman and Denning (1973)] and the analysis of certain scheduling algorithms for secondary storage devices [see, for example, Fuller (1972)].

Other applications of deterministic models are found in the derivation of formulas for the first-approximation, order-of-magnitude estimation of simple performance indices of computer systems. This category of models includes *mean-value models* of systems, which can be thought of as obtained from probabilistic models by replacing each random parameter with its mean value.

A mean-value model of a work load consists of a set of identical jobs, whose characterizing parameters coincide with the average parameters of the jobs in the work load to be modeled. These identical jobs arrive at the model with constant rate, equal to the mean arrival rate λ in the real work load. Alternatively, no jobs arrive or leave, but the same jobs continuously circulate in the model of the system in constant number. In this case, especially when the number of jobs is small, the assumption of identical jobs may sometimes be relaxed.

The results obtained by mean-value models are usually optimistic. In other words, as we shall see in Section 4.4, the predicted values of the performance indices are generally better than the real ones.

More accurate estimates can sometimes be obtained by a model which is partially probabilistic and partially mean-value. This is, for instance, the case of those queuing models of virtual-memory systems in which the paging behavior of programs is represented by an analytic approximation of the curve relating the mean page fault rate to the amount of memory allotted to a program (see Example 7.3). It is also the case of deterministic models which use results derived from queuing models to represent some parts of the system. A model of this type is described in Chamberlin et al. (1973).

Deterministic approaches to computer system modeling may be applied to worst-case or best-case studies, in which each random parameter is replaced by one of its extreme values. An extreme value may be defined as equal to the mean plus or minus a multiple of the standard deviation. The resulting models could be called *extreme-value models*.

In Sections 4.2.2 and 4.2.3 we shall describe two simple examples of deterministic models to illustrate the approximations which have to be introduced in order to formulate them, the techniques to be employed in writing the equations, and the results that can be obtained.

4.2.2 A Model of CPU-I/O Overlap

In this section we shall present a deterministic model of a uniprogramming system proposed by Hellerman and Smith (1970). The purpose of the model is to evaluate and compare various CPU-I/O overlap schemes. Since the system to be modeled is uniprogrammed, the overlap being considered is between the CPU and the I/O activities of the same job.

Example 4.1   The system we want to represent consists of a CPU, a primary memory, one or more secondary memory devices, and one or more independent I/O channels between the primary and the secondary memories. The workload is assumed to contain only one job, which endlessly processes records from a data base stored in secondary memory. To be processed, the records must be loaded into primary memory. The records are stored back into secondary memory when their processing is completed. Transfers of information between primary and secondary memory are not done record by record but block by block. All records have the same size, denoted by r. Also blocks have a constant size b, which is an integral multiple of r. The *blocking factor* g is defined as

$$g = \frac{b}{r}.$$
b block size
r record size
(4.1)

The primary memory is divided into v regions, each one of which contains a block. Thus, we have

$$v = \frac{M}{b},$$
(4.2)

where M is the size of the portion of primary memory in which records may be loaded.

While the CPU is processing the block stored in one of the regions of primary memory, the other regions are used by the I/O channels as buffer areas for I/O operations. The secondary memory and the I/O channels are characterized by a constant access time t_a to each block and by the word transfer time t_w. Thus, the record and block transfer times are given by rt_w and bt_w, respectively.

The CPU time required to process a record is assumed to be the same for all records and is denoted by t_{cpu}. The performance index to be computed by using the model is the throughput rate T expressed in records processed per unit time. If the unit time is much longer than t_{cpu}, this rate is constant. The model parameters we have introduced are given in Table 4.1 together with the numerical values to be used in our calculations. Since b and r are assumed to be fixed, M has to vary with v as shown in (4.2) and Table 4.1.

Table 4.2 lists the four overlap schemes we want to evaluate. The *degree of overlap* of a scheme coincides with the number v of regions in primary memory.

Table 4.1

PARAMETERS OF THE DETERMINISTIC MODEL OF CPU-I/O
OVERLAP STUDIED IN EXAMPLE 4.1

Parameter name	Symbol	Value
Primary memory size (data area)	M	$2K, 4K, 6K$ words
Record size	r	64 words
Block size	b	$2K$ words
CPU time to process one record	t_{cpu}	1.6 ms
Access time of secondary memory	t_a	15 ms
Word transfer time of secondary memory	t_w	10 μs
Number of regions (blocks) in primary memory (degree of overlap)	v	1, 2, 3

Table 4.2

OVERLAP SCHEMES CONSIDERED IN EXAMPLE 4.1

Scheme	Degree of overlap v
(a) Serial (no overlap)	1
(b) Two-way restricted parallel (C–I or O–C)	2
(c) Two-way parallel (C-I or Q-C or I-O)	2
(d) Three-way parallel (I-C-O)	3

In the *serial* scheme, as illustrated in Fig. 4.1(*a*), there is no overlap. A block is input (*I* axis), goes through the computation phase (*C* axis), and is output (*O* axis). Since there is only one region in memory ($v = 1$), the next block cannot be loaded until the previous one has been completely dumped to secondary memory.

The input, compute, and output times for a block may be written as

$$t_I = t_a + bt_w,$$

$$t_C = gt_{cpu}, \tag{4.3}$$

$$t_O = t_a + bt_w = t_I.$$

The simple inspection of the timing diagram in Fig. 4.1(*a*) allows us to express the record processing time $1/T$ as a function of the model parameters. Let us define the *block processing time* t_B as the ratio between the duration of a relatively long period of time and the number of blocks processed by the system during that period. Clearly, $1/t_B$ is the throughput rate of the system expressed in blocks per unit time. Thus,

$$\frac{1}{T} = \frac{t_B}{g}, \tag{4.4}$$

since there are g records in each block. In Fig. 4.1(*a*), t_B equals $t_I + t_C + t_O$. By (4.3), this sum can be written as $gt_{cpu} + 2t_a + 2bt_w$, which, divided by g as suggested by (4.4), yields the equation of $1/T$ reported in Table 4.3(*a*).

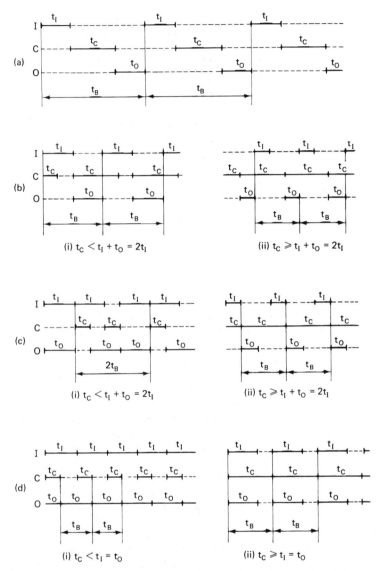

Figure 4.1 Timing diagrams for the four overlap schemes: (*a*) serial scheme; (*b*) two-way restricted parallel scheme; (*c*) two-way parallel scheme; (*d*) three-way parallel scheme. For the last three schemes, (i) I/O-bound case; (ii) compute-bound case.

The second overlap scheme is called *two-way restricted parallel* because it allows concurrent I/O and CPU activities to take place but not simultaneous input and output operations. *C-I* and *O-C* overlaps are permitted, but *I-O* overlap is not. The degree of overlap is 2, and there is only one I/O channel, which at any given time can work only in input or in output mode but not in both. Two cases must be considered: the *I/O-bound* case, illustrated in Fig. 4.1(b)(i) and defined by the condition $t_C < t_I + t_O$, and the complementary *compute-bound* case, corresponding to the condition $t_C \geq t_I + t_O$ and depicted in Fig. 4.1(b)(ii). From these timing diagrams we derive expressions of t_B as for the previous scheme. Noting that (4.3) and (4.4) also hold for this scheme (and for all of the others), we obtain the equations of $1/T$ reported in Table 4.3(b).

Table 4.3

EQUATIONS DERIVED FROM THE TIMING DIAGRAMS IN FIG. 4.1

Scheme	Case	Equations	
(a)	—	$1/T = t_{cpu} + 2t_a/g + 2rt_w$	$z = 1 + 2y + 2x$
(b)	(i)	$1/T = 2t_a/g + 2rt_w$	$z = 4y + 2x$
	(ii)	$1/T = t_{cpu}$	$z = 1$
(c)	(i)	$1/T = t_{cpu}/2 + t_a/g + rt_w$	$z = \frac{1}{2} + 2y + x$
	(ii)	$1/T = t_{cpu}$	$z = 1$
(d)	(i)	$1/T = t_a/g + rt_w$	$z = 3y + x$
	(ii)	$1/T = t_{cpu}$	$z = 1$

Also the *two-way parallel* scheme is characterized by a degree of overlap $v = 2$. However, the system includes two I/O channels and at least two secondary memory devices, so that an input transfer and an output transfer may be simultaneously performed. When this happens, the CPU will have to remain idle. As shown in Fig. 4.1(c), the additional capabilities of the system with respect to scheme (b) affect only the performance index in the I/O-bound case. This is to be expected, since in scheme (c) the I/O performance, but not the CPU speed, is improved.

The same conclusion is easily reached for the *three-way parallel* overlap scheme. Since the degree of overlap in this scheme is 3, the CPU may be processing a block while another block is being loaded and yet another one is being dumped. This scheme requires the same I/O capabilities as scheme (c) but a larger amount of primary memory if the block size is to be the same as in the other schemes. When the CPU is saturated (compute-bound case), the system's performance does not differ from the one produced by scheme (c) or (b). In the I/O-bound case, as shown in Table 4.3(d)(i), the record processing time is $t_{cpu}/2$ time units less than the one corresponding to scheme (c).

Table 4.4 displays the values of throughput rate T and CPU utilization ρ_1 produced by the four schemes discussed above assuming the model parameter values reported in Table 4.1. The values of ρ_1 are simply obtained as the ratios between T and $T_{max} = 625$ records per second. Since the model has closed-form solutions, represented by the equations in Table 4.3, the calculation of the value of the performance index corresponding to any given combination of model parameter values is straightforward.

It is also easy to study the behavior of the performance index as a function of the parameters. We may, for instance, ask which overlap scheme is the best when the memory size M and the record size r are fixed and the block size b is allowed to vary with v as dictated by (4.2). To answer this question, we normalize the record-processing time, dividing it by t_{cpu}, which is the CPU time needed to process a record. This ratio,

$$z = \frac{1}{Tt_{cpu}}, \tag{4.5}$$

Table 4.4

RESULTS OBTAINED FROM THE MODEL DESCRIBED IN
EXAMPLE 4.1 AND THE PARAMETER VALUES IN TABLE 4.1

		Fixed b, variable M			Fixed M ($2K$ words), variable b	
Scheme	Case	T [records/s]	ρ_1	Case	T [records/s]	ρ_1
(a)	—	261.9	0.419	—	261.9	0.419
(b)	(i)	450.9	0.721	(i)	317.2	0.507
(c)	(i)	523.9	0.838	(i)	420.6	0.672
(d)	(ii)	625	1	(i)	488.7	0.781

is equal to 1 only if the overlap between CPU and I/O activities is perfect and the
utilization of the CPU is 1. More often, especially in the I/O-bound case, z is greater than
1. In fact, it can easily be shown that z is the reciprocal of ρ_1, the utilization of the CPU.
    We then write the normalized equations in Table 4.3 as functions of the following
two parameters:

$$x = \frac{rt_w}{t_{cpu}}, \qquad y = \frac{rt_a}{Mt_{cpu}}, \tag{4.6}$$

noting that these parameters do not depend on the values of b or v and that, by (4.2) and
(4.6), $t_a/gt_{cpu} = vy$. Also the new equations are reported in Table 4.3. The diagram in Fig.
4.2 contains the answer to our question above. The values of x and y corresponding to the
problem at hand identify a point in the first quadrant of the (x, y) plane. The ranking of
the four overlap schemes for those values of x and y is given in the diagram. For instance,
the values of the model parameters in Table 4.1 (with M = $2K$ words) yield x = 0.4 and
y = 0.293. This point falls into the region of the diagram in Fig. 4.2 characterized by the
ranking (d, c, b, a) in order of decreasing performance. This is confirmed by the values of
T and ρ_1 reported in Table 4.4, in which we see that scheme (d) is the best for our system.

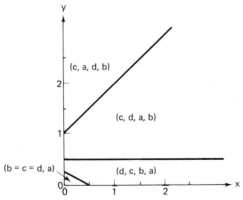

Figure 4.2 Performance rankings of overlap schemes for fixed memory and record
size. [*Source*: Hellerman and Smith (1970), by permission of ACM, Inc.]

Fixing the memory size at 2K words causes T and ρ_1 to decrease with all schemes except (a), in which the memory size does not differ from the one previously considered. Also, the reduction of M from 6K words to 2K words for scheme (d) transforms the system from CPU-bound to I/O-bound, because t_I and t_O decrease less rapidly than t_C as the block size gets smaller, due to the fact that t_a does not depend on b.

Figure 4.2 shows that more sophisticated overlap schemes do not always improve performance. For instance, when $y > x + 1$, scheme (c) is the best, and the serial scheme is better than both the three-way parallel and the two-way restricted parallel schemes. ■

4.2.3 A Mean-Value Model of a Multiprogramming System

In this section we shall briefly describe a simple mean-value model proposed by Fenichel and Grossman (1969) to estimate the throughput of multiprogramming systems. The CPU and I/O activities of a process are assumed never to overlap. A probabilistic model of which the model presented here may be considered as a derivation is discussed in Section 4.3.5.

Example 4.2 The system to be modeled is a simple EXOPE system (*see* Fig. 1.2) with only one secondary memory device, say, a drum. The system is multiprogrammed and keeps the degree of multiprogramming N constant. Each job in the system is at any given time *active* or *dormant*. A job is dormant, or in state S_0, when it does not reside in primary memory. An active job is either in state S_1, waiting for or receiving CPU service, or in state S_2, waiting for or receiving drum service. The state diagram of each job is depicted in Fig. 4.3(a). When a job becomes dormant, another job is assumed to be immediately injected into the active set in order to keep the degree of multiprogramming constant.

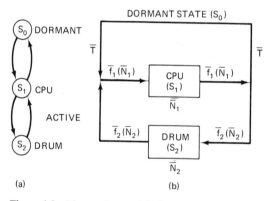

(a)   (b)

Figure 4.3 Mean-value model of a multiprogramming system: (a) state diagram of a single job; (b) the model of the system.

All jobs are assumed to be identical. Each one of them is characterized by its CPU time demand t_{cpu} and by its number n_{dr} of drum requests. These requests are issued at regular CPU time intervals, that is, whenever the job has been processed by the CPU for $t_{cpu}/(n_{dr} + 1)$ time units since the completion of its last drum operation or since the beginning of its execution. Each drum request always involves the transfer of a block, whose size is fixed and constant for all blocks. At the end of the $(n_{dr} + 1)$st CPU interval, a job terminates and becomes dormant.

The job state diagram in Fig. 4.3(*a*) naturally leads to the system model shown in Fig. 4.3(*b*). Let $\bar{N}_1$ denote the mean number of jobs in state S_1 and $\bar{N}_2$ the mean number of jobs in state S_2. Then we have

$$\bar{N}_1 + \bar{N}_2 = N. \tag{4.7}$$

At the equilibrium, the mean arrival rate must be equal to the mean departure rate both for the CPU and for the drum. Since we expect these rates to depend on the respective *loads* $\bar{N}_1$ and $\bar{N}_2$, we shall indicate them by $\bar{f}_1(\bar{N}_1)$ and $\bar{f}_2(\bar{N}_2)$. The equality of the mean arrival and departure rates will hold also for the dormant state because of our constant-N assumption. The dormant state rates coincide in fact with our performance index $\bar{T}$, the system's mean throughput rate.

Each job enters state S_1 $n_{dr} + 1$ times. The first n_{dr} times it leaves S_1, the job enters S_2. The last time, it goes to S_0. Thus,

$$\bar{f}_2(\bar{N}_2) = \frac{n_{dr}}{n_{dr} + 1}\bar{f}_1(\bar{N}_1), \tag{4.8}$$

and

$$\bar{T} = \bar{f}_1(\bar{N}_1) - \bar{f}_2(\bar{N}_2) = \frac{\bar{f}_1(\bar{N}_1)}{n_{dr} + 1}. \tag{4.9}$$

If $\bar{f}_1(\bar{N}_1)$ were known, (4.9) would allow us to compute the mean throughput rate. We have (*see* Fig. 4.4)

$$\bar{f}_1(\bar{N}_1) = 0 \qquad \text{for } \bar{N}_1 = 0,$$
$$= \frac{n_{dr} + 1}{t_{cpu}} \qquad \text{for } \bar{N}_1 \geq 1, \tag{4.10}$$
$$= \bar{N}_1\frac{n_{dr} + 1}{t_{cpu}} \qquad \text{for } 0 < \bar{N}_1 < 1.$$

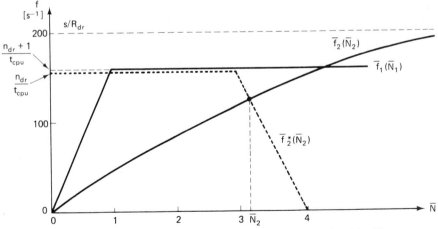

Figure 4.4 Mean arrival and departure rates for the model in Fig. 4.3. The parameter values are those shown in Table 4.5. The dotted line is used in a graphical procedure for the solution of the model.

The first two cases in (4.10) are trivial ones. When $\bar{N}_1 = 0$, all of the active jobs are waiting for the drum, which takes an infinite amount of time to service a request. Thus, the drum is saturated, and the mean throughput rate of the system is 0. When $\bar{N}_1 \geq 1$, the CPU is always busy, and the system produces its maximum throughput rate

$$\bar{T}_{max} = \frac{1}{t_{cpu}}. \tag{4.11}$$

The last case in (4.10) is the most interesting one, since it corresponds to a system in which the utilization of the CPU is between 0 and 1. To solve the model in that case, we need to know $\bar{f}_2(\bar{N}_2)$. This rate may be obtained by measurement, or simulation, or from an analytic model of the drum. The maximum output rate of a sectored drum characterized by a revolution time R_{dr} and s sectors is equal to s/R_{dr} blocks per unit time. This corresponds to transferring one block during each sector period. If we assume that drum requests issued by jobs always involve exactly one block, we have

$$\bar{f}_{2\,max} = \bar{f}_2(\infty) = \frac{s}{R_{dr}}. \tag{4.12}$$

The curve $\bar{f}_2(\bar{N}_2)$ will typically look like the one depicted in Fig. 4.4. An analytically derived version of it can be found in Fig. 4 of Coffman (1969). The introduction of a curve like that in Fig. 4.4 makes the model a nonlinear one [$\bar{f}_1(\bar{N}_1)$ is piecewise linear]. A simple graphical method for solving the model consists of plotting in the $(\bar{N}_2, \bar{f}_2)$ plane the function

$$\bar{f}_2^* = 0 \qquad\qquad \text{for } \bar{N}_2 = N,$$

$$= \frac{n_{dr}}{t_{cpu}} \qquad\qquad \text{for } \bar{N}_2 \leq N - 1, \tag{4.13}$$

$$= \frac{n_{dr}}{t_{cpu}}(N - \bar{N}_2) \qquad \text{for } N - 1 < \bar{N}_2 < N.$$

Function $\bar{f}_2^*$ is obtained by substituting (4.7) into (4.10) and (4.10) into (4.8). The point of intersection of $\bar{f}_2^*$ with the true $\bar{f}_2$ curve yields the value of $\bar{N}_2$ corresponding to the solution of the model. From this value we can derive $\bar{N}_1$ and, from (4.9), $\bar{T}$.

The procedure is illustrated in Fig. 4.4 for the values of the model parameters listed in Table 4.5. The dotted line represents function $\bar{f}_2^*(\bar{N}_2)$. The value of $\bar{N}_2$ at the

Table 4.5

PARAMETERS OF THE MEAN-VALUE MODEL OF A
MULTIPROGRAMMING SYSTEM DESCRIBED IN EXAMPLE 4.2

Parameter name	Symbol	Value
Degree of multiprogramming	N	4
CPU time demand of a job	t_{cpu}	250 ms
Number of drum requests of a job	n_{dr}	40
Drum revolution time	R_{dr}	20 ms
Number of sectors in the drum	s	4

intersection being 3.2, we have $\bar{f}_2(\bar{N}_2) = 128$ blocks per second, $\bar{N}_1 = 0.8$, $\bar{f}_1(\bar{N}_1) = 131.2$ CPU intervals per second, and $\bar{T} = 3.2$ jobs per second. The maximum throughput rate given by (4.11) is $\bar{T}_{\max} = 4$ jobs per second.

The graphical construction in Fig. 4.4 provides immediate insight into the effects of parameter modifications. For instance, increasing N will increase $\bar{N}_1$ toward 1 and $\bar{T}$ toward $\bar{T}_{\max}$. The same result can be obtained by a faster (lower R_{dr}) or more parallel or higher-density (larger s) drum or by a better drum-scheduling algorithm, which causes the $\bar{f}_2(\bar{N}_2)$ curve to rise more rapidly. An increase of $\bar{T}$ may also be brought about by a decrease of n_{dr}. An increase of t_{cpu} will increase $\bar{N}_1$. This will cause $\bar{T}$ to approach $\bar{T}_{\max}$ but will at the same time reduce $\bar{T}_{\max}$. Increasing t_{cpu} beyond the point where $\bar{T}$ reaches $\bar{T}_{\max}$ produces an inversely proportional decrease of $\bar{T}$. ∎

4.3 PROBABILISTIC MODELS

4.3.1 Markov Models and Queuing Models

Because of their potential for representing complex, highly variable phenomena in a relatively compact way, probabilistic models are much more widely applied to the study of computer systems than deterministic models. Among the probabilistic approaches to analytic modeling, the queuing approach is by far the most appealing and popular one. However, Markov or semi-Markov models are also sometimes used in evaluation studies. Another, more important reason for studying Markov models here is that their theory is the basis of elementary queuing theory. In this section we shall present a simple treatment of Markov models before introducing queuing models, which constitute the subject of Sections 4.3.2–4.3.5.

A *Markov chain,* that is, a discrete-state Markov process, is a stochastic process $X(t)$ (*see* Section 2.4.3) with states $S_0, S_1, S_2, \ldots$ such that the probability that at time t_{k+1} the state is S_j only depends on the state at time t_k for any sequence of time instants $t_1, t_2, \ldots, t_{k+1}$ with $t_1 < t_2 < \cdots < t_{k+1}$.

We say that the process is in state S_{h_i} at time t_i if $X(t_i) = h_i$, h_i being a nonnegative integer. Thus, the above definition can be written as

$$\text{Prob}\,[X(t_{k+1}) = j | X(t_1) = h_1, X(t_2) = h_2, \ldots, X(t_k) = h_k]$$
$$= \text{Prob}\,[X(t_{k+1}) = j | X(t_k) = h_k]. \quad (4.14)$$

Relationship (4.14) is called the *continuous-time Markov property* and defines a *continuous-time Markov chain.* The term *continuous time* refers to the fact that state transitions are allowed to take place at any point in time. If we restrict transitions to occur only at discrete time instants, to be denoted by the *time indices* $1, 2, \ldots, k, \ldots$, then we may define the *discrete-time Markov property* for the stochastic process X_k as

$$\text{Prob}\,(X_{k+1} = j | X_1 = h_1, X_2 = h_2, \ldots, X_k = h_k) = \text{Prob}\,(X_{k+1} = j | X_k = h_k). \quad (4.15)$$

A stochastic sequence X_k which satisfies (4.15) for all positive integers k and all possible states is called a *discrete-time Markov chain*. In such a chain, the probability of a transition from state S_i to state S_j at time k may be written as

$$p_{ij}(k) = \text{Prob} \, (X_{k+1} = j | X_k = i). \tag{4.16}$$

The Markov property makes it possible to specify the statistical relationships among states in the form of a matrix $\mathbf{P}(k)$, the transition-probability matrix. If the transition probabilities are independent of time, we may indicate them simply by p_{ij}, and the chain is said to be *homogeneous*. The *state-transition diagram* of a Markov chain is a directed graph whose vertices represent the states and whose arcs represent state transitions. The label of each arc coincides with the probability of the corresponding transition. For homogeneous chains, these labels are time-invariant. A chain is completely specified by its state-transition diagram and by its initial state. The diagram may be seen as a graphical equivalent of the transition-probability matrix $\mathbf{P}$.

When we model a system by a Markov chain, we want to use our model to answer several performance-related questions. We are, for instance, interested in determining how often a certain state will be visited, how much time will be spent in it by the system, and how long the intervals between visits will be on the average. If the Markov model satisfies certain conditions to be specified below, answering these questions analytically is relatively straightforward.

A Markov chain is *irreducible* if each state can be reached from any other state (in the state-transition diagram, there must exist a directed path leading from state S_i to state S_j for all i and j). A state is *recurrent* if the probability of ever revisiting it after a visit has taken place is 1. The *mean recurrence time* $\bar{t}_{rj}$ of a recurrent state S_j is the mean time between successive visits to S_j. If the visits to S_j are not periodic, that is, if the recurrence times t_{rj} are not all equal, S_j is said to be *aperiodic*. An aperiodic Markov chain is a Markov chain in which all states are aperiodic.

We denote by $p_j(k)$ the probability that a Markov chain is in state S_j at time k. Note that the p_j's are *state probabilities*, whereas the p_{ij}'s defined above are *state-transition probabilities*. The initial state probabilities are denoted by $p_j(0)$.

Two important results allow us to give answers to the questions we asked above.

First, if a Markov chain is homogeneous, irreducible, and aperiodic, then the limiting state probabilities

$$p_j = \lim_{k \to \infty} p_j(k) \qquad (j = 0, 1, \dots) \tag{4.17}$$

exist and are independent of the $p_j(0)$'s.

Second, if all states of the Markov chain are also recurrent and their mean recurrence times are finite, then the p_j's are a stationary probability distribution and can be determined by solving the e·uations

$$p_j = \sum_i p_i p_{ij} \qquad (j = 0, 1, \dots), \tag{4.18}$$

and

$$\sum_i p_i = 1. \tag{4.19}$$

A state probability distribution is said to be *stationary* in this context if when it is selected as the initial distribution, the Markov chain's state probability distribution coincides with it at all times. Thus, if for all j we set $p_j(0) = p_j$, then we have $p_j(k) = p_j$ for all k.

The solutions of equations (4.18) and (4.19) may be called the *equilibrium state probabilities* since they are independent of the initial state probabilities. At the equilibrium, the amount of time which is spent in state S_j is proportional to p_j. Also, the mean time between visits to S_j, that is, the mean recurrence time of S_j, can be computed by exploiting another useful result, which holds under the same conditions as the second result reported above:

$$\bar{t}_{rj} = \frac{1}{p_j}. \tag{4.20}$$

What is the distribution of the durations of the time intervals t_j spent in state S_j? At each discrete-time instant, if the Markov chain is in S_j, it has a probability p_{jj} of remaining in S_j and a probability $1 - p_{jj}$ of making a transition to a different state. Due to the Markov property (4.15), these probabilities never change, no matter how much time has already been spent in S_j. Independence allows us to calculate the probability of a duration t_j exactly equal to n time instants as the product of all the successive probabilities involved:

$$\text{Prob} \, (t_j = n) = (1 - p_{jj}) p_{jj}^{n-1} \qquad (n = 1, 2, \dots). \tag{4.21}$$

Thus, (4.21) shows that state durations are geometrically distributed with mean $1/(1 - p_{jj})$. It is important to note that the geometric distribution is the only discrete distribution having the *memoryless property*. If the time intervals between certain events are geometrically distributed, at each instant the time to the next event is statistically independent of the time which has elapsed since the last event. The fact that the distributions of state durations in a discrete-time Markov chain have the memoryless property is a direct consequence of the Markov property (4.15). Similarly, it can be shown that, in a continuous-time Markov chain, state durations are exponentially distributed and that the exponential distribution is the only continuous distribution for which the memoryless property holds.

We can therefore conclude that in Markov models state durations are necessarily distributed either geometrically or exponentially. This is in many situations an unrealistic assumption, even though it greatly facilitates the analytical solution of the model. The restriction is removed in *semi-Markov models*, which allow state durations to have arbitrary distributions. A description of a semi-Markov model from a simulation viewpoint may be found at the end of Example 3.3. At the time of a state transition, the model behaves exactly as if it were a Markov model. This is the reason a semi-Markov model is said to possess an *embedded Markov process* defined at the instants of state transitions. Of course, the set of Markov processes is a subset of the set of semi-Markov processes.

A simple Markov model will now be discussed to illustrate the concepts and techniques introduced so far in this section.

Example 4.3 The CPU of a multiprogramming system is at any given time executing instructions from

  a. a user program; or
  b. an operating system routine explicitly called by a user program and performing a task (for instance, an I/O operation) on its behalf; or
  c. an operating system routine performing a system-wide control task such as scheduling, resource allocation, or recovery from a system crash; or
  d. the wait loop.

When the instruction being executed is in category a, the CPU is in the *problem state* (S_3). It is in the *supervisor state* when executing an instruction in category b or c. Category d corresponds to the *idle state* (S_0). We assume that all operating system routines can be neatly subdivided into categories b and c. The state corresponding to category b will be called the *user supervisor state* (S_2), and the one corresponding to category c, the *system supervisor state* (S_1). This classification is convenient from a charging viewpoint. It is in fact fair to charge each user for the services received in category b and to divide the charges for category c among all users.

Our model of the CPU has four states. Let us assume that no state, once it is entered, can ever last less than 50 μs, and let us approximate all state durations so as to make them integral multiples of 50 μs. We may then consider a discrete-time Markov model for the CPU, taking 50 μs as the interval between successive instants of discretized time.

The choice of a Markov model automatically implies that the Markov property (4.15) holds. This means that when the CPU is, for instance, in the system supervisor state, the probability of its transition to the idle state is independent of whether the previous state was the idle, or the problem, or the user supervisor state. In reality, this transition will be much less probable if the previous state was the idle state than in the other cases. However, our Markov model does not allow us to take these differences into account. To distinguish between the two cases while remaining within the framework of Markov models, we should split the system supervisor state (S_1) into three states, characterized by the ordered pairs (S_3, S_1), (S_2, S_1), and (S_0, S_1). In these pairs, the first element would indicate the state visited just before S_1. Thus, the transition probabilities from (S_2, S_1) to S_0 and from (S_0, S_1) to S_0 would be distinct and could be made different from each other.

The state-transition diagram of our homogeneous Markov model is depicted in Fig. 4.5. Table 4.6 shows its transition-probability matrix. Note that the idle state is always preceded and followed by the system supervisor state. It is in fact the CPU scheduler

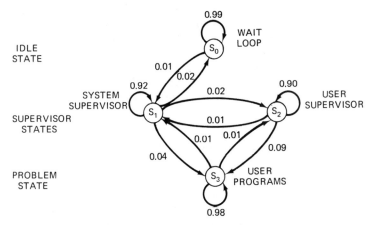

Figure 4.5   State-transition diagram of the discrete-time Markov model of a CPU described in Example 4.3.

Table 4.6

TRANSITION-PROBABILITY MATRIX DEFINING THE
DISCRETE-TIME MARKOV MODEL OF A CPU IN
EXAMPLE 4.3

| | | \multicolumn{4}{c}{To state} | | |
		S_0	S_1	S_2	S_3
	S_0	0.99	0.01	0	0
From state	S_1	0.02	0.92	0.02	0.04
	S_2	0	0.01	0.90	0.09
	S_3	0	0.01	0.01	0.98

which when the CPU terminates the execution of a task and the CPU queue is empty puts it into the wait loop. In this condition, when an interrupt is detected, the CPU branches to a location in the system supervisor.

The equilibrium state probabilities can be computed by solving the system of equations (4.18) and (4.19):

$$
\begin{aligned}
p_0 &= 0.99p_0 + 0.02p_1, \\
p_1 &= 0.01p_0 + 0.92p_1 + 0.01p_2 + 0.01p_3, \\
p_2 &= \phantom{0.01p_0 +{}} 0.02p_1 + 0.90p_2 + 0.01p_3, \\
p_3 &= \phantom{0.01p_0 +{}} 0.04p_1 + 0.09p_2 + 0.98p_3, \\
1 &= p_0 + p_1 + p_2 + p_3.
\end{aligned} \tag{4.22}
$$

One of the first four equations in (4.22) is dependent on the other three. This is the reason equation (4.19) must also be considered together with (4.18) in order to solve the system. The solutions of (4.22) are

$$
p_0 = \tfrac{2}{9}, \qquad p_1 = \tfrac{1}{9}, \qquad p_2 = \tfrac{8}{99}, \qquad p_3 = \tfrac{58}{99}. \tag{4.23}
$$

The utilization of the CPU given by our model is $\rho_1 = 1 - p_0 = 77.7\%$. However, only about the 58.6% of the total time is spent at the equilibrium by the CPU processing user programs. The remaining $77.7 - 58.6 = 19.1\%$ of the time is spent in the supervisor state, 11.1% in S_1 and 8% in S_2.

The mean duration of state S_j ($j = 0, 1, 2, 3$) may be computed, by (4.21), as $50/(1 - p_{jj})\,\mu s$. Thus, we have $\bar{t}_0 = 5$ ms, $\bar{t}_1 = 625\ \mu s$, $\bar{t}_2 = 500\ \mu s$, and $\bar{t}_3 = 2.5$ ms. The mean recurrence times of the four states are given by (4.20), which is to be multiplied by 50 μs:

$$\bar{t}_{r0} = 225\ \mu s, \qquad \bar{t}_{r1} = 450\ \mu s, \qquad \bar{t}_{r2} = 618.75\ \mu s, \qquad \bar{t}_{r3} = 85.34\ \mu s. \qquad (4.24)$$

Note that these times are very short since a departure from the current state always occurs at the end of each 50-μs interval. Thus, when the next state coincides with the current one, this state is reentered and we have a new visit to it, with a recurrence time of 1 interval.

Results more interesting than those in (4.24) can be obtained by considering the time interval between two successive transitions S_j from some other state. The first $1/(1 - p_{jj})$ instants of this interval will be spent on the average in S_j, and the rest, whose duration is denoted by $\bar{t}'_{rj}$, in other states. The mean recurrence time of S_j can be computed as

$$\bar{t}_{rj} = \frac{1 \cdot 1/(1 - p_{jj}) + \bar{t}'_{rj} \cdot 1}{1 + 1/(1 - p_{jj})}. \qquad (4.25)$$

Thus, from (4.25) and (4.20), we have

$$\bar{t}'_{rj} = \frac{2 - p_{jj} - p_j}{p_j(1 - p_{jj})}, \qquad (4.26)$$

which yields

$$\bar{t}'_{r0} = 17.7\ \text{ms}, \qquad \bar{t}'_{r1} = 5.45\ ms, \qquad \bar{t}'_{r2} = 6.3\ \text{ms}, \qquad \bar{t}'_{r3} = 1.85\ \text{ms}. \qquad (4.27)$$

∎

We are now ready to introduce *queuing models*.

The basic components of a queuing model are servers, queues, and sources. *Servers* are generally used to model the resources demanded by the *jobs*. The jobs are generated by the *sources* or exist in the queuing model since its creation. Each server can serve only a limited maximum number of jobs at the same time. This is often called the *number of channels* of the server. Those jobs which find the server busy must wait in a *queue* until their turn comes. Each server has at least one queue, and the term *service center* is often used to indicate the complex consisting of a server and its queues. In some cases, a service center contains several servers, all of which process jobs from the same queue or queues. A job generally requests the attention of a server for a certain amount of time (called *service time*) and joins a service center at an instant called the *arrival time* of the job at the center.

The most important characteristics of a source are

a. its type, *finite* or *infinite*; if the source is finite, the maximum number of jobs generated by that source which the model may contain has a finite upper bound;

b. the distribution of the intervals between the generation of successive jobs (*inter-arrival times*);

c. the *demands* of each job for the services of each service center in the model; if the demands for a certain type of service are identically distributed for all jobs, it is natural to consider them as characteristic of the corresponding service center rather than of the source; however, since they represent the resource demands made by the jobs, thinking of them as characterizing the source is more correct.

A service center is characterized by

a. the number and the capacity of its queues; the *capacity* of a queue is the maximum number of jobs it can contain;

b. the number of its servers and the number of channels of each one of them;

c. the *speed* of its servers; if a job's demand d is expressed in units of service, and v is the speed of the server expressed in units of service deliverable per unit time, the service time of the job is $t_s = d/v$; the *mean service rate* of the server over a time period τ is defined as $1/\bar{t}_s$, where $\bar{t}_s$ is the mean service time over τ, and is expressed in jobs processed per unit time; when the speed of a server is fixed and the demands for service are identically distributed for all jobs or for each class of jobs, we may consider the service-time distribution (or distributions) among the characteristics of the server;

d. the *service discipline*, which specifies under what conditions the servers terminate their service to a job, how the next job to be served is selected from the service center's queues, and what an incompletely serviced job does.

A queuing model is defined by its sources, its service centers, and their interconnections. The interconnections specify the paths which the jobs are allowed to follow in their journey through the model from center to center.

The simplest type of queuing model is the single-service-center (or single-server) model depicted in Fig. 4.6. The service center consists of a single-channel server and of one queue with unbounded capacity. When a job has been completely processed by the server, it leaves the model. Among the jobs in the queue, the one which, according to the center's scheduling policy, has the highest priority at that time enters the server and is processed there until completion. If the queue is empty, the server will be idle until the next job's arrival. The service discipline of the center in this model must be *nonpreemptive*. In other words, since

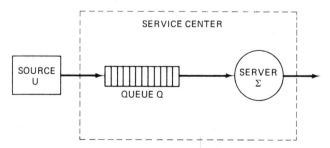

Figure 4.6   Non-preemptive single-service-center queuing model.

a job which is dismissed by the server leaves the system, jobs must be processed to completion. In models in which a job may visit the same center several times before leaving the system, service may be *preemptive*.

A model containing more than one service center is said to be a *queuing network*. In a queuing network, some service centers act as the sources of other centers. If there are also external sources, the network is said to be *open*. Otherwise, it is a *closed* network. In a closed network, the total number of jobs is fixed and constant. Two simple examples of open and closed networks are presented in Figs. 4.7 and 4.8, respectively.

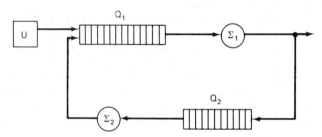

Figure 4.7 Open queuing network.

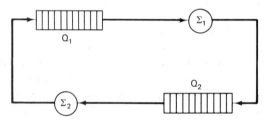

Figure 4.8 Closed queuing network.

In the queuing model of a computer system, the user community may be represented by one or more sources which generate jobs. Alternatively, it may be modeled by one or more service centers which try to reproduce the behavior of the users. The former approach results in an open-network model, and the latter in a closed-network model. While the work load in an open-network model of a system is represented by the characteristics of the source (or sources), the most important of which have been listed above, in a closed network it is modeled by the characteristics of the service center (or centers) representing the user community.

The most popular computer performance indices (response time, turnaround time, throughput rate, utilization factors) are usually easy to define, though not always easy to compute, in a queuing model. Other easily definable indices are the waiting times in the queues and the queue lengths. Of course, component-oriented indices such as utilizations, waiting times, and queue lengths require, to be definable, that the corresponding component be explicitly modeled in the network.

Not all of the resources and all of the job behaviors in computer systems can be modeled with the same ease by a queuing network. It is in fact particularly hard to represent resources which are used in conjunction with others by the same job. An example of such a resource is primary memory, part of which a job is to obtain and keep while being serviced by, or waiting for, the CPU and most of the I/O devices. Another example is the CPU in a system in which a job can overlap its I/O activities with its computations.

The requirement of analytic solvability of the model imposes a number of additional restrictions. One of them is the mutual independence of interarrival times and service times at all the servers. Other constraints are discussed in the next sections.

Our discussion of queuing models focuses on those which have been proposed for the evaluation of computer systems. A number of queuing models have been applied to the study of system components such as disks, drums, buffers, and primary memories. The reader is referred to the discussion of these models in Chapter 5 of Coffman and Denning (1973) and to its bibliography.

4.3.2 Nonpreemptive Single-Service-Center Models

All servers and channels in a service center draw the jobs to be processed from the same queue or set of queues. Thus, in a single-service-center model only one type of resource can be represented. This resource need not coincide with a single physical resource of the system. For instance, the service center may be used to model a whole computer system. However, there is no way of representing different resources separately in such a model. Single-service-center models have mostly been applied to the study of scheduling algorithms, especially for interactive systems.

In our discussion, we shall assume that the model in Fig. 4.6 represents an interactive system. The infinite source U represents the user community. The approximation which is made considering U as infinite becomes more justifiable as the number N of terminals gets larger.

The arrival process has been experimentally found to be quite close to a *Poisson process* in several interactive installations [*see* Fuchs and Jackson (1970), Anderson and Sargent (1972), and Lewis and Yue (1972)]. In a Poisson arrival process, the number n_a of arrivals during an interval τ has a Poisson distribution:

$$\text{Prob}\,[n_a(\tau) = k] = \frac{(\lambda\tau)^k}{k!}\,e^{-\lambda\tau} \qquad (k \geq 0, \tau \geq 0), \qquad (4.28)$$

where λ is the *mean arrival rate*. It can be easily shown [see, for instance, Kleinrock (1975)] that a Poisson arrival process is characterized by interarrival times which are exponentially distributed:

$$F_{t_{int}}(x) = \text{Prob}\,(t_{int} \leq x) = 1 - e^{-\lambda x} \qquad (x \geq 0). \qquad (4.29)$$

Both the mean and the standard deviation of the exponential distribution (4.29) are equal to $1/\lambda$. Thus, the *coefficient of variation c*, which is the ratio of the standard deviation to the mean, is equal to 1.

As mentioned in Section 4.3.1, the exponential distribution is the only continuous distribution having the so-called *memoryless property*, which greatly simplifies the analysis of queuing models. In terms of interarrival times, the memoryless property means that at any instant the time to the next arrival is statistically independent of the time already spent waiting for it. In other words, the probability of an arrival does not depend on the history of the arrival process.

If even the distribution of service times is assumed to be exponential, the model is much easier to solve analytically than in the case of a different service-time distribution. Unfortunately, CPU service-time distributions have experimentally been found to have coefficients of variation much larger than 1, generally between 3 and 10 [*see* Anderson and Sargent (1972), Bryan (1967), and Parupudi and Winograd (1972)]. We shall return to this point later.

The simplest nonpreemptive service discipline is *first-come-first-served* (FCFS), also called *first-in-first-out* (FIFO), which selects the jobs to be serviced in chronological order of arrival. Other nonpreemptive disciplines which are of interest and have been studied are the *shortest-processing-time-first* (SPTF) discipline, which favors the jobs with the smallest CPU time demands (assumed to be known), and the *external-priority* (EP) discipline, in which the priority of each job is determined by the source.

Let us now consider the queuing model in Fig. 4.6 with job interarrival and service times independent and identically distributed. Both distributions are assumed to be exponential. The mean interarrival time will be denoted by $1/\lambda$. The mean service time will be $1/\mu$. Thus, λ is the mean arrival rate and μ the mean service rate. This model is often denoted by the descriptor $M/M/1$, where the first M means that the interarrival times are exponentially distributed (M stands for "Markovian"), the second M that also the service time distribution is exponential, and 1 means that the server has one channel.

The state of a single-server queuing model in which all jobs are statistically identical is conveniently characterized by the number N of the jobs in the service center. N includes the jobs waiting in the queue, or queues, and those being serviced. The model will be said to be in state S_N ($N = 0, 1, \ldots$) when it contains N jobs.

Arrivals and departures of jobs are the only events which can change the state of the model. We assume that the probability that two such events occur simultaneously is negligible. Thus, the state-transition diagram of the system is as shown in Fig. 4.9(a). Let us focus our attention on a time interval $(t, t + h)$, with h so small that the probability of more than one event occurring during the interval is negligible. If no event occurs, the system does not change its state. If there is an arrival, the next state is the one immediately to the right of the current state in Fig. 4.9(a). If a departure, that is, a completion of service, occurs, the system moves to the state immediately to the left of the current one. Of course, if

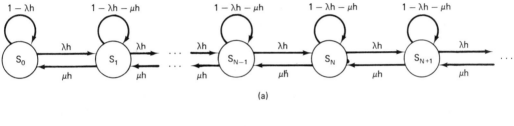

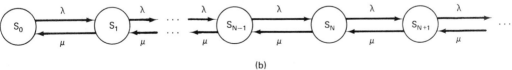

(a)

(b)

Figure 4.9 State diagrams of an *M/M/1* queuing model: (*a*) the state-transition diagram; (*b*) the state-transition-rate diagram.

the current state is S_0, there cannot be any departures. The probability of an arrival in $(t, t + h)$ is λh; it does not depend on past history because of the memoryless property of the arrival process. Similarly, the probability of a departure in $(t, t + h)$ is μh.

Because of our exponential assumptions, the model is a continuous-time homogeneous Markov chain. This type of Markov chain, in which transitions may take place only from the current state to one of its nearest neighbors, is called a *birth-death process*. The *M/M/1* queuing model may be viewed as a birth-death process with constant *birth rate* λ and constant *death rate* μ. Note that *constant* in the previous sentence means not only "time-invariant" but also "equal for all states." It can be shown that the limiting state probabilities exist and are stationary if $\lambda < \mu$.

Solving a model of this type is easier than solving an arbitrary continuous-time Markov model. The probability $p_N(t + h)$ that the system is in state S_N at time $t + h$ is given by the sum of

    a. the conditional probability that no events occur in $(t, t + h)$, given that the system's state at time t was S_N: $(1 - \lambda h - \mu h)p_N(t)$;

    b. the conditional probability of an arrival in $(t, t + h)$, given that the system's state at time t was S_{N-1}: $\lambda h p_{N-1}(t)$;

    c. the conditional probability of a departure in $(t, t + h)$, given that the system's state at time t was S_{N+1}: $\mu h p_{N+1}(t)$.

Note that if $N = 0$, the conditional probability in a above is to be written as $(1 - \lambda h)p_0(t)$ and that the one in b is equal to zero.

Thus, we have

$$p_0(t + h) = (1 - \lambda h)p_0(t) + \mu h p_1(t), \tag{4.30}$$

$$p_N(t + h) = (1 - \lambda h - \mu h)p_N(t) + \lambda h p_{N-1}(t) + \mu h p_{N+1}(t) \quad (N = 1, 2, \dots). \tag{4.31}$$

Subtracting $p_0(t)$ from both sides of (4.30) and $p_N(t)$ from both sides of (4.31), dividing both sides by h, and letting h tend toward zero, we obtain

$$p_0'(t) = -\lambda p_0(t) + \mu p_1(t), \tag{4.32}$$

$$p_N'(t) = -(\lambda + \mu)p_N(t) + \lambda p_{N-1}(t) + \mu p_{N+1}(t) \qquad (N = 1, 2, \ldots). \tag{4.33}$$

Recalling that the limiting state probability distribution is stationary, we have $p_N'(t) = 0$ for $t \to \infty$ and $N = 0, 1, \ldots$. Thus, at the equilibrium, the ordinary difference-differential equations (4.32) and (4.33) become the algebraic linear equations

$$\lambda p_0 = \mu p_1, \tag{4.34}$$

$$(\lambda + \mu)p_N = \lambda p_{N-1} + \mu p_{N+1} \qquad (N = 1, 2, \ldots), \tag{4.35}$$

which must be supplemented with the equation

$$\sum_{N=0}^{\infty} p_N = 1. \tag{4.36}$$

Equations (4.34) and (4.35), which are called the *equilibrium state probability equations*, could have been written directly from the *state-transition-rate diagram* of our model, presented in Fig. 4.9(b). In this diagram, the arc labels are rates instead of probabilities. At the equilibrium, the input and the output rates of each state must be equal. The input rate into S_N is $\lambda p_{N-1} + \mu p_{N+1}$. The output rate from S_N is $(\lambda + \mu)p_N$. If we impose the equality of these two rates, we obtain equation (4.35). Similarly, the equilibrium condition for S_0 yields equation (4.34).

Let us denote by ρ the ratio λ/μ, which is assumed to be less than 1. This ratio is called *traffic intensity* in queuing theory. The solutions of equations (4.34), (4.35), and (4.36) are

$$p_0 = 1 - \rho, \tag{4.37}$$

$$p_N = \rho^N p_0 = (1 - \rho)\rho^N \qquad (N = 1, 2, \ldots). \tag{4.38}$$

We see from (4.38), which for $N = 0$ reduces to (4.37), that the equilibrium state probabilities in the $M/M/1$ model are geometrically distributed. The mean number of jobs in the service center and its variance can be obtained from (4.37) and (4.38) as follows:

$$\bar{N} = \sum_{N=0}^{\infty} N p_N = p_0 \sum_{N=1}^{\infty} N \rho^N = \frac{\rho}{1 - \rho}, \tag{4.39}$$

$$\text{Var}\,(N) = \sum_{N=0}^{\infty} (N - \bar{N})^2 p_N = \frac{\rho}{(1 - \rho)^2}. \tag{4.40}$$

By similar methods, we have that the probability of finding k or more requests in the service center is ρ^k.

Since $p_0 = 1 - \rho$ is the equilibrium probability that the server is idle, ρ is the equilibrium probability that the server is busy, that is, its utilization.

The other important performance indices of the system can be easily defined on this model. The mean throughput rate coincides with λ, the mean arrival rate, whenever an equilibrium solution exists ($\rho < 1$). In fact, at the equilibrium, jobs cannot accumulate in the model, and the mean output rate must equal the mean input rate. Thus, the maximum value of the mean throughput rate is μ, the mean service rate. As we saw at the end of Section 4.3.1, this rate depends on the speed of the server and on the service demands of the jobs.

The mean response or turnaround time of the modeled system corresponds to the mean time a job spends in the model. To calculate it, we can apply *Little's result*: For any interarrival-time, and service-time distribution, any number of channels in the service center, and any service discipline, the mean number of jobs in the service center is equal to the product of the mean arrival rate by the mean time in the model [Little (1961)]:

$$\bar{N} = \lambda \bar{t}. \tag{4.41}$$

Thus, from (4.41) and (4.39), we have

$$\bar{t} = \frac{1}{\mu(1 - \rho)}. \tag{4.42}$$

It is often important, both to an individual user and to a system designer or manager, to know the expected response time to a job with a given service-time demand. A user whose job requires t_s seconds of server time is obviously more interested in the expected response time for this job than in the value of $\bar{t}$ given by (4.42), which is the average over all jobs. An interactive system designer or manager is usually interested in providing faster service to shorter jobs, since this is what the users will expect to happen.

The mean $\overline{t(t_s)}$, considered as a function of t_s, is called the *response function*. To derive it, we must specify the scheduling policy implemented by the service center. The results we have obtained so far are independent of the policy. Under the FCFS discipline, the mean waiting time $\bar{t}_w$ of a job in Q is equal to the mean service time multiplied by the mean number of jobs it found in the service center at its arrival. Thus, we have, from (4.39),

$$\overline{t(t_s)} = t_s + \bar{t}_w = t_s + \frac{1}{\mu} \cdot \frac{\rho}{1 - \rho}, \tag{4.43}$$

which reduces to (4.42) for $t_s = 1/\mu$.

Another important index for an interactive system is the variance of response times. Even more interesting is the variance of the response times to a given command or to commands of comparable *weight*, that is, whose execution times are not too different. These indices can be computed for an $M/M/1$ model since the distributions of response times and of waiting times have been analytically derived. Both of these distributions are exponential:

$$f_t(x) = \mu(1 - \rho)e^{-\mu(1-\rho)x} \qquad\qquad (x \geq 0), \tag{4.44}$$

$$f_{t_w}(y) = (1 - \rho)\mathrm{imp}_0(y) + \lambda(1 - \rho)e^{-\mu(1-\rho)y} \qquad (y \geq 0; \text{FCFS}), \tag{4.45}$$

where $imp_0(y)$ is the unit impulse function at the origin ($y = 0$). Thus, we have

$$Var(t) = \frac{1}{\mu^2(1 - \rho)^2},\tag{4.46}$$

$$Var(t_w) = \frac{\rho(2 - \rho)}{\mu^2(1 - \rho)^2}.\tag{4.47}$$

Note that (4.47) can be derived directly from (4.46) and the relationship

$$Var(t) = Var(t_s) + Var(t_w) = \frac{1}{\mu^2} + Var(t_w).\tag{4.48}$$

This relationship holds since the two components of t, t_s and t_w, are statistically independent, and $Var(t)$ is therefore the sum of their variances. The variance of the response times to a given command is equal to $Var(t_w)$, which is given by (4.47). Note that the standard deviation of the response times, $\sigma_t = \sqrt{Var(t)}$, coincides with $\bar{t}$ and grows as sharply as $\bar{t}$ when ρ increases. Note also that this equality does not hold for the distribution of t_w, whose mean and standard deviation also both increase very sharply with ρ.

Example 4.4   In a simple uniprogramming interactive system, commands and input messages arrive from a large number of independent terminals. When the turn for a command or message to be processed comes, the corresponding process is swapped into primary memory and is given control of the CPU and of the second-memory devices it needs. When the execution is completed, the process is swapped out, and an output message is sent to the corresponding terminal. The next job in the queue will start being serviced only at the end of the swap-out operation. Note that there is no time quantum, or, equivalently, that the quantum is infinite.

If we assume that all input requests are statistically identical and independent, that their arrival process may be modeled as a Poisson process, and that their service times are independent of their arrival times and exponentially distributed, we can use an $M/M/1$ queuing model. Note that the service time of a job in this model does not coincide with its CPU time demand. It is its total uniprogramming execution time, which includes CPU and I/O (but not terminal I/O) times. In fact, the CPU in this system remains idle while the process being executed is waiting for the completion of an I/O operation it has started.

For the values of the model's parameters listed in Table 4.7, we have $\rho = 0.75$. The traffic intensity of this model cannot be interpreted as the utilization of the CPU but should rather be seen as the utilization of the CPU/secondary-memory-devices complex. From

Table 4.7
PARAMETERS OF THE $M/M/1$ QUEUING MODEL IN FIG. 4.6

Parameter name	Symbol	Value
Mean arrival rate	λ	1.5 jobs/s
Mean service time (mean uniprogramming execution time)	$1/\mu$	500 ms

(4.39) we obtain $\bar{N} = 3$, from (4.40) Var $(N) = 12$, from (4.42) $\bar{t} = 2$ s, and from (4.46) $\sigma_t = 2$ s. The mean waiting time of a request in the queue is, by (4.43), $\bar{t}_w = \rho\bar{t} = 1.5$ s. Thus, a command which has a uniprogramming execution time of 4 s should expect to have a response time of 5.5 s if the scheduling policy of the system is FCFS. The standard deviation of this response time is, by (4.47), 1.93 s.

Curve (a) in Fig. 4.10 represents the mean response time of this model as a function of ρ, assuming that λ varies between 0 and μ and that μ remains constant. When ρ changes because of variations in μ and λ is kept constant, we obtain curve (a') of the same diagram, whose equation may be easily derived from (4.42).

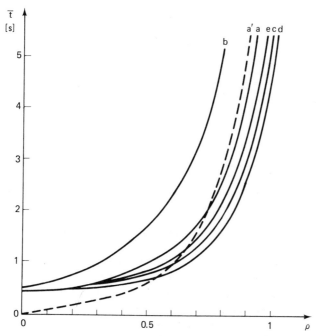

Figure 4.10 Mean response time of single-service-center models vs. ρ: (a) $M/M/1$ model of Example 4.4 and PS model of Example 4.7, constant μ; (a') same as (a), constant λ; (b) $M/G/1$ model of Example 4.5, $c = 2$, constant μ; (c) $M/G/1$ model of Example 4.5, $c = 0.5$, constant μ; (d) $M/D/1$ model of Example 4.5; (e) preemptive RR model of Example 4.6, $q = 0.3$ s.

The most notable characteristic of these two curves is their sharp increase toward infinity as ρ approaches 1. Loading the system so that its mean throughput rate λ will be close to the maximum rate μ makes $\bar{t}$ intolerably high. The conflict between the installation manager's and the user's viewpoints cannot be represented with more dramatic clarity than by these diagrams. For relatively low values of ρ, $\bar{t}(\rho)$ is not substantially larger than $1/\mu$, the mean service time. At $\rho = 0.5$, the mean waiting time $\bar{t}_w$ [see (4.43)] is equal to $1/\mu$. As ρ increases further, $\bar{t}_w$ grows very rapidly and soon completely dominates $1/\mu$. At $\rho = 0.9$, $\bar{t}_w$ is 9 times $1/\mu$.

The response function of the model, assuming that the scheduling policy is FCFS, is given by (4.43) and plotted in Fig. 4.11 [curve (a)].

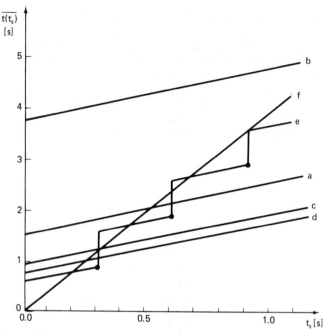

Figure 4.11   Response functions of single-service-center models: (*a*) *M/M/*1 FCFS model of Example 4.4; (*b*) *M/G/*1 FCFS model of Example 4.5, $c = 2$; (*c*) *M/G/*1 FCFS model of Example 4.5, $c = 0.5$; (*d*) *M/D/*1 FCFS model of Example 4.5; (*e*) preemptive RR model of Example 4.6, $q = 0.3$ s; (*f*) PS model of Example 4.7.

We have already stated that the exponential assumption has been experimentally found to be a poor approximation to the distributions of the service times of computer components. Measurement results indicate that the coefficients of variation of CPU time distributions are generally much higher than 1 and that those of I/O time distributions are lower than 1.

Nonexponential distributions with $c > 1$ may be approximated by a weighted sum of exponentials (*hyperexponential distribution*) such as

$$F_{t_s}(x) = \text{Prob}\,(t_s \leq x) = \sum_{i=1}^{k} w_i(1 - e^{-\mu_i x}) \qquad \left(\mu_i > 0, w_i > 0, \sum_{i=1}^{k} w_i = 1\right).$$

$$(4.49)$$

The mean and variance of the random variable t_s are

$$\bar{t}_s = \sum_{i=1}^{k} \frac{w_i}{\mu_i}, \qquad \text{Var}\,(t_s) = \sum_{i=1}^{k} \frac{2w_i}{\mu_i^2} - \left(\sum_{i=1}^{k} \frac{w_i}{\mu_i}\right)^2. \qquad (4.50)$$

It is easy to show that the coefficient of variation is

$$c = \frac{\sqrt{\text{Var}\,(t_s)}}{\bar{t}_s} \geq 1 \qquad (4.51)$$

and that it is $c = 1$ only when $\mu_i = \mu$ for all i, that is, when the distribution is exponential.

A hyperexponential distribution of service times such as the one in (4.49) can be obtained by connecting k exponential servers $\Sigma_1, \ldots, \Sigma_k$ in parallel. Server Σ_i must have a service rate equal to μ_i and a probability of being used by a job to be serviced equal to w_i (*see* Fig. 4.12). Note that at most one of the k servers may be busy at any given time. The single-service-center model in Fig. 4.12 can be solved at the equilibrium by defining the state of the system as the pair (N, i), where N is the total number of jobs in the center and i is the identifier of the busy server, if any $(i = 0, 1, \ldots, k)$. Then we write the equilibrium state probability equations in the unknowns $p(N, i)$.

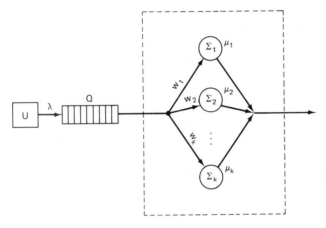

Figure 4.12 Exponential-service equivalent of a Poisson-arrival, hyperexponential-service single-service-center model.

Similarly, nonexponential distributions with $c < 1$ like those of most I/O service times may be approximated by a *hypoexponential distribution*, for example, of the type

$$F_{t_s}(x) = \text{Prob}\,(t_s \le x) = 1 - \frac{\mu_2}{\mu_2 - \mu_1}\,e^{-\mu_1 x} - \frac{\mu_1}{\mu_1 - \mu_2}\,e^{-\mu_2 x} \qquad (\mu_1 \ne \mu_2).$$

$$(4.52)$$

The mean and the variance of the distribution (4.52) are

$$\bar{t}_s = \frac{1}{\mu_1} + \frac{1}{\mu_2}, \qquad \text{Var}\,(t_s) = \frac{1}{\mu_1^2} + \frac{1}{\mu_2^2}, \qquad (4.53)$$

and the coefficient of variation is

$$c = \sqrt{1 - \frac{2\mu_1\mu_2}{(\mu_1 + \mu_2)^2}} < 1. \qquad (4.54)$$

The service-time distribution (4.52) can be obtained by connecting two exponential servers in series, with service rates μ_1 and μ_2, one of which at most may be busy at any given time. If we connect k exponential servers in series, we can model hypoexponential distributions with mathematical forms more complex than (4.52). The corresponding multiple-server service center is shown in Fig. 4.13. When all servers in series have the same service rate μ, the center's service distribution is the *Erlang-k distribution*

$$F_{t_s}(x) = 1 - e^{-k\mu x} \sum_{i=0}^{k-1} \frac{(k\mu x)^2}{i!}. \tag{4.55}$$

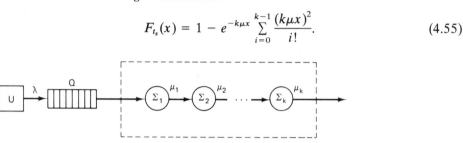

Figure 4.13   Exponential-service equivalent of a Poisson-arrival, hypoexponential-service single-service-center model.

The model in Fig. 4.13 can be solved, like the one with hyperexponential service times, by defining the system's state as the pair (N, i), with $i = 0, 1, \ldots, k$.

Hyperexponential and hypoexponential approximations to real-world service-time distributions are useful in queuing networks, since they allow one to obtain networks in which all servers are exponential. However, the approximate equality of the coefficients of variation of two distributions is a necessary but by no means sufficient condition for using one of them as an approximation to the other.

In studying nonpreemptive single-server systems with general service-time distribution (also called $M/G/1$ systems), there is no need for these approximations if we are interested only in index $\bar{i}$, since a closed-form expression of $\bar{i}$ at the equilibrium has been obtained. If $1/\mu$ and c denote the mean and the coefficient of variation of the service time distribution, we have

$$\bar{N} = \rho + \frac{\rho^2(1 + c^2)}{2(1 - \rho)}. \tag{4.56}$$

This expression of the mean number of jobs in the service center may be obtained by recognizing that the number of jobs left in the center by a departing job is a semi-Markov process with an embedded Markov chain defined at the instants of departure.

Applying Little's result (4.41), we have the so-called *Kintchine-Pollaczek formula*

$$\bar{i} = \frac{1}{\mu}\left[1 + \frac{\rho(1 + c^2)}{2(1 - \rho)}\right], \tag{4.57}$$

and, for FCFS scheduling,

$$\bar{t}_w = \frac{\rho(1 + c^2)}{2\mu(1 - \rho)}.$$ (4.58)

What is most remarkable in this result is that the mean response time and the mean waiting time depend only on the mean $1/\mu$ and on the standard deviation c/μ of the service-time distribution. All the higher moments of this distribution influence neither $\bar{t}$ nor $\bar{t}_w$.

Note that, for $c = 1$, equations (4.56), (4.57), and (4.58) become (4.39), (4.42), and the expression of $\bar{t}_w$ used in (4.43), respectively.

Example 4.5   Let us consider again the system we represented by an $M/M/1$ model in Example 4.4. We now remove the assumption of exponentially distributed service times. Of the arbitrary service-time distribution, we know the mean $1/\mu$ and the standard deviation σ_s. The arrivals of jobs are still modeled as a Poisson process with mean rate λ. The values of $1/\mu$ and λ are those given in Table 4.7.

If $\sigma_s = 1$ s, we have $c = 2$. From (4.56) we obtain $\bar{N} = 6.375$, from (4.57) $\bar{t} = 4.25$ s, and from (4.58) $\bar{t}_w = 3.75$ s. Thus, the greater variability of service times corresponding to an increase of c from 1 to 2 causes a 112% increase in $\bar{N}$, the same percent increase in $\bar{t}$, and a 150% increase in $\bar{t}_w$. The (b) curves in Figs. 4.10 and 4.11 represent $\bar{t}(\rho)$ and $\overline{t(t_s)}$ for this $M/G/1$ model. As in (4.43), we have $\bar{t}(t_s) = t_s + \bar{t}_w$.

Opposite results are obtained when service times are less variable than in the $M/M/1$ case. For $\sigma_s = 0.25$ s, we have $c = 0.5$; hence $\bar{N} = 2.15$, $\bar{t} = 1.43$ s, and $\bar{t}_w = 0.93$ s. Thus, with respect to our $M/M/1$ model, $\bar{N}$ decreases by 28%, $\bar{t}$ by the same percentage, and $\bar{t}_w$ by 38%. The (c) curves in Figs. 4.10 and 4.11 refer to this case.

When $c = 0$, there is no service-time variability. All jobs have the same service time $1/\mu$. This is an $M/D/1$ model, where D stands for *deterministic*. With the values of λ and μ in Table 4.7, we obtain $\bar{N} = 1.87$, $\bar{t} = 1.25$ s, and $\bar{t}_w = 0.75$ s. The functions $\bar{t}(\rho)$ for variable λ and $\overline{t(t_s)}$ for FCFS scheduling are plotted in Figs. 4.10 and 4.11 [curves (d)], respectively.   ∎

4.3.3 Preemptive Single-Service-Center Models

The simplest preemptive queuing model is depicted in Fig. 4.14. When a job leaves the server, it does not necessarily leave the service center. There is a nonzero probability b that the job rejoins the queue and waits there for additional service. A job may leave the server for a variety of reasons, which depend on the service discipline adopted by the service center.

A very popular preemptive service discipline is the *round-robin* (RR) scheduling policy, which does not allow the server to process a job for a time longer than a given *quantum q*. If the service time needed by a job exceeds q, the processing of the job is interrupted, and the job goes back to the queue, which is

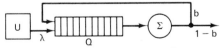

Figure 4.14   Preemptive single-service-center queuing model.

managed according to the FCFS policy. The RR discipline was one of the first policies adopted in time-sharing systems because of its simplicity and therefore has received a great deal of attention [see McKinney (1969)].

In a computer system with RR scheduling, the probability b is not constant. For instance, for a given job, b decreases as the job receives more service. However, the solvability requirement is more easily met when b is assumed to be constant. As we shall see, even if we make this assumption and the additional one that the memoryless property holds both for the interarrival and the service-time distributions, solving this model is much more complicated than solving the $M/M/1$ model. This greater complexity is found whenever a service discipline depends on the service requirements of each job and on the path followed by each job through the model.

The service times are assumed for simplicity to be integral multiples of the quantum q. Thus, to retain the memoryless property, we assume that the probability that a job requires k time quanta is given by the geometric distribution

$$\text{Prob}\,(t_s = kq) = b^{k-1}(1 - b) \qquad (k = 1, 2, \ldots; 0 < b < 1). \qquad (4.59)$$

Let the state of the system be represented by the number N of jobs in it and the probability of state N be denoted by p_N ($N = 0, 1, \ldots$). Let a job requiring k quanta of service find on its arrival, at the equilibrium, j jobs in the service center. This job, which will be called the *tagged job*, has to take the feedback path at the end of each one of the first $k - 1$ quanta of service received. Thus, it returns to the queue $k - 1$ times and departs after receiving the kth quantum. A *pass* of the tagged job is defined as the period which begins when the job joins the queue and starts waiting for its next quantum of service and ends when it leaves the server after receiving that quantum. The time to perform the ith pass will be denoted by τ_i ($i = 1, \ldots, k$).

During the first pass, the tagged job has j jobs ahead. One of these jobs is being serviced at the time the tagged job arrives and will leave the server after αq units of time ($0 \le \alpha \le 1$). Thus, we can write

$$\tau_1 = \alpha q + (j - 1)q + q. \qquad (4.60)$$

The durations of the successive passes are integral multiples of q. If h_i is the duration (in number of quanta) of the ith pass, the tagged job during that pass has $h_i - 1$ jobs ahead, of which $b(h_i - 1)$ on the average will return to the queue. Note that this result is based on the assumption that the probability that a job will require another quantum is independent of its history and therefore given by $\text{Prob}\,(t_s > q)$, which, by (4.59), is equal to b. This assumption is valid because of the memoryless property that the service-time distribution has.

During the ith pass of the tagged job there are on the average $\lambda \bar{\tau}_i$ arrivals. Since $h_i = \bar{\tau}_i/q$, we have, for $k \ge 3$,

$$\bar{\tau}_{i+1} = b(h_i - 1)q + \lambda \bar{\tau}_i q + q = (\lambda q + b)\bar{\tau}_i + q(1 - b) \qquad (i = 2, \ldots, k - 1), \qquad (4.61)$$

or, equivalently,

$$\bar{\tau}_{i+1} = a^{i-2}\bar{\tau}_2 + q(1-b)\frac{1-a^{i-2}}{1-a} \qquad (i = 2, \ldots, k-1), \qquad (4.62)$$

where

$$a = \lambda q + b. \qquad (4.63)$$

The same approach we used to write (4.60) yields

$$\bar{\tau}_2 = bjq + \lambda\bar{\tau}_1 q + q = \lambda q \bar{\tau}_1 + q(1 + bj). \qquad (4.64)$$

Equation (4.64), together with (4.62), allows us to express the mean time spent by the tagged job in the model when there are j jobs at its arrival:

$$\bar{t}_k(j) = \sum_{i=1}^{k} \bar{\tau}_i = \bar{\tau}_1 + \frac{q(k-1)}{1-\rho} + q\frac{1-a^{k-1}}{1-a}\left(\lambda\bar{\tau}_1 + bj - \frac{\rho}{1-\rho}\right), \qquad (4.65)$$

where

$$\rho = \frac{\lambda q}{1-b}. \qquad (4.66)$$

Note that ρ is the utilization factor of the server, since the mean service time given by (4.59) is $q/(1-b)$.

The mean queue length is given by

$$\sum_{N=1}^{\infty} (N-1)p_N = \sum_{N=1}^{\infty} Np_N - \sum_{N=1}^{\infty} p_N = \bar{N} - \rho. \qquad (4.67)$$

The mean of αq is $\rho q/2$, since the server is busy only during a fraction of the total time equal to ρ. Observing that the queue length at the arrival of the tagged job is $j - 1$, we may derive from (4.60) an expression of $\bar{\tau}_1$:

$$\bar{\tau}_1 = q\left(\bar{N} - \frac{\rho}{2} + 1\right). \qquad (4.68)$$

The value of $\bar{N}$ can be shown to coincide with the one which would result from equation (4.56), which is valid for $M/G/1$ models:

$$\bar{N} = \rho + \frac{\rho^2(1+b)}{2(1-\rho)}. \qquad (4.69)$$

Note that the coefficient of variation of distribution (4.59) is $\sqrt{b}$.

Equation (4.65) yields the mean response time of a job requiring k quanta:

$$\bar{t}_k = \sum_{j=0}^{\infty} p_j \bar{t}_k(j) = \bar{\tau}_1 + \frac{q(k-1)}{1-\rho}$$

$$+ q\frac{1-a^{k-1}}{1-a}\left(\lambda\bar{\tau}_1 + b\bar{N} - \frac{\rho}{1-\rho}\right) \qquad (k = 1, 2, \ldots). \qquad (4.70)$$

The value of $\bar{t}_k$ may be expressed as a function of the model's parameters by using equations (4.63), (4.66), (4.68), and (4.69). Note that, since from (4.63) and (4.66) we have $a < 1$, the dependence of $\bar{t}_k$ on the service time kq tends to become linear [with slope $1/(1 - \rho) > 1$] as k increases.

Equation (4.70) may be viewed as the response function of this model. The mean response time can be computed [see (4.59)] as

$$\bar{t} = \sum_{k=1}^{\infty} b^{k-1}(1 - b)\bar{t}_k. \tag{4.71}$$

Example 4.6 A uniprogramming interactive system similar to the one considered in Examples 4.4 and 4.5 but with finite-quantum round-robin scheduling is to be modeled. In this system, a job in execution relinquishes control of the CPU when one of two conditions is satisfied. The first condition is job termination, which usually occurs when additional input from the user terminal is needed. The second condition is met when the job has had the control of the CPU for an entire time quantum since the last time the CPU was allocated to it, and there is at least one job waiting for the CPU. In a nonpreemptive system like the one modeled in Examples 4.4 and 4.5, the CPU is released only when the first condition is met. Thus, that system may be viewed as a preemptive system of the type considered here in which the time quantum is infinite, so that the second condition is never satisfied.

When a job is waiting for the completion of an I/O operation it has started, the CPU is not switched to another job but remains allocated to that job. Therefore, the time quantum specifies the maximum amount of real time, not of useful CPU time, that a job can consume before having to return to the queue. This is the real time which has elapsed since the most recent allocation of the CPU to the executing job.

The system will be modeled as in Fig. 4.14. We assume that the mean arrival rate λ is $1.5\,\text{s}^{-1}$. We also choose a time quantum $q = 300\,\text{ms}$ and a probability of returning to the queue $b = 0.4$. With these parameter values, the mean service time is $500\,\text{ms}$, and, by (4.66), ρ is 0.75. Thus, we have the same parameter values as in Examples 4.4 and 4.5 (see Table 4.7).

The evaluation of (4.70) allows us to obtain the ordinates of the solid dots on the (e) curve in Fig. 4.11. The response function of our model can be plotted by observing that, within each interval of duration q on the t_s axis, the value of $\bar{t}$ increases linearly with unit slope.

Note that the expected response time to a command which has an execution time shorter than 300 ms is between 0.58 and 0.88 s. For FCFS scheduling, the (a) curve in Fig. 4.11 yields an expected response time between 1.5 and 1.8 s in the same range of service time demands. The comparison of response functions (a) and (e) confirms the intuitive claim that a time-sharing system gives a better response to "light" jobs than a system in which all jobs are allowed to run to completion without ever having to release the CPU. In the case of Fig. 4.11, a job which requires less than 2 quanta of service ($t_s < 0.6\,\text{s}$) receives on the average a faster response from the RR system with $q = 0.3\,\text{s}$ than from the FCFS system. Longer jobs obtain on the average a faster response from the FCFS system.

From (4.71), we have $\bar{t} = 1.55\,\text{s}$, which is substantially lower than the 2-s mean response time of the FCFS system considered in Example 4.4. By varying λ, we can change the value of ρ without modifying the mean service time. The corresponding values of $\bar{t}$ we obtain from (4.71) are plotted for our model in Fig. 4.10 [curve (e)]. This curve is below the one corresponding to FCFS service for all values of ρ.   ∎

If in the model in Fig. 4.14 the quantum q tends toward zero, it is as if the server were simultaneously processing all the jobs in the service center at all times, each job at a speed inversely proportional to the total number of jobs. This scheduling policy is called the *processor-sharing* (PS) policy.

For Poisson arrivals and *any* service-time distribution with mean $1/\mu$, the mean response time of a PS model is given by (4.42).

To prove the validity of this statement, we first calculate the expected response time to a job whose service-time demand is t_s. By (4.66) and (4.63), b and a must tend toward 1 as q tends toward 0 if ρ is to remain constant. By (4.69), $\bar{N}$ will then tend toward $\rho/(1-\rho)$, and by (4.68) $\bar{\tau}_1$ will tend toward 0. If in (4.70) we replace k with t_s/q and let q tend toward 0, we obtain the response function of the PS model:

$$\overline{t(t_s)} = \frac{t_s}{1-\rho}. \tag{4.72}$$

If service times have a distribution with probability density function f_{t_s}, we can write

$$\bar{t} = \int_0^\infty f_{t_s}(x)\overline{t(x)}\, dx = \frac{\bar{t}_s}{1-\rho} = \frac{1}{\mu(1-\rho)}. \tag{4.73}$$

Since in deriving (4.73), which is identical to (4.42), no assumption has been made about the service-time distribution, we conclude that in a PS model, for any distribution of t_s, $\bar{t}$ coincides with the mean response time of an $M/M/1$ model having the same λ and the same μ.

Example 4.7   If in the time-sharing system modeled in Example 4.6 the time quantum were made very short with respect to the mean service time, we could approximate it by a processor-sharing single-service-center model.

In a PS system, all jobs being processed must be in primary memory. Thus, the system is multiprogrammed, even though no I/O devices can be explicitly represented in a single-service-center model. As in Examples 4.4–4.6, the server in this model does not represent the CPU but the complex of all processors in the system. The service time demanded by a job is not its CPU time but its total uniprogramming execution time, which includes its initial loading into memory (swap-in) and its final unloading (swap-out).

For $\lambda = 1.5\text{ s}^{-1}$ and $1/\mu = 500\text{ ms}$, as in Table 4.7, ρ would be 0.75 and (4.73) would yield $\bar{t} = 2\text{ s}$. The diagram of $\bar{t}(\rho)$ would coincide with the one we plotted in Example 4.4 for the $M/M/1$ model [curve (a) in Fig. 4.10].

The response function (4.72) for our PS model is reported in Fig. 4.11, curve (f). It is a straight line going through the origin and with slope $1/(1-\rho)$. For very short jobs, the response given by a PS model is faster than that of an FCFS $M/M/1$ or even of an RR model. However, for $t_s > 0.9\text{ s}$, all commands are processed more rapidly under an RR discipline, and this is the case also in certain ranges of t_s for $t_s < 0.9\text{ s}$. Furthermore, an FCFS $M/M/1$ model's response becomes faster for $t_s > 0.5\text{ s}$.

In a real time-sharing system, a PS policy, or even a round-robin policy with a very short quantum, cannot be efficiently implemented. As q decreases, the CPU switching overhead becomes relatively more important. At some point, this overhead cannot be neglected anymore, as the CPU spends most of its time switching from one process to another. Thus, the PS model may only be viewed as a rough approximation of an RR system whose quantum is relatively short with respect to the mean or, better, the median of service times.   ∎

The preemption of a running job can also be caused by the arrival of another job having a higher priority. In this case, a scheduling decision is to be made at each job arrival. Several preemptive disciplines of this type have been studied for the single-service-center model in Fig. 4.14, for instance, PSETF (*preemptive-shortest-elapsed-time-first*), which is suitable when service times of jobs are not known in advance, PSPTF (*preemptive-shortest-processing-time-first*), and PEP (*preemptive-external-priorities*).

If the preempted jobs join a queue different from the one they came from and the server has a total of n queues, we have an n-level *foreground-background* (FB$_n$) discipline. An FB$_n$ model is depicted in Fig. 4.15. This model, which represents more accurately than the one with a single queue in Fig. 4.14 a number of real time-sharing systems, has been studied under a number of different assumptions. In one of its versions, each queue has a different quantum associated with it. Usually, it is $q_i < q_{i+1}$ for all i, and q_n may be infinite. The jobs in queue Q_i are serviced if queues $Q_1, \ldots, Q_{i-1}$ are empty. Preemption can only occur because of quantum expiration. Preempted jobs coming from queue Q_i go to Q_{i+1}, and those coming from Q_n go back to Q_n. The jobs in each queue are processed in FCFS order.

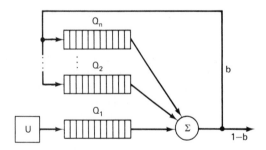

Figure 4.15   Single-service-center queuing model with FB$_n$ scheduling.

4.3.4   Open-Network Models

In modeling computer systems, queuing networks can provide a much greater degree of detail than models containing only one service center. An open network has been defined in Section 4.3.1 as a network having at least one source.

The work of Jackson (1963) allows us to solve open-network models in which the interarrival-time distribution and all service-time distributions are exponential, and the service disciplines of the centers do not depend on the future service-time requirements or on the future path of a job through the network. The latter assumption rules out quantum-oriented disciplines and most of the other preemptive scheduling policies. This is a reasonable exclusion for service centers which model, for instance, disk and drum processors but not for those representing the CPU in models of interactive systems. We shall now illustrate Jackson's approach by an example.

Example 4.8   A queuing model of the EXOPE system in Fig. 1.2 is to be constructed and solved analytically, using the method proposed by Jackson. Each one of the four processors P_1, P_2, P_3, and P_4 will be represented as a single-server, single-channel service center. Each center will have a single queue of infinite capacity. For the method to be applicable, we must assume that the service times of jobs at each center are independent and exponentially distributed. At center i, the mean service rate is μ_i. The service discipline of each center will be assumed to be nonpreemptive.

The user community is represented by an infinite source which generates jobs according to a Poisson arrival process with rate λ.

Jackson's results would allow us to treat the model when λ is a function of the number of jobs in the model, N, and when each service rate μ_i is a function of N_i, where N_i is a nonnegative integer representing the number of jobs being serviced or waiting at the ith service center. However, for simplicity, we assume that both λ and the μ_i's are constant. Note that this assumption is reasonable for the μ_i's of centers which represent components whose scheduling is acually nonpreemptive. It is generally not accurate for the μ_i's of other centers and for λ, which, especially in heavily loaded interactive systems, certainly depends on N.

The interconnections between the four service centers reflect the path followed by a job within our system. As depicted in Fig. 4.16, a job enters the system via the I/O processor P_4. The time spent by the job in service center 4 should somehow account for its input and loading operations. When the job has received the requested service from Σ_4, it is to be considered as loaded in primary memory and ready to run. When its turn to be processed by the CPU comes, the job is serviced by Σ_1. The need for an I/O operation causes the job to release the CPU to the next job in Q_1 and to migrate either to service center 2, which models the drum processor, or to 3, which models the disk processor. The

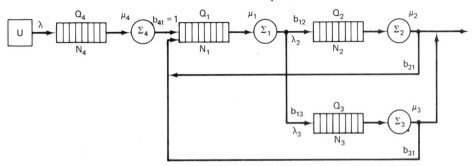

Figure 4.16   Open-network model of the EXOPE system in Fig. 1.2.

probability of a drum request is denoted by b_{12} and is assumed to be identical for all jobs and constant in time. The probability of a disk request is of course $b_{13} = 1 - b_{12}$.

When the drum or disk server completes the processing of a job request, the job may terminate and leave the system or return to the CPU queue Q_1 for further CPU service. The probabilities of returning to Q_1 are denoted by b_{21} and b_{31}, respectively. Like b_{12} and b_{13}, they are identical for all jobs and are constant. Note that while in the system a job at its completion has to go through processor P_4 so that its output can reach the external world this output operation is not represented in the model of Fig. 4.16.

An important system resource which also is not modeled is the primary memory. Due to its characteristics of being shared among jobs and often used in conjuncton with other resources, the memory is difficult to represent in a queuing model. We observe that all jobs in service centers 1, 2, and 3 should be viewed as models of real jobs which have to coexist in primary memory. Assuming an infinite capacity for the queues in our model is certainly unreasonable from this viewpoint. In general, to represent memory contention in some way, we should limit the queue sizes. However, this would greatly increase the difficulty of obtaining an analytic solution. Another approach is the one of keeping constant the total number of jobs in service centers 1, 2, and 3, that is, the degree of multiprogramming. This approach is described in Section 4.3.5.

Table 4.8 lists the parameters of the model we have constructed for our system. In this model, as in all open networks, the mean throughput rate is equal to the arrival rate λ, which is one of the model's parameters. This is not, however, the case of the mean response or turnaround time, whose calculation will be the main objective of our analysis of the model. Another interesting index is the maximum throughput rate that the system can provide when processing a work load consisting of statistically identical jobs with given μ_i's and b_{ij}'s.

Table 4.8

PARAMETERS OF THE OPEN-NETWORK MODEL IN FIG. 4.16

Parameter name	Symbol	Value
Mean arrival rate	λ	0.7 jobs/s
Mean uninterrupted CPU time	$1/\mu_1$	30 ms
Mean drum service time	$1/\mu_2$	20 ms
Mean disk service time	$1/\mu_3$	80 ms
Mean input service time	$1/\mu_4$	500 ms
Drum request probability	b_{12}	0.75
CPU request probability after drum service	b_{21}	1
CPU request probability after disk service	b_{31}	0.9

The state of the model in Fig. 4.16 is defined as the four-dimensional vector $\mathbf{N} = (N_1, N_2, N_3, N_4)$. The corresponding total number of jobs in the system is $N = \sum_{i=1}^{4} N_i$. The events in the model are all job arrivals and all completions of service to a job at a service center.

Let the system be in state $\mathbf{K} = (K_1, K_2, K_3, K_4)$ at time t. We now compute the conditional probabilities $p(\mathbf{N}, t + h | \mathbf{K}, t)$ that the system is in state $\mathbf{N} = (N_1, N_2, N_3, N_4)$ at time $t + h$, where h is so short that at most one event may take place in the model during the interval $(t, t + h)$. In this interval, the probability of an arrival is $h\lambda$, and the probability that service center i completes the processing of a job is $h\mu_i$. The following four cases have to be considered.

  a. $\mathbf{N} = \mathbf{K}$ (no event occurs). Thus,

$$p(\mathbf{N}, t + h | \mathbf{K}, t) = 1 - h\lambda - h \sum_{i=1}^{4} \mu_i. \qquad (4.74)$$

  b. $\mathbf{N} = \mathbf{K}$ except $N_4 = K_4 + 1$ (one arrival). Thus,

$$p(\mathbf{N}, t + h | \mathbf{K}, t) = h\lambda. \qquad (4.75)$$

  c. $\mathbf{N} = \mathbf{K}$ except $N_2 = K_2 - 1$ or $N_3 = K_3 - 1$ (one departure). Thus,

$$p(\mathbf{N}, t + h | \mathbf{K}, t) = h\mu_x(1 - b_{x1}), \qquad (4.76)$$

where x is equal to either 2 or 3.

  d. $\mathbf{N} = \mathbf{K}$ except $N_x = K_x - 1$, $N_y = K_y + 1$ (one service completion at center x followed by the job's immediate transfer to another center y). For the model in Fig. 4.16, we ave $x = 4$ and $y = 1$, or $x = 1$ and $y = 2$, or $x = 1$ and $y = 3$, or $x = 2$ and $y = 1$, or $x = 3$ and $y = 1$. Note that $b_{41} = 1$. Thus,

$$p(\mathbf{N}, t + h | \mathbf{K}, t) = h\mu_x b_{xy}. \qquad (4.77)$$

From probability theory, we know that

$$p(\mathbf{N}, t + h) = \sum_{\text{all } \mathbf{K}} p(\mathbf{K}, t)p(\mathbf{N}, t + h | \mathbf{K}, t). \qquad (4.78)$$

Substituting (4.74), (4.75), (4.76), and (4.77) into (4.78), we have

$$p(\mathbf{N}, t + h) = p(\mathbf{N}, t)(1 - h\lambda - h \sum_{i=1}^{4} \mu_i) + h\lambda p[(N_1, N_2, N_3, N_4 - 1), t]$$

$$+ h\mu_2(1 - b_{21})p[(N_1, N_2 + 1, N_3, N_4), t]$$

$$+ h\mu_3(1 - b_{31})p[(N_1, N_2, N_3 + 1, N_4), t]$$

$$+ h\mu_4 b_{41}p[(N_1 - 1, N_2, N_3, N_4 + 1), t]$$

$$+ h\mu_1 b_{12}p[(N_1 + 1, N_2 - 1, N_3, N_4), t]$$

$$+ h\mu_1 b_{13}p[(N_1 + 1, N_2, N_3 - 1, N_4), t]$$

$$+ h\mu_2 b_{21}p[(N_1 - 1, N_2 + 1, N_3, N_4), t]$$

$$+ h\mu_3 b_{31}p[(N_1 - 1, N_2, N_3 + 1, N_4), t]. \qquad (4.79)$$

We now subtract $p(\mathbf{N}, t)$ from both sides of (4.79), divide both sides by h, and then let h tend toward zero. We obtain a difference-differential equation which expresses $dp(\mathbf{N}, t)/dt$ as a function of λ, the μ_i's, the b_{ij}'s, and the probabilities of those states from which $\mathbf{N}$ can be reached in one step. Jackson (1963) proved that a time-independent solution to this equation exists and is unique.

The solution, which is the *equilibrium state probability distribution*

$$p(\mathbf{N}) = \lim_{t \to \infty} p(\mathbf{N}, t), \qquad (4.80)$$

is given by

$$p(N_1, N_2, N_3, N_4) = p_1(N_1) \cdot p_2(N_2) \cdot p_3(N_3) \cdot p_4(N_4), \tag{4.81}$$

where

$$p_i(N_i) = (1 - \rho_i)\rho_i^{N_i} \qquad (i = 1, 2, 3, 4), \tag{4.82}$$

with

$$\rho_i = \frac{\lambda_i}{\mu_i} \tag{4.83}$$

and

$$\begin{aligned}
\lambda_1 &= & b_{21}\lambda_2 + b_{31}\lambda_3 + b_{41}\lambda_4, \\
\lambda_2 &= b_{12}\lambda_1, \\
\lambda_3 &= b_{13}\lambda_1, \\
\lambda_4 &= & \lambda.
\end{aligned} \tag{4.84}$$

Note that the system of linear algebraic equations (4.84) is assumed to have one and only one solution. The reader can verify that the results in (4.81) and (4.82) satisfy the difference-differential equation derived from (4.79).

Thus, under our assumptions, the equilibrium probability distribution of the number of jobs at service center i is independent of those at the other centers and is identical to that of an $M/M/1$ queuing system having arrival rate λ_i and service rate μ_i [see (4.38)].

This conclusion allows us to apply the results obtained for the $M/M/1$ model in Section 4.3.2 to any Jackson-type queuing network. In particular, the utilization of service center i is simply equal to the value of ρ_i given by (4.83). Also, by (4.39), the mean number of jobs at service center i is

$$\bar{N}_i = \frac{\rho_i}{1 - \rho_i}. \tag{4.85}$$

By Little's result (4.41), the mean response time, defined as the mean time between the arrival and the departure of a given job, is

$$\bar{t} = \frac{1}{\lambda}\bar{N} = \frac{1}{\lambda} \sum_{i=1}^{4} \frac{\rho_i}{1 - \rho_i}. \tag{4.86}$$

With the parameter values listed in Table 4.8, the solution of equations (4.84) yields $\lambda_1 = 28$ jobs/s, $\lambda_2 = 21$ jobs/s, $\lambda_3 = 7$ jobs/s, and $\lambda_4 = 0.7$ jobs/s. From (4.83), we have $\rho_1 = 0.84$, $\rho = 0.42$, $\rho_3 = 0.56$, $\rho_4 = 0.35$. Hence the mean number of jobs in the system, $\bar{N}$, is about 7.78, and, by (4.86), $\bar{t} = 11.1$ s. On the average, there are 5.25 jobs in the CPU service center, 0.72 in the drum, 1.27 in the disk, and 0.54 in the input processor.

The maximum arrival rate is the one which saturates the busiest service center, the CPU ($\rho_1 = 1$). Since in our model

$$\rho_1 = \frac{1}{\mu_1}\lambda_1 = \frac{1}{\mu_1}\frac{1}{1 - b_{21}b_{12} - b_{31}b_{13}}\lambda = 1.2\lambda, \tag{4.87}$$

we have

$$\bar{T}_{max} = \lambda_{max} = \frac{\rho_{1\,max}}{1.2} = \frac{1}{1.2} = 0.833 \text{ jobs/s.} \qquad (4.88)$$

The diagram in Fig. 4.17 shows the relationship between the mean response time and the mean arrival rate, which (for $\lambda \leq \lambda_{max}$) coincides with the mean throughput rate $\bar{T}$. Note that, for $\lambda = 0$, we have $\bar{t} = 3.1$ s. This is the mean uniprogramming execution time of a job. For $\lambda = 0.7$ jobs/s, the total real time spent by the average job in the system is about 3.6 times the minimum value of $\bar{t}$. The congestion caused by the competition for resources increases the mean input time from 0.5 s to about 0.768 s, the mean total CPU time from 1.2 s to 7.5 s, the mean total drum time from 0.6 s to 1.034 s, and the mean total disk time from 0.8 s to 1.817 s. These results have been obtained by applying Little's formula to each individual service center in Fig. 4.16. ∎

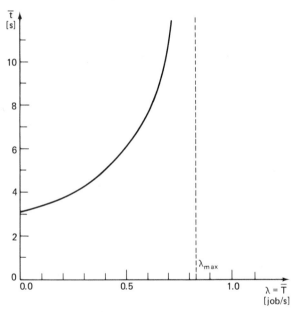

Figure 4.17 Mean response time vs. mean throughput rate for the model in Fig. 4.16 and Table 4.8.

Baskett et al. (1975) have shown that open and closed queuing networks with service centers characterized by more general service-time distributions and by scheduling disciplines including FCFS, PS, and LCFS (*last-come-first-served*) can be solved symbolically. Also, in these networks, there may exist different classes of jobs, and a job is allowed to change class according to a given fixed probability when moving from one service center to another. Each class of jobs at some types of service centers may be characterized by a different service-time distribution. The same network may be open for some classes of jobs and closed for the others. The arrival process may be a Poisson process or consist of a finite number of Poisson arrival streams.

The ability to solve symbolically queuing networks containing different classes of jobs allows computer system modelers to increase substantially the degree of detail of work-load models. The work load of most installations may be partitioned into classes defined by significantly different values of job characteristics (*see* Section 5.3.5). An obvious, simple, and very popular example is the one of an installation which serves both interactive and batch users. The requests submitted by the interactive users generally demand completely different amounts of system resources with respect to those demanded by the batch jobs. Modeling this work load assuming that the distribution of service times at each service center and that of interarrival times is the same for all jobs is clearly a very crude approximation. By introducing various classes of jobs into a model, correlations among job parameters can be accounted for in a natural way.

When the exact closed-form solution of a queuing network model is not known, it may be possible to determine an approximate solution. Approximation methods allow us to solve more complex, and hence potentially more accurate, models of computer systems. Clearly, the use of these methods is convenient only if the inaccuracies they introduce are less significant than the accuracy gains due to the greater degree of detail in the model.

The *diffusion approximation* can now be applied to open and closed networks with single-channel single-server centers characterized by arbitrary service-time distributions and nonpreemptive scheduling policies which are not based on an a priori knowledge of the service time [*see* Kobayashi (1974)]. The method consists of modeling the number of jobs in the network, or in a service center, as a continuous-time stochastic process rather than as a discrete-time one [*see*, for instance, Newell (1971)]. The probability density function of this number, under certain assumptions, satisfies a diffusion equation. This equation may be solved in certain cases in which the original discrete-time process gives rise to currently unsurmountable mathematical difficulties. Sometimes, even the transient solution of the model can be determined.

Another approach to the approximate solution of complex queuing networks is based on the idea of *decomposition*. As in the other fields where decomposition is used, this method consists of partitioning the network into subnetworks, studying each subnetwork separately, replacing it by an approximate model (for instance, by a single service center), and analyzing the simplified network. Thus, decomposing a network model is like transforming it into a hierarchy of models to be solved successively. A decomposition method for queuing networks and the criteria to be followed in its application are described in Courtois (1971).

4.3.5 Closed-Network Models

A typical application of closed queuing networks can be found in the modeling of multiprogramming systems in which the degree of multiprogramming N is constant or whose behavior is to be analyzed for several given values of N. The former is the case of those systems having a fixed number of primary-memory regions which, because of the heavy-work-load assumption, are characterized by a very low probability of being empty. The service centers of a closed network modeling a system with a constant value of N represent those resources which a job accesses while being in primary memory. These resources are usually the CPU (or CPU's) and the channels which control secondary-memory devices. Other centers, representing, for instance, I/O peripherals, may be added externally, so as to obtain a more complex network. This network then incorporates a subnetwork whose total number of jobs is kept constant by a control mechanism. An example of such a network is the model of the Multics system analyzed by Sekino (1973).

The first type of closed network to be studied in this section is a *central-server model*. This model was analyzed by Buzen (1971) using the approach to the solution of exponential closed networks proposed by Gordon and Newell (1967).

Example 4.9 The system to be modeled is the EXOPE system we considered in Example 4.8. However, we want to analyze its performance assuming a constant degree of multiprogramming. Thus, only the processors P_1, P_2, and P_3 in Fig. 1.2, which are those accessed by the jobs loaded in primary memory, will be explicitly represented in our model.

A three-service-center central-server model is shown in Fig. 4.18. Each center contains one server and one queue. The central server, Σ_1, represents the CPU, and the others, Σ_2 and Σ_3, the drum and the disk processor, respectively. The feedback path around the central server has a totally different meaning from the one in the preemptive model in Fig. 4.14. All service disciplines in a central-server model are nonpreemptive. The feedback path is taken by those jobs which have been processed to completion and leave the system. To keep N constant, every departing job is immediately replaced by an arriving one, which joins the CPU queue Q_1. Since all jobs in the model are statistically identical, this control mechanism may be implemented by the feedback path in Fig. 4.18 along which a job leaving the system immediately reenters it. The presence of the feedback path allows both the throughput rate and the response time to be easily defined.

As in Example 4.8, we assume that the service times are exponentially distributed at all centers and that the probabilities of reaching other centers at the completion of service

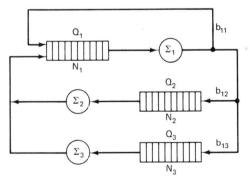

Figure 4.18 Closed-network, central-server model of the EXOPE system in Fig. 1.2.

at a center are constant and equal for all jobs. The mean service rates at all centers are also assumed to be constant. These assumptions can be relaxed somewhat without impairing the solvability of the model [*see*, for example, Gordon and Newell (1967) and Baskett et al. (1975)]. We have made them more restrictive to simplify our discussion. Table 4.9 summarizes the parameters of the model in Fig. 4.18. The value of b_{11}, the probability that a job takes the feedback path around the central server, may be derived from those of b_{12} and b_{13}, since $\sum_{i=1}^{3} b_{1i} = 1$.

Table 4.9
PARAMETERS OF THE CENTRAL-SERVER MODEL IN FIG. 4.18

Parameter name	Symbol	Value
Mean uninterrupted CPU time	$1/\mu_1$	10 ms
Mean drum service time	$1/\mu_2$	25 ms
Mean disk service time	$1/\mu_3$	100 ms
Drum request probability	b_{12}	0.8
Disk request probability	b_{13}	0.1
Degree of multiprogramming	N	3

As usual, the state of a queuing network with s service centers is defined by the vector $\mathbf{N} = (N_1, N_2, \ldots, N_s)$, where N_i is the number of jobs in service center i. We shall first solve an arbitrary closed network with s exponential service centers and N jobs. Then the general results will be applied to the particular case of a central-server model.

Since we have

$$\sum_{i=1}^{s} N_i = N, \tag{4.89}$$

and N is constant, the number of distinguishable states is equal to the number of partitions of the N jobs among the s centers, i.e.,

$$\binom{N + s - 1}{s - 1}.$$

If the Markov process characterized by these states is irreducible, that is, if each state is reachable from any other state with nonzero probability, then an equilibrium state probability distribution exists (*see* Section 4.3.1). Gordon and Newell (1967) obtained this distribution by imposing that, at the equilibrium, the rate of transitions from state $\mathbf{N}$ to other states equals the rate of transitions from other states to $\mathbf{N}$. Let us introduce the binary function

$$a(N_i) = 0 \quad \text{for } N_i = 0,$$

$$= 1 \quad \text{for } N_i > 0. \tag{4.90}$$

For each distinct state $\mathbf{N}$, we can write an equilibrium equation which is called the *balance equation* for state $\mathbf{N}$:

$$\left[\sum_{k=1}^{s} a(N_k)\mu_k \right] p(\mathbf{N}) = \sum_{i=1}^{s} \sum_{k=1}^{s} a(N_k)a(N_i + 1)\mu_i b_{ik} p(N_1, \ldots, N_k - 1, \ldots, N_i + 1, \ldots, N_s).$$

$$\tag{4.91}$$

One of the equations (4.91) is dependent on the others. However, the solution can be obtained by supplementing the balance equations (4.91) with the usual condition

$$\sum_{\text{all } N} p(\mathbf{N}) = 1. \tag{4.92}$$

The right-hand side of (4.91) represents the rate at which state $\mathbf{N}$ is reached from other states due to the completion of service to a job in service center i followed by its joining the queue of jobs at center k. The presence of the term $a(N_k)$ is needed since this transition cannot be taken into account if in $\mathbf{N}$ we have $N_k = 0$.

Equations (4.91) and (4.92) can be solved by separation of variables. Let

$$p(\mathbf{N}) = C(N)x_1^{N_1}x_2^{N_2}\ldots x_s^{N_s}, \tag{4.93}$$

where $C(N)$ is a coefficient whose value may vary with N. Substituting (4.93) into (4.91) and observing that $a(N_i + 1) = 1$ for all i, we have

$$\sum_{k=1}^{s}\left[a(N_k)\left(\mu_k - \sum_{i=1}^{s}\mu_i b_{ik}\frac{x_i}{x_k}\right)\right] = 0. \tag{4.94}$$

Since (4.94) must be valid also in those states in which all jobs are in the same service center, all coefficients of the $a(N_k)$ must be equal to zero at the equilibrium. Thus,

$$\mu_k x_k = \sum_{i=1}^{s}\mu_i x_i b_{ik} \qquad (k = 1, 2, \ldots, s). \tag{4.95}$$

Let us now consider a central-server model with s servers and N jobs. In such a model, we have $b_{ik} = 0$ for $i \neq 1$ and $k \neq 1$. Hence, the equations (4.95) for $k \neq 1$ are of the type

$$\mu_k x_k = \mu_1 x_1 b_{1k} \qquad (k = 2, \ldots, s). \tag{4.96}$$

If we define

$$y_k = \frac{\mu_1}{\mu_k}b_{1k} \qquad (k = 2, \ldots, s), \tag{4.97}$$

we may rewrite (4.96) as

$$x_k = y_k x_1 \qquad (k = 2, \ldots, s), \tag{4.98}$$

and (4.93) becomes

$$p(\mathbf{N}) = C(N)x_1^N y_2^{N_2} \cdots y_s^{N_s}. \tag{4.99}$$

Substituting (4.99) into (4.92), we obtain

$$C(N) = \left(x_1^N \sum_{\text{all } N}\prod_{k=2}^{s} y_k^{N_k}\right)^{-1}. \tag{4.100}$$

Thus, if we define

$$G(N) = \sum_{\text{all } N}\prod_{k=2}^{s} y_k^{N_k}, \tag{4.101}$$

the equilibrium state probabilities (4.99) of a central-server model are given by

$$p(\mathbf{N}) = \frac{1}{G(N)} \prod_{k=2}^{s} y_k^{N_k} \tag{4.102}$$

When these probabilities are known, we can calculate the performance indices we are most interested in. The mean throughput rate at the equilibrium is equal to b_{11} multiplied by the output rate of the central server. This output rate coincides with μ_1 when the central server is busy $(N_1 > 0)$ and equals zero when it is idle. Thus, remembering the definition of the CPU utilization ρ_1, we have

$$\bar{T} = b_{11}\mu_1 \sum_{\substack{\text{all } \mathbf{N} \\ \text{with } N_1 > 0}} p(\mathbf{N}) = b_{11}\mu_1\rho_1. \tag{4.103}$$

If we cut the feedback path around the central server but keep controlling the degree of multiprogramming as in the closed-network model, the value of $\bar{T}$ given by (4.103) equals the one of the mean job arrival rate. Applying Little's result (4.41), we obtain for the mean response or turnaround time the expression

$$\bar{i} = \frac{N}{\bar{T}}. \tag{4.104}$$

The expression of ρ_1 used in (4.103) can be transformed into one which, as we shall see below, is easier to compute. We observe that the exponents N_k appearing in (4.101) are all possible values of the number of jobs in service center k. This number is comprised between 0 (in those states in which center k is empty) and N (in that state in which all of the centers but k are empty). If only the states with $N_1 > 0$ are considered, the latter case $(N_k = N)$ can never occur; since the minimum value of N_1 is 1, N_k can at most equal $N - 1$. Thus, we have

$$\sum_{\substack{\text{all } \mathbf{N} \\ \text{with } N_1 > 0}} \prod_{k=2}^{s} y_k^{N_k} = G(N - 1), \tag{4.105}$$

and, by (4.103) and (4.102),

$$\rho_1 = \frac{G(N - 1)}{G(N)}. \tag{4.106}$$

The utilization of service center i $(i = 2, \ldots, s)$ is

$$\rho_i = \sum_{\substack{\text{all } \mathbf{N} \\ \text{with } N_i > 0}} p(\mathbf{N}) = \frac{y_i G(N - 1)}{G(N)} = y_i\rho_1. \tag{4.107}$$

Note that (4.107) can also be obtained by equating the mean job input rate of service center i to its mean job output rate and recalling definition (4.97):

$$b_{1i}\mu_1\rho_1 = \mu_i\rho_i. \tag{4.108}$$

Let us apply these results to our three-server model with $N = 3$. In this case, the model has 10 states. Its state-transition-rate diagram is shown in Fig. 4.19. The diagram has been constructed by observing that the rate at which jobs go from center 1 to center 2

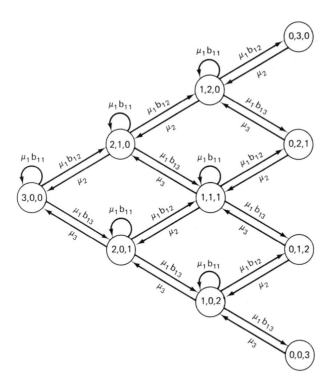

Figure 4.19 State-transition-rate diagram for the central-server model in Fig. 4.18 with $N = 3$. Each node contains the values of N_1, N_2, N_3 corresponding to the state it represents.

is $\mu_1 b_{12}$ and that the rate of transitions from 2 to 1 is μ_2. Similarly, the transitions from 1 to 3 and from 3 to 1 occur with rates $\mu_1 b_{13}$ and μ_3, respectively.

The balance equation for state $(3, 0, 0)$ can be written by inspection of the diagram in Fig. 4.19 as

$$(\mu_1 b_{11} + \mu_1 b_{12} + \mu_1 b_{13})p(3, 0, 0) = \mu_1 b_{11}p(3, 0, 0) + \mu_2 p(2, 1, 0) + \mu_3 p(2, 0, 1). \quad (4.109)$$

Note that the left-hand side of (4.109) is identically equal to $\mu_1 p(3, 0, 0)$, as we would have directly written if we had applied (4.91).

To calculate ρ_1, whose value is needed in order to derive the utilizations of the other service centers, as well as $\bar{T}$ and $\bar{\imath}$, we must, by (4.106), compute $G(N)$ and $G(N-1)$. From (4.101), we have

$$G(2) = 1 + y_2 + y_3 + y_2^2 + y_2 y_3 + y_3^2,$$
$$G(3) = G(2) + y_2^3 + y_2^2 y_3 + y_2 y_3^2 + y_3^3. \quad (4.110)$$

Note that $G(2)$ in (4.110) has been written considering only those states in Fig. 4.19 for which $N_1 > 0$. State $(3, 0, 0)$, for instance, contributes the term $y_2^0 y_3^0 = 1$ to both $G(2)$ and $G(3)$.

The parameter values listed in Table 4.9 yield [*see* (4.37)] $y_2 = 2$ and $y_3 = 1$. Thus, from (4.110), we obtain $G(2) = 11$ and $G(3) = 26$. Equation (4.106) yields $\rho_1 = 0.423$.

Table 4.10

ALGORITHM FOR THE EQUILIBRIUM SOLUTION OF A CENTRAL-
SERVER MODEL WITH $s = 3$

(a)

N	Y_1	Y_2	Y_3
0	1	1	1
1	1	$1 + y_2$	$1 + y_2 + y_3$
2	1	$1 + y_2(1 + y_2)$	$1 + y_2(1 + y_2) + y_3(1 + y_2 + y_3)$
3	1	$1 + y_2[1 + y_2(1 + y_2)]$	$1 + y_2[1 + y_2(1 + y_2)] + y_3[1 + y_2(1 + y_2) + y_3(1 + y_2 + y_3)]$
⋮	⋮	⋮	⋮

(b)

$$y_1 = \frac{\rho_1}{\rho_1} = 1 \qquad y_2 = \frac{\rho_2}{\rho_1} = 2 \qquad y_3 = \frac{\rho_3}{\rho_1} = 1$$

N	Y_1	Y_2	$Y_3 = G$	ρ_1
0	1	1	1	0
1	1	3	4	0.25
2	1	7	11	0.363
3	1	15	26	0.423
4	1	31	57	0.456
5	1	63	120	0.475
6	1	127	247	0.496
⋮	⋮	⋮	⋮	⋮

By (4.107), we have $\rho_2 = 0.846$ and $\rho_3 = 0.423$. Finally, the mean throughput rate given by (4.103) is $\bar{T} = 4.23$ jobs/s, and the mean response time given by (4.104) is $\bar{t} = 0.709$ s.

A computationally efficient algorithm for calculating $G(N)$ has been proposed by Buzen (1973). We define the two functions $Y_2(N)$ and $Y_3(N)$ recursively as follows:

$$Y_2(0) = 1,$$

$$Y_3(0) = 1,$$

$$Y_2(N) = 1 + y_2 Y_2(N - 1),$$

$$Y_3(N) = Y_2(N) + y_3 Y_3(N - 1) \qquad (N = 1, 2, \ldots).$$

(4.111)

The reader can easily verify that, for all N, $Y_3(N) = G(N)$. Thus, the computation of $G(N)$ can be organized as in Table 4.10(a). Each entry in columns Y_2 and Y_3 is obtained by multiplying the entry immediately above it by y_2 or y_3, respectively, and adding the entry immediately to its left on the same row. For example, $Y_3(3) = Y_2(3) + y_3 Y_3(2)$, as dictated by (4.111). Table 4.10(b) shows the results of the execution of the algorithm for the parameter values in Table 4.9.

This algorithm can be used to solve central-server models with any number of servers. The recursive definitions (4.111) may be generalized as follows:

$$Y_i(0) = 1,$$

$$Y_1(N) = 1, \qquad\qquad\qquad\qquad (4.112)$$

$$Y_i(N) = Y_{i-1}(N) + y_i Y_i(N-1) \qquad (N = 1, 2, \ldots; i = 2, \ldots, s),$$

and we always have

$$G(N) = Y_s(N). \qquad\qquad\qquad\qquad (4.113)$$

Note that the numbering of the service centers has no influence on the result, the only exception being the central server, which must be assigned number 1. It is easy to see in (4.101) that function $G(N)$ is symmetric with respect to y_2 and y_3. ∎

The mean-value model analyzed in Section 4.2.3 can be thought of as having been derived from a central-server model with two service centers. Equation (4.8) is equivalent to (4.108), since the mean output rates of the CPU and drum service centers are $\mu_1\rho_1$ and $\mu_2\rho_2$, respectively, and the probability of a CPU-to-drum transition is $b_{12} = n_{dr}/(1 + n_{dr})$. Similarly, (4.9) is equivalent to (4.103), as in a two-service-center model $b_{11} = 1/(1 + n_{dr})$. The method given in Example 4.2 for solving the mean-value model assumes that the CPU and drum processing rates are known as functions of the mean number of jobs in the corresponding service centers. The analysis performed in Example 4.9 provides us with a way to compute $\rho_1(N)$ and $\rho_2(N)$ from such system and work-load parameters as μ_1 [which is given by $(n_{dr} + 1)/t_{cpu}$; *see* (4.10)], μ_2 [given by s/R_{dr}; *see* (4.12)], and b_{12} [which is $n_{dr}/(1 + n_{dr})$].

If we apply this analysis to a two-service-center central-server model with the parameter values in Table 4.5, we have $\rho_1 = 0.878$, $\rho_2 = 0.702$, and $\bar{T} = 3.512$ jobs/s. The discrepancies between these results and those found in Example 4.2 must be attributed to the use in that example of a curve for the drum rate $\bar{f}_2(\bar{N}_2)$ which differs from the one implied by the central-server model and to the fact that service times at the two servers are assumed to be constant.

The evaluation of the performance of interactive systems by analytic techniques is another important application of closed-network models. In an interactive system with N active terminals there are exactly N jobs. An any given time, N_s of these jobs are "in the system," and the corresponding N_s users are waiting for a response at their terminals. The remaining $N_t = N - N_s$ jobs are "at the terminals," and the system cannot resume its work on each of them until it receives an input message from the corresponding terminal (*see* Fig. 1.4). Thus, the user community can be represented by a server with N parallel and independent channels and no queues. Each channel models an individual user.

We shall now discuss a simple closed-network model of an interactive installation, which has been analyzed by Kleinrock (1968).

Example 4.10   The simplest closed-network model of an interactive installation is one which represents the whole system by a single service center. If the system is time-shared, the service discipline at the center should be quantum-oriented. To simplify the solution of the model, we shall choose the processor-sharing discipline (*see* Section 4.3.3) and assume that all jobs are statistically identical. The model is shown in Fig. 4.20, and its parameters are listed in Table 4.11.

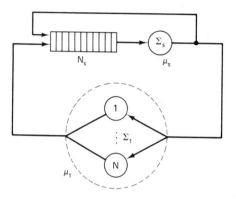

Figure 4.20   Closed-network model of an interactive installation.

Table 4.11

PARAMETERS OF THE CLOSED-NETWORK MODEL OF AN
INTERACTIVE SYSTEM IN FIG. 4.20

Parameter name	Symbol	Value
Mean system service time (mean uniprogramming execution time)	$1/\mu_s$	0.5 s
Mean terminal (or "think") time	$1/\mu_t = \bar{t}_t$	10 s
Number of active terminals (users)	N	10

Most of the remarks made in Example 4.7 apply also to the use of this model in the evaluation of an interactive system. In particular, the model assumes that the system is multiprogrammed, that swapping times can be ignored, and that the time quantum is very short with respect to the mean service time.

If both system service times and terminal times are exponentially distributed, the stochastic process $N_s(t)$ is a finite continuous-time Markov chain. The chain is finite since $0 \leq N_s(t) \leq N$. Its state-transition-rate diagram reported in Fig. 4.21 shows that the Markov chain is in fact a birth-death process (*see* Section 4.3.2).

The mean rates in Fig. 4.21 can be derived as follows. Let the model be in state N_s at time t. Each one of the N_s jobs in server Σ_s is processed at a speed equal to $1/N_s$ of the server's speed. The probability that service to any one job is completed during a very short

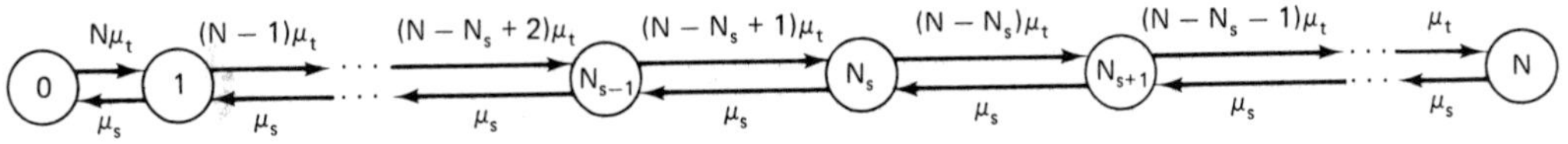

$$N\mu_t \quad (N-1)\mu_t \quad (N-N_s+2)\mu_t \quad (N-N_s+1)\mu_t \quad (N-N_s)\mu_t \quad (N-N_s-1)\mu_t \quad \mu_t$$

0 1 $\cdots$ N_{s-1} N_s N_{s+1} $\cdots$ N

$$\mu_s \qquad \mu_s \qquad \mu_s \qquad \mu_s \qquad \mu_s \qquad \mu_s \qquad \mu_s$$

Figure 4.21 State-transition-rate diagram for the closed-network model in Fig. 4.20.

interval $(t, t + h)$ is $N_s(\mu_s/N_s)h$, and the corresponding mean completion rate is μ_s. Since each channel in Σ_t has the same mean service rate μ_t, and since $N - N_s$ of the channels are busy in state N_s, the mean arrival rate to the system service center is $(N - N_s)\mu_t$.

The distribution of terminal (or "think") times measured by Scherr (1967) in the CTSS installation at M.I.T. looks like an exponential one for times larger than 10 s but differs substantially from it for shorter times. Its mean is 35.2 s, its median is 11 s, and its coefficient of variation is 0.65. Bryan (1967) and Parupudi and Winograd (1972) found mean think times between 10 and 25 s.

The balance equations may be derived immediately from the diagram in Fig. 4.21:

$$p_0 N\mu_t = p_1 \mu_s,$$

$$p_{N_s}[(N - N_s)\mu_t + \mu_s] = p_{N_s-1}(N - N_s + 1)\mu_t + p_{N_s+1}\mu_s \qquad (N_s = 1, \ldots, N-1),$$

$$p_{N-1}\mu_t = p_N\mu_s. \tag{4.114}$$

The reader can easily verify that (4.114) may be written in the following simpler and more compact form:

$$p_{N_s}(N - N_s)\mu_t = p_{N_s+1}\mu_s \qquad (N_s = 0, 1, \ldots, N-1). \tag{4.115}$$

One of the N equations (4.115) is dependent on the other $N - 1$. By appropriate substitutions, we can express all state probabilities in terms of p_0:

$$p_{N_s} = p_{N_s-1}(N - N_s + 1)\frac{\mu_t}{\mu_s} = p_{N_s-2}(N - N_s + 1)(N - N_s + 2)\left(\frac{\mu_t}{\mu_s}\right)^2$$

$$= \cdots = p_0 \frac{N!}{(N - N_s)!}\left(\frac{\mu_t}{\mu_s}\right)^{N_s} \qquad (N_s = 0, 1, \ldots, N). \tag{4.116}$$

The equilibrium probability that the system is idle, p_0, is obtained by imposing the condition

$$\sum_{N_s=0}^{N} p_{N_s} = p_0 \sum_{N_s=0}^{N} \frac{N!}{(N - N_s)!}\left(\frac{\mu_t}{\mu_s}\right)^{N_s} = 1. \tag{4.117}$$

From (4.117) we obtain the utilization of the system, $\rho_s = 1 - p_0$. The mean throughput rate of the system's model coincides with the output rate of Σ_s:

$$\bar{T} = \mu_s \rho_s. \tag{4.118}$$

Each one of those users whose jobs are at the terminals generates μ_t requests per unit time. The probability that a job is at the terminals is given by $(1/\mu_t)/(\bar{t} + 1/\mu_t)$, where $\bar{t}$ is the mean time in Σ_s and $\bar{t} + 1/\mu_t$ is the mean duration of an interaction. Thus, the mean arrival rate at Σ_s is

$$\lambda = N\mu_t \frac{1/\mu_t}{\bar{t} + 1/\mu_t} = \frac{N}{\bar{t} + \bar{t}_t}, \tag{4.119}$$

where $\bar{t}_t = 1/\mu_t$.

At the equilibrium, λ must be equal to $\bar{T}$. From (4.118) and (4.119), we have

$$\bar{t} = \frac{N}{\mu_s \rho_s} - \bar{t}_t.$$ (4.120)

For the parameter values in Table 4.11, we have $p_0 = 0.538$, $\rho_s = 0.462$, $\bar{T} = 0.924$ jobs/s, and $\bar{t} = 0.822$ s.

One of the most frequent questions asked about an interactive system refers to the maximum number of terminals the system can support. As formulated in the previous sentence, the question is meaningless for two reasons: First, a precise definition of what is meant by *support* must be given; second, the work load generated by the terminals must be adequately specified. Within the context of our model, we shall say that an interactive system is able to support N terminals, all generating statistically identical jobs characterized by exponential distributions of system and terminal times with parameters μ_s and μ_t if the mean response time $\bar{t}$ is less than a given maximum value $\bar{t}_{max}$. Note that in fact both μ_s and, to some extent, μ_t depend also on system parameters. However, since these system parameters are assumed to be constant, we can think of μ_s and μ_t as being work-load parameters only.

If we plot the function $\bar{t}(N)$ for our model with the parameter values given in Table 4.11, we obtain the curve in Fig. 4.22. Beyond a certain number of terminals, the mean response time increases much more sharply than for lower values of N, tending asymptotically toward a straight line with positive slope. Following Kleinrock (1968), we define point $(N^*, \bar{t}^*)$, where this asymptote intersects the horizontal line $\bar{t} = \bar{t}(1)$, as the system's *saturation point*.

A well-designed system should not have a processing speed, to which μ_s is proportional, so high that $\bar{t}^*$ is substantially smaller than $\bar{t}_{max}$. Thus, the value of N^* defined above is a reasonable estimate of the maximum number of terminals the system can support.

The value of $\bar{t}^* = \bar{t}(1)$ is, of course, $1/\mu_s$. The equation of the asymptote for the $\bar{t}(N)$ curve is obtained by observing that when $N \to \infty$, we have $p_0 \to 0$ and $\rho_s \to 1$. Thus, (4.120) yields, for $N \gg N^*$,

$$\bar{t} \cong \frac{N}{\mu_s} - \bar{t}_t,$$ (4.121)

and, by the definition of N^*, we have

$$N^* = 1 + \frac{\mu_s}{\mu_t}.$$ (4.122)

In our model, $N^* = 21$ terminals.

For $N \ll N^*$, the $\bar{t}(N)$ curve may be approximated by

$$\bar{t} \cong \frac{1}{\mu_s} \frac{1}{1 - (N - 1)(\mu_t/\mu_s)},$$ (4.123)

which is obtained from (4.117), (4.120), and the condition $(N - 1)\mu_t/\mu_s \ll 1$, derived from (4.122). The dotted curve in Fig. 4.22 represents function (4.123).   ∎

The model discussed in Example 4.10 can also be applied to the evaluation of multiprogramming systems with constant degree of multiprogramming N and a

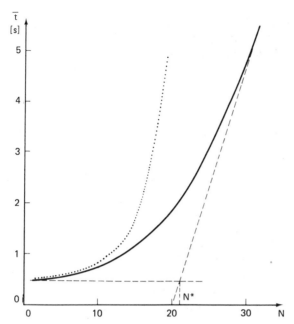

Figure 4.22   Mean response time of the model in Fig. 4.20 and Table 4.11 vs. the number of active terminals.

number of I/O channels (or of independent paths to the I/O devices) much larger than N. If the latter assumption is satisfied, the probability that a job requests an I/O server which is servicing another job is very low. Thus, queuing for I/O servers may be ignored, and the system can be modeled as in Fig. 4.20. However, Σ_t now represents N parallel and identical I/O servers, and Σ_s the CPU. The network is no longer a model of an installation but represents a system. If the system is time-shared, we may choose the PS discipline for the CPU service center, as we did in Example 4.10 for the system service center.

The user community may be explicitly modeled by adding either an external source (open network) or another loop containing a service center such as Σ_t in Fig. 4.20 (closed network). In both cases, if the presence of a control mechanism which keeps the degree of multiprogramming constant is postulated, the solution of the model does not depend on the characteristics of the sources or of the additional service center. However, the addition of a model for the user community allows us to define and compute such indices as $\bar{i}$ and $\bar{T}$. Note that the degree of multiprogramming can be kept constant only if a queue of jobs waiting for memory is added to the model and if the user community is so active that this queue is never found to be empty when a job leaves the system's model.

Boyse and Warn (1975) have used this model to evaluate an interactive, multiprogramming, virtual-memory system supporting a number N_u of graphic terminals. In that system, N_{max} is 3, there are 11 paths to the I/O devices, and most of the I/O traffic is due to paging. Thus, the assumption of identical I/O servers with no queuing is not too unrealistic. The restriction, imposed by the model, that I/O requests cannot be overlapped with the computations needed by the same job is reasonable for page fetches but not for page stores (which are, therefore, ignored).

With exponential service times at both servers, the utilization of the CPU can be computed from (4.117). If b is the probability that a job leaving the CPU service center will also leave the system, the mean throughput rate is given by $\bar{T} = b\mu_s\rho_s$, and the mean response time is $\bar{t} = (N_u/\bar{T}) - \bar{t}_u$. Note that now μ_s and ρ_s are the mean service rate and the utilization of the CPU; N_u is the number of terminals, and $\bar{t}_u$ the mean time a job spends at the terminal.

A similar model has been used by Sekino (1973) for the Multics multi-processor virtual-memory system. Sekino's model is a closed network containing two loops. The internal loop consists of two service centers. The CPU service center contains one queue for the ready jobs and a multiple-channel server. Each channel models a CPU. The other center consists of a queue and of a single server representing the paging device. The number of jobs in the internal loop is assumed to be constant. The external loop contains a service center with a server such as Σ_t in Fig. 4.20, representing the user terminals. This center is followed by a queue in which the jobs arriving at the system wait until they are loaded into primary memory.

4.4 ANALYTIC MODEL CALIBRATION AND VALIDATION

The discussion, made in Section 3.3.1, of the accuracy of a model and of its calibration and validation is applicable to analytic as well as simulation models. In particular, the accuracy of an analytic model can be defined as in Fig. 3.16. Assuming that the values of the system's performance indices $\mathcal{P}$ are not affected by appreciable errors, the three types of inaccuracies listed in Section 3.3.1 are the major ones which may cause the values $\mathcal{P}'$ produced by an analytic model to differ from $\mathcal{P}$.

Formulation inaccuracies are generally to be attributed to an excessively low degree of detail or to the too drastic approximations needed to make the model solvable.

Solution inaccuracies in symbolic solutions may be caused by mistakes in mathematical manipulation or by the approximation methods employed. Examples of the latter type of inaccuracies are those resulting from the use of the diffusion approximation to solve queuing models. When an analytic model is solved numerically, solution inaccuracies are usually to be attributed to the numerical methods applied. For instance, with iterative methods, the accuracy of the solution is generally related to the number of iterations performed.

Finally, *parameter inaccuracies* may affect the estimates of model parameter values and distributions—hence the values of $\mathcal{P}'$. Even though all model parameters can be measured if the modeled system is available, it may be useful in certain cases to determine some of them by trying to fit the calculated to the measured performance. For instance, the values of the b_{ij}'s in the models in Figs. 4.16 and 4.18 could be determined in this way.

The empirical estimation of work-load parameters and of their distributions should be performed using the statistical techniques described in Sections 2.4.3, 2.6, and 2.7, as well as those employed in the papers by Fuchs and Jackson (1970), Anderson and Sargent (1972), and Lewis and Yue (1972). Statistical tests for the goodness of fit of empirical to analytic distributions are described in various books on statistical methods [for example, Snedecor and Cochran (1967)].

These tests are not needed to calibrate deterministic models, which are not based on distributional assumptions. However, the same methods for the empirical estimation of the numerical values of parameters may be used for deterministic and for queuing models.

Calibration and validation are mostly concerned with formulation inaccuracies, which they try to identify and whose causes they try to remove. However, all of the three types of inaccuracies may be present in the procedure illustrated in Fig. 3.16. Before a calibration procedure is applied, the investigator should make an effort to separate the solution and parameter inaccuracies from those due to the formulation of the model.

Solution inaccuracies can often be detected if an alternative method of solution for the model is available. With analytic models, one such method always exists: The model (*not* the system) may be simulated, and its results compared with those obtained from the analytic solution. Conversely, if the model is a simulator, it may be possible to find a solvable analytic model which is not too dissimilar from it and to use its results to verify the accuracy of some simulation experiments. A simple example of this procedure is given in Fig. 3.18.

Measurement, or the simulation of the system (*not* of the model) if the system to be evaluated is not available, is necessary in the calibration of an analytic model. If simulation is used, the simulator should be valid at least under the conditions corresponding to the parameter values selected for the calibration procedure. The reader should always keep in mind that simulation, not validated by measurement, is not sufficient to guarantee the validity of an analytic model.

In general, there are no explicit calibration parameters in queuing models. Among the few exceptions, we can mention the correction introduced by Scherr (1967) into his model to take the effect of swapping into account. No explicit calibration parameters are present in the examples of deterministic models described in Section 4.2, but some of the model parameters could easily be interpreted and used as calibration parameters.

Validation has been defined as a set of operations intended to make the domain of validity of a model as wide as required by the model's applications. No validation procedures for analytic models are known at the present time. As for simulators, the domain of validity of an analytic model can be to some extent influenced by carefully choosing the calibration conditions. So far, in the history of queuing models for computer systems, only a few have been experimentally validated. One of the most comprehensive comparisons of analytic results with measurement and simulation results is the one performed by Scherr (1967). His model of the CTSS time-sharing system is a cyclic queuing system like the one in Fig. 4.20. Besides the unrealistic distributional assumptions, dictated by the requirement of solvability in symbolic form, the model does not represent swapping (except for a constant swapping and overhead time added to service times), the finite and different quanta (the PS discipline is assumed), or the scheduling policy (an FB_9 policy with multiple entries to the queues, based on memory space demand, with time-variant priorities and a complex preemption mechanism). Nevertheless, the analytic results obtained by Scherr are definitely closer than one would have expected to the measurement or simulation data. Chapter 4 of Scherr (1967) compares graphically the analytic, simulation, and measured values of the following indices: the ratio of the mean response time to the mean CPU time per interaction vs. the mean number of interacting users; the response function of the system; the probability density function of response time; the utilization of the CPU vs. the mean number of interacting users; and the utilizations of the disk and of the drum for swapping purposes vs. the mean number of interacting users.

Scherr's results, as well as those published by a few other authors [see Muntz (1975)], seem to indicate that even very crude models of interactive systems can provide reasonable accuracy and a relatively large domain of validity, at least if one considers as acceptable the errors which affected those results. An analytic model of a noninteractive system from which the same conclusions may be drawn is described in Hughes and Moe (1973) (see Examples 7.9 and 7.13).

One of the most controversial aspects of probabilistic model formulation is the choice of the distributions of model parameters. In spite of the substantial progress made in the area of queuing models, this choice is in most models still limited to a few types of distributions if a symbolic solution is desired. What influence does this choice have on the values of the performance indices produced by a given model? For instance, what is the effect of replacing all the actual distributions of service times in a queuing network with exponential distributions?

A particular answer for a specific nonpreemptive single-service-center model can be found in Figs. 4.10 and 4.11, where the impact of the coefficient of variation of the service-time distribution on the mean response time can be observed. The reader will verify that $\bar{t}$ increases substantially with the variability of service times, represented by their coefficient of variation c.

This result is confirmed by an analytic and simulation study performed by Boyse and Warn (1975) on the closed-network model in Fig. 4.20. A diagram of the utilization ρ_s of Σ_s (the CPU server) as a function of the coefficient of variation of CPU service times is shown in Fig. 4.23. Note that the points corresponding to an Erlang-2 and to a hyperexponential distribution were each obtained from only one of the many distributions having the same coefficient of variation. The maximum difference between the values of ρ_s plotted in Fig. 4.23 is less than 15% for values of c in the range $(0, 1.8)$.

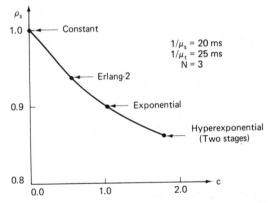

Figure 4.23 Sensitivity of the utilization ρ_s to the coefficient of variation c of service times at service center Σ_s in the model in Fig. 4.20. [*Source*: Boyse and Warn (1975), by permission of ACM, Inc.]

Thus, the distributions of service times affect the values of performance indices predicted by a model. The quantitative amount of this influence depends on the type of model and on the values of the parameters. Replacing the actual distributions with ones having a smaller coefficient of variation tends to produce optimistic results. The results tend to be pessimistic when the distributions assumed in the model have a c larger than the actual ones.

Sensitivity studies like the one just mentioned are extremely important for computer systems evaluators and, in general, for those persons interested in applying analytic models. Unfortunately, so far only a few models have been analyzed from this viewpoint.

PROBLEMS

4.1. Formulate a deterministic model of the EXOPE multiprogramming system analyzed in Example 4.9. Using the data in Table 4.9, calculate the values of the mean response time and mean throughput rate of your model, and compare them with the values obtained in Example 4.9 from the queuing model in Fig. 4.18.

4.2. In a uniprogramming time-sharing system a process is swapped into primary memory completely before its execution is started and is swapped out when it terminates or when its time quantum expires. The CPU remains idle when the process issues a disk request. Swapping may be overlapped with computation and takes place between primary memory and a drum. Construct a deterministic model of the system to calculate the mean response time. Assume that the average process has the characteristics in Table 4.9 and that its mean swapping time is 10 ms. Specify all the assumptions you make, and discuss their importance and realism.

4.3. A CPU can make one reference to memory every 100 ns. The primary memory consists of four modules interleaved four ways, so that references to consecutive addresses are in fact made to consecutive modules. The modules are semiconductor memories with a read time of 400 ns and a write time equal to the read time. Each module can be independently accessed, and its cycle is staggered by 100 ns with respect to the cycle of the preceding module. Thus, the maximum memory band-width (transfer rate) is equal to 10^7 words/s, that is, 1 word every 100 ns. Assume that the CPU issues references at its maximum rate and that if the previous reference was to module i ($i = 0, 1, 2, 3$), the probability that the next will be to module $(i + 1)$ mod 4 is $p_{i,(i+1)\bmod 4} = 0.55$. Also, the probabilities of referencing other modules are all equal to each other. Construct a Markov model of the CPU-memory system, and derive the actual memory bandwidth.

4.4. Analyze a nonpreemptive single-server model of an interactive system with Poisson arrivals ($\lambda = 2$ interactions/s) and a two-stage hyperexponential distribution for service times. The parameters of this distribution are [see (4.49)] $w_1 = 0.92$, $w_2 = 0.08$, $\mu_1 = 0.92\ s^{-1}$, and $\mu_2 = 0.051\ s^{-1}$. Write the equilibrium equations for the model, and solve them. Derive from (4.49) the expression of $\bar{i}$, given in (4.50). Show that the value of $\bar{i}$ is the same as the one computable from the results of the analysis of $M/G/1$ systems.

4.5. The mean waiting time of a job with service time t_s in an $M/G/1$ queuing model with SPTF discipline is

$$\overline{t_w(t_s)} = \frac{\lambda}{\mu^2\left[1 - \lambda\displaystyle\int_0^{t_s} x\, dF_{t_s}(x)\right]^2},$$

where $F_{t_s}(x)$ is the service-time distribution function. Plot the response function of this system assuming that $F_{t_s}(x)$ is exponential with mean $1/\mu$ and using the data in Table 4.7. Compare the SPTF response function with that of an $M/M/1$ system with FCFS scheduling and the same parameter values. Which one of the two policies would you prefer for an interactive system? What is the main drawback of this policy? How serious do you think this drawback is? Can you suggest a nonpreemptive service discipline which is likely to retain the respective advantages and to alleviate the respective drawbacks of FCFS and SPTF?

4.6. Construct a queuing model of the batch EXOPE system simulated in Example 3.2. Queuing models, like event charts, can be viewed as vehicles for describing computer systems. One of the purposes of these descriptions is to facilitate the formulation of simulators. Compare on the basis of the example mentioned above these two "languages" (queuing models and event charts) in terms of their descriptive power and, more specifically, of the convenience of their usage in simulator construction.

4.7. A memory system consists of eight noninterleaved modules, each having four ports. Requests for access come from four processors which are connected to the four independent ports of each module. Construct a model which allows you to calculate the mean transfer rate of the memory system assuming that the cycles of the modules are synchronous, each processor generates one request per memory cycle, the requests generated by each processor are independent and uniformly distributed over the modules, a priority rule is used to resolve conflicts at the entrance of each module, and rejected requests are repeated at the next cycle, until they are accepted.

4.8. Determine the influence of the quantum length q on the response function of a round-robin scheduler.

(a) Attack the problem at the symbolic level, keeping in mind that while q changes, the mean job service time remains constant.

(b) For the parameter values given in Table 4.7, draw the initial parts of the response functions corresponding to $q = 0.15$ s and $q = 0.6$ s, and compare them with curve (e) in Fig. 4.11. Which value of q favors short jobs the most?

(c) Is there, in your opinion, an optimum quantum length for the given work load? If so, how could you determine it?

4.9. Show how Jackson's approach to the analysis of open queuing networks can be extended to closed networks. For example, study the network in Fig. 4.18 by using Jackson's approach, and show that the results are the same as those obtained in Section 4.3.5 by applying Gordon and Newell's method.

4.10. In a 20-terminal interactive system, each terminal has its own dedicated CPU of the processor-on-a-chip type. All CPU's are connected to temporarily dedicated memory modules via a synchronous bus, whose bandwidth is 10 times the bandwidth of the CPU's and of each memory module. A control processor (of the same type as the CPU's) handles page faults, and another processor acts as the controller of a disk that transfers the pages requested by the CPU's to the appropriate memory modules via the bus. Disk transfers have higher priority on the bus than CPU accesses to memory. Formulate a queuing model of this system, discuss its solvability, and, assuming that the system exists, describe the experiments which should be performed in order to obtain the parameters and the distributions necessary to use the model. Discuss the reasonableness of the approximations you have made in the model formulation process.

4.11. Solve the model in Fig. 4.20 assuming that the system service center is managed according to a nonpreemptive discipline (for instance, FCFS). Note that the feedback path around Q_s and Σ_s is to be eliminated. Compare your results with those obtained in Example 4.10. Can you propose any application for your model?

4.12. A study is to be performed to compare the performances of uniprocessor and multiprocessor systems. For simplicity, the only performance measure to be considered is mean response (or turnaround) time, all distributions are assumed to be exponential, and scheduling is to be FCFS. The arrival rate λ is the same for both systems, and the service rate of each one of the n processors in the multiprocessing system is μ/n if μ is the service rate of the single multiprogrammed CPU.

(a) Determine the mean response time and the response function of the n-channel single-server single-service-center model adopted for the multiprocessor system.

(b) Compare the equations expressing $\bar{t}$ and $\overline{t(t_s)}$ for the two models being considered, and comment on what happens when λ changes or when μ changes.

(c) The analysis made has neglected system overhead. How would you expect your results to change if overhead could be taken into account?

4.13. Construct a queuing network model of the system described in Problem 4.2.

(a) Explain why this model would be a more accurate representation of the system if we could make the path followed by a job at its departure from a service center depend on where the job came from when it arrived at the center.

(b) Say whether and how you would be able to achieve the objective described in part a if you knew how to solve queuing networks with several classes of jobs, provided that a job could change class when moving to a new service center [*see* Baskett et al. (1975)].

4.14. How many terminals saturate an interactive system assuming that the mean terminal time is 20 s and that the mean CPU time demand of its users is 0.1 s? 0.5 s? 1 s? What is the value of the mean response time at the saturation point in these three cases?

4.15. Incorporate the model in Fig. 4.20 into an open-network model where jobs arriving from the source wait in a memory queue until their turn to join the CPU queue Q_s comes. The jobs leaving the CPU server Σ_s go to service center Σ_t, which represents N parallel, identical, and independent I/O devices, with probability b_{st}. When they leave the system (an event which occurs with probability $1 - b_{st}$), another job from the memory queue enters the CPU queue so as to keep the number N of jobs in the loop constant. Solve the model for its mean response time, assuming that the probability of an empty memory queue is negligible. Is it possible to consider the two-service-center loop as an N-channel server? Or as a single-channel server? Under what assumptions? Can you calculate the minimum λ required to make the probability that the memory queue is empty less than 0.05? Assume $b_{st} = 0.9$ and the parameter values in Table 4.11.

4.16. Replace each service center in the open-network model in Fig. 4.16 with a box representing a delay. Calculate these delays using the results obtained for the $M/M/1$ model and the parameter values in Table 4.8. Then compute the mean response time of the network of delays, and verify that its value equals the one obtained in Example 4.8.

5

Work-Load Characterization

5.1 INTRODUCTION

There is practically no computer system evaluation study in which the problem of characterizing the work load of the system does not arise. In many cases, work-load characterization is the hardest technical problem to solve for the investigator. To emphasize its importance, and our belief that its most fundamental conceptual aspects are common to all evaluation studies and techniques, we shall devote this chapter to a discussion of the work-load characterization problem.

The *work load* of a computer system has been defined in Section 1.2 as the set of all inputs (programs, data, commands) the system receives from its environment. This definition requires some clarifications and qualifications.

First, the composition of the work load depends on the choice of the system's boundaries made by the evaluators. A user job or process is normally thought of as being external to the system. Hence, it is a part of the work load. The modules of the operating system in charge of resource management are generally considered part of the system. Those system programs which do work for each individual user who requests their assistance (e.g., compilers, assemblers, editors, data base systems) constitute the "gray area," since their assignment to the system or to the work load depends on the study being performed. In any case, such an assignment is always desirable to clarify the ideas and objectives of the investigators and to avoid frequent mistakes.

Second, the above definition of work load is incomplete if the time frame being considered is not specified. We may, for instance, include in an installation's work load all of the inputs processed by the system in that installation during a day. This will be called a *daily work load*. Similarly, we can define *hourly, weekly, monthly*, and *yearly work loads*. We also have the *lifetime work load*, the set of all inputs received and processed by a system over all of its lifetime. The other types of work load listed above can be seen as samples from the lifetime work load. As the duration of the time period we consider decreases, further specifications become necessary due to the increasing importance of boundary conditions. For example, during a 1-min period some jobs are read into a batch-processing system, some jobs leave it, some make progress toward their completion, and some others wait on tape or disk. Which of these jobs should be included in the 1-min work load? The answer to this question depends on the particular study being performed. In most cases, only the resource demands totally or partially satisfied during the given period are to be included in the corresponding work load.

Third, the above definition of work load should not be interpreted as implying that the inputs received by a system from its environment are not influenced by the system's behavior. The user community of an installation is known to react quite appreciably and not very slowly to a number of system modifications, but so little of this knowledge is quantitative that these influences cannot be reliably predicted. Thus, the simplifying and simplistic assumption is usually made that the work load is insensitive to all changes in the system's performance. The assumption is made also in this book, unless explicitly stated otherwise. Of course, an evaluator should always keep in mind that this assumption is justified only by our present ignorance.

In any system evaluation study, we are confronted with the problem of deciding under what work load or work loads the performance of the system should be evaluated. Performance indices are meaningful only if the work load by which their values are produced is precisely specified. Even when a system running under its *production work load* is being measured, some control over the work load is to be exerted by selecting the times and the durations of measurement sessions. Experimenting in a *controlled environment*, or at least in an *observed environment*, is an essential condition for the experiments to be *reproducible*, that is, to have scientific value. Not controlling or observing the work load in a computer system experiment is like measuring the electrical conductivity of a material without paying attention to the temperature or trying to determine the relationship between pressure and temperature in a gas without considering the volume.

There are two work-load-related operations to be performed during the planning phase of an evaluation study. One is the *specification* of the type of work load which is to drive the system, or a model of the system. In the majority of the studies, this is the current production work load, defined over a time period (e.g., a week, a month, a year) also to be specified. The investigator is sometimes interested in evaluating the performance of a system under other types of work loads. To determine, for instance, the capacity (or maximum throughput rate) of a system, a work load is to be selected which saturates the system. In studies whose objective is to test a hypothesis about the causes of inefficiencies, the selection of a special, unrealistic work load may produce faster and more reliable results than those which could be obtained with the production work load. In some predictive studies, the work load may be a short-term or long-term projection of the current one. For reasons to be clarified below, a work load selected as described will be called *real work load*.

The other operation to be performed is the *characterization* of the work load for the system under study. A work load can be characterized with various degrees of detail. A reader who has already studied Chapters 2, 3, and 4 will not have much difficulty in recognizing that in performance evaluation a real work load is to be characterized by a *work-load model*. This is evidently the case in simulation or analytic studies, in which a model of the real work load must always drive a model of the real system if the values of the performance indices are to be obtained. Also in measurement experiments, however, the system is usually driven by a model of the real work load [*see* Ferrari (1972)]. In some experiments, the work load which a system processes during a measurement session is a sample from the production work load or from some portions of it (for instance, from its peak periods). This sample, which is supposed to represent a much bigger real work load, may be thought of as a model of that work load. In other types of experiments, the system is driven by sets of inputs which have been constructed for the measurement of the system and replace its real work load. Also these collections, because of their origin and purpose, can legitimately be considered as work-load models.

Like any other model, a work-load model is to be formulated, constructed, tested, calibrated, and validated. An iterative process for the creation of a work-load model is schematically illustrated in Fig. 5.1.

The problems which arise in formulating a work-load model are discussed in Section 5.2. In Section 5.3 we shall describe the major techniques used to

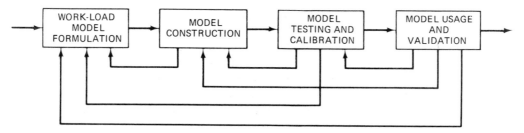

Figure 5.1 Phases of work-load model design.

construct work-load models from given model formulations. The calibration and validation problems for work-load models are briefly commented on in Section 5.4. Formulation, construction, testing, calibration, and validation are described separately only for the sake of clarity. In reality, they are often intimately and inextricably intertwined.

Table 5.1

MAIN CHARACTERISTICS OF A
WORK-LOAD MODEL

Representativeness
Flexibility
Simplicity of construction
Compactness
Usage costs
System independence
Reproducibility
Compatibility

A work-load model can be judged according to several criteria. The principal characteristics of such a model are listed in Table 5.1. Some of these characteristics are important for models in general. *Representativeness* is just another term, often used in the literature on work-load characterization, for *accuracy*. *Flexibility* is the possibility of easily and inexpensively modifying a model to reflect variations in the real work load. The *simplicity of construction* of a work-load model includes the cost and complexity of gathering the information necessary to design it and to make it operational. The characteristic of *compactness* is related to the degree of detail and hence to the representativeness and usage costs of a model. A very compact model is usually less detailed, less representative, and cheaper to use than a less compact one. It is worth noting that the compactness of a model is often dictated by the scarcity of the available information about the real work load rather than left entirely to the model builder to choose.

Other characteristics are more peculiar of work-load models. *System independence* is the extent to which a model can be transported from system to system while remaining sufficiently representative. Typical problems in which independence is essential are some of the selection problems discussed in Chapter 6. In other studies, the independence requirements are much less restrictive. For instance, when the objective of the study is the improvement of a system's performance, the work-load model is to be independent, in the sense defined above, of the system modifications being considered for improvement purposes. Since not all of the work-load representations used in measurements can be reproduced equally easily, *reproducibility* is an important characteristic. Together with flexibility, this characteristic describes the degree of control an evaluator has over a work-load model. *Compatibility* with the system or the system model to be driven is needed to make a work-load model usable. This means that, for instance, a model which is to drive a real system must be composed of programs executable by that system.

Two of the model characteristics introduced above are discussed in much more detail in Sections 5.2.2 (representativeness) and 5.2.3 (independence). All of the characteristics are considered in the treatment of work-load models in Section 5.3.

5.2. THE FORMULATION OF A WORK-LOAD MODEL

5.2.1 Approaches to Work-Load Characterization

Any real work load can be thought of as consisting of a set of jobs, each one of which performs an information-processing task when it is processed by the system under study. Characterizing a work load for evaluation purposes requires determining which of its numerous aspects have an influence on the system's performance. Since we are interested in quantitative evaluation, we view a work-load model as a set of quantifiable *work-load parameters*. Two examples, drawn from Chapters 3 and 4, respectively, are now discussed to illustrate the concept of work-load model and some types of characterization used in evaluation studies.

Example 5.1   In this example, we shall consider the work-load model which drives the EXOPE system simulator designed in Example 3.2. Some representations of the model are described in Example 3.4. Table 3.6 lists the parameters which characterize the work load of the batch-processing EXOPE installation being simulated. This characterization is based on the assumption that of all the information contained in the real work load only the parameters in Table 3.6 have an appreciable influence on the performance indices of interest.

Several observations need to be made about this table. First, the work-load model is actually a collection of *job models*, which characterize individual jobs separately. This is the case even in a distribution-driven simulator which processes statistically identical jobs, that is, in which each job parameter is drawn from the same distribution. The separate characterization of jobs is a very popular approach since it is simpler and more natural than the alternative method consisting of modeling the work load directly as a whole, as if it were produced by a single job. In a simulator like the one being dealt with here, separately characterizing each job is mandatory, since each job's history in the system is in fact what the simulator tries to reproduce.

Another important, though obvious, remark is that the work-load model and the system model have to be created together. They must match and be compatible with each other. The degree of detail of the work-load model is to reflect that of the simulator and, like the latter, is limited by the availability of the relevant data. For instance, if the length r_{ds} of each disk record handled by a job is neither deterministically nor statistically known, this parameter cannot be included in a job's characterization. In this case, the disk model in Table 3.5, which refers to r_{ds}, cannot be used.

To be compatible with the system model, which in our example represents the resources of the system explicitly, the work-load model must be *resource-oriented*. As shown in Table 5.2, each job is represented by its demands in terms of the hardware resources modeled in the simulator. The symbols in Table 5.2 should be interpreted as follows. Job step j consists of n_{cpuj} processing intervals of durations

Table 5.2

JOB CHARACTERIZATION FOR THE SIMULATOR OF EXAMPLE 3.2*

Resource	Global	Job step 1	Job step 2	...	Job step n
			Job parameters		
CR	c				
LP	l				
M		$m(1)$	$m(2)$	...	$m(n)$
CPU		$t_{cpu}(1, 1), B(1, 1)$ $t_{cpu}(1, 2), B(1, 2)$ $\vdots$ $t_{cpu}(1, n_{cpu1})$	$t_{cpu}(2, 1), B(2, 1)$ $t_{cpu}(2, 2), B(2, 2)$ $\vdots$ $t_{cpu}(2, n_{cpu2})$	$\cdots$ $\cdots$ $\cdots$	$t_{cpu}(n, 1), B(n, 1)$ $t_{cpu}(n, 2), B(n, 2)$ $\vdots$ $t_{cpu}(n, n_{cpun})$
DRUM		$r_{dr}(1, 1)$ $\vdots$ $r_{dr}(1, n_{dr1})$	$r_{dr}(2, 1)$ $\vdots$ $r_{dr}(2, n_{dr2})$	$\cdots$ $\cdots$	$r_{dr}(n, 1)$ $\vdots$ $r_{dr}(n, n_{drn})$
DISK	$r_{ds}(in)$ $r_{ds}(out)$	$r_{ds}(1, in)$ $r_{ds}(1, 1)$ $\vdots$ $r_{ds}(1, n_{ds1})$ $r_{ds}(1, out)$	$r_{ds}(2, in)$ $r_{ds}(2, 1)$ $\vdots$ $r_{ds}(2, n_{ds2})$ $r_{ds}(2, out)$	$\cdots$ $\cdots$ $\cdots$ $\cdots$	$r_{ds}(n, in)$ $r_{ds}(n, 1)$ $\vdots$ $r_{ds}(n, n_{dsn})$ $r_{ds}(n, out)$

*For symbols not explained in Example 5.1, see Tables 3.5 and 3.6.

$t_{cpu}(j, i)$ $(i = 1, 2, \ldots, n_{cpuj})$, each of which is followed by either a drum request for a record of length $r_{dr}(j, h)$ $(h = 1, 2, \ldots, n_{drj})$ or a disk request involving a record of length $r_{ds}(j, k)$ $(k = 1, 2, \ldots, n_{dsj})$. The binary parameter $B(j, i)$ determines whether the request at the end of processing interval $t_{cpu}(j, i)$ is to the drum or to the disk. The last processing interval of a job step j is always followed by a disk request with record length r_{ds} (j, out), and the first is preceded by a disk request with record length $r_{ds}(j, in)$. The record lengths of those disk requests servicing the card reader at the beginning of a job's execution and the line printer at the end are denoted by $r_{ds}(in)$ and $r_{ds}(out)$, respectively.

This characterization of each job in terms of the resources needed for its execution is very natural and popular. It suffers, however, from a drawback which is a serious one in many evaluation studies: the dependence of the work-load model on the system and the configuration for which it is intended. Another question which arises with respect to the model described in this example is the one concerned with its representativeness. There can be little doubt about the fact that if the six resources listed in Table 5.2 are the ones and the only ones which matter, the model is likely to be accurate (of course, provided it is properly constructed and calibrated). But is this a valid assumption?   ■

Example 5.2   The work load for the central-server model of an EXOPE system illustrated in Fig. 4.18 is characterized by the parameters listed in Table 4.9 except N, the degree of multiprogramming. In choosing that characterization, we have assumed that service times at all service centers are exponentially distributed. Furthermore, the system is assumed to be so heavily loaded that the degree of multiprogramming can aways be kept at its maximum value N. Also, this work-load model can be viewed as a collection of job models, like the one in Example 5.1, but the jobs here are all statistically identical.

Note that service times depend both on the demands of the jobs and on the speeds of the servers. We assume that in our study the speeds of the devices modeled by the three servers in Fig. 4.18 will not be modified. Under this assumption, the service times may be considered as job parameters.

Remarks very similar to those made in Example 5.1 can be made about this model. It is evidently compatible with the system model, and in fact heavily constrained in its degree of detail by the closed-form solvability requirement of that model. It is resource-oriented, although here the modeled resources are only the CPU, the drum, the disk, and, to some extent, the primary memory. Finally, its ability to completely and properly represent a real work load remains to be demonstrated.   ■

In the two examples above, we have seen work-load models formulated as collections of job models. Each job model consists of a v-tuple $(w_1, w_2, \ldots, w_v)$ of *job parameters*, most of which represent the resource demands of the job. Thus, the work-load model is the set of the N v-tuples which represent its N jobs. The most frequent types of job parameters are the *single-valued parameter* and the *sequence*. The latter is a temporal sequence of single-valued (deterministic or random) variables. For instance, the work-load model discussed in Example 5.1 consists of N 7-tuples of the type $(c, l, \{m\}, \{t_{cpu}\}, \{B\}, \{r_{dr}\}, \{r_{ds}\})$, where c and l are single-valued parameters, $\{m\}, \{t_{cpu}\}, \{B\}, \{r_{dr}\},$ and $\{r_{ds}\}$ are sequences. The job model referred to in Example 5.2 may be viewed as consisting of the quadruple $(\{t_1\}, \{t_2\}, \{t_3\}, \{q\})$ of sequences, where $\{t_i\}$ is the sequence of service times at service center i and $\{q\}$ is a sequence of ternary variables indicating the center the job reaches after leaving server Σ_1 (the CPU). Since all jobs are assumed to be statistically identical, the whole work-load model may be rep-resented as a quintuple $(\tau_1, \tau_2, \tau_3, b_{12}, b_{13})$. The τ_i's are random variables whose distributions, when assumed to be exponential, are completely defined by their means $1/\mu_i$. The b_{1i}'s are scalars representing intercenter transition probabilities ($b_{11} = 1 - b_{12} - b_{13}$ is not included in the model since it is functionally depen-dent on other work-load parameters).

To this type of characterization we may reduce the great majority of the work-load models used in evaluation studies. Two important problems encountered in the discussion of Examples 5.1 and 5.2 were those of representativeness and of system independence. These problems are discussed further in Sections 5.2.2 and 5.2.3.

5.2.2   The Problem of Representativeness

The primary requirement of any model is that it represent with sufficient accuracy the behavior of the modeled system. The representativeness of a work-load model defines its ability to adequately represent a real work load in a performance evaluation study.

In our terminology, a *real* work load does not necessarily coincide with the production work load. The representativeness of a work-load model is to be interpreted as its accuracy in representing a real work load (which need not even physically exist), not a production work load. In some studies, it is more important to have a work-load model which exercises in a realistic manner all the parts of a system than a model which tries to reproduce the behavior of a particular production work load. Representativeness, intended according to the above definition as the ability of a work-load model to satisfy the evaluator's requirements, is one of the most important design considerations even in these studies.

A work-load model is usually more compact than the real work load it represents. That is, it contains less information. The main reason for building compact models is to save time and money. How can we determine whether the information missing in a model would be essential to its representativeness? Can the representativeness of a model be quantified? In looking for answers to the above questions, we are led to recognize that representativeness may be viewed as a particular case of *work-load equivalence*.

Let us consider the situation depicted in Fig. 5.2. The performance indices selected to express the performance of system $\mathscr{S}$ are collectively denoted by the symbol $\mathscr{P}$. Set $\mathscr{P}$ may include distributions of random variables, means, variances and higher moments, values of deterministic variables (e.g., utilization factors), and so on. The two work loads W_1 and W_2 are said to be *equivalent with respect to system $\mathscr{S}$ and performance index set $\mathscr{P}$* if the values $\mathscr{P}_1$ and $\mathscr{P}_2$ of the

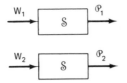

Figure 5.2   Illustration of work-load equivalence.
W_2 is equivalent to W_1 if $\mathscr{P}_1 = \mathscr{P}_2$.

performance indices they produce when driving system $\mathscr{S}$ are equal within some specified limits of precision. Now let W_2 be a model of W_1, and drive either $\mathscr{S}$ or a valid model of $\mathscr{S}$. Then W_2 *represents* W_1 *with respect to system $\mathscr{S}$ and set $\mathscr{P}$* if it is equivalent to W_1 with respect to $\mathscr{S}$ and $\mathscr{P}$.

The dependence of this definition of representativeness on the system and on the performance indices should never be overlooked. If W_2 represents W_1 for a given $\mathscr{S}$ and a given $\mathscr{P}$, we should not be surprised if the same two work loads will not be equivalent for different choices of performance indices or for different systems. There are changes which do not affect equivalence or representativeness. This is the case, for instance, when a distribution belonging to $\mathscr{P}$ is replaced by its mean, or by the (mean, variance) pair. The inverse transformation, however, does not generally preserve work-load equivalence. Considering those indices which are conveniently represented by random variables, we could define two work loads as *nth-order equivalent* if they produce the same values of at least the first n moments of the distributions of the indices. If two work loads are nth-order equivalent with respect to a system and a set of performance indices, they are also ith order equivalent $(i = 1, \ldots, n - 1)$ with respect to the same system and set of indices. Another useful extension of these definitions could be made if a metric were chosen to quantify the "distance" between $\mathscr{P}_1$ and $\mathscr{P}_2$. This would allow us to define the *degree of equivalence* between W_1 and W_2, or the *degree of representativeness* of W_2 as a model of W_1.

Before continuing our discussion, we shall apply the definition of representativeness given above to the model presented in Example 5.2.

Example 5.3   Assuming that the central-server model in Fig. 4.18 is a valid model of system $\mathscr{S}$, we want to determine the conditions under which two work loads W_1 and W_2 are equivalent with respect to $\mathscr{S}$ and to the performance index set $\mathscr{P} = (\bar{T}, \bar{\imath})$. In Section 4.3.5, we obtained the following results for our two performance indices:

$$\bar{T} = b_{11}\mu_1\rho_1, \tag{5.1}$$

$$\bar{\imath} = \frac{N}{b_{11}\mu_1\rho_1}, \tag{5.2}$$

and we saw that ρ_1, the utilization of the central server (CPU), can be expressed as a function of the work-load parameters and of N, as shown in (4.106) and (4.101). Thus, two work loads in which the parameters listed in Table 4.9 have the same numerical values are equivalent with respect to $\mathscr{S}$ and $\mathscr{P}$. This condition is sufficient but not necessary for equivalence. Two necessary and sufficient conditions for the equivalence of two work loads W' and W'' are

$$b'_{11}\mu'_1\rho'_1 = b''_{11}\mu''_1\rho''_1, \qquad N' = N''. \tag{5.3}$$

If the equalities in (5.3) are satisfied, W'' is equivalent to W' and can be used to drive $\mathscr{S}$ in lieu of it. It is evident that the differences existing between W_1 and W_2, which are not reflected by their parameters, might play an important and undesirable rôle as some changes in $\mathscr{S}$ or in $\mathscr{P}$ are introduced. For instance, the fact that the first condition in (5.3) is satisfied for certain values of $b'_{1j}, b''_{1j}, \mu'_j, \mu''_j$ $(j = 1, 2, 3)$ does not guarantee that it will still be satisfied when the speed of the CPU or of the drum or of the disk is altered or when a file allocation modification will cause the values of b'_{12}, b''_{12}, b'_{13}, b''_{13} to change. A variation in the speed of one service center will not affect the equivalence of two work loads if each one of the parameters in Table 4.9 has the same value in both. As observed above, this nonnecessary equivalence condition is much stronger than (5.3). Thus, the validity of a work-load model can be expected to increase, at least up to a certain point, with the degree of detail to which its fidelity to the real work load has been pushed.   ∎

Our definition of representativeness is based on work-load equivalence and hence on the performance indices selected for the evaluation study to be performed. It is easy to recognize the conceptual similarity between this definition and a criterion sometimes used to determine how *loaded* a given system is, which consists of looking at the utilizations of the devices in the system's configuration. Essentially, the criterion measures the *magnitude* of a work load from the effects that work load has on the activities of the system's devices. In other words, the criterion characterizes the *external load* in terms of the *internal loads* it produces on the various devices.

The magnitude of the work load that a system is processing at a certain time is often roughly estimated from the responsiveness of the system to a stimulus to which the system reacts in known ways under various work loads. If the turnaround time of a job, or the response time to a command, is much longer than usual, the user's first guess is that the system is much more loaded than usual. Karush (1969) has proposed a method, based on this observation, to measure work-load magnitudes in an interactive installation. A program, which will be called a *terminal probe*, is to be written. The terminal probe is then run from a terminal while the system is processing a number, variable from zero to a given maximum, of other copies of the same probe. The response times to the probe obtained at the terminal are measured and plotted as in Fig. 5.3. When the magnitude of the system's load is to be measured, the experimenter inputs the probe from a terminal and measures the response time. Reporting this time on the diagram in Fig. 5.3 will provide a measure of the load existing on the system

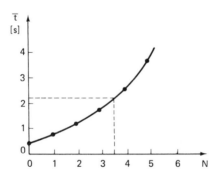

Figure 5.3   Terminal probe for the measurement of the magnitude of an interactive system's work load. A mean response time of 2.2 s corresponds to a load of 3.4 terminal probes.

at the time of the experiment in terms of the equivalent number of terminal probes. Thus, the probe is used as a yardstick, or as the unit work load.

The *load factor* of an interactive system proposed by Syms (1974) is also based on the concept of equivalence. All the mixtures of commands which, entered simultaneously at a system's terminals, produce the same value of the mean response time correspond to the same load factor. The introduction of the load factor is superfluous since the selected performance index (in this case, the mean response time) may be used directly to quantify the magnitude of the load. A more useful achievement is expressing, if possible, the load factor L (proportional to the mean response time) as a function of the numbers of terminals at which the various types of commands are input. In general, if we consider k commands $c_1, \ldots, c_k$ and N terminals, the load on the system may be defined by the k-tuple $N_1, \ldots, N_k$, where N_i $(i = 1, \ldots, k)$ is the number of terminals at which command c_i is entered, and $\sum_{i=1}^{k} N_i = N$. For some interactive systems Syms (1974) was able to find a linear expression such as

$$L = L(N_1, \ldots, N_k) = \sum_{i=1}^{k} a_i N_i. \tag{5.4}$$

Syms's study is discussed in more detail in Sections 6.3.5 and 6.5.

The definition of representativeness based on work-load equivalence allows us to state a criterion for determining the degree of detail and the parameters to be included in a work-load model. For a given system $\mathcal{S}$, a given set $\mathcal{P}$ of performance indices, and a given real work load W, those and only those parameters of W which have a nonnegligible influence on some element of $\mathcal{P}$ should be included in W', a model of W. The influence we are concerned with is the dependence of some index in $\mathcal{P}$ on the values of work-load parameters within the bounds expected to hold for these parameters in the work load (or all the work loads) to be considered during the study.

How easy is it to find a characterization that satisfies the representativeness criterion? The general problem has been discussed in Sections 2.6 and 2.7, where some techniques for determining what system and work-load parameters influence a given performance index were introduced. Often the dependence of performance indices on the most obvious work-load parameters (e.g., on the resource demands of jobs) is highly nonlinear. Thus, the effects are usually not additive, and the interactions among work-load parameters, as well as those between work-load and system parameters, play a nonnegligible role. The presence of interactions is seldom considered in the formulation of a work-load model. A choice of the job parameters which does not reflect the existence of interactions may turn out to be inadequate. For instance, a work-load model which does not contain any information on the arrival order of the jobs may not represent the real work load adequately. This may be due, among other things, to the fact that in a multiprogramming system the values of most performance indices (e.g., the mean throughput rate, the utilizations of the CPU and the I/O devices) are usually quite sensitive to such ordering.

5.2.3   The Problem of System-Independent Characterization

Most of the evaluation studies of practical interest involve comparisons of different systems or different configurations of the same system. Therefore, independence is an important characteristic of a work-load model. This characteristic is heavily influenced by how the model is formulated.

It was observed in Section 5.1 that considering the behavior of a user community as independent of the performance of the system it is using is an unrealistic but (due to the state of our knowledge) necessary approximation. The kind of system dependence we are concerned with in this section is totally different. If the parameters by which we model a work load depend on the type of system, on its configuration, and on its software, they do not describe the work load as they should. Thus, work loads characterized this way (for example, in terms of resource demands) are not readily *transportable* to other systems or even to slightly different configurations of the same system. Three simple examples of such situations follow.

a. A work-load model in which file accessing activities are represented by the total disk time of each job, including the waiting time for the channel and for the disk, cannot be used when a system is to be studied with two different placements of files on disk, or with different numbers of disks, or with disks having different performances, or with disks having different scheduling policies.

b. When a work-load model characterizes the processing activity of a job in terms of its CPU-time demand instead of, say, its instruction usage frequencies, the model cannot be used without modifications to drive a system to be evaluated with CPU's of the same type but different speeds.

c. A work-load model in which the paging activity of each job in a virtual-memory environment is characterized by the total page fault rate produced when running on a certain system is useless when the primary-memory size is one of the factors in the study.

When the work-load model is a collection of job models, an additional source of system dependence in a multiprogramming environment may be the choice of a job model which is not independent of the rest of the jobs. This is, for example, the case when the disk times of the jobs include queue waits.

Another less evident type of dependence is the one due to system-work-load interactions which are not taken care of in the work-load model. An example of these interactions is that between the order in which jobs are submitted to a multiprogramming system and the system's scheduling policies. Let a work-load model, consisting of a certain number of job models having a certain ordering, adequately represent a given real work load with respect to a multiprogramming system $\mathcal{S}_1$. With respect to system $\mathcal{S}_2$, which differs from $\mathcal{S}_1$ in the scheduling policy, this work-load model, with the same job ordering, is likely not to be representative of the given real work load. The existence of interactions is responsible for some of the most subtle problems in the area of work-load characterization. System dependencies due to interactions are quite hard to discover and to eliminate. In principle, all those interaction effects which are likely to be significant in a certain study ought to be considered when designing a work-load model for that study. In practice, this may be so difficult and expensive to do in a systematic way that the designers may have to rely on their intuition and on the results of some quick, informal verifications.

The consequences of the two types of system dependence discussed at the beginning of this section are schematically illustrated in Fig. 5.4. This figure refers to an improvement study involving the comparison of two versions $\mathcal{S}_1$ and $\mathcal{S}_2$ of the same system. $\mathcal{S}_1$ is the existing, measurable version, whereas $\mathcal{S}_2$ is a version incorporating modifications which have not been made yet in the real system and whose influence on performance is to be predicted. In principle, we should

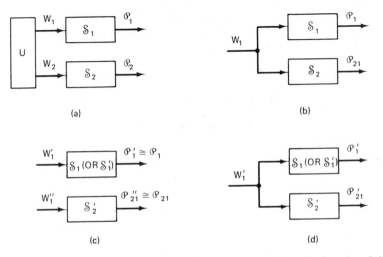

Figure 5.4 Possible sources of error due to the system dependencies of work-load models in improvement studies.

compare $\mathcal{P}_1$ and $\mathcal{P}_2$, the values of performance indices produced by $\mathcal{S}_1$ and $\mathcal{S}_2$ under the two respective work loads W_1 and W_2, which would be generated by the same user community U when using $\mathcal{S}_1$ and $\mathcal{S}_2$ [*see* Fig. 5.4(a)]. Since we do not know how the user community will react to the system changes which transform $\mathcal{S}_1$ into $\mathcal{S}_2$, we cannot predict W_2 from the knowledge of W_1. Hence, we assume that even $\mathcal{S}_2$ will process W_1, producing a performance $\mathcal{P}_{21}$ [*see* Fig. 5.4(b)]. The real work load W_1 will be represented in the study by a model W_1', which will be used to drive either $\mathcal{S}_1$ or a valid model of it, called $\mathcal{S}_1'$. The same model W_1' can drive also $\mathcal{S}_2'$, a valid model of $\mathcal{S}_2$, if the characterization on which W_1' is based is independent of the modifications being considered. If a system-dependent characterization is used, two distinct models of W_1 should be created, W_1' for $\mathcal{S}_1$ and W_1'' for $\mathcal{S}_2$, so as to obtain performances very close to $\mathcal{P}_1$ and $\mathcal{P}_{21}$, respectively [*see* Fig. 5.4(*c*)]. However, evaluators often tend to adopt the solution in Fig. 5.4(*d*). This solution consists of using the same work-load model W_1' to drive both $\mathscr{S}_1$ (which produces $\mathscr{P}_1'$) and $\mathscr{S}_2$ (which produces P_{21}'). Neglecting the errors due to the inaccuracies of the models, we see that $\mathscr{P}_{21}'$ differs from $\mathscr{P}_2$ for two reasons, first because W_1 is different from W_2 due to the sensitivity of user communities to system performance, and second because W_1' is different from W_1'' due to the system-dependent characterization of the work load. Before making decisions based on the comparison of $\mathscr{P}_1'$ and $\mathscr{P}_{21}'$, an evaluator should determine the influence of these errors on the values of the performance indices and see whether the comparison is meaningful.

Are there system-independent ways of characterizing a work load? The parameters of resource-oriented work-load models may have various degrees of system dependence. In one of the cases briefly mentioned at the beginning of this section, the performance changes due to different placements of files on a disk had to be investigated. We stated that a representation of the file accessing behavior of a certain work load in terms of the total disk time per job is inadequate for the problem. An adequate work-load model is obtained by representing job file usage in terms of the names of the files accessed by each job, of the history of those accesses, and of the amounts of data transferred per access. This representation is much more detailed than the one which was found to be inadequate, but this is not the important point here. In fact, some of the data listed above may often be omitted with little loss of accuracy. The essential advantage of the new characterization over the previous one is that it is based on job demands in terms of *logical resources* rather than of *physical resources*.

The more system-independent the resources whose demands are used to model a work load, the more system-independent will the work-load model be. However, the degree of independence which is necessary varies from study to study. For an improvement investigation in which no changes of the disk system are considered, the work-load model criticized above might be adequate.

The objectives and the scope of a study must be carefully considered when characterizing an installation's work load for it. Those work-load characteristics related to parts of the system (or systems) expected to change during the study should be represented as much as possible at the logical level. Let the objective of a study be to choose the most appropriate CPU for an installation among those of a computer family, assuming that all the candidate CPU's have identical instruction sets. Then, the computational demands of the jobs can be much more adequately represented by the amounts of the various types of instructions to be executed than by the CPU times requested by the jobs when running on one of the CPU's in the family.

An alternative approach is to use system-dependent parameters and to modify their values properly when going from a system to another. This approach, depicted in Fig. 5.4(*c*), can be applied only if a proper way of transforming W_1' into W_1'' is known. Assume that, in the example of the previous paragraph, the ratio between the instruction times of each CPU and the corresponding ones of each other CPU is the same for all instructions. Then the CPU time demands of a job for all the CPU's can be easily calculated from the time demand for one CPU. Sometimes this is done even if the ratios of instruction times are not identical and even when the instruction sets differ, using estimates of the relative speeds of the CPU's for the applications being considered. These are clearly crude approximations, and their limits of validity should be carefully investigated before relying on them.

In general, modifying work-load parameters when a work-load model is transported to another system is made extremely difficult by the presence of system-dependent interactions among the work-load parameters. A substantial amount of research is needed to discover, classify, and quantify these interactions and possibly to identify work-load parameters which are relatively independent of each other as well as of the characteristics of the system.

The problem of system dependence would disappear if the information-processing needs of a user community could be expressed in a totally abstract way, with no reference whatsoever to the particular means by which these needs are fulfilled in a specific computer installation. This abstract characterization should, however, be easily translatable into a more concrete one (for instance, in terms of resource demands) as soon as the system to be driven by it is specified. A suggestion along these lines is the one, discussed above, of using logical instead of physical resource-based models as much as possible.

Several researchers have proposed approaches to the abstract characterization of information-processing needs, which is a problem of fundamental importance in computer science. The main objective of most of these efforts, which will now be briefly reviewed, has been to provide a quantitative definition of the *information-processing work* required by a process. As observed by Hellerman (1972), the usual approach consists of choosing a *canonical implementation* of algorithmic processes and of defining as the work of the process some quantitative attribute of its canonical implementation.

The canonical implementations used in the theory of computational complexity are more or less abstract machines, and the attributes which define the work are space quantities (the length of the tape for a Turing machine, the number of memory cells, the number of logic elements) and time quantities (the number of steps, the number of additions or multiplications, the maximum number of cascaded stages). These approaches are usually intended for the analysis of algorithms. Their practical goal is to determine the most efficient algorithm among those which compute the same function. The highest efficiency corresponds to the minimum amount of work. The analysis of algorithms is extremely useful in program and system design. However, the definitions of work introduced to analyze algorithms, although system-independent, have not given any substantial help to practical performance evaluation. This is probably due to their predominant orientation toward computational aspects only (information transfers, which consume so many system resources, are usually ignored by these definitions) and to the unavailability of methods for translating amounts of work into resource demands for a given system.

Other researchers have proposed definitions of work based on information-theoretical concepts. For example, Hellerman (1972) defines the *work of a process* $f: X \rightarrow Y$, whose domain X is finite and may be divided into n subdomains X_i $(i = 1, \ldots, n)$ such that all inputs in X_i produce the same point in the range Y, as

$$w(f) = \sum_{i=1}^{n} |X_i| \log_2 \frac{|X|}{|X_i|}, \qquad (5.5)$$

where $|A|$ denotes the number of elements in set A. The reader familiar with the fundamentals of information theory will notice that $w(f)/|X|$ is the *entropy function* of the source X.

Bailliu (1973) distinguishes *reversible transformations* of information, which may only alter the order of the input elements, from *irreversible transformations*, in which $|X| \neq |Y|$. He defines the *activity* of a process f as

$$a(f) = \frac{1}{|X|} \sum_{i=1}^{n} |X_i| \log_2 |X_i|, \qquad (5.6)$$

which coincides with the loss of information in the input if f is irreversible and with the loss of order if f is reversible. In the latter case, the subdomains X_i are the largest ones which are ordered according to some conventional definition of order. Unlike what happens with Hellerman's definition of work, there is no activity associated with identity transformations, that is, with data transfers.

Information sources and their entropies are considered also by Rozwa-dowski (1973) in his definition of the *quantity of computation* as the sum of the reductions of uncertainty caused by all the (information-theoretic) sources which constitute a process. For instance, in the process of executing one memory-reference machine instruction he identifies three sources: source S_1, which selects the instruction to be executed, the operation to be performed, and the registers to be used and specifies the address of the next instruction; source S_2, which selects the operand values; and source S_3, which selects the value of the result. Let a machine have a memory of $32K$ words, a word length of 24 bits, 8 central registers, and an opcode field of 6 bits. The reductions of uncertainties due to the three sources S_1, S_2, S_3 listed above, when an instruction is executed which adds the contents of a memory location to those of a central register, are, assuming that all outcomes of selection decisions are equiprobable,

$$H(S_1) = \log_2 32K + \log_2 2^6 + \log_2 8 + \log_2 32K = 39 \text{ bits,}$$

$$H(S_2) = \log_2 2^{24} + \log_2 2^{24} = 48 \text{ bits,} \qquad (5.7)$$

$$H(S_3) = \log_2 2^{24} = 24 \text{ bits.}$$

Thus, the total work (or quantity of computation) performed by the instruction is

$$H(S_1) + H(S_2) + H(S_3) = 111 \text{ bits}, \tag{5.8}$$

which coincides with the total number of bits moved by the machine during the instruction cycle. The work performed by S_1 may be viewed as overhead or control work and that performed by S_2 and S_3 as the actual, useful process work.

The definition of *software work* proposed by Kolence in the context of his *software physics* [*see* Kolence (1972)] is very similar from a pragmatic viewpoint to the one given by Rozwadowski: "a processor performs one unit of software work on some storage media when one byte of that media is altered." Note that pure transfers require work, even when the information being transferred is not really different from the one present in the storage before the transfer. Thus, the term *altered* is not to be interpreted literally. The word *processor* in the above definition designates not only CPU's but all types of processors, including channels, controllers, control units, and so on.

This very brief and superficial survey of some of the approaches to the problem of a system-independent definition of information-processing work has been intended only to give the readers the flavor of those proposals and to stimulate their curiosity. Even from our sketchy presentation, it is probably easy to draw the impression that these ideas are either too abstract or still too system-dependent for our purposes. Our ideal work-load model is sufficiently detached from real systems so as not to be influenced by any of their peculiarities yet is easily adaptable to any system and its idiosyncrasies. Stating that the approaches proposed so far do not seem adequate to solve our problem does not mean that they should not be studied, understood, and pursued. If our ideal work-load characterization can be found, there is some chance that it will result from investigations along the lines described above. Even if this were only a marginal chance, the insights that these studies might provide into the nature and the foundations of information processing would make their pursuit worthwhile.

5.3   THE CONSTRUCTION OF WORK-LOAD MODELS

5.3.1   Basic Definitions

Many different types of models are used in performance evaluation to represent the work load of an installation. The choice of the most suitable one for a given study is constrained by the requirement that the work-load model be compatible either with the system or with the system's model to be driven. Other important constraints are often those due to the limited information available about the real work load to be modeled.

When a work-load model is to be designed, the objectives of the study and its requirements in terms of the characteristics listed in Table 5.1 are to be carefully considered. In the following several sections, we shall describe the most important types of models and discuss their properties. The choice of a model is in most studies likely to be confined to the model types introduced below.

The spectrum of characteristics displayed by the existing types of work-load models is quite wide and does not suggest any simple classification. We shall base ours on the nature of the model. If the model is just a sample job stream taken from a production work load and used to drive the system at the very time this work load is produced by the user community, we call it a *natural work-load model*. The construction and properties of this type of model, which by its definition can be used only in measurement experiments, are discussed in Section 5.3.2. In all other cases, we have an *artificial work-load model*. If the artificial model is composed of one or more programs, it is called an *executable artificial model*. Executable models are used to drive a real system during measurement experiments in which the system is dedicated to the experiment. However, they can in principle drive certain types of program-driven simulators. The characteristics of executable artificial models are commented on in Section 5.3.4. Various methods for their construction are described in Section 5.3.5. The properties of the *nonexecutable artificial models*, which are employed in analytic and most simulation studies, are briefly surveyed in Section 5.3.3.

5.3.2   Natural Work-Load Models

According to the definition given in Section 5.3.1, a natural model is a sample of the production work load which the system processes at the time a monitoring experiment is performed. We call this a model of the real work load only because of its duration, which is generally shorter than that of the work load to be modeled. The modeling activity in this case consists only of choosing the times at which the collection of the data should be started and stopped. Sometimes, the real work load does not coincide with the production work load but rather with some parts of it. If we are interested in, say, the behavior of a system under heavy load, our real yearly work load may be defined as the set of jobs executed by the system between 9:30 and 11:30 a.m. during all the working days of a year. Thus, our work-load model may consist of those jobs executed between the same times during all the working days of a properly selected week. Note that we exclude from the class of natural work-load models those samples of the production work load which are recorded and used to drive the system (or a suitable model of it) at some later time. These models are considered artificial and are described in Sections 5.3.3–5.3.5.

Many studies using a natural work-load model have been reported in the literature, but only seldom have the design decisions for the model been described and satisfactorily justified. Scherr (1967) collected data on the behavior of CTSS, an interactive system built at M.I.T., and of its user community during 47 measurement periods, whose durations had a mean of 143 min and a range from less than 1 hr to about 8 hr. The user community was characterized by two parameters, think time and CPU time demand per interaction. The standard deviations of the means of these parameters over each period about the overall means were roughly 15% of the overall means (*see* Table 5.3). This result is not,

Table 5.3
CHARACTERISTICS OF A NATURAL WORK-LOAD MODEL FOR THE
MEASUREMENT OF CTSS PERFORMANCE

Work-load parameter	Think time	CPU time/interaction
Overall means [s]	35.0	0.88*
Median of the 47 means [s]	34.0	0.93
Mean of the 47 means [s]	34.2	0.92
Standard deviation of the 47 means [s]	4.994	0.150
Coefficient of variation	0.146	0.163

Source: Scherr (1967).

* Value computed from data collected during normal working hours. All other figures include the results of evening and weekend measurements.

unfortunately, sufficient to guarantee that the natural model chosen is a representative one. The method of independent replications allows us to compute from the data in Table 5.3, for a given confidence level, the confidence intervals of the estimates contained in the first column of the table for the mean think time and for the mean CPU time demand per interaction. However, the characterization chosen for the work load could be proved representative only if we were given a similar table with the values of the performance indices. What Table 5.3 tells us is that the means of the two work-load parameters selected were fairly stable over the time interval in which the system was measured and that even period durations as short as 1 hr provided reasonably accurate estimates of those means. We can therefore conjecture that if Scherr's characterization of the work load is representative, his model implementation, described above, produces a representative natural work-load model. However, the data reported in Table 5.3 and in our discussion above do not provide any information on the representativeness of the characterization. Of course, they do not prove that Scherr's characterization is not representative either.

A conclusion we can draw from this example is that a work-load model adequately represents the real work load if and only if both its formulation and its implementation are representative. A potentially representative formulation can result in a nonrepresentative model if the implementation is inadequate. Also, a potentially representative method of construction may produce a nonrepresentative model if applied to an inadequate characterization of the work load.

In the case of natural models, formulation can be avoided. If the work-load parameters which influence the performance indices are assumed to be stationary, there is no need to identify and measure them. However, measuring some work-load parameters as Scherr did allows us to observe the magnitude and the fluctuations of the load and to see how far its behavior is from a stationary one. Also, characterizing the real work load by a set of parameters to be measured makes experiments more reproducible and is required to be able to interpret their results statistically (*see* Example 2.11).

The design of a natural model, under stationary assumptions, may be based on the methods described in Section 2.6.4 for selecting the time and the duration of a measurement session. When the session consists of a number of separate, relatively short subsessions, as with the independent-replication method for variance estimation, some of the considerations about final conditions made in Section 3.4.2 should also be taken into account.

The applicability of the methodologies of Section 2.6.4 stems from the fact that the problem of *stochastic convergence* dealt with in that section and the problem of representativeness as stated in Section 5.2.2 coincide in the case of natural work-load models. This can be easily understood assuming that the only performance index of interest is the mean of a random variable such as response time. Our definition of representativeness requires that the value of this mean, computed when the system is driven by the natural work-load model selected, be equal to the one produced by the system under the real work load. Since we are dealing with stochastic variables and estimators of distribution descriptors such as the mean, this equality must be statistically defined in terms of a confidence level and a confidence interval. Thus, to obtain a representative natural model, it is sufficient to solve the stochastic convergence problem for this confidence interval. When there are two or more performance indices, all of the type referred to above, the work-load model is representative only if the stochastic convergence criterion is satisfied for all indices.

When stationary assumptions can reasonably be made, the ability of natural models to accurately represent real work loads is potentially very high. It is only potentially so because of the additional condition that the stochastic convergence problem be properly solved. The system independence of these models is not so high. There is in general no guarantee that the stochastic convergence criterion will still be satisfied after introducing even a slight modification into the system (note that evaluators are usually interested in changes which affect the system's performance indices). Thus, it is recommended that variance estimation and confidence interval calculations be repeated after any system modification.

The fact that natural models are so little controllable (only times and durations can be decided by the evaluator) makes their flexibility and reproducibility very poor. A minor degree of indirect flexibility may be provided by the option of excluding some of the collected data from the calculations of performance indices.

The cost of designing natural models is certainly nonnegligible (see the methods described in Section 2.6.4) but lower than that of most other types of work-load models. The converse is true with respect to usage costs. Natural models are usually much less compact than most of the artificial ones, since they require longer sessions and the collection, storage, and reduction of more data.

Thus, natural models should be preferred when obtaining a high degree of representativeness with relatively low design costs is the most important objective and if a low degree of controllability and high usage costs can be tolerated. An advantage of natural models, which is the main reason for their choice in a number of installations and of studies, is that the system need not be entirely dedicated to the measurement experiment when they are used.

5.3.3 Nonexecutable Artificial Models

In Section 5.3.1, all work-load models which do not consist of a live sample from a production work load were classified as *artificial.* Also, we decided to treat *executable* models, those which can drive a real computer system, separately from *nonexecutable* ones. Both natural and executable artificial models are obviously suited to measurement studies (and to some special types of program-driven simulation experiments), whereas analytic and simulation studies make use of nonexecutable artificial models.

The spectrum of nonexecutable models is very broad. This class includes, for instance, the characterization in terms of two deterministic variables (CPU time to process a record and record size) for the analytic model described in Section 4.2.2 as well as the very detailed traces used to drive trace-driven simulators (*see* Section 3.2.4). In this section, we shall attempt neither a formal classification of nonexecutable models nor a survey of the large variety of models which are found in this class. A number of these models have been described in Chapters 3 and 4, some have been discussed in this chapter (*see* Examples 5.1 and 5.2), and others are introduced in the next chapters. The study of how a real work load is characterized in the analytic and simulation models presented in this book (following what was done in Examples 5.1 and 5.2), the discovery of analogies, and the creation of new work-load models by extrapolation are left as useful exercises for the reader. Here, we shall discuss only the construction of some types of nonexecutable models and their most important properties.

In analytic studies of computer systems, the constraint of mathematical tractability very often dictates the formulation of the work-load model as well as of the system model. Once the system model is formulated, very few choices are left to the evaluator, and even those are constrained by the solvability requirement. In a queuing network, for instance, the service-time distributions at the service centers can be specified as an important part of the work-load model. But using measured distributions, or being willing to take correlations and autocorrelations of service times into account, generally causes the model to be unsolvable in closed form. The evaluator is usually aware of these problems when the decision to apply analytic techniques is made and formulates the model knowing the limitations of such an approach.

As the boundaries of the set of solvable queuing models are expanded, the constraints on work-load characterization become less restrictive. The fact, mentioned in Chapter 4, that queuing networks with different classes of customers can be solved in closed form under certain assumptions allows one to model the behavior of real jobs much more accurately than when only one class can be handled. However, the representativeness of even the most sophisticated work-load models used in analytic studies is still quite poor. Obtaining a representative work-load model is never the major consideration in its formulation, which is generally dominated by mathematical issues. Of course, the evaluator should not feel authorized to forget the representativeness problem. Both in the formulation of a work-load model and in its construction, which consists only of assigning numerical values to the work-load parameters (e.g., specifying that service times at service center i are exponentially distributed with mean $1/\mu_i$), the accuracy of the model should be maximized within the limits imposed by mathematical solvability. The estimation of model parameters from measurement data, which is necessary to construct the work-load model, is discussed in Section 4.4.

Analytic work-load models are very flexible with respect to changes in those aspects of the real work load which they model. Representing variations in the mean service time requested by jobs at a service center in a queuing network is easy, whereas accounting for changes in the memory space demands of the jobs may be difficult or impossible. Also, these work-load models are usually not too complicated to construct, very compact and perfectly reproducible. Their system dependence, which has been commented on for a particular model in Example 5.3, is not substantially different from that of the other work-load models based on similar characterizations. Since their degree of representativeness is usually poor, it cannot be damaged too much by those system changes the model is able to reflect.

The work-load models used in distribution-driven simulators have more or less the same properties as those suitable for queuing models. The major difference is a much greater potential for representativeness due to the removal of most of the solvability constraints. Thus, arbitrary distributions for the work-load parameters are always acceptable, and correlations and autocorrelations between parameters can be (although they rarely are) taken into account by making the stochastic model of each job more sophisticated than the one described in Section 3.2.4. Demands for resources which may be concurrently used by several jobs, such as primary- and secondary-memory space and shareable programs and data bases, can be easily modeled. The simultaneous usage of more than one resource (for instance, a CPU and an I/O channel) by the same job is also easy to represent in a simulator. These models, like the analytic ones, are very controllable and hence flexible and reproducible. In fact, their greater degree of detail and lack of strict constraints make them even more flexible than their analytic counterparts. They can adequately reflect many more types of changes in the real work load, including any variation in the distributions of work-load parameters and in the behaviors of classes of jobs. They are as simple to construct as analytic models but tend to require more information because of their higher degree of detail and much greater usage costs due to the fact that they drive a simulator.

As pointed out in Section 3.2.4, where the construction of work-load models for simulators is discussed, the properties of traces and of program-like representations of the work load differ quite substantially from those of the models for distribution-driven simulators. Traces are, among the nonexecutable models, the closest in nature and properties to the executable ones. Their representativeness is potentially much higher than that of the models discussed so far in this section. The penalty for the excellent representativeness traces may exhibit is their very poor compactness. However, since the cost of running a trace-driven simulator is not in general higher than that of running another type of simulator, the penalty is limited to the additional amount of storage required by the trace and to the need for accessing it during the simulation. Construction costs are mostly those of the measurement experiments necessary to trace the system, an operation which is often quite expensive.

Traces are well reproducible but, unfortunately, do not have any flexibility. This lack of flexibility makes it very difficult or impossible to adjust the model to certain changes in the system with respect to which the trace is not valid. Therefore, it is essential to determine the types of system modifications that might need to be simulated during the study before formulating the models and designing the tracing experiments. This decision and the extent to which it is taken into account determine the domain of validity of the trace, which cannot easily be extended. An often reasonable approach to the problem is that of collecting a very detailed trace and reducing it to a more manageable size before using it. This approach allows the evaluator to decrease the degree of detail of the work-load model and hence of the simulator while at the same time being able to extend their domain of validity simply by reprocessing the collected data, without having to retrace the system. An example of the lack of flexibility of a trace will now be briefly discussed.

Example 5.4   Let us consider the trace depicted in Fig. 3.14(*a*), reproduced for convenience in Fig. 5.5(*a*). The trace is a model of a single job representing the job's successive demands for the resources of the EXOPE system described in Example 3.1.

How should we modify this model if we want to use it to represent a job which may overlap part of its computational activity with some of its I/O activities? Clearly, the strictly sequential trace in Fig. 5.5(*a*) would require some nontrivial structural modifications.

A possible solution would be to add to each "I/O" element of the trace a third field, as shown in Fig. 5.5(*b*). This field would contain the CPU time, relative to the beginning of the CPU interval in the next element of the trace, at which the I/O operation is to be completed to allow the CPU to continue executing the job. For instance, the 141 entry in Fig. 5.5(*b*) means that the first disk request allows the CPU to execute the job for 141 time

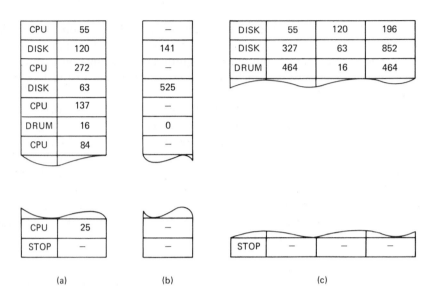

Figure 5.5 Modifications required to allow an original job trace (*a*) to represent a job which can partially overlap its computational and I/O activities.

units after having been issued. If at that time the request has not yet been satisfied, the CPU is to stop and wait for the completion of the disk operation.

A better trace model for such a job is schematically displayed in Fig. 5.5(*c*). The entries in the second field are the pure CPU times, measured from the beginning of execution, at which the I/O operations of the types encoded in the first field are issued. The fourth field contains for each I/O operation the time at which the operation must absolutely be completed in order for the computational activity of the job to be allowed to

Table 5.4
PROPERTIES OF NONEXECUTABLE ARTIFICIAL MODELS

	Work-load models for			
	Analytic techniques	Distribution-driven simulation	Program-driven simulation	Trace-driven simulation
Potential for:				
Representativeness	Poor	Fair	Good	Excellent
Compactness	Excellent	Very good	Fair	Poor
Flexibility	Good	Good	Fair	Poor
Reproducibility	Excellent	Excellent	Excellent	Excellent
System independence	Poor	Fair	Good	Good
Costs of:				
Construction	Low	Low-medium	Medium-high	High
Usage	Low	High	High	High

continue. The trace in Fig. 5.5(c) represents the same job as the one in Figs. 5.5(a) and (b). It is evident that adding to the trace in Fig. 5.5(a) the extra field in Fig. 5.5(b), or transforming it into the trace in Fig. 5.5(c), involves a nontrivial effort. If the original job has been modeled as a triple (t_{cpu}, t_{dr}, t_{ds}) of random variables, providing the overlap capability would only entail adding one or more random variables, which would represent the deadlines shown in Fig. 5.5(b) or in the fourth field of Fig. 5.5(c). ■

Table 5.4 summarizes our qualitative discussion of the properties of nonexecutable work-load models. The table gives the relative potentials of various types of models in terms of the characteristics introduced in Section 5.1.

5.3.4   Executable Artificial Models

Any work-load model consisting of one or more programs executable on the system to be evaluated but not satisfying the definition of a natural model (*see* Section 5.3.2) is said to be an *executable artificial model*. Executable models are almost exclusively used in measurement experiments. The only exception is the case of program-driven simulators which accept actual programs as their input. The main reasons artificial work-load models are preferred to natural ones in a number of measurement experiments are their better reproducibility, greater flexibility, and potentially higher compactness. These were found in Section 5.3.2 to be the areas in which natural models are particularly weak. On the other hand, artificial models tend to be less representative and more system-dependent than their natural counterparts. They are generally more expensive to construct and require that the system be dedicated to them during measurement sessions, an annoying characteristic for many installations.

An evaluator who uses measurement techniques has to choose the type of work-load model best suited to the experiment, considering the objectives and the scope of the study as well as the peculiar problems and characteristics of the installation. If the goal of an experiment is, say, to measure the effects on performance of some incompletely debugged modifications to the operating system, an artificial work-load model driving the modified system during the periods reserved to the installation's staff will avoid the inconveniences which may be caused to the users by an undebugged system and provide a much more reproducible environment than a natural model. The latter feature is particularly desirable in all studies involving comparisons. If, on the other hand, the system is to be continuously available to its user community, there are no alternatives to a natural model. In this case, a reasonable level of reproducibility can be obtained only at the expense of compactness (that is, by making the measurement sessions long enough), and the users will have to be exposed to the risks of working with the undebugged modified operating system.

An experiment which definitely requires an artificial model is one intended to test the behavior of a system under a real work load which does not coincide with the production work load but rather, for instance, with a projected future work load. On the contrary, exploratory studies aimed at answering questions about the performance of the system under its production work load (e.g., has a recent system change been really beneficial?) generally require a natural model. This is certainly the case if an artificial model of the production work load has not been constructed. In fact, the data needed to construct such a model can be gathered only by driving the system with a natural model.

Our comparison of executable artificial models and natural models should not lead the reader to the erroneous conclusion that all executable artificial models have the same characteristics. We shall see, in this and the next section, that there is a great variety of such models, with macroscopically different properties. Thus, an evaluator who decides, according to the criteria outlined above, to use an artificial model for a measurement experiment still has a number of choices to make before and during the construction of such a model.

A distinction was made in Section 5.2.1 between those characterizations of a work load which represent it as a whole and those consisting of a collection of job characterizations. One of the first artificial models proposed in performance evaluation, the *instruction mix* [*see* Raichelson and Collins (1964) and Arbuckle (1966)], falls into the former category. The instruction mix model of a real work load is the frequency distribution of the types of instructions executed during the processing of that work load. Given a real work load and a CPU, we can measure (or estimate) the relative frequency of execution of each CPU instruction during the processing of the work load. The set of these frequencies represents the relative usage of machine instructions made by the work load, or, in other words, its relative demands in terms of CPU resources.

An instruction mix is certainly nonexecutable. The reason it is described in this section is that deriving an executable model from it is straightforward. Any program characterized by the same set of instruction frequencies is such a model. Note that the work load which is so represented may consist of a single job. Thus, an instruction mix can also be used as a job model. If machine instructions are grouped into classes (for instance, according to their execution times), the instruction mix may consist of the class frequencies. A hardware setup for measuring these frequencies has been described in Section 2.3.3 (*see* Fig. 2.6).

An executable instruction mix can be used to measure the total CPU time demand of a job or of a work load. A nonexecutable instruction mix allows us to compute the same demand if we know, for all i, the execution time t_{xi} of instruction i, whose relative frequency is denoted by f_i. The *mean instruction execution time* is

$$\bar{t}_x = \sum_i f_i t_{xi} \qquad \left(\sum_i f_i = 1\right). \tag{5.9}$$

The total CPU time needed to execute n instructions is

$$t_x(n) \cong n\bar{t}_x, \tag{5.10}$$

and the *mean instruction execution rate* of the CPU for the given work load (considering only the computational demands of its jobs) is $\bar{v}_{\text{cpu}} = 1/\bar{t}_x$.

When measuring the real work load is too expensive or impossible (for instance, because the system does not exist or has not yet been installed), the evaluator can use instruction mixes measured at similar installations. This is a case in which *standard instruction mixes* may be useful. The best-known published example of standard mix is the *Gibson mix*, one of whose condensed versions is presented in Table 5.5. Gibson (1970) obtained the frequencies in this mix from a large amount of trace data collected in IBM 7090 installations. Thus, this mix reflects the average relative usage of 7090 instructions in scientific and technical applications.

Table 5.5
TWO STANDARD INSTRUCTION MIXES

Instruction class	Gibson mix, f_i [%]	Flynn mix, f_i [%]
Load/store	31.2	} 45.1
Index	18	
Branch	16.6	27.5
Compare	3.8	10.8
Fixed point	6.9	7.6
Floating point	12.2	3.2
Shift/logical	6.0	4.5
Other	5.3	1.3
	100.0	100.0

Source: Flynn (1974).

An instruction mix model clearly depends on the architecture of the CPU. The same information-processing needs, expressed in the language of another machine, will result in a different instruction mix; not only will the frequencies differ but also the types of instructions appearing in the mix. The dependence on the system can be reduced, as indicated in Section 5.2.3, by choosing work-load parameters which represent logical rather than physical resources. In the case of a mix, this can be done by grouping instructions into those broad classes which are found in most CPU's. The form in which the Gibson mix is presented in Table 5.5 is an example of this type of classification. We can see that it allows a direct comparison to be made with another mix, also reported in Table 5.5, which was obtained from scientific-technical programs run in IBM System/360 installations and published by Flynn (1974).

A mix expressed in a reasonably system-independent form allows us, as shown in the following example, to compare two or more CPU architectures and to evaluate their suitability for an installation which produces that mix. Two mixes like those in Table 5.5, which are based on data gathered in a large number of installations, do not represent the characteristics of an individual installation. They can therefore be used, as Flynn did, to compare the properties of different architectures and to analyze possible temporal trends in CPU usage patterns.

Example 5.5   Two CPU's A and B are the most serious candidates for a new scientific installation. Since the work load that the user community will produce is unknown and cannot be measured until the system is installed, we shall choose the Flynn mix as an approximate model of it (the instruction sets of A and B are not too different from the one of the 360 system). Each instruction of the two machines is to be assigned to one of the classes in Table 5.5, and its relative frequency in that class is to be estimated. From these frequencies and the instruction execution times given in the manuals of the two CPU's (to be trusted only because of the gross approximations made throughout the study), we can derive the mean weighted execution times for the instructions in each class. Let these times be those listed in Table 5.6. Then, by applying (5.9), we find

$$\bar{t}_{xA} = 1.88 \ \mu s, \qquad \bar{t}_{xB} = 1.67 \ \mu s. \tag{5.11}$$

We can therefore conclude that, when processing the Flynn mix and with all of the approximations made, machine A is about 11% slower than machine B.

Table 5.6

MEAN WEIGHTED INSTRUCTION CLASS EXECUTION TIMES
FOR THE TWO CPU'S COMPARED IN EXAMPLE 5.4

Instruction class	Machine A, t_{xi} [μs]	Machine B, t_{xi} [μs]
Load/store ⎫ Index ⎭	1.8	1.3
Branch	1.2	1.3
Compare	2.4	2.0
Fixed point	2.4	2.6
Floating point	5.4	5.6
Shift/logical	1.8	2.0
Other	3.5	4.0

If we repeat the calculation using the Gibson mix in Table 5.5, we obtain different absolute results ($\bar{t}_{xA} = 2.29 \ \mu s$, $\bar{t}_{xB} = 2.12 \ \mu s$) but similar relative conclusions. That is, under the Gibson mix, machine A would be approximately 7% slower than machine B. On the other hand, a mix consisting of branches and logical operations might be processed more rapidly by machine A than by machine B. Several additional examples may be found in Drummond (1973).   ■

Mixes representing more specific applications than just scientific and commercial ones, or applications along different dimensions, may be very useful. For instance, both mixes in Table 5.5 include data from compilation as well as from execution of scientific programs. By keeping compilation mixes separate from

Traces have been used in measurement studies by some researchers. For instance, Sackman (1964) measured the performance of the SAGE system in *playback* (or *regenerative*) *recording* experiments, which consisted of driving the system by executable traces [*see also* Karush (1970)]. The very complicated technical problems alluded to above (in particular, those of interference and initialization) explain why playback measurements have had very little popularity to date.

To obtain an executable work-load model by putting together models of individual jobs, we must, at least conceptually, perform the following two operations (*see* Fig. 5.7):

A. Determine the values of the job parameters for each one of the jobs which should appear in the model. We assume that the job parameters have been selected in the model formulation phase. As pointed out in Section 5.1, reality is often much more complicated than our conceptualizations suggest.

B. Construct the model of each job characterized in A above.

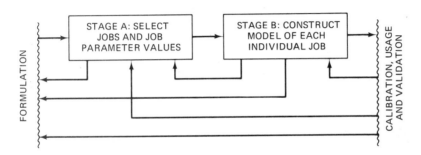

Figure 5.7 Construction phase of an executable artificial model composed of models of individual jobs.

Various approaches to these two problems will be examined in Section 5.3.5. In the rest of this section, we shall briefly discuss executable work-load models which are constructed by following an inverse conceptual path (that is, stage B is executed before stage A). Preexisting or purposely constructed job models are selected and grouped together (possibly assigning an appropriate weight to each one of them) according to an a priori, and usually rather superficial, knowledge of the types of applications an installation will have to process. The goal of such an approach is to obtain a not too inaccurate picture of the installation's expected load or, in some cases, an input suitable for testing certain parts or features of a system [*see,* for example, Karush (1969)]. These standard job models, for the most part proposed for computer selection studies, are called *kernels* [*see,* for example, Arbuckle (1966) and Lucas (1971b)] or sometimes *standardized benchmarks* [*see* Hillegass (1966)]. *Standardized synthetic modules* [*see* Lucas (1971a)] have also been proposed for the same purpose. The definitions of benchmarks and synthetic jobs will be given in Section 5.3.5.

Work-load models which are suitable for interactive systems and may be viewed as belonging to the category of kernels are those composed of scripts. A *script* is a sequence of interactive commands, separated by (usually fixed) think times. This sequence is supposed to represent a typical user session at a terminal. Thus, a collection of scripts may be used to model a number of terminal users simultaneously accessing an interactive system.

Typical examples of kernel problems are, for a scientific installation, matrix inversion, square root approximation, polynomial evaluation, and, for a commercial installation, the file updating kernel. In the latter kernel, a master file is read from disk or tape and updated according to the contents of a detail file, and a report file containing records of the transactions processed is generated (*see* Fig. 5.8). An example of script for an interactive scientific installation is the Multics script described by Saltzer and Gintell (1970) and summarized in Table 5.9.

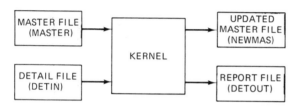

Figure 5.8 File updating kernel.

Table 5.9

SEQUENCE OF OPERATIONS IN AN INTERACTIVE SCRIPT

Operation	Comments
User log-in	—
Program creation	Some typing errors are edited; some syntactic errors are introduced
Program compilation	Syntactic errors are diagnosed
Program debugging	Syntactic errors are removed
Program compilation	Compilation is successful
Program execution	Execution is successful; results are printed out
Program listing	Program text is printed out
File listing	List of files associated with program is printed out
Program deletion	—
User log-out	—

Source: Saltzer and Gintell (1970).

The use of a set of kernels is justifiable during the planning of a new installation when the work load that will have to be processed by the system can only be conjectured and when a system-independent work-load model is needed to compare the characteristics of different machines. In the latter case, users in the process of selecting a computer system sometimes include kernel problems in their specifications. The prospective vendors have to code these kernels for their proposed machines and measure or estimate their running times. Even though sets of kernels, standardized benchmarks, or scripts may represent fairly well an evaluator's idea of the production workload of an installation, they sometimes bear little resemblance to the actual work load. Their field of applicability is definitely broader than the one of instruction mixes. Pipelined machine evaluation and I/O operation modeling are two examples of problems in which kernels may be made much more accurate than mixes. The potentially high system independence of kernels is another important feature of these work-load models.

5.3.5 The Design of an Executable Artificial Model

In the previous section, the task of designing an executable work-load model by aggregation of individual job models has been subdivided into two conceptually distinct stages, A and B, depicted in Fig. 5.7.

Stage A consists of determining the parameters of each one of the jobs to be included in the model. The two conflicting requirements of representativeness and compactness play an important role in the selection of these jobs. A larger work-load model is potentially more representative but tends to take more time to run. The cost of an experiment with an artificial work load increases with its duration, especially because users have to be locked out of the system during such an experiment. The duration of the session is not only dependent on the number of jobs but also on their durations. A work-load model is potentially more representative and system-independent if the characteristics of its jobs do not drastically differ from those of the majority of the real jobs. Thus, a greater number of jobs of normal duration should generally be preferred to fewer jobs that are much longer than usual. The higher potential for representativeness and system independence is due to a greater likelihood of producing similar types and intensities of interactions among system and work-load components.

In stage A, the maximum processing time of the work-load model may be one of the model design specifications. In those experiments in which the total execution time is to be measured in order to evaluate the system's mean throughput rate, the maximum execution time cannot be specified in advance. However, its order of magnitude can be, and often is, included in the design requirements. The choice of this order of magnitude establishes a limit to the degree of representativeness that the work-load model can achieve. Within this constraint, the designer should try to make the model as representative as possible.

Other design objectives may emphasize some of the properties we have listed in Table 5.1, within the limitations discussed at the beginning of Section 5.3.4 for this type of work-load model. These objectives will determine some of the decisions to be made during the design of the model. The discussions of the various alternatives, which appear later in this section, will help the reader understand how the desired properties should influence these choices.

Assuming that we have already selected a characterization for the work load and that this characterization is in terms of a v-tuple of job parameters $(w_1, w_2, \ldots, w_v)$ as discussed in Section 5.2.1, what methods can we use to derive the values of the parameters of each job to be included in the model? Five possible methods are listed in Table 5.10. Methods Aa and Ab apply to characterizations in which job parameters may be of any type, while methods Ac and Ad are suitable for single-valued characterizations and method Ae for sequence-type models.

Method Aa is the least sophisticated one since it does not make any attempt to represent the autocorrelations and correlations existing within and among job parameters. The distributions of job parameters $w_1, \ldots, w_v$ are assumed to be known either from measurements or from estimations. The v-tuple of their

Table 5.10

METHODS TO DETERMINE INDIVIDUAL JOB PARAMETERS (STAGE
A OF THE EXECUTABLE MODEL DESIGN PROCEDURE)

Method	Description
For parameters of both types	
Aa	Construct the probability distributions of the parameters in the real work load. By sampling these distributions, derive the parameters of each job in the model.
Ab	Extract real jobs from the real work load by sampling it. Use the parameters of each job to characterize a job in the model.
For parameters of the single-value type	
Ac	Partition the jobs of the real work load into classes, each characterized by similar combinations of parameters. Choose a suitable number of jobs in each class, and use the parameters of each job to characterize a job in the model.
Ad	Construct the joint probability distribution of the parameters in the real work load. Derive from this distribution the parameters of a set of jobs with the same joint distribution.
For parameters of the sequence type	
Ae	Define the states of a job in terms of the values or ranges of values of its parameters. Construct the state-transition probability matrices for the real work load, and use them to derive the sequences of values of each job's parameters.

values for a job in the work-load model is obtained by sampling these distributions in the same way as in simple distribution-driven simulators (*see* Section 3.2.4). Since the distributions of the w_i's are sampled independently, the implicit assumption underlying method Aa is that system performance does not appreciably depend on the statistical relations among the w_i's. The size of the sample, that is, the number of job models drawn from the distributions, must be statistically significant, so that the distributions of the job parameters in the model can be considered good approximations of those in the real work load. Unfortunately, this condition is by itself not sufficient, in general, to guarantee a certain degree of representativeness for the model.

This method has been used by Schwetman and Browne (1972), who characterized the production work load of the CDC 6600 installation at the Austin campus of the University of Texas by the measured distributions of such parameters as the job interarrival time, the user-specified time limit, the user-specified memory space limit, the ratio between the time limit and the time actually used, the ratio between the space limit and the space actually used, the ratio between used time and CPU time, the I/O burst rate, and the CPU burst rate.

Method Ab takes into account correlations and autocorrelations by deriving the v-tuples from real jobs. The rationale of this method is that in real jobs these interrelations are automatically present and do not have to be explicitly reconstructed. Thus, instead of sampling parameter distributions, one samples the real work load, which in this case usually coincides with a production work load. Various sampling policies can be used. We can pick, for instance, one job out of every n which are submitted (the nth, the $2n$th, and so on) or that job which is running, if any, when we periodically sample the system. The policies which base their sampling on time intervals would seem likely to produce more representative work-load models, since they give more weight to jobs which, making greater use of the resources, have a heavier influence on performance. However, these policies may tend to emphasize the "heavy" jobs excessively. Thus, for those installations whose work load is far from being homogeneous, a combination of the two types of policies, or another method, should probably be used.

Method Ab is the only one which allows us, when coupled with method Ba below, to avoid characterizing explicitly the real work load by a v-tuple of parameters, because the sampled jobs can be employed directly in the construction of the work-load model. However, the evaluator has little control over the composition of such a model, which may turn out to be less representative than required unless a large number of jobs is collected. This remark will be convincing if the reader recognizes the similarity between a model obtained by method Ab and an executable trace. In fact, the latter might be viewed as a particular case of the former. Applications of this method are reported by Shope et al. (1970) and Wood and Forman (1971).

Method Ac gives the modeler better control over the representativeness, and hence also the compactness, of the model. Let us assume that the work-load parameters are such that a job is fully characterized by single values of

$w_1, \ldots, w_v$. In other words, the parameters represent the total resource demands of an individual job rather than the histories of its resource demands. Then, in the *v-dimensional space of job parameters*, each job in the real work load is represented by a point. To classify the jobs, we can apply a *clustering technique* (one of those used, for instance, in pattern recognition or information retrieval) to the cloud of points which represents the real work load in the parameter space. The purpose of clustering techniques is to partition the points into clusters according to some vicinity criterion. The criterion can be, for instance, that the sum of the squares of the distances between each point in a cluster and the cluster's center of mass be minimum. Often, clustering algorithms require their user to specify the number of clusters to be considered. The accuracy of the classification and the cost of determining it increase with this number. However, such an algorithm may be applied iteratively. One may, for instance, start with two clusters only and keep applying the algorithm with an incremented number of clusters until some accuracy criterion is satisfied. The accuracy criterion may be the requirement that the maximum of the sums of squares which characterize the clusters be less than a prespecified amount.

In the context of method Ac, each cluster is viewed as a class of jobs. The real work load can be modeled by a set of jobs drawn from each class proportionally to its population, very much like a political system based on parties and proportional representation. As in political systems, compactness imposes that the number of representatives from each class be a very small fraction of its membership. These representatives may be selected according to various policies. For example, the q_i *v*-tuples which represent class i could all be identical and correspond to the coordinates of the center of mass of class i. Alternatively, they could be those characterizing the q_i real jobs closest to the center of mass or those of some q_i real jobs satisfying other requirements.

Table 5.11

JOB PARAMETERS FOR A BATCH-PROCESSING INSTALLATION

		Mean value	
Parameter	Overall	Research jobs	Instructional jobs
Cards read	224	430	95
Lines printed	760	1430	442
CPU time [s]	11.0	26	3.8
Peripheral processor time [s]	11.9	22	7.1
Primary memory space [words]	17.85K	21.12K	16.32K
Tape drives requested	0.28	0.4	0.22
Cost to user [$]	1.44	3.40	0.48
Fraction of jobs using FORTRAN	0.54	0.73	0.44
Number of jobs	1588	527	1061

Source: Hunt et al. (1971), by permission of AFIPS, Inc.

The results of method Ac tend to be reasonably good if the clusters are well defined and deteriorate rapidly as the fuzziness of their boundaries increases. Methods similar to Ac, even though formal clustering techniques were not applied, have been used by several work-load model designers. For example, Joslin (1965) classifies real jobs qualitatively according to their application. In a batch-processing installation, he partitions the work load into such classes as FORTRAN-coded engineering problems, COBOL-coded business problems, FORTRAN-coded mathematical problems, and so on. Other classifications often encountered in the literature are those based on the programming languages in which jobs are written or on the priorities assigned to them by the programmers and by the system. Hunt et al. (1971) characterized the work load of the CDC 6400 installation at the University of Washington by the parameters listed in Table 5.11. Application of an iterative clustering technique resulted in the six job classes described in Table 5.12. The first step of the procedure partitioned the

Table 5.12

JOB CLASSES RESULTING FROM AN APPLICATION OF METHOD Ac TO THE WORK LOAD IN TABLE 5.11

Class	Population	Predominant job type
1	408	Small FORTRAN jobs
2	472	Small non-FORTRAN (e.g., BASIC) jobs
3	86	Small aborted jobs
4	181	Medium jobs using tapes
5	293	Medium jobs not using tapes
6	148	Large jobs
	1588	

Source: Hunt et al. (1971).

work load into two clusters, which turned out to almost coincide with the research and instructional classes reported in Table 5.11.

Method Ad is conceptually similar to Ac and applies to the same type of characterization, even though no partitioning of the real work load is attempted. A scaled-down picture of this work load is obtained by constructing a model which approximates the joint probability distribution of its parameters and is, at the same time, much more compact. We shall illustrate the method by an example following Sreenivasan and Kleinman (1974), who proposed it and applied it to the construction of a work-load model for a batch-processing installation.

Example 5.7 Let jobs be characterized by the pair (t_{cpu}, n_{io}) of single-valued parameters, where t_{cpu} is the total CPU time consumed by a job and n_{io} is the total number of its I/O requests. The parameter space is the plane represented in Fig. 5.9(a), in which each real

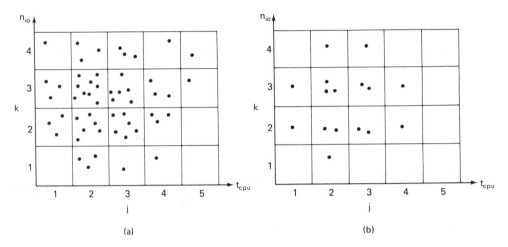

Figure 5.9 Example of the application of method Ad: (a) the real work-load plane; (b) the work-load model plane.

job corresponds to a point. A way to approximate the joint probability distribution of t_{cpu} and n_{io} is to divide the plane into rectangles of proper size and to reduce the number of points in each rectangle by the same factor. This factor is close to the ratio between the number of jobs in the real work load and the number of jobs in the work-load model. The result of this operation is shown in Fig. 5.9(b) for a reduction factor equal to 3.

As in method Ac, the values of the parameters of the jobs in the model can be chosen in different ways. If the rectangle whose center has coordinates (t_{cpuj}, n_{iok}) in the plane of the model [Fig. 5.9(b)] contains y_{jk} points, we may characterize the corresponding job models by y_{jk} pairs of the same values (t_{cpuj}, n_{iok}) or by the y_{jk} pairs corresponding to y_{jk} real jobs picked at random from that rectangle in the real plane [Fig. 5.9(a)]. Other policies may also be chosen.

The total number Y of jobs in the model may be determined from design specifications such as the maximum CPU time that the model is allowed to consume when running on the given system. We may, for instance, write

$$t_{cpu\,tot} = \sum_{j} \left(t_{cpuj} \sum_{k} y_{jk} \right),\tag{5.12}$$

where $t_{cpu\,tot}$, the total CPU time demanded by the model, cannot be larger than the given maximum. If by X we denote the total number of jobs in the real work load and by x_{jk} the number of real jobs in the rectangle defined by (t_{cpuj}, n_{iok}), the reduction factor is

$$r = \frac{X}{Y},\tag{5.13}$$

with

$$X = \sum_{j}\sum_{k} x_{jk}, \qquad Y = \sum_{j}\sum_{k} y_{jk},\tag{5.14}$$

and

$$y_{jk} = \frac{x_{jk}}{r} \tag{5.15}$$

for all j and k.

We are interested in the minimum value of r which satisfies the design requirements since this is the choice corresponding to the maximum degree of representativeness. To determine this minimum, we can apply a simple iterative procedure which consists of starting with an initial value of r, calculating $\sum_k y_{jk}$ from (5.15) and $t_{\text{cpu tot}}$ from (5.12), adjusting the value of r, and repeating until $t_{\text{cpu tot}}$ is close enough to its maximum limit.   ■

Although serious comparisons have not been made between methods Ac and Ad, the latter is likely to provide a higher degree of representativeness, especially when the real work load cannot be partitioned into clusters with sharply defined boundaries. Both methods, in their versions described above, suffer from the same shortcoming. The construction of a scaled-down picture of the real work load is based on the job density in each class or rectangle, and this is equivalent to giving all of the jobs the same weight. In reality, however, jobs do not generally have the same weight. An installation's work load is often dominated by a few very large jobs, which in the parameter space are isolated points and tend to disappear when the reduction factor is applied, rather than by the much more numerous very small jobs.

Both methods can be modified in various ways to reduce this problem. For example, appropriate weights may be assigned to each class or to each rectangle so that in fact each has its own reduction factor. In our illustration of method Ad (Example 5.7), we could give each rectangle of coordinates $(t_{\text{cpu}j}, n_{iok})$ a weight proportional to $t_{\text{cpu}j} + n_{iok}\bar{t}_{io}$, where $\bar{t}_{io}$ is the mean time per I/O request. Changing the method to take this modification into account is left as an exercise for the reader (*see* Problem 5.6). Another approach is suggested by the remark that the rectangles need not be all identical in size, provided that the sizes of the corresponding rectangles in the two planes coincide.

The weights introduced above, and others which might be similarly defined, are in fact measures which somehow try to quantify the relative importance of the various jobs by the *amount of service* or the *resource count* that each job requires. We have seen in Section 5.2.2 that this importance should be expressed in terms of their influence on performance and that, however, the complexity of the problem generally obliges us to grossly approximate it by indices such as resource counts. In any case, the democratic principle of attributing equal importance to all jobs is, in computer systems, wrong.

Method Ae can be used when job parameters are of the sequence type and there are reasons not to use method Aa or Ab. The model of a job underlying method Ae is more sophisticated than the one of Aa. It is in fact a stochastic model in which each job is at any given time in one of its possible states and has certain probabilities, measured or estimated from the real work load, of making transitions to other states. The state of a job is defined by the current values of its parameters or by their recent histories. State-transition probabilities depend on the current state and sometimes on those visited in the recent past. If we assume that they depend only on the current state, we can represent jobs by one or more Markov models from which the sequences of values of the characterizing parameters can be derived.

Let a job be characterized by the pair $(\{t_{cpu}\}, \{t_{io}\})$, where $\{t_{cpu}\}$ is the sequence of uninterrupted CPU intervals (also called *CPU bursts*) and $\{t_{io}\}$ is the sequence of blocked intervals due to I/O requests. These sequences are those which the job would exhibit if it were running alone on the system. We can postulate that CPU and I/O intervals are generated by two distinct and independent Markov processes, whose states are simply ranges of interval durations. If we subdivide the axis of CPU bursts into q_{cpu} ranges, the CPU burst model consists of q_{cpu} states. A transition from state S_{cpui} to state S_{cpuj} occurs if a CPU burst whose duration falls into the range of S_{cpui} is followed by a burst of duration falling into the range of S_{cpuj}.

Alternatively, and probably more accurately, states may be defined as pairs of ranges. If S_{cpui} is the range of a CPU burst and S_{iok} is the range of the immediately successive I/O burst, the state of a job would be defined by (S_{cpui}, S_{iok}), and the total number of states would be $q_{cpu}q_{io}$ instead of $q_{cpu} + q_{io}$ (q_{io} is the number of ranges into which the axis of I/O bursts has been subdivided). Note that the model (or models) may be the same for all the jobs or that there may be different models for different classes of jobs or even for different jobs.

Very few data have been published to help evaluators make their choices. We shall mention the results obtained by Lasseter et al. (1973), who found partially observable Markov models of CPU bursts to fit reasonably well the behaviors of about 400 jobs from a CDC 6600 installation's production work load. These models were only partially observable since their states did not correspond to different durations but rather to different distributions of durations.

A work-load model obtained by method Ae is described by Lindsay (1975), who characterized the work load of a CDC 6400 installation by two independent homogeneous Markov chains. One was the chain of the *input rates* s_i/t_{cpui}, where s_i is the number of disk sectors involved in a disk-to-memory transfer and t_{cpui} is the CPU time consumed between that transfer and the next transfer of the same type. The other was the chain of the *output rates* s_o/t_{cpuo}, where s_o is the number of sectors involved in a memory-to-disk transfer and t_{cpuo} is the CPU time consumed between the preceding transfer of the same type and that transfer.

In *stage B* of the work-load model design procedure, each job model is to be implemented in executable form. The model of each job has been determined in stage A, either by one of the five methods discussed above or by some other method. There are three basic approaches, listed in Table 5.13, to implement a job model.

Method Ba is the most straightforward when in stage A the v-tuples of job parameters which constitute the work-load model are drawn from real jobs. This

Table 5.13

METHODS TO IMPLEMENT AN EXECUTABLE MODEL OF
EACH JOB (STAGE B OF THE EXECUTABLE MODEL
DESIGN PROCEDURE)

Method	Description
Ba	Take jobs from the real work load (*benchmarks*)
Bb	Write nonparametric programs or select the most appropriate ones from an existing pool
Bc	Write parametric programs (*synthetic jobs*)

is the case of method Ab and may be that of Ac and Ad. However, both in Ac and Ad the representatives of each class or rectangle do not have to be real jobs.

Method Ba can also be applied after using Aa or Ae, since we can always search the real work load to find the real job whose parameters are closest (according to some mathematical or intuitive definition of distance) to a v-tuple generated from a set of distributions or of transition matrices. In these cases, however, it is more natural and easier to use method Bb or Bc.

The real jobs selected as members of the work-load models are called *benchmarks*. Benchmarks are certainly the best models for the jobs selected in stage A, since they coincide with the jobs to be modeled. Their very limited modifiability, however, makes benchmark sets quite inflexible. The easiest changes are perhaps those suggested by Joslin (1965), who suppressed some job steps (e.g., compilation or execution) or the generation of the output in some benchmarks to increase the representativeness of the work-load model. Another problem which may arise with benchmarks in some installations is the unavailability of real jobs due to privacy reasons. This obstacle is made harder to overcome by the fact that the files used by the benchmarks must also be part of the work-load model.

Method Bb implements jobs models by purposely written programs which are *nonparametric*, that is, whose resource demands cannot be easily modified. In other words, these programs are like benchmarks except for the fact that they do not come from the real work load. Method Bb is applicable in conjunction with any of the methods we have discussed for stage A. It may replace Ba when the real work load does not exist (for instance, when a new installation is being created) or is unavailable due to privacy reasons.

The difficulty of writing programs which exhibit a given behavior strongly depends on the degree of detail with which their behavior is specified. It is relatively easy to implement a program which consumes a given amount of CPU time, but it is much harder to match a certain CPU burst pattern or an assigned memory referencing behavior. The category of jobs which method Bb may make use of includes kernels, standardized benchmarks, and scripts as well as programs constructed to match certain instruction or statement mixes (*see* Section 5.3.4). In these cases, however, the design of the work-load model is usually not done following the procedure illustrated in this section. Rather, the model is assembled according to a priori judgments and expectations concerning the behavior of the real work load, which is not known in detail. When the real work load is thoroughly known and representativeness is a major design issue, method Bb is very difficult to use in connection with a preexisting pool of programs such as kernels or scripts.

Method Bc employs a *synthetic job* to implement each job model. A synthetic job is a *parametric* program. The behavior of such a program can be easily controlled by acting on the values of a few input variables, to be called the *arguments* of the synthetic job. If job characterization is simple, the implementation of a synthetic job which is able to reproduce the behavior of a large variety of real jobs is also reasonably simple, as described in the following example.

Example 5.8   An executable work-load model for a batch-processing system is to be designed. Jobs have been characterized by the pair (t_{cpu}, n_{io}) of single-valued parameters, as in Example 5.7. Stage A of our design procedure has yielded a model of the work load in terms of a certain number of pairs of values of t_{cpu} and n_{io} [for example, we may assume that method Ad was applied and resulted in the 16 points in Fig. 5.9(b)]. The problem is to construct a synthetic job by which we can implement the desired work-load model. This problem has a multiplicity of solutions. In writing our synthetic job, we shall try not to make the job too unrealistic.

For simplicity, let us assume that the I/O operations of the real jobs involve only a card reader and a line printer. Since most programs in a batch environment request most of their input from the card reader at the beginning and produce most of their output to the printer at the end, we shall design our synthetic job according to the flowchart in Fig. 5.10. The arguments of the job are denoted by t'_{cpu}, n'_{io}, and n'_i. We want t'_{cpu} and n'_{io} to, dictate the actual t_{cpu} and n_{io} of the job and n'_i to be the number of input operations. The last argument is not required, since our model does not distinguish between input and output requests. However, this argument has been added in order to increase the flexibility of the synthetic job (*see* Section 5.4).

The two variables k_1 and k_2 which appear in the flow chart in Fig. 5.10 are to be estimated by a timing procedure or, better, measured; k_1 is the CPU time the program spends outside the compute loop, and k_2 is the loop execution time. Note that k_1, which will often be negligible with respect to t'_{cpu}, is assumed to be a constant in Fig. 5.10, while it is in fact dependent on n'_{io} and n'_i.

Our synthetic job is extremely simpleminded and could be improved from many standpoints. For example, t'_{cpu}, n'_{io}, and n'_i could be initialized by the program instead of being read from a card. If this modification were made, the contents of the data deck would become absolutely unimportant. In our example work-load model in Fig. 5.9(b), we would have 16 copies of the synthetic job, each characterized by the 16 different (t_{cpu}, n_{io}) pairs read from the diagram in the figure.   ∎

Another example of a synthetic job is the one constructed by Buchholz (1969), who introduced this type of job model and proposed its use as a measurement standard. A flowchart of Buchholz's job, which was inspired by the file updating kernel described in Section 5.3.4 and in Fig. 5.8, is given in Fig.

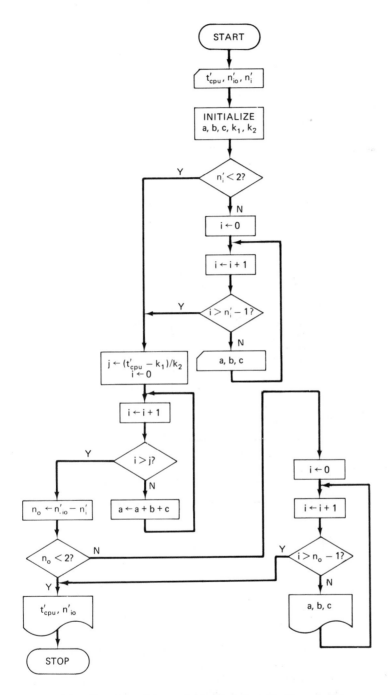

Figure 5.10 Flowchart of the synthetic job designed in Example 5.8.

265

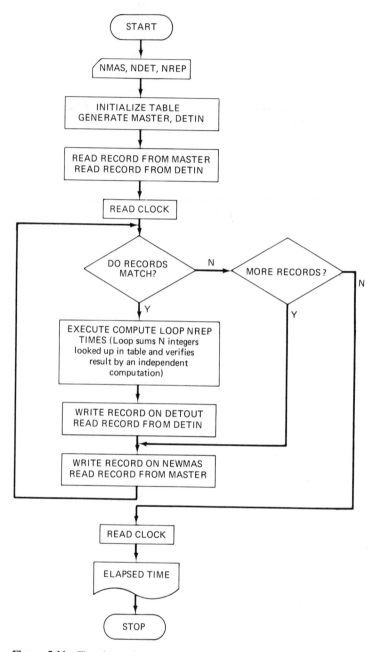

Figure 5.11 Flowchart of the synthetic job proposed by Buchholz (1969). The records in MASTER have consecutive keys; the keys of those in DETIN jump by an increment equal to the ratio NMAS/NDET. TABLE is an array of size N^3. Thus, N influences both the execution time of the compute loop and the memory space occupied by the program.

266

5.11. [Note that, in some sense, the standardized benchmark proposed by Gosden and Sisson (1962) and Hillegass (1966) was also a synthetic job.] Buchholz's synthetic job has three arguments: the number NMAS of master records to be read in, the number NDET of detail records to be processed, and the number NREP of executions of the compute loop for each time the loop is entered. As can be derived from the caption of Fig. 5.11, the compute loop is entered NDET times. The relationships among these arguments and the amounts of resources consumed by the job are less immediate and straightforward than those existing in the simple job we designed in Example 5.8 but are still quite direct. The difficulty of deriving the values of the job's arguments corresponding to a v-tuple of job parameters obtained from stage A depends on the characterization selected for the work load. If the job model is as simple as the one assumed in Example 5.8, this derivation is relatively easy (*see* Problem 5.13).

Synthetic jobs similar to the one proposed by Buchholz have been used by several evaluators. For example, Wood and Forman (1971) made only slight modifications to it when they designed their work-load model by applying methods Ab and Bc (Ba could not be used for privacy reasons). Sreenivasan and Kleinman (1974) added to it three arguments: the number of times the file updating process is repeated, the I/O buffer size, and the record size. The values of the job parameters t_{cpu} and n_{io} obtained by applying method Ad had to be translated into those of the six arguments. This is, in general, a nontrivial problem. However, as will be seen in Section 5.4, the degrees of freedom gained by having more arguments than job parameters can be used to calibrate the work-load model. A synthetic job slightly more complex than that of Example 5.8 was used by Kernighan and Hamilton (1973) as the basic component of their work-load model for a Honeywell 6070 running under the GECOS III operating system. The arguments of the synthetic job were total CPU time, total I/O time, and primary-memory space occupied. The space requested by each job was assumed to be time-invariant.

It is to be observed that method Bc is the only one which, when coupled with method Aa or Ae, allows an executable work-load model to be generated in real time, that is, at the time it is needed. This can be done by sampling the given distributions or applying the given stochastic models to generate the values of the parameters of a job at the time of its arrival. The arrival time may also be determined by sampling a given interarrival time distribution. The parameter values generated in this way are then passed onto a copy of the synthetic job, which becomes the model of a job to be input into the system immediately. In this application, it is important that the relationships between the job parameters and the arguments of the synthetic job be as simple as possible.

The reader has certainly noticed the close similarity between this method of work-load model generation in real time and the one used in distribution-driven simulation (*see* Section 3.2.4). The only conceptual differences are that in measurement studies the method involves the real system rather than a model of it, and, since the work-load model must be executable, the mediation of synthetic jobs is necessary.

This method of work-load model generation, which makes the model very compact, has been applied by Schwetman and Browne (1972) and Lindsay (1975).

The strongest argument in favor of synthetic jobs is their flexibility, which can be exploited in work-load model calibration as well as in its modification. Also, unless different classes of jobs in the real work load have been characterized differently, there is usually no reason to have more than a few distinct synthetic jobs in a model. Thus, the resulting model is often more compact than one obtained by method Ba or Bb, especially when, as noted above, the executable work load is generated in real time. Oliver et al. (1974), for instance, argue that their library of five synthetic jobs, oriented toward five different types of commercial applications, can represent, by suitable combinations of the jobs, a very broad spectrum of commercial work loads.

Synthetic jobs can be applied equally conveniently in conjunction with all the methods we have described for stage A. The major disadvantage of synthetic jobs with respect to benchmarks is their intrinsically lower degree of representativeness. For equal job characterizations, properly chosen benchmarks are likely to represent the real applications of the installation better than synthetic jobs. The latter presumably need a more accurate characterization to reach the potential representativeness of the former. However, several studies have reported encouraging results on the use of synthetic jobs even with very simple characterizations [see, for example, Kernighan and Hamilton (1973) and Schwetman and Browne (1972)].

We shall end this section with a brief discussion of the various ways in which an executable work-load model may be submitted to the system to be measured. Often, in a batch-processing installation, a work-load model physically consists of a number of card decks or a tape or disk file. If method Bc has been employed to implement the model, the synthetic job (or jobs) may also be called by a *driver*. A driver is a program which reads job parameters from a card reader or some other input device or generates them from given distributions or from stochastic models. Then the driver calculates from these parameters the values of the arguments of the synthetic job, passes these values to a copy of the job, and simulates the job's arrival (that is, adds it to the input queue). As mentioned above, arrival times can be scheduled by the next event technique used in simulation if the interarrival time distribution is part of the work-load model (*see* Example 5.6).

When the driver is a program running on the system to be measured, we call it an *internal driver*. If job models are generated and submitted to this system by another computer connected to it as a peripheral device, we have an *external driver*. Thus, an external driver is a hardware-software complex. Drivers have been quite infrequently used so far in batch-processing installations, and practically all of them were of the internal type.

In interactive systems, the only alternative to a driver for an experiment under an artificial work-load model consists of hiring as many people as there are terminals which have to be active. These people are to play the role of users following scripts provided by the experimenters. Since this alternative is very inconvenient and considerably lowers the reproducibility of the work-load model, the driver solution is generally to be preferred. Internal drivers do not require extra hardware but interfere with the system being measured. Furthermore, they are unable to simulate the arrival of commands and the departure of outputs without distortions due to the bypassing of parts of the system's I/O paths. This is not the case of external drivers, which can represent more accurately the conversations between the system and the terminals. One problem with an internal driver is, as seen in Example 5.6, that of having to intercept all output which is sent to the terminals and simulate its transmission and reception by each user as well as the user's think and typing-in time. Note that internal drivers sometimes simulate resource demands instead of conversational command sequences. Also, both types of drivers, and the job models they generate, may run concurrently with real processes and do not necessarily require a dedicated system.

Descriptions of internal drivers can be found in DeMeis and Weizer (1969), Saltzer and Gintell (1970), and Fogel and Winograd (1972). An example of an external driver is the one developed by Greenbaum (1969) for the Multics system: A PDP-8 minicomputer connected via telephone lines to the GE-645 computer system can simulate up to 12 simultaneous interactive users whose commands follow scripts like the one in Table 5.9.

One problem to be solved whenever the work-load model for a multi-programming system consists of a sequence of job models which is to be manufactured by the experimenters is deciding in what order the jobs should appear in the sequence. Clearly, the order in which jobs are processed influences the amount of overlap between the computational and input-output activities needed to process the work load and hence the values of performance indices such as throughput rate and response time. This is the reason different job-scheduling policies produce different system performances and why the behavior of a given policy in general depends on the order and the times of arrival of the jobs.

A simple illustration of this fact is given in Fig. 5.12 for the case of two jobs competing for a CPU and an I/O channel. When job 1 precedes job 2, the total elapsed time is substantially longer than when the jobs enter the system in the reverse order. Note that a big part of the difference between the two elapsed times is due to the *tail effect* discussed in Section 3.4.2.

Even in deciding the job arrival order, an experimenter should try to maximize the representativeness of the work load. If the installation has special policies affecting this order or if the real work load exhibits identifiable patterns of arrival (for instance, the larger jobs tend to be submitted at the end of the day), the work-load model should reflect them. In most installations, the jobs have external priorities which affect the order in which they are processed. In those installations, job models will have to be assigned external priorities according to the observed frequencies and patterns of such priorities. Also, stochastic models of the arrival processes could be created from empirical data and used to

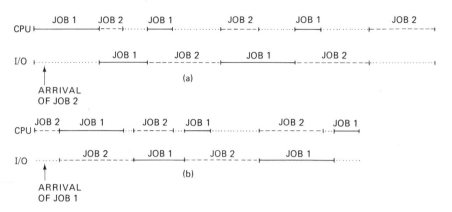

Figure 5.12 Dependence of the total elapsed time on the job arrival order in a multiprogramming system: (*a*) job 1 precedes job 2; (*b*) job 2 precedes job 1. Dots indicate the intervals in which the resource is idle.

determine a reasonably representative ordering of the job models. When no information on this aspect of user community behavior is available, a randomization procedure should be applied to reduce the bias possibly introduced by the investigator or by the method of job model generation (stage A). The reader has certainly noted that such a procedure is already built into method Ab.

5.4 WORK-LOAD MODEL CALIBRATION AND VALIDATION

Like any other model, even a work-load model should be calibrated and validated whenever possible. The distinction between these two operations has already been discussed in Sections 3.3 and 4.4. Both are based on a comparison which, in the case of a work-load model, is supposed to indicate the extent to which the model fits the real work load. According to the definition of representativeness given in Section 5.2.2, we should compare the values of the performance indices produced by the two work loads to determine how close the work loads are to being equivalent. This is certainly the most reliable comparison if the work-load model is executable and if the real work load and the system are available. When these conditions are met, experimental comparisons are possible, but experiments must be performed with great care to ensure that the system is under the same conditions when it is driven by the two work loads. If the conditions are not all met, only conceptual comparisons can be made (*see* Section 3.3.1).

When the work-load model is not executable, it will have to drive a model of the system, and the outcome of calibration or validation experiments will be very much influenced by the accuracy of the system model. In fact, since a system model requires a valid work-load model when it is being calibrated or validated, the only reasonable solution seems to be that of performing both operations on both models at the same time. In many cases this solution is actually made mandatory by the fact that the two models cannot be easily and neatly separated. Of course, there may be situations in which the system model is known, or may safely be assumed, to be valid. Also, when some latitude for modifying the system model without changing the work-load model exists, we can make use of it to study the degree of system independence of the work-load model. However, our considerations in this section mostly refer to the case of executable work-load models.

To exhibit a reasonably large domain of validity, work-load models, like system models, should contain more detail than would be required to make them representative under just a few experimental conditions. This additional degree of detail may be introduced indirectly by using an augmented set of performance indices to be compared in calibration and validation procedures. In other words, a work-load model which is able to produce sufficiently accurate values not only of primary performance indices but also of some secondary performance indices is likely to have a larger domain of validity than one for which only primary index values have been examined.

Schwetman and Browne (1972), for instance, validated their work-load model for a CDC 6600 by comparing not only mean throughput rates and CPU utilizations, which were their primary indices, but also the utilizations of the various disk channels and the mean rates of peripheral processor requests, of operating system requests, and of task switching. This comparison was made by running a work-load model composed of synthetic jobs on a system configured to reproduce for these jobs as faithfully as possible the conditions of production work-load processing. Since the basic synthetic job used did not involve any remote batch or interactive I/O activity, those resources normally taken by these activities (part of the primary memory, one of the slots available to load ready jobs into memory, and four peripheral processors) were turned off. Another example is the one of Kernighan and Hamilton (1973), who based their comparisons on 13 indices. These indices included the user CPU time, the system CPU time, the I/O times for each secondary storage device, and the numbers of I/O operations, CPU idle intervals, and programs swapped.

A comparison showing an insufficient match ought to result in a modification of the model. Especially when the model is being calibrated, changes must be as easy to make as possible. A work-load model should ideally be designed with a clear knowledge of the most probable changes to be made to it. Since both predicting these changes and making good use of the information is quite difficult, one should design models which are reasonably flexible in general, so as to reduce the probability of having to redesign them. Among the executable models, the most flexible ones are those composed of synthetic jobs. The calibration of a work-load model of this type may consist of varying the arguments of some of its synthetic jobs to make the model more representative. In addition, it is possible to introduce in the design of a synthetic job some special *calibration parameters* which would be the obvious first candidates for modification. Examples of such parameters in the synthetic job in Fig. 5.10 could be k_1 and k_2 or, perhaps more properly (since k_1 and k_2 were intended to be correction factors), n_i', the third argument.

It seems in principle feasible to extend the methods used to calibrate simulators to the calibration of synthetic work-load models. In particular, the technique described in Section 3.3.3 to determine the changes to be made can probably be applied to this problem. Both for work-load model design and for calibration the relationships between the arguments of a synthetic job and its characterizing parameters should be as simple as possible. An ideal situation is one in which each job parameter depends in a simple manner on only a single argument. In this case, it is possible to isolate each component of the job's behavior, and the calculation of the argument values and of their changes during calibration is much easier.

Example 5.9 Let us examine the relationships between the arguments of the synthetic job designed in Example 5.8 (*see* Fig. 5.10) and its behavior. In principle, the two components of the job's behavior, t_{cpu} and n_{io}, are quite well isolated from each other and directly related to the arguments t_{cpu}' and n_{io}'. Varying t_{cpu}' influences only t_{cpu} and not n_{io}. Also, n_{io} is exactly equal to n_{io}', which, however, has some impact on t_{cpu}. To determine the extent of this impact, as well as to validate our design, we can run several experiments with the synthetic job and plot the measured values of t_{cpu} and n_{io} versus t_{cpu}' (with constant n_{io}') and n_{io}' (with constant t_{cpu}'). The presence of n_i' among the arguments adds a third dimension to our problem. However, this argument will be ignored for the moment, since accounting for it is straightforward and would only make our discussion more cumbersome. Our design objectives can be expressed by the two equations

$$t_{cpu} = t_{cpu}', \qquad n_{io} = n_{io}'. \tag{5.16}$$

If the experiments and the collection of the data are careful enough, the curves referred to above will tell us how far our synthetic job is from these objectives. In the case of significant discrepancies, we can also use these curves as calibration curves. We can, for instance, read from them the value of t_{cpu}' to be fed into the synthetic job in order to obtain a given value of t_{cpu}.

If the dependence of t_{cpu} and n_{io} on t_{cpu}' and n_{io}' were very intricate, adjusting the values of t_{cpu}' and n_{io}' to obtain the desired t_{cpu} and n_{io} might be quite difficult. An example of this difficulty can be found in the paper by Sreenivasan and Kleinman (1974), where the synthetic job has six arguments and two characterizing parameters nonlinearly related to the arguments.

A set of synthetic jobs in which a high degree of isolation between parameters has been achieved is described by Oliver et al. (1974), who report the results of a number of experiments on individual synthetic jobs. Experimenting is important especially because of the difficulties of predicting and taking into proper account the effects on job parameters of the rest of the work load (ideally there should be no effects) and of the operating system. Furthermore, if synthetic jobs are not written in machine language, different translators generally have a hard-to-predict influence on the relationships between arguments and job parameters. In all of these cases, experimentation is essential. ■

A work-load model construction method based on a calibration procedure might be proposed. The method would consist of iterative adjustments of arguments, experiments, and new adjustments or of successive additions of copies of synthetic jobs followed by the selection of the values of their arguments and by experiments. This proposal, though attractive, does not seem to be generally implementable now since the rules and criteria that should guide the various choices to be made are unknown and too many expensive measurement experiments would probably be required.

A work-load model should be validated whenever the system is modified or a different system is considered. However, this operation may be extremely difficult or impossible to perform. Even in the case of a slight system modification being tested before its release, there is no way of measuring the performance indices of the modified system under the real work load. This can only be done a posteriori, that is, after the release to the users.

When the real work load is an estimated one, it cannot be used to drive the system for comparison purposes. The problems which arise when different systems are to be compared are even more complex. Thus, in almost all cases of practical interest, the validity of a work-load model must be postulated. It is important that the model be intrinsically valid over as large a domain of systems and configurations as needed in the evaluation study. This problem has been discussed throughout this chapter, and even earlier in this section. However, we must recognize that our knowledge of it, like the one of several other aspects of work-load characterization, is still in a quite primitive state.

PROBLEMS

5.1. Determine an instruction mix representing a work load whose processing would be 10% faster on machine *A* than on machine *B* in Table 5.6.

5.2. A system is to be selected for an installation in which all users program in the same language (e.g., FORTRAN). The performances of several (hardware, compiler) pairs are to be compared. Describe in a step-by-step fashion how you would approach the problem using a statement mix, for instance, the one in Table 5.7, to characterize the work load of the installation. State what measurement experiments you would perform and how you would design them, including a description of the measurement tools to be used. Compare, especially from the viewpoint of the reliability of the results, the advantages and the shortcomings of this approach to those of an approach which would base its characterization of the work load on physical resource demands.

5.3. Specify three types of modification to the batch EXOPE system represented in Fig. 3.6 with respect to which the work-load characterization in Table 5.2 is independent and three types with respect to which it is system-dependent. Can you think of characterizations which would be independent with respect to each one of the last three types of changes or to all of them?

5.4. An investigation is being performed to determine the feasibility of driving an interactive system by a set of stochastic models of user behavior (method Ae in Section 5.3.5). The driver could be organized according to the scheme illustrated in Example 5.6, but the executable trace would be replaced by the stochastic models which, in real time, would generate the next command for each user. Modify the flowcharts in Fig. 5.6(c), and design the measurement experiments you would perform in order to gather the information required by the driver.

5.5. Which one of the methods in Table 5.10 produces, in your opinion, the highest potential representativeness in its results? Why? Which method is likely to produce, everything else being equal, the most system-independent work-load models?

5.6. Modify the iterative procedure which determines the reduction factor in method Ad (*see* Example 5.7) to account for the introduction of a weight proportional to $t_{cpuj} + n_{iok}\bar{t}_{io}$ for each rectangle whose center has coordinates (t_{cpuj}, n_{iok}). Note that $\bar{t}_{io}$ is the mean time per I/O request. Could you obtain a similar result by selecting variable-size rectangles instead of giving them different weights as above in this problem? How would you choose the sizes of the rectangles?

5.7. You have used method Ac to classify the jobs in a real work load. How would you weigh the various classes in order to obtain a more representative work-load model than one based on equal weight for all jobs?
Assume that the characterization selected for each job is
(a) the pair (t_{cpu}, n_{io});
(b) the triple (t_{cpu}, t_{io}, m), where t_{io} is the total I/O time excluding queue waits and m is the memory space requested by the job.

5.8. Would it be possible to apply method Ac or Ad to characterizations containing sequence-type parameters? If so, how?

5.9. Design a synthetic job with the same arguments as the one designed in Example 5.8, making n_i' always equal to $n_{io}'/2$ and the job's structure a single loop, to be repeated n_i' times. The loop consists of reading one card, computing for the appropriate amount of time, and printing one line. Comment on the relationships between t_{cpu}' and t_{cpu} and between n_{io}' and n_{io}, after having introduced into your job suitable corrections if necessary.

5.10. An executable work-load model is to be designed for a batch-processing EXOPE system which differs from the one depicted in Fig. 3.6 only in that the drum is missing. Each input (card reader) request issued by a job causes an input routine to be called. This routine looks into the input buffer to find the requested data. If the buffer is empty, the routine suspends the job and requests that the disk sector containing the next input data to be processed be transferred into the buffer. The completion of this transfer causes the job to become ready to run again. Each output (printer) request causes an output routine to be called. This routine stores into the output buffer the data to be printed out and gives control back to the job. When the buffer is full, the routine suspends the job and transfers the contents of the output buffer to the disk. The completion of this operation puts the job into the ready state. The size of each buffer (hence, also of a disk sector) is equivalent to 25 cards or 15 lines. The performance index of interest is the mean throughput rate. A test for the representativeness of the characterization used in Example 5.8 and in Problem 5.9 consists of seeing whether the order in which the input and output operations are performed by each job has a nonnegligible impact on the mean throughput rate. Assume that the total disk time, excluding queue waits, is constant and equal to 10 ms; that two identical synthetic jobs, each characterized by $t'_{cpu} = 100$ ms, $n'_{io} = 300$, $n'_i = 150$, enter the empty system at the same time; and that the disk is never tied up by the card reader or by the line printer. Compare the mean throughput rate given by two jobs of the type designed in Example 5.8 to the one produced by two jobs of the type designed in Problem 5.9 (alternate inputs and outputs). It is advisable to solve the problem with only one job first. If the comparison showed a negligible difference between the throughput rates, would this be sufficient to conclude that the degree of representativeness of the characterization is satisfactory? Discuss also the assumption that reader-to-disk and disk-to-printer transfers have a negligible effect on the throughput rate.

5.11. An evaluation study is to determine the influence of I/O buffer size on the performance of the EXOPE installation described in Problem 5.10. The system independence of the (t_{cpu}, n_{io}) job characterization is to be assessed using one of the two synthetic jobs dealt with in Problem 5.10, or both of them. Again, it is suggested that an investigation in a uniprogramming environment precede the one in which two identical synthetic jobs are multiprogrammed. The arguments of the jobs may be the same as in Problem 5.10. Is the choice of their values critical, and to what extent?

5.12. Assuming that the distributions used by Schwetman and Browne (1972) (see the description of method Aa in Section 5.3.5) are available, specify a job characterization which is consistent with them and draw a flowchart of a synthetic job based on this characterization. Specify also, in flowchart form, a procedure which could be followed by a driver like the one implemented by Schwetman and Browne to generate the argument values for each copy of the synthetic job from the given distributions.

5.13. Show how the values of the arguments NMAS, NDET, NREP of the synthetic job proposed by Buchholz (1969) can be derived from those of the parameters t_{cpu}, t_{io}, m which may be used to characterize the jobs in a real work load to be modeled. Assume that the four files referenced by the synthetic job are stored on four tapes mounted on four separate tape drives, each provided with its own independent controller.

5.14. Is it possible and useful to implement a synthetic script, that is, a script whose behavior can be made to encompass a broad spectrum of interactive user behaviors simply by changing the values of a few arguments? What arguments would you choose, for example, if you had to implement in this way the script outlined in Table 5.9?

5.15. Given a work-load model implemented by methods Ad and Bc, how would you react to a proposal for its calibration based on the experimental comparison of the performance indices it produces with those produced by a work-load model obtained in the same way except for the use of Ba in lieu of Bc?

6

Performance Evaluation in Selection Problems

6.1 SELECTION PROBLEMS

In Section 1.5, performance evaluation studies were classified into the three major categories of selection, improvement, and design studies. Selection studies were defined as those intended to produce the technical information needed by computer users in making decisions on how to satisfy their information-processing requirements by selecting one out of several available alternatives. Thus, selection is an activity typically performed by customers, while design is the task of a manufacturer or supplier. We already noted in Section 1.5 that this distinction between types of evaluation problems is not unambiguous and is made only for expository convenience. Like many of the classifications in this book, it must be taken with several grains of salt. In fact, a number of design activities are usually carried out by organizations which do not manufacture and sell computer systems, components, or software but are instead primarily computer users. For instance, some installations have system components (hardware or operating system modules) which have been designed and implemented by the installation's staff. Also, most computer manufacturers purchase equipment (e.g., peripherals) and sometimes software from other manufacturers. They thus act as customers on the so-called OEM (original equipment manufacturer) market and are confronted with typical selection decisions.

276

Even the border line between selection and improvement studies is not sharply defined. An improvement effort may reveal that the best course of action would be to upgrade the system by adding to it a certain piece of equipment, say a disk drive. Evidently, as a result, a disk drive selection problem arises. Note that this problem is very similar to the one of choosing a disk drive for an installation being designed, assuming that the rest of the configuration has already been specified. However, we have more freedom in the latter case, since it is easier to modify a configuration being designed than one which has already been installed.

The most frequent selection problems will be classified, for the purposes of our treatment, into the following categories.

a. *Processing mode selection*. Among the questions to be answered when an installation is being set up, some are concerned with the processing mode (or modes) that the user community needs (or will benefit the most from). The main modes are batch, interactive, open-shop or closed-shop, direct access, and real-time. Selecting the processing mode will provide the installation designers with information to be used in effectively restricting the field of acceptable hardware and software solutions.

b. *Vendor selection.* This is the central problem in the design of an installation. Important differences usually exist between a completely new installation (e.g., a computerized information system which is being introduced into an organization) and the procurement of a new system for an existing installation. In all cases, however, economical and technical constraints often restrict the choice to a limited number of alternatives whose ability to meet the performance requirements of the installation is to be evaluated for comparison purposes. In competitive selections, these alternatives are proposed by various vendors, who design one or more configurations using their hardware and software components. This is the reason for the name given to this category of problems, which in fact consist of selecting one out of several candidate systems. Configuration design, which usually involves the selection of components, will be dealt with in Chapter 8.

c. *Installation selection.* This is the category of problems to be solved when the most convenient installation among several available ones is to be chosen to satisfy a given information-processing need. An organization may have various computing facilities, and a department, or a group, or an individual programmer within the organization may have to decide which one is the most desirable for a given application. Another example is the selection of a service bureau (a company or external installation which sells computer time) for the processing of a given work load. In a strictly technical sense, these problems are similar to that of selecting a vendor. However, their economic aspects and the different viewpoint (which in this class is that of a mere computer user) may make the global picture quite different.

d. *System component selection.* In this class we have the system upgrading or expansion problems, motivated by performance improvement requirements or desires. They are characterized by the fact that the component or components to be selected must be added to an existing system running in an existing installation. Other problems in this class are those selections encountered in configuration design. Consistently with our definition of a computer system, we include in this category the selection of operating systems or operating system modules (accounting packages, software measurement tools, and, if they are considered as part of the system, compilers, data base systems, and utility programs) as well as hardware modules such as primary-memory boxes, central and I/O processors, disk drives, tape drives, multiplexers, and so on.

   e. *Application program selection*. This type of selection is normally performed by a user and not (as in the case of the software modules mentioned in d) by an installation's management. Of course, some of the criteria on which the selection is to be based are likely to be the same for the two cases. The distinction between these cases is in fact rather vague since it depends on the definition adopted for the system's boundaries. Thus, the selection of a compiler or a data base system will in one situation fall into class d and in another situation into this class. Examples of problems which are peculiar to this class are

   a. the selection of one among the several languages offered by an installation for the coding of a given program;

   b. the selection of one among the several packages existing in an installation for the execution of a given task, (for instance, the generation of pseudo-random numbers, the analysis of variance, the solution of partial differential equations, the sorting of a file);

   c. the selection of one among the several packages existing on the market for the satisfaction of a certain information-processing requirement (for example, the analysis and verification of FORTRAN programs, the automatic generation of program flow charts, the computation of payrolls or income taxes).

   In Section 6.2 we shall deal with some of the fundamental technical aspects of selection problems. After giving the reader a global and rapid perspective of a competitive selection methodology in Section 6.2.1, we shall discuss, in Section 6.2.2, the weight that performance evaluation has in selection decisions and the major obstacles which an evaluator encounters in tackling selection problems. In Section 6.3 we shall be concerned with performance comparisons for selection. After a discussion of some general comparison problems in Section 6.3.1, we shall examine comparisons for processing mode selection in more detail in Section 6.3.2, while Section 6.3.3 is devoted to vendor selection problems, Section 6.3.4 to installation selection, and Section 6.3.5 to system component selection. The selection problems we have grouped in class e are dealt with in Section 9.4.1. A technique-oriented view of selection problems is given in Section 6.4. Some of the peculiar and often extremely complex work-load characterization questions which selection poses are reviewed and discussed in Section 6.5.

6.2 SELECTION METHODOLOGIES

6.2.1 A Competitive Selection Procedure

Computer selection raises, as will become evident in the sequel of this chapter, extremely difficult questions. No universal, standardized procedures exist yet for answering these questions. At best, standard rules for selection exist within an organization. These rules, however, often differ significantly from those used by other organizations. Also, many organizations adopt nonstandardized ad hoc approaches. In this section we shall outline a possible procedure for attacking the various classes of selection problems presented in Section 6.1. Our purpose is to provide a framework for the understanding of the role of performance evaluation in these problems. In presenting this procedure, we shall follow Timmreck (1973), who applies it in particular to competitive vendor selection. The procedure consists of four steps.

Step 1. Analysis and specification of needs. This is the crucial and perhaps most difficult step. It involves such problems as work-load characterization, work-load forecasting, information flow analysis, user requirement analysis and prediction. The needs should be specified in a vendor-independent and system-independent fashion if an unbiased selection procedure is desired. We have already seen in Section 5.2.3 what the main obstacles to a really system-independent work-load characterization are. Most of those considerations can be repeated for the other problems listed above, which are all related to the specification of the system's environment. In this step, a description (as quantitative and precise as possible) of the environment and of its foreseeable future developments is to be prepared. Clearly, this task will be somewhat less difficult if a new system is to be selected for an existing installation than if a new installation is to be set up. The aspects of this step that are more relevant to performance evaluation are discussed in Section 6.5.

Step 2. Preparation of a request for proposals. The needs identified in step 1 must be translated into a set of requirements to be submitted to various vendors. The vendors are expected to propose a configuration which meets these requirements. Of course, the translation should not bias the requirements toward certain vendors. It is useful to distinguish between *mandatory* and *desirable* requirements and to minimize the number of the mandatory ones [*see* Joslin (1968)]. Requirements will include performance specifications, hardware characteristics, processing modes, operating system properties, system cost, reliability and maintainability specifications, service and training needs, languages and software packages desired, and descriptions of expansion capabilities and options.

Step 3. Validation of proposed systems. When the proposals from the vendors are received, a validation process is to take place in order to determine their suitability. This process involves checking whether and to what extent the requirements are met by each proposed system. Checks are performed using manuals, evaluation techniques and tools, measurement data provided by the

279

vendors, and information from other installations having the same system. Those proposals which do not meet all mandatory requirements are rejected. The others are to be compared in step 4.

Step 4. Selection of a valid proposal. The comparison among the proposals which passed the tests in step 3 may be performed according to various methods. *Ad hoc methods* usually consist of simple comparisons of the characteristics and of the degrees to which each valid proposal meets the desirable requirements. They are often used when the selection procedure is to determine whether the feeling that there is no important reason to select a vendor different from the one favored by the customer is justified or not. *Scoring methods* [*see*, for example, Sharpe (1969)] require that a tree of system characteristics be prepared by successive subdivision of the characteristics into classes and subclasses until all the relevant characteristics are included. These characteristics may coincide with the requirements specified in steps 1 and 2. Then a numerical weight is attached to each characteristic to represent its relative value to the evaluators. The sum of all the weights attached to the subnodes of any given node in the tree must be equal to 1. Finally, for each proposal, the evaluators assign a score to each leaf of the tree, and these scores are multiplied by the corresponding weights. Those products computed for nodes having a common father node are then added together to obtain the score of that node. The process is repeated until the score of each system is computed. The proposal with the highest score is selected. The major classes of characteristics used in a RAND Corporation study [*see* Sharpe (1969), p. 285] based on a scoring method are presented in Table 6.1. The *cost-value method* proposed by Joslin (1968) assigns a monetary value to the desirable requirements listed in step 2. This value is subtracted from the cost of those proposals which satisfy the corresponding desirable requirement. The selected

Table 6.1

A SIMPLE ILLUSTRATION OF SCORING METHODS

System characteristic*	Weight*	Scores (on a scale of 10)		
		Vendor A	Vendor B	Vendor C
Hardware	0.27	7	8	6
Operating system	0.27	5	6	7
Data management	0.08	6	4	4
Language processors	0.16	5	7	8
General programming support	0.02	7	5	7
Conversion considerations	0.12	9	6	7
Vendor reliability and support	0.08	6	7	5
	1.00			
Weighted score		9.46	10.38	10.0

*Source: Sharpe (1969).

proposal is the one whose final cost is the lowest. The reader has certainly noticed that subjective weightings play a nonnegligible role in all of the methods described above. An assessment of the advantages and disadvantages of the methods is beyond the scope of this book and can be found in Timmreck (1973).

Two important remarks must be made about the procedure outlined above. The first is that many selections are in fact performed by the so-called *sole-source procedure*. In vendor selection, this means that the vendor is known a priori and that the problem consists of designing the configuration. This a more restricted but nontrivial problem, especially if one wishes to consider the purchase or rental of hardware or software components from independent manufacturers (*see* Chapter 8). Sole-source procurement may be motivated by several reasons, the most important of which is often the prohibitive costs of program conversion that a system from a different vendor would require. This compatibility issue is sometimes successfully solved by emulation of the machine to be replaced. However, there may be other reasons why a new system is procured from the same vendor as the old one: satisfaction with the services received; attractive contract clauses, discounts, and future benefits; easier training of the programming and operations staff; and better chances of survival in the market. In certain situations, the superiority of a new vendor in some of these areas may instead suggest that a change of vendor be made.

The second remark is that a selection procedure like the one illustrated above can reasonably be used only when the cost of the system to be selected justifies the effort required. Simpler and cheaper procedures should be applied to select, say, a single minicomputer.

Procedures for attacking the problems of selecting installations or system components may be conceptually patterned after the one just described. In practice, since the amount of money involved in these selections is generally smaller than the total cost of a medium or large system and the possible alternatives at the outset are generally fewer and better specified, the actual procedures followed are shorter, simpler, and cheaper. Proposals are usually not expected from prospective vendors, who simply provide technical and price information on those of their products supposed to satisfy the user's requirements. By evaluating these data and comparing them against the stated needs, the user will arrive at a decision. For instance, an installation selection problem will be approached by

   a. specifying the work load to be processed (step 1);
   b. gathering information on the performance and charging characteristics of the accessible installations (step 2);
   c. evaluating the information collected and discarding those installations which are not competitive with the others (step 3);
   d. comparing costs and performances of the remaining installations to determine the one which is best suited to the task (step 4).

Some techniques which may be applied to perform these operations are described in Section 6.3.4. Also the selection of a system component can easily be described as following the same sequence of steps. It should be noted, however, that informal competitive procedures or sole-source procurement are even more widely used in installation and system component selections than in vendor selections.

6.2.2 The Role of Performance Evaluation in Selection Procedures

In Section 6.2.1, we have briefly described the steps of a procedure for attacking selection problems. The procedure is especially suited to vendor selection problems. However, the same procedure with some simplifications has been recognized to be conceptually valid also for installation and system component selections. Even a superficial examination of the procedure shows that it includes various activities and considerations which do not strictly belong to the realm of performance evaluation as we have defined it in Section 1.4. Economical aspects are present, and rightly so, in all of the procedure's steps. Several intrinsically qualitative characteristics, such as language features and programming support, must be taken into account. Their quantification (when attempted, as in scoring methods) is always the expression of subjective opinions, to which the evaluation techniques discussed in this book cannot be applied. In this section, we shall examine the role played by quantitative performance evaluation in a selection procedure. At what points of the procedure described in Section 6.2.1 are evaluation studies of the type considered in this book (*see* Section 1.4) required or convenient, and what is their contribution to the selection process?

Some of the needs to be analyzed and specified in step 1 of the procedure can be termed *performance requirements*. The users of an installation being planned, or of a system component to be acquired, or of a computing service being offered generally have requirements of three types: functional requirements, performance requirements, and economic requirements. They want their information-processing needs to be satisfied with a certain level of performance and the minimum cost compatible with the satisfaction of their needs and with that level of performance. These three types of requirements are interrelated since each system or component feature being considered has functional, performance, and cost implications. The distinction between mandatory and desirable needs mentioned in Section 6.2.1 applies to each type of need. This distinction is important in that it reveals the latitude a decision maker will have in trading off the functional capabilities and performance aspects of desirable features with their costs in the selection process. The analysis and specification of performance needs involves deciding the main performance indices and criteria (*see* Section 1.4) by which the various alternatives will be judged and compared and selecting quantitative values or ranges for them. Since the performance of a system depends on its work load, the work load will have to be characterized and described. Thus, techniques for work-load characterization and forecasting and user community modeling may have to be used to analyze and specify needs (step 1) if an installation is being designed. In the case of installation selection, the work load will in general be only partially known. Predicting what programs will be sharing the resources of the system with the user's programs will usually be impossible. However, this additional work load must be somehow estimated if the performance a system will give to the user is to be determined. When a component is to be selected, the problem of characterizing its input is often less necessary. Technical characteristics which do not depend on the input may be sufficient to specify the performance of components, especially hardware. For instance, the performance of a primary-memory module may be satisfactorily described by its word length, access time, write time, and transfer rate, and the performance of a disk drive by its seek characteristic, revolution time, transfer rate, and data organization. In all selection problems, step 1 is an extremely important step. It is highly desirable that users have a clear understanding of the performance (and cost) implications of each one of their stated needs. In particular, it is easy to conceive of contradictory or unfeasible specifications, which should obviously be avoided. Thus, some evaluation studies might be necessary or at least useful in step 1 to help in the specification of the requirements. The objective of these studies might be to determine the influences of certain system features on given performance indices, or the adequacy of certain indices, or the properties of a proposed characterization of the work load.

The preparation of a request for proposals (step 2) may require the same types of study as the analysis of needs. In practice, however, evaluation studies are seldom performed during the first two steps, in spite of the fact that they would often be quite useful. The studies these two steps would require do not have peculiar characteristics which can only be found in selection problems. The choice of performance indices, their analysis, and the characterization and forecasting of the work load are all present (with characteristics not too dissimilar from those they have in selection procedures) in performance improvement or in system design, or in both.

Much more typical characteristics are displayed by evaluation studies needed for the validation (step 3) and final selection (step 4) of proposals. Step 3 is the only one in which performance evaluation techniques play a significant role, at least in a number of practical selections. Of course, it is our contention that this role must be expanded and permeate steps 1, 2, and 4 as well. But we cannot ignore the fact that currently evaluation techniques are almost exclusively used (if at all) to validate the various proposals in step 3. In most cases the other steps follow subjective methods even in those instances in which a more objective quantitative approach would be applicable and desirable.

The validation of a proposal from a performance viewpoint is a typical performance analysis problem (*see* Section 1.4). Given the set of specifications determined in steps 1 and 2, the goal is to see whether or not the mandatory ones are satisfied and how well the desirable ones are met. However, the underlying theme of step 3, which gives it its peculiar flavor, is the one of *performance comparison* of the various alternatives. The comparison problem, which step 4 explicitly attacks from a global viewpoint (a viewpoint which encompasses functional, performance, and cost characteristics), is not peculiar to selection procedures. Even improvement and design problems can be viewed as consisting of a comparison of alternatives. What is peculiar is the fact that, in selection problems, comparisons are to be made between alternatives which usually differ from each other much more than in the other types of problems.

Thus, the validations to be performed in step 3 should be aimed at providing the investigator not only with the basis for a go/no-go decision but also with quantitative information on the relative performances that the various alternatives are likely to exhibit in the intended environment.

What impact do the results of performance comparisons have on the selection decision to be made in step 4? The methods we have outlined in Section 6.2.1 do not make clear distinctions between functional, performance, and cost characteristics. Both in scoring and cost-value methods, performance issues are intermixed with issues of different types. To be more precise, scoring methods usually try to express quantitatively the value of each competing solution to the future users. The score assigned to a proposal encompasses its functional and performance aspects, while its cost is normally kept separate. Several attempts to incorporate cost into the score have failed because of the difficulty of assigning to the cost a weight consistent with the weights of the other system characteristics. Thus, a selection decision based on a scoring method involves explicit consideration of the cost-value trade-off. Note that keeping the costs separate from the scores helps us clarify the alternatives but does not solve the selection problem. The same difficulties encountered when trying to assign a weight to the cost present themselves at the decision-making stage. For example, assume that the proposals in Table 6.1 cost $1,550,000, $1,870,000 and $1,750,000, respectively. Which one should we choose? Note also that when the final scores are as close to each other as they are in Table 6.1 it is legitimate to suspect that their differences are mostly due to noise in the scoring system. Differences as small as those in Table 6.1 should probably be treated as nonsignificant.

The cost-value method, by expressing all system characteristics in terms of cost, allows the decision makers not to face the cost-value trade-off dilemma directly. However, this dilemma is in fact considered at every step of the method, on an item-by-item, microscopic basis rather than macroscopically at the end. For each desirable system requirement, we have to determine the cost of having it, the cost of not having it, the costs related to the dates at which it may be satisfied, and so on.

Thus, the cost-value trade-off is crucial in both types of selection methods. But what about the cost-performance trade-off? It is important to realize that selection is not, and should not be, based only on cost-performance considerations. Such functional aspects as system support, conversion assistance, training, expansion potential, ease of use, maintainability, available software (in particular, programming languages), documentation, and compatibility with the current system usually have (and deserve) a big impact on selection decisions. Performance, in the restricted sense which the term has in this book, is also an important factor, even though primitive indices (for example, in vendor selection problems, memory cycle time, fixed-point addition time, maximum memory size) are still being used in some cases instead of indices more directly related to how well the system performs.

No matter which selection method is used in step 4, comparing the degrees to which the desirable requirements are satisfied is necessary. In a scoring approach, comparisons of different alternatives have to be made for each system characteristic in order to assign scores. In the cost-value method, comparisons are implicit in the assignment of costs to different proposals for each desirable requirement. Thus, performance comparison is an essential component of a selection procedure even though the actual decision is based neither on its results only nor on cost-performance trade-offs only. Performance comparison will be the main theme of Section 6.3.

6.3 PERFORMANCE COMPARISONS

6.3.1 The Comparison Problem

In this section, we shall examine from a ·conceptual viewpoint the following question: How reliable is the result of a performance comparison study?

Consider two alternatives A and B whose performances are to be compared. The purpose of the comparison is to determine which one is better and to quantify, if possible, this conclusion (e.g., to be able to say that B is 20% better than A). Let us assume that a set $\mathcal{P}$ of performance indices has been selected and that it adequately represents our notion of performance for entities like A and B. The selection of $\mathcal{P}$ is a fundamental and difficult problem to be discussed in the following sections, but here we consider it as having been satisfactorily solved. We shall also assume that a suitable figure of merit F has been derived from the indices in $\mathcal{P}$ so that a comparison of the values of F for the two alternatives will indicate which one of them should be considered better and by how much. This is, evidently, another nontrivial problem, which is addressed in the following sections. Note that if in $\mathcal{P}$ there is only one index or an index of predominant importance, that index can be taken as the figure of merit. Also, an investigator may be interested in comparing performance index by index. In this case, F will be a different index from $\mathcal{P}$ in each comparison.

Thus, under ideal conditions, the comparison of F_A and F_B will provide us with the desired answer. In practice, however, there are several sources of errors which may distort the values of F_A and F_B and make their comparison unreliable. Under the assumptions we have made above, two major sources of errors may be the different environmental conditions in which F_A and F_B are determined and the statistical nature of at least some of the indices on which F depends.

The first source of errors is due to the presence in $\mathcal{P}$ of indices whose values depend not only on the performance of A and B but also on the environment in which A and B operate. This is the case of practically all of the most popular indices of computer system performances, whose values depend critically on the work load. To make them descriptors of the performances of A and B, we have to specify one or more work loads and determine their values under exactly those work loads for both A and B. Only a few indices may be viewed as being insensitive to the work load. Among these, we find certain component parameters such as memory access times, maximum transfer rates, add times, and upper or lower bounds of system performance indices (e.g., the capacity or maximum throughput rate, the maximum number of editing terminals supportable by an interactive system with a given mean response time). However, it is easy to realize that even the definitions of these bounds require careful specifications of the types of input to be considered. Thus, all of the factors which influence F, except those which characterize the two alternatives A and B, should be controlled so as to eliminate their possible contributions to the difference $F_A - F_B$. This difference should reflect only the relative performances of A and B. Reaching such an objective is unfortunately quite difficult in practice. For instance, it is very hard to characterize the work load of an installation so that two systems A and B can be said to be driven by the same work load (the problem is discussed in detail in Sections 5.2.3 and 6.5). Selecting this work load is another fundamental but not well-understood question (*see* Sections 5.2.2 and 6.3.3). In principle, the indices and the work load (or work loads) to be selected for a comparison study should try to emphasize the performance differences of the alternatives while at the same time minimizing the influences of possible discrepancies between the work loads. We shall, for instance, note in Section 6.3.3 that the representativeness of the work-load model is not a very strict requirement as long as the lower degree of representativeness does not substantially distort $F_A - F_B$.

The second source of errors to be briefly discussed in this section is the statistical nature of most of the performance indices on which the figure of merit F depends. Investigators are generally interested in the values of population descriptors, such as the means of these indices, but only estimates of the descriptors (e.g., sample means) can usually be obtained because of the finite number of observations practically collectable. Thus, wrong conclusions may be drawn from performance comparisons in which indices have not been accurately estimated. Let F be a system performance index, for instance, the mean job turnaround time $\bar{t}$. We shall consider system A to perform better than system B with respect to $\bar{t}$ under a certain work load if $\bar{t}_A < \bar{t}_B$. Ideally, the work load used in the comparison should be the one that would be processed by either system if that system were selected and installed. Since, as explained in Section 5.1, experimenting under that work load is practically impossible, the two mean turnaround times will have to be estimated from samples obtained by driving the systems with models of this work load. If $\hat{\bar{t}}_A$ and $\hat{\bar{t}}_B$ are the estimates of $\bar{t}_A$ and $\bar{t}_B$ from these samples, their comparison should

a. produce the same qualitative results: If $\bar{t}_A > \bar{t}_B$, then $\hat{\bar{t}}_A > \hat{\bar{t}}_B$; if $\bar{t}_A < \bar{t}_B$, then $\hat{\bar{t}}_A < \hat{\bar{t}}_B$; if $\bar{t}_A \cong \bar{t}_B$, then $\hat{\bar{t}}_A \cong \hat{\bar{t}}_B$;

b. produce similar quantitive results: The estimated percentage by which one of the alternatives outperforms the other should not be too different from the actual percentage.

It should be noted that we are in fact estimating the difference $d_{AB} = \bar{t}_A - \bar{t}_B$ by the difference $\hat{d}_{AB} = \hat{\bar{t}}_A - \hat{\bar{t}}_B$ between the corresponding sample means. Our problem can therefore be stated as follows: Calculate the confidence interval for d_{AB} with a given confidence level K, or, alternatively, calculate the probability that d_{AB} is outside of a given interval around $\hat{d}_{AB}$. We can (at least conceptually) experiment with a number of different samples of the real work load. Each sample will provide us with two estimates of the mean turnaround time, one for system A and one for system B. The distributions of $\hat{\bar{t}}_A$ and $\hat{\bar{t}}_B$ can therefore be defined. If $\hat{\bar{t}}_A$ and $\hat{\bar{t}}_B$ are independent and normally distributed, their difference is also normal. Thus, the confidence interval for d_{AB} is given by

$$\hat{d}_{AB} - z\sigma_{AB} \leq d_{AB} \leq \hat{d}_{AB} + z\sigma_{AB}, \tag{6.1}$$

where z is defined by (2.5) and σ_{AB} is the standard deviation of $\hat{d}_{AB}$ about d_{AB}. If the variances σ_A^2 and σ_B^2 of $\hat{\bar{t}}_A$ and $\hat{\bar{t}}_B$ were known, the independence assumption would allow us to compute σ_{AB}^2 as the sum $\sigma_A^2 + \sigma_B^2$. However, this is not usually the case. Therefore, the variances will have to be estimated by the formula [*see* (2.7) *and* (2.13)]

$$\hat{\sigma}_A^2 = \frac{\displaystyle\sum_{i=1}^{n_A} (t_{Ai} - \hat{\bar{t}}_A)^2}{n_A (n_A - 1)} \tag{6.2}$$

and by the analogous formula for $\hat{\sigma}_B^2$. Let $n_A = n_B = n$ and $\hat{\sigma}_{AB}^2 = \hat{\sigma}_A^2 + \hat{\sigma}_B^2$. Since the random variable $(\hat{d}_{AB} - d_{AB})/\hat{\sigma}_{AB}$ has a Student's t-distribution, the calculation of the confidence interval in (6.1) is to be based (especially if n is not very large) on this rather than on the normal distribution:

$$\hat{d}_{AB} - z'\hat{\sigma}_{AB} \leq d_{AB} \leq \hat{d}_{AB} + z'\hat{\sigma}_{AB}, \tag{6.3}$$

where z' is related to K as shown in Section 2.4.3 and can be read from a table of the t-distribution with $n - 1$ degrees of freedom.

The assumptions we have made are all essential. If, for example, $n_A \neq n_B$, the Student's t-distribution cannot be used unless $\sigma_A = \sigma_B$ [*see* Snedecor and Cochran (1967), p. 115, for a useful approximation]. The normality and independence assumptions are more difficult to remove. Considerations analogous to those made in Section 2.6.4 to compute the minimum sample size without assuming normality or independence can be applied, with the necessary ·modifications, to the computation of confidence intervals for d_{AB}. For example, if the only assumption which can be made is that $\hat{d}_{AB}$ has finite mean and finite variance,

Chebyshev's inequality [invoked in (2.10)] yields

$$\hat{d}_{AB} - \sigma_{AB}/\sqrt{1-K} \le d_{AB} \le \hat{d}_{AB} + \sigma_{AB}/\sqrt{1-K}. \tag{6.4}$$

Nonparametric methods such as rank tests can also be employed for the same purpose when the normality assumption is unlikely to hold. Descriptions of these methods can be found in most textbooks on statistical analysis. However, note that the distribution of $\hat{d}_{AB}$ is closer to normality than those of $\hat{t}_A$ and $\hat{t}_B$ if the distributions of $\hat{t}_A$ and $\hat{t}_B$ are skewed on the same side.

When the confidence interval for d_{AB} has been estimated, a comparison of its width with the value of $\hat{d}_{AB}$ gives us useful information about the probable sign of d_{AB} and about its significance. If the confidence interval corresponding to confidence level K includes zero, d_{AB} has a nonnegligible probability of lying on either side of the origin (in which the two systems being compared have the same performance). Therefore, we cannot reject the hypothesis $d_{AB} = 0$ at the given significance level $1 - K$, and the difference between the two performances is not statistically significant. Decreasing the level of significance will make our estimations more accurate and our tests more sensitive but will require much larger sample sizes (*see* Sections 2.4.3 and 2.6.4).

If the work-load models used for A and B not only represent the same work load (which is an essential requirement imposed by the considerations we made at the beginning of this section) but are also composed of the same number of job models representing the same jobs, we can pair the observations t_{Ai} and t_{Bi} regarding job i. The variance of $\hat{d}_{AB}$ is no longer equal to the sum of the variances of $\hat{t}_A$ and $\hat{t}_B$ as in the independent case, since the covariance between the sample means is likely to be nonnegligible:

$$\sigma_{AB}^2 = \sigma_A^2 + \sigma_B^2 - 2\,\text{Cov}\,(\hat{t}_A, \hat{t}_B). \tag{6.5}$$

Pairing will make Cov $(\hat{t}_A, \hat{t}_B)$ positive, thereby reducing σ_{AB} and increasing the accuracy of the comparison for equal sample sizes with respect to the independent case. Assuming independence when observations are in fact paired may cause wider confidence intervals to be computed and d_{AB} to be considered nonsignificant, while in reality it is significant. Assuming that the deviations $d_{ABi} - d_{AB}$, where $d_{ABi} = t_{Ai} - t_{Bi}$, are independent and normally distributed with mean zero and variance σ_d^2, $\hat{d}_{AB}$ is normally distributed about d_{AB} with variance σ_d^2/n, and σ_d^2 can be estimated from the sample as

$$\hat{\sigma}_d^2 = \frac{\sum\limits_{i=1}^{n} (d_{ABi} - \hat{d}_{AB})^2}{n - 1}. \tag{6.6}$$

Since the variable $(\hat{d}_{AB} - d_{AB})/(\hat{\sigma}_d/\sqrt{n})$ follows a Student's t-distribution, the confidence interval for d_{AB} at the confidence level K is given by (6.3) where $\hat{\sigma}_{AB}$ is to be replaced by $\hat{\sigma}_d/\sqrt{n}$.

Other important and sometimes neglected sources of errors in performance comparisons are the different biases introduced into the results by improper use of evaluation techniques, for example, imprecise measurement tools, inaccurate simulation or analytic models, and incorrect recording or manipulation of the data. It should be noted that any systematic error which affects the values of the performance indices of both systems by the same amount does not have any unwanted influence on the outcome of a comparison. Thus, much more attention should be paid to the problem of making inputs, evaluation techniques and tools, and procedures as equal as possible for the systems to be compared than to the one of obtaining accurate absolute estimates of the performance indices of each system. The reader should also note that the global contribution to $\hat{d}_{AB}$ of the sources of variation discussed in this section, and sometimes (by properly designed experiments) even the contributions of each source, can be estimated by analysis of variance techniques (*see* Section 2.7.2).

6.3.2 Processing Mode Comparisons

In some installation design studies, one of the first decisions to be made is the selection of the processing mode. This decision has a very important influence on the selection of the vendor, on the design of the hardware and software configuration, and on the organization of the installation. However, the problem of selecting the processing mode is relatively seldom debated and attacked in a formal way. The main reason for this fact is that each processing mode has peculiar and unique characteristics which make it evidently suitable for certain types of applications and evidently unsuitable for others. Therefore, given an application, what processing mode would be employed for it is usually clear. *Direct access* is very appropriate in installations with a single user or in very small open-shop installations intended to provide hands-on computing to a restricted number of relatively experienced users. The *batch-processing mode* is convenient in medium-large installations whose work load consists mostly of production programs requiring nontrivial amounts of computational power or of I/O power, or of both. Installations in which program development is the predominant activity generally prefer the *fast-turnaround batch* or the *interactive mode*. The latter is also the most appropriate mode for applications such as computer-aided design, computer graphics, information retrieval, document preparation, and reservation systems. The *real-time mode*, which is in some sense similar to the interactive mode, is usually found in industrial process or laboratory experiment control applications.

Another reason the selection of the processing mode is seldom paid serious attention is that large systems likely to be installed where a variety of applications have to be processed are often equipped with operating systems which support several processing modes at the same time (typically, batch and interactive but sometimes also real-time).

Thus, the processing mode problem is only rarely considered in a selection procedure, since its solution is very often immediate. Yet several comparative studies have been made in this area, and their results should be of concern to both installation designers and system designers. Furthermore, some methodological aspects of these studies are interesting and applicable to a number of problems, including the selection of the processing mode when either a multiple-mode operating system or multiple installations using different modes are available, the design and evaluation of user-machine interfaces, and the measurement and modeling of user community behavior. For these reasons, we shall briefly discuss the comparison of two processing modes, the batch and interactive modes, taking the survey by Sackman (1968) as our main source of information on some early experimental studies of the subject.

The first question to be answered is concerned with the objectives of the study: What does a comparison of batch and interactive processing mean? Of course, several different viewpoints, all legitimate and interesting, exist with respect to this question. If we take the viewpoint of an installation planner whose main objective is to maximize the value of the installation to the organization, we are confronted with the question, What impact does the processing mode have on the value of an installation? A general answer to this question cannot be given. The impact depends on the installation's type and applications, for example, on the proportions of program development and production-processing activities, on the abilities and backgrounds of the users, on how the installation is managed, and so on. If results of interest to many more people than just the managers of a specific installation are to be obtained, the idea of defining and using value as our comparison criterion is to be abandoned in favor of the one of selecting a few quantitative indices to which any interested person can then give different weights during a particular decision-making process. These indices should quantify in some way the following important aspects of our comparison:

    a. the consumption of human resources,
    b. the consumption of system resources,
    c. the quantity of the work produced by the programmers,
    d. the quality of the work produced by the programmers,
    e. the attitude of the users.

Note that the performance of the system is not included in the list of index classes since system productivity aspects are represented by the system resource consumption indices, and system responsiveness aspects are expected to influence the other four classes of indices heavily. Table 6.2 shows some indices which belong to these classes and which have actually been used in the comparative studies mentioned above. These indices were measured while a specific programming task was carried out by a number of programmers using the two modes to be compared.

Ideally, the comparison experiment should be designed so as to eliminate all the sources of variation of these indices except the processing mode. Thus, the same group of programmers should be given the same task to be carried out using

Table 6.2

INDICES FOR BATCH-INTERACTIVE MODE COMPARISON

Class	Indices
Consumption of human resources	Programmer's time
Consumption of system resources	Computer time
Quantity of work produced	Elapsed time
Quality of work produced	Program execution time, program size
Attitude of the users	Preferred mode

both modes. The two modes should be supported by either the same system or very similar systems with loads of similar magnitudes. The programming task should be neither batch-oriented nor interaction-oriented. Yet it should adequately represent applications which are present and meaningful in both types of installations. Clearly, most of these requirements can be only approximately satisfied in a real experiment, and techniques to control secondary factors (*see* Sections 2.6.2 and 2.6.3) will have to be used. Several complex questions have to be answered when designing the experiment. For example, how many programmers are needed and how experienced should they be? If they are novices, the results may not be useful for installations in which most of the user population is composed of highly experienced programmers. If they have some previous experience, they may be biased toward the mode in which they have been accessing computers in the past. Also, since it is not possible to have the same individuals solve the given problem in both modes, the two groups have to be carefully matched, and pairing techniques may be employed to derive the results. Other questions are concerned with the choices of programming tasks and of the language to be used. To eliminate variations due to different languages, the same language must be used in both modes and therefore supported by both. The objection could be raised at this point that preventing programmers from using languages particularly suited to each processing mode is not realistic. However, the emphasis in our comparison is on the impact on the indices in Table 6.2 of the different response-time characteristics of the two modes, and not on the relative merits of a specific batch system and of a specific interactive system. This remark is useful in dealing with another question: Should the performance of the two systems be controlled during the experiment, and how? Clearly, even if the same hardware configuration is used in the two modes, different work loads existing on the system when the programmers involved in the experiment test and debug their programs make response characteristics variable. Two opposite philosophies have been adopted in the five studies surveyed by Sackman (1968). The no-control philosophy, followed in four of the studies, is based on the opinion that a controlled performance would not be realistic. The only study in which control was exerted was the one by Grant and Sackman (1966), who kept the batch system's turnaround time constant at 2 hr. Perhaps a better solution would be to control turnaround time so that it exhibits its usual variability but not some relatively rare phenomena which could appreciably distort the results.

Other problems involve the measurement of the indices and of additional interesting variables, the control of the incentives for the participating programmers, and the choice of the statistical tests to be applied to the results. Note that the measurement of programmer's times and user attitudes has to rely upon personal logs and questionnaires. A detailed discussion of all of these problems, and of the ways in which they have been solved by the authors of the five studies, can be found in Sackman (1968) and in the papers describing each study.

Table 6.3

RESULTS OF FIVE COMPARATIVE STUDIES OF BATCH AND INTERACTIVE PROCESSING

	Index			
Study	Programmer's time	Computer time	Elapsed time	Preferred mode
Erikson (1966)	1.9:1 (0.06)	3.4:1 (0.04)	—	Interactive
Gold (1967)	1.2:1 (0.07)	1:4.7 (0.001)	1:1	Interactive (0.001)
Grant and Sackman (1966)	1.6:1 (0.05)	1:1.4	—	Interactive
Schatzoff et al. (1967)	1:2.1 (0.02)	1.1:1	1.5:1 (0.08)	—
Smith (1967)	1.2:1	1:1.5	1.2:1	Fast-turnaround batch

Source: Sackman (1968).

* The batch:interactive ratios are reported. The statistical significance of the comparison, when known, is in parentheses. For example, Erikson's study showed a ratio of 1.9 between the mean programmer's time in batch mode and the same mean time in interactive mode, and the difference between the mean times was significant at the 6% level.

Table 6.3 summarizes some of the results obtained in the five studies. It should be noted that Smith's study was actually a comparison of batch and fast-turnaround batch and that some of the problems discussed above received less than satisfactory solutions in some of the studies. No indices of program quality are reported in the table. The two studies which measured them did not find any significant differences between program execution times and between program sizes. Gold (1967), however, reported that interactive users achieved significantly better solutions and a better understanding of their problem than batch users.

No definite conclusions can be drawn from the results in Table 6.3, with the exception of user preference. Programmer's time tends to be lower and computer time higher in an interactive environment. Elapsed time results, reflecting the amount of work which can be produced in an installation, were slightly favorable to the interactive mode. The differences in programmer's time and computer time among individual programmers were found, by the three studies which investigated them, to be much larger than those due to the processing mode. Ranges as big as $14:1$, and never smaller than $3:1$, were reported. Thus, the quality of the programmers should be expected to have a bigger impact on a programming project than the processing mode.

6.3.3   Vendor Comparisons

Comparing systems proposed by different vendors is one of the most complicated problems in performance evaluation. Because of the variety of the technologies, architectures, management policies, and user interfaces exhibited by the existing systems, this problem is often said to be similar to the one of comparing apples and oranges. That systems are hard to compare to each other is especially evident when the comparison is attempted in terms of organizational parameters or hardware performance indices such as word lengths, access times, transfer rates, instruction sets, and scheduling policies. The problem becomes unsolvable if the comparison is intended to determine the "best" among several systems independently of the application, that is, the highest performance system for any possible installation. Nevertheless, a number of hardware-oriented, work-load-independent indices have been proposed and used for system comparison purposes. Before discussing comparisons based on the types of indices emphasized in this book, we shall briefly review some of those approaches.

A fundamental notion in computer systems engineering, one which is natural but very hard to satisfactorily define and quantify, is the notion of *information-processing power*. If we had a good definition of power, we could use it to compare different systems and to select the most convenient system for an installation whose power requirements were known. Unfortunately, this is not the case. The closest approximation to it is the capacity, or maximum throughput rate, which, however, requires the types of jobs being considered and several additional details to be specified. Some attempts have been made to base the definition of power on hardware characteristics only, so as to avoid getting involved with the intricacies of operating systems and work loads.

The earliest comparisons were based on rudimentary indices such as the internal clock rate of the CPU, its fixed-point add time, the cycle time of the primary memory, and the time required to fetch two numbers, add them, and store the result (a hembryonic kernel). Examples of slightly more sophisticated definitions of power are those introduced by Schneidewind (1966),

$$P = \frac{M}{t_{\text{cycle}}}, \tag{6.7}$$

where M is the primary-memory size in words or characters and t_{cycle} its cycle time, and by Gruenberger (1966),

$$P = M\left(\frac{1}{t_{add}} + \frac{1}{t_{mpy}}\right), \tag{6.8}$$

where M is in words and t_{add} and t_{mpy} are the addition and multiplication times. Note that these indices are still hardware-oriented and work-load-independent like the more primitive ones mentioned above. Also, they are exclusively concerned with the performance of the CPU-primary-memory complex, which for a long time has been the most expensive part of a system and therefore the focal point of evaluation studies.

The work load makes its timid appearance in indices which require the use of instruction mixes. An index based on an instruction mix is the mean CPU instruction execution rate

$$P = \bar{v}_{cpu} = \frac{1}{\bar{t}_x}, \tag{6.9}$$

where $\bar{t}_x$, the mean instruction execution time, is given by (5.9).

Another definition of power which requires the specification of an instruction mix is the one used by Knight (1963):

$$P = \frac{[(L - 7)Mk_1]^{k_2}}{k_3(\bar{t}_x + \bar{t}_{ion})}, \tag{6.10}$$

where L is the instruction length in bits, M and $\bar{t}_x$ have been defined above, $\bar{t}_{ion}$ is the mean nonoverlapped I/O time per instruction executed, k_1 is a coefficient whose value depends on whether the word length is fixed or variable, k_2 has (in Knight's study) different values for scientific and commercial installations, and k_3 is a constant. Two different mixes, corresponding to these two types of applications, were used by Knight to calculate $\bar{t}_x$. This distinction is also present in the constants which appear in the rather complicated formula used to estimate $\bar{t}_{ion}$. This formula expresses the mean I/O time not overlapped with CPU activity as a function of I/O and secondary-memory transfer rates, start, stop, and rewind times, and estimated utilizations of I/O devices. Note that definition (6.10) was derived by Knight from opinions of experts and was used in several extensive studies of technological progress in computer systems [*see also* Knight (1968) and Cerveny and Knight (1973)]. These studies, which examined hundreds of systems introduced between 1944 and 1972, shed some quantitative light on a very important question: that of *economies of scale* in the computer field.

We postulate that the dependence of the power P of a computer system (whose definition is left unspecified for the moment) on the system's cost C has the form

$$P = KC^g, \tag{6.11}$$

where K and g are positive constants. Thus, the power per unit cost is given by

$$\frac{P}{C} = KC^{g-1}. \tag{6.12}$$

We say that computer systems offer economies of scale if their power increases more than linearly with their cost. Therefore, the crucial element in our postulated relationship is the value of g (*see* Fig. 6.1):

    a. If $g > 1$, we have *economies of scale*;
    b. if $g = 1$, we have *returns to scale*;
    c. if $g < 1$, we have *diseconomies of scale*.

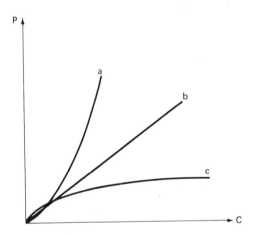

Figure 6.1   Relationship between information-processing power P and cost C: (*a*) economies of scale ($g > 1$); (*b*) return to scale ($g = 1$); (*c*) diseconomies of scale ($g < 1$).

The form of relationship expressed by (6.11) was proposed in the late 1940s by H. Grosch, who also conjectured that the value of g is close to 2. For this reason, (6.11) with $g = 2$ is known as *Grosch's law*. One of the main results obtained by Knight was the experimental proof of the validity of Grosch's law, at least over the time period considered. It is very important to note that the definition of P given in (6.10), which is essentially an index based on hardware and instruction mix characteristics, was used in this verification. Table 6.4 summarizes the relevant results (obtained by least-squares linear regression analysis) reported by Knight for about 500 systems introduced during the period 1950–1972. Note that greater economies of scale have been obtained for minicomputers and, in more recent periods, for scientific applications.

Clearly, the question of economies of scale is very important in the design of information-processing systems for large organizations, especially when the prospective users are geographically distributed. The area over which the users are

Table 6.4

VALUES OF g IN EQUATION (6.11)

Period	g	
	Scientific systems	Commercial systems
1950–1962	1.92	2.17
1962–1966	3.10	2.47
1964–1972 (minicomputers)	5.88	—

Sources: Knight (1963), Knight (1968), and Cerveny and Knight (1973).

distributed need not be so large as a continent or a region for this statement to hold. Often, even when they are all located in a big building, the decentralization problem is worth studying. The basic question is, Given the information-processing needs of an organization, is a large centralized computing facility with a number of terminals and remote entry stations more or less convenient than a decentralized configuration, consisting of many systems, possibly installed in various locations and interconnected in a network? It is evident that this question, when relevant, is to be answered before selecting the equipment and designing the system's configuration or configurations. Also, the reader will recognize that this dilemma is conceptually similar to the one concerning uniprocessor versus multiprocessor systems. A multiprocessor system has in fact a distributed architecture like a decentralized system, but its CPU's are usually in close proximity, access the same primary and secondary memories, and are more tightly interconnected. Thus, some of the arguments in favor or against decentralization hold also for multiprocessing, and some do not.

The results reported above indicate that a centralized solution is likely to provide a given power at a lower cost or more power for a given cost. However, the definition of power (6.11) used by Knight cannot be taken as a comprehensive, realistic descriptor of the value of a computer system. There are many additional arguments in favor and against decentralization to be considered. In our discussion, we shall follow the approach proposed by Streeter (1973).

Table 6.5 summarizes the most important potential advantages of the two solutions in the case of general-purpose information-processing systems. Most of these arguments are very difficult or impossible to quantify. The simple approximate treatment described by Streeter, which involves the costs of the equipment, the communications links, user-computer communications, and service interruptions and the mean job turnaround time as the performance index, will now be illustrated by an example.

Example 6.1 The issue of centralization is being considered for a general-purpose information-processing system to be installed in a large company. An analysis of the

Table 6.5

POTENTIAL ADVANTAGES OF CENTRALIZATION AND
DECENTRALIZATION OF GENERAL-PURPOSE COMPUTING
FACILITIES

Advantages of centralization	Advantages of decentralization
Economies of scale in equipment	Lower probability of service interruptions
Reduction in program preparation and maintenance	Better local knowledge of local conditions
Reduction in data base storage duplication	Easier tailoring of programs and services to local requirements
Reduction in equipment maintenance costs	More flexibility in adapting to new conditions
Reduction in site preparation costs	Greater personnel interest and motivation
Reduction in physical security costs	Tighter contact of personnel with local users
Higher equipment utilization due to larger and more varied user population	Easier and more reliable user-system communication
More effective use of high-quality personnel	
Reduction in mean and variance of turnaround times	
Greater variety of programs and services available to users	
Integration of administrative and technical services	

Source: Streeter (1973).

company's needs has produced a ball-park figure for the total information-processing power P required. The problem is to assess the convenience of centralized and decentralized solutions both in terms of cost and in terms of performance. Two of the alternatives are represented in Fig. 6.2. We assume that in a decentralized solution all systems are identical and interconnected by a complete network. That is, each system is connected to all of the others. With this highly simplified characterization of the problem, our end goal is to select N, the number of systems to be installed. Thus, we shall try to determine the influence of N on the total cost C and on the mean turnaround time $\bar{t}$.

Assuming that Grosch's law holds, (6.11) yields the following equation for equipment costs:

$$C_e = N\sqrt{\frac{P}{KN}} = K_e\sqrt{N}. \tag{6.13}$$

To calculate the cost C_c of communication links, we multiply the number of links, $N(N-1)/2$, by the cost per link, which depends on the volume of traffic per link. The traffic per link can be obtained by dividing the total traffic, which is proportional to $N-1$ since each file modification must be transmitted to the $N-1$ other systems, by the number of links. Thus, the traffic per link is inversely proportional to N. If we assume a quadratic

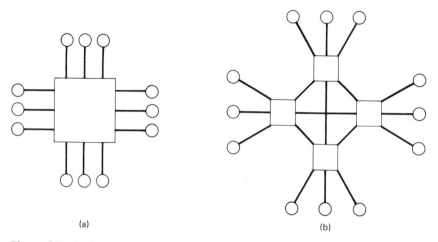

(a)   (b)

Figure 6.2 Configuration alternatives for an information-processing system; (*a*) centralized system (*N* = 1); (*b*) decentralized system with complete interconnections (*N* = 4). Squares represent systems, and circles represent I/O peripherals.

relationship like Grosch's law between traffic and cost per link, representing the economies of scale for communications charges, the square of the cost per link is inversely proportional to N. Thus,

$$C_c = \frac{N(N-1)}{2} \frac{H}{\sqrt{N}} = K_c\sqrt{N}(N-1). \tag{6.14}$$

Note that, for $N = 1$, we have $C_c = 0$, as we should expect.

User-computer communication costs can be assumed to be approximately proportional to the average user-computer distance, which, if users and computers have a uniform geographic distribution, is inversely proportional to $\sqrt{N}$. Hence,

$$C_u = \frac{K_u}{\sqrt{N}}. \tag{6.15}$$

Finally, the cost of service interruptions can be calculated in a first approximation assuming that failures are statistically independent and that service is interrupted only when no system is operational. If p_f is the probability of system failure, assumed to be the same for any system, the cost C_i of interruptions is

$$C_i = K_i p_f^N. \tag{6.16}$$

The total cost C is then defined as the sum of the four costs C_e, C_c, C_u, C_i:

$$C = K_e\sqrt{N} + K_c\sqrt{N}(N-1) + \frac{K_u}{\sqrt{N}} + K_i p_f^N. \tag{6.17}$$

Let us assume that, in our design, $P = 10^6$ instructions/s. Taking $K = 10^8$ instructions $\times$ s/$\$^2$, we have $K_e = 0.1$ \$/s. Also, let $K_c = 0.01$ \$/s, $K_u = 0.1$ \$/s, $K_i =$

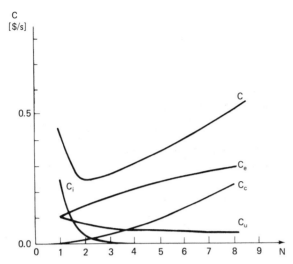

C
[$/s]

0.5

0.0
0   1   2   3   4   5   6   7   8   9   N

C

C_e

C_c

C_i

C_u

Figure 6.3   Costs of an information-processing system vs. the number of installations.

2.5 $/s, and $p_f = 0.1$. Equations (6.13) through (6.17) are plotted in Fig. 6.3 for these numerical values. Evidently, the total cost is minimum for $N = 2$, and the cost for $N = 3$ is only slightly higher, whereas the cost of a centralized solution is about 1.8 times the minimum, due to the relatively high cost of service interruptions and the low reliability of the systems.

A very simple and crude way of approximately determining the impact of N on the mean turnaround time is to model the system in Fig. 6.2 as a set of N distinct single-server queuing systems (*see* Fig. 6.4). Let us assume that all systems are identical and uniformly loaded, that the arrival process for each one of them is a Poisson process with mean rate λ/N, and that service times at each server are exponentially distributed with mean rate μ/N (so that the total processing power is constant, since the sum of the mean service rates is always equal to μ). Then we can apply the results obtained in Chapter 4 for $M/M/1$ models. In particular, equation (4.42) with mean service rate μ/N and utilization factor

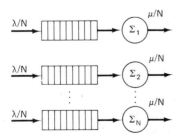

Figure 6.4   Simple queuing model of the systems in Fig. 6.2.

$\rho = (\lambda/N)(\mu/N) = \lambda/\mu$ yields

$$\bar{t} = \frac{N}{\mu(1 - \rho)}. \qquad (6.18)$$

Thus, the mean turnaround time $\bar{t}$ is proportional to N. Figure 6.5 shows some diagrams of $\bar{t}(N)$ for $\mu = 1000$ jobs/hr, various values of λ, and therefore of ρ. The $C(N)$ curve plotted in Fig. 6.3 is also reported in Fig. 6.5 to give the reader a pictorial representation of the cost-performance trade-off in this extremely simplified study. According to (6.18), the performance penalty to be paid for decreasing the total cost by 44% when going from a centralized system to one composed of two installations is a 100% increase in the mean turnaround time. ∎

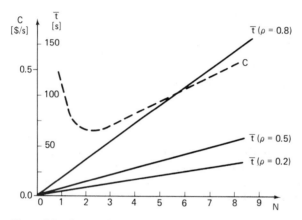

Figure 6.5   Cost-performance comparison for the systems in Fig. 6.2.

Evidently, investigations of economies of scale and of centralization problems conceptually similar to those discussed above could be made with more comprehensive and more appropriate performance indices than the ones we have introduced so far in this section. Indices like those defined in (6.7) and (6.8) had the advantage of being exclusively hardware-dependent. An additional dependence on the work load, but a very simple and primitive one since it involves only the work load's computational aspects, characterizes indices like those defined in (6.9) and (6.10). However, the performance indices we introduced in Section 1.4 seem to be much closer to what managers and users are really interested in. With some simplification, we can say that managers are mostly interested in throughput rates and utilizations, and system users in turnaround or response times. These indices are influenced not only by the performances of some hardware components but also by the way they are interconnected, by how their activities are coordinated, by the user-system interface, by the translators, programming aids, utility programs, and their performances. Unfortunately, they also depend on the nature and magnitude of the work load. Thus, these indices can be used as system performance indices only if the work load under which their values are produced is clearly and uniquely specified. In proposal validation studies (step 3 of the selection procedures described in Section 6.2.1), the objective is to verify that a proposed system processes the given work load (or work loads) with values of the performance indices satisfying the mandatory requirements. Such a requirement may be that the mean throughput rate be greater than 10 jobs/min, where the "jobs" referred to in the unit of throughput rate are specific, well-defined jobs. In performance comparison studies, the work loads under which the various systems produce the values of the performance indices to be compared must be identical in order for these values to be usable as system performance comparison criteria (*see* Section 6.3.1).

What work load should be selected to define and evaluate our performance indices? Usually, if the installation already exists, the work load chosen coincides with, or is close to, the current maximum production work load of the installation. This choice also allows comparisons to be made between the performances of the proposed systems and those of the current one. In more sophisticated studies, corrections should be introduced into this work load to account for the effects that each new system would have on the user community. If the installation does not exist, the initial production work load is to be estimated from the available knowledge of the users' information-processing needs. Often, both for a preexisting and for a new installation, one or more projected work loads are also considered. The projections partially or totally extend over the estimated lifetime of the equipment. The characterization of these present and future work loads is made extremely difficult by the requirement that they be identical for all the systems being compared. This calls for a portable, vendor-independent work-load model.

But what types of work-load models are likely to be used? To answer this question, we have to determine how suitable for selection problems each evaluation technique is. As we shall see in Section 6.4, measurement techniques are applicable in this case, since the various alternatives among which the choice is to be made are supposed to exist (if not exactly identical, at least in similar configurations or versions) and to be accessible by the vendor or by the user. Also, these techniques usually turn out to be the most appropriate. The work loads selected, be they current or projected, cannot be used to drive directly any of the systems being compared (the projected ones do not even exist). Thus, an executable artificial model must be employed. Among all types of executable artificial models discussed in Sections 5.3.4 and 5.3.5, the most popular in selection studies are those consisting of sets of benchmarks or synthetic jobs. However, more primitive models such as mixes and kernels have also been used.

For the performance requirements specified in the request for proposals to be meaningful, the work-load model (or models), or its detailed specification, is to be included in the request. Often, a set of benchmarks or synthetic jobs is designed by the requestor and converted by each vendor to the system being proposed. The execution time of the set of programs on that system, a measure of mean throughput rate, is usually the basic performance test of the proposal validation step (step 3). It is also the most popular index used in performance comparisons, even though other measurements taken during the conversion and the execution of the programs are often compared against each other. This is illustrated in the following example, which summarizes a performance comparison study described by Strauss (1972).

Example 6.2 The performances of four new systems proposed for an existing university computer center are to be compared with each other and with those of the currently installed system. The five systems considered and their configurations are listed in Table 6.6 (A is the current system). The primary performance index selected is the mean

Table 6.6

SYSTEMS AND CONFIGURATIONS COMPARED IN EXAMPLE 6.2

System	Vendor and model	Memory size	Disk storage size
A	IBM 360/50	$256K$ bytes, $2\,\mu s$ $1M$ byte, $2.5\,\mu s$	$484M$ bytes (2314)
B	Burroughs B 6714	$128K$ words, 48 bits/word	$484M$ bytes
C	IBM 370/155	$768K$ bytes	$600M$ bytes (3330)
D	UNIVAC 1108	$196K$ words, 36 bits/word	$80M$ words
E	XDS SIGMA 9	$512K$ bytes	$600M$ bytes (2314)

System	Number of tape drives	Operating system	Type of procurement	Approximate monthly cost
A	6	OS/MFT	1 to 2-year lease	$31,000
B	6	MCP	1-year lease	$28,600
C	6	OS/MFT OS/MVT	1 to 2-year lease	$39,900
D	6	EXEC 8	5-year purchase	$33,000
E	4	UTS	5-year purchase	$30,000

Source: Strauss (1972).

throughput rate exhibited by each system when driven by the installation's work load. As an executable model of this work load, a set of benchmarks has been designed. The characteristics of the set are summarized in Table 6.7. The set includes also another job, not listed in the table: the *idle job*, which never terminates and which consumes all the

Table 6.7

CHARACTERISTICS OF THE SET OF BENCHMARKS
FOR EXAMPLE 6.2

Composition		IBM 360/50 CPU times [s]		
Language	Number of jobs	Compilation	Execution	Total
FORTRAN	12	82	2229.8	2311.8
COBOL	6	447.8	92.8	540.6
WATFIV	6	210.9	—	210.9
	24	740.7	2322.6	3063.3

Operational rules

R1. No source code optimization is allowed.

R2. Two basic runs (run 1 and run 2) are to be made; the results of other optimizing runs may be reported.

R3. In run 1 and run 2,
   a. all jobs remain in given classes (if pertinent),
   b. the maximum degree of multiprogramming must be 5,
   c. input ordering of jobs is fixed and equal to the given one,
   d. all jobs are assigned equal external priorities.

R4. A run terminates when all jobs but the idle job are completed.

R5. In run 1, execution starts after all jobs have been read in; read, execution, and print elapsed times have to be recorded.

R6. In run 2, execution starts as soon as possible; total elapsed time is to be recorded.

Expected output

Description of exact hardware and software configuration

All printer and console log output

CPU, start, and stop time for each job step and job

All standard accounting information

All necessary source code changes

Total human and machine time spent initially and by run

Results of optimizing runs

Source: Strauss (1972).

CPU time not used by the other jobs or by the operating system, so as to produce an indication of the additional capacity available in each system. Four of the FORTRAN jobs are heavily compute-bound and test the accuracy and precision of the CPU and of various standard mathematical functions and routines. The remaining eight FORTRAN jobs are designed to test the efficiency of the FORTRAN I/O routines (this is one of the areas in which system A was known to be particularly inefficient). One of the COBOL jobs creates an indexed sequential test file for four of the others, which are programs from the production administrative work load. The sixth COBOL program contains bugs and has the task of testing the COBOL compiler's diagnostic capabilities. The WATFIV benchmarks are small students jobs which, roughly speaking, are supposed to represent the instructional part of the work load, while the FORTRAN jobs mostly account for the faculty and graduate student research portion and the COBOL jobs for the administrative data-processing portion. The reader has certainly noticed that, in constructing this work-load model, relatively little emphasis has been given to the representativeness requirement, at least in terms of physical or logical resource usage. In fact, most of the benchmarks were selected with purposes different from the one of matching the relative usage of resources of the production work load. We have already observed in Section 5.2.2 that the representativeness requirement is present even when the work-load-characterizing parameters are not resource-oriented due to the particular objectives of the investigators. We should also remember here the important remark, made in Section 6.3.1, that in comparative studies the degree of representativeness of the work-load model may be lower than in perfor-

Table 6.8

SOME RESULTS OF THE COMPARISON STUDY DESCRIBED IN EXAMPLE 6.2

	System				
Index	A	B*	C*	D†	E†
Total recorded elapsed time [min]	94.9	43.46	14.7	21.25	32.4
Total elapsed time minus idle-job CPU time [min]	61.6	43.4	14.3	17.7	18.1
Estimated total elapsed time minus idle-job CPU time without benchmark modifications [min]	61.6	43.4	14.3	19.1	63.7
Total CPU time minus idle-job CPU time [min]	51.05	40.2	11.75	16.3	14.5
Human time for conversion [hr]	40‡	80	4	160	40
Machine time for conversion [hr]	6‡	20§	20	5	3
Mean throughput rate per unit cost [$10^6 \times$ jobs/(min \$/month)]	12.57	19.33	42.06	41.09	44.19

Source: Strauss (1972), by permission of AFIPS, Inc.

* Priorities were adjusted so that the idle job would run only when nothing else could run.

† Source code modifications were made to some of the benchmarks; their estimated effects are eliminated in the figures reported for the third index in this table.

‡ Benchmark preparation times.

§ On a 370/145 and including conversion to ANS COBOL, which was not required.

mance analysis studies, provided that the differences between the values of performance indices are relatively insensitive to the discrepancies existing between the work-load model and the real work load.

The main objective in designing the operational rules reported in Table 6.7 was to enhance the fairness of the comparison by trying to have the benchmarks run in reasonably similar environments without excessively favoring or penalizing any system with respect to the others. This is an extremely difficult problem, one of those in which the investigator is forced to face directly and without escape the "apples versus oranges" reality. Not allowing code optimization (rule R1) is both fair and realistic. However, the results reported by the vendor of system E showed that the simple replacement of WRITE statements by CALL BUFFOUT statements in the source code of the FORTRAN benchmarks reduced the total elapsed time of system E by factor of about 3.5 (*see* Table 6.8). Now, if system E were selected and installed, is it realistic to assume that the programmers would not rapidly learn to use CALL BUFFOUT instead of WRITE? On the other hand, there are clearly source code optimizations which should not be permitted, at least if we suspect that vendors are likely to be substantially more knowledgeable about their systems than typical users. Considerations of a similar nature could be made on the rules which try to reduce the effects of different memory sizes (R3b) and to prevent vendors from arranging the benchmarks in the order which is best suited to their allocation strategies (R3a, c, d). Note that the vendors of systems B and C did not respect the rule of assigning equal external priorities to all jobs (rule R3d) in order to ensure that the idle job would run only if no other job were ready to run. Rules R4, R5, and R6 are intended to exactly define elapsed times so that their comparison will be meaningful. It should be noted that the provision for additional runs contained in rule R2 allows vendors to present a more complete picture of their proposed systems by removing in those runs the constraints which, in their opinion, unduly penalize them.

The outputs expected to be provided by each vendor, listed in Table 6.7, were dictated by the objectives of the study. For example, the investigators were interested in the completeness, fairness, and accuracy of the accounting information each system would give to the users. They were also highly concerned with the costs and time that would be needed to convert to a new system and took the figures quoted by each vendor for the conversion of the benchmarks as a rough relative measure of conversion complexity.

Some of the most interesting results of the study are summarized in Table 6.8. Due to the doubts expressed above on the fairness of the operational rules and to the fact that they were not respected by all the vendors, the interpretation of the results is not so straightforward as it should be. Performance-wise, system C clearly emerges as the winner. However, it is also the most expensive. C is followed by D, which, however, is the second most expensive and had the highest human conversion costs. A cost-performance picture of the five systems, which is based on the elapsed times in the second and third row of Table 6.8 and on the costs in the last column of Table 6.6, is presented in Fig. 6.6. The broken lines reported there are diagrams of equation (6.11) normalized with respect to the cost and the performance of system A. That is, we have plotted the function

$$\frac{P}{P_A} = \left(\frac{C}{C_A}\right)^g, \tag{6.19}$$

where P coincides with our performance index $\bar{T}$, the mean throughput rate for the set of 24 benchmarks described in this example. Evidently, if the same level of economies of scale determined by Knight can be expected to hold for the systems compared in this study

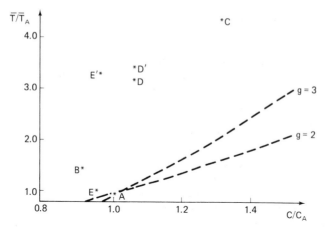

Figure 6.6 Mean relative throughput rate (during the execution of the set of 24 benchmarks described in Example 6.2) vs. approximate relative monthly cost for the five systems in Table 6.6. The two broken lines are normalized plots of equation (6.11) for $g = 2$ (Grosch's law) and $g = 3$. D' and E' correspond to runs with modified benchmarks.

and for this definition of performance, the substantial departures of the experimental points from the curves in Fig. 6.6 can be explained only by the fact that the proposed systems (with the exception of system E when running the unmodified benchmarks) have a different K, so that equation (6.19) is in fact to be written as

$$\frac{P}{P_A} = \frac{K}{K_A}\left(\frac{C}{C_A}\right)^g. \tag{6.20}$$

The ratio K/K_A, which, judging from the diagram in Fig. 6.6, is at least 2, may be interpreted as a rough measure of the technological progress which has intervened between the introduction of system A and the ones of the other systems.

Even if we were completely convinced of the fairness of the rules and of their scrupulous application on the part of all vendors, the interpretation of the results would still be difficult. What system should we choose, having established the rather common and not surprising fact that the systems which perform better are also more expensive? A selection decision must take into account a large number of factors, not only the cost and the performance of each proposed system. Most of these factors have been mentioned in Section 6.2.1. If we restrict our attention to cost and performance, it may be helpful to consider the values of a *cost-performance index* such as the mean throughput rate per dollar. The last row of Table 6.8 shows system E' (with modified benchmarks) to be the most cost-effective, followed by C and D' at a distance which could easily be attributed to the various errors undoubtedly present in the evaluation process. ∎

It should be noted that the performance comparison discussed in Example 6.2 has been made using the values of elapsed times measured by the vendors without testing their statistical significance or estimating confidence intervals as described in Section 6.3.1. This omission is justified by the objectives of the study and by the performance index selected. The mean throughput rate (which is a time average, not the mean of an attribute of the job population) is in fact calculated from a single measurement of the total elapsed time, and little statistical analysis can be performed on a sample of size 1. A study of the effects on this index of the sources of variation which are not perfectly controlled would be useful but also extremely expensive, since it would require the set of benchmarks to be run a great number of times. Furthermore, the fact that the experiments are performed by different vendors using different tools and techniques is likely to introduce into the results systematic errors bigger than those which an analysis of variance would be able to detect and quantify.

Example 6.2 has certainly raised in the reader's mind several questions related to the specification and design of benchmarks which have to be transferred from system to system. These problems are discussed in Section 6.5.

6.3.4 Installation Comparisons

When a user or an organization has computer applications for which it would be uneconomical or unreasonable to set up an entire installation and there is no system at hand which constitutes the obvious choice to process them, the problem of selecting the most convenient one among the accessible installations or service bureaus arises. This problem is substantially different from the one of vendor selection examined in Section 6.3.3. No hardware or software procurement is involved but only the procurement of services. The viewpoint of the decision makers is strictly a user's viewpoint (with respect to performance, this means that only responsiveness aspects, and neither productivity nor utilization aspects, matter). Also, the only system input the users know about is their programs, which are only part of each system's work load. Situations of this type occur in several environments. An example is that of a programmer or of a team, belonging to an organization with many general-purpose installations or having access to a computer network, who has to decide which installation to use for a certain application. Another example is the one of a company that has to select which time-sharing service or, in general, computer-time vendor to subscribe to. Sometimes, a choice to be made before that of the service bureau mentioned in the latter example is the one between buying computer time and procuring a computer system of adequate size and cost to handle the application. This interesting problem may involve a comparison of processing modes and the use of some of the approaches described in the previous section and in this section. We shall leave it to the reader as a subject for further meditation (*see* Problem 6.12). The case in which the programs to be run in the selected installation are not known at the time the decision is made will not be discussed. We shall restrict ourselves to the simple situation in which all the programs exist; written in a higher-level language. Of course, the costs of running them and the savings expected from the study are to be so high as to justify the investigation and its cost.

What are the aspects of a computer system a user is most interested in when considering an installation selection problem? Morgan and Campbell (1973) list the following characteristics: ease of use (ease of access, availability of consulting services and documentation), availability (probability that the system is operational at a given time), reliability (probability of failure and recovery or repair within a certain time), flexibility (range of applications and of languages), performance (turnaround or response time), cost, technological risk (the risk that the system is too technologically advanced and hence not sufficiently tested and understood), and schedule risk (the probability that the system will be phased out before the user's processing requirements are satisfied). For most of these aspects, the actual usage of the system is the best source, or one of the best sources, of information for the user. In particular, the performance and cost characteristics can be evaluated much more reliably by direct experimentation with each of the candidate systems than by any other method. As suggested by Morgan and Campbell, the most effective way to measure the costs and performances of the various installations with respect to a given set of programs seems to be the one of constructing an executable model of that set of programs, code it for each system, and execute it. Since we assume that the programs exist, they could be used directly in these experiments. However, the costs of converting them and their data bases to each system, plus those of their execution on each system, would in most cases be prohibitive. Clearly, an executable model's compactness is extremely valuable in these cases. A synthetic-job model of the programs will generally have lower conversion costs than a benchmark model (*see* Section 5.3.5), since the actual files used by the real programs will not have to be converted. Synthetic jobs can create and access files whose contents are absolutely irrelevant. Also, synthetic jobs are much more flexible than benchmarks and, if properly adjusted, can often be made a more representative model of a limited, well-determined set of programs than combinations of actual programs drawn from that set.

How should we design the synthetic model of our programs? The model will have to be system-independent and representative. System independence in this context means that the model must be executable and equally representative on all the systems to be compared. This is exactly the same requirement that work-load models for vendor comparisons have to satisfy. Representativeness can be defined at two different levels. The first is the comparative level. The model will be representative if the rankings of the systems in terms of performance and cost based on the results of its usage are the same as would be produced by the modeled programs. It would also be desirable, for the purposes of cost-performance analyses, to have a model which would preserve not only the rankings but also the orders of magnitude of the ratios between costs.

The second level of representativeness relates to the ability to estimate the actual performance and the actual cost from those given by the model. This additional degree of validity of the model is certainly desirable but does not seem to always be essential. In the area of cost, there are results, reported by Morgan and Campbell (1973), showing that the second level of representativeness is achievable within the limitations due to the instability of most charging algorithms. Insofar as performance is concerned, the results published by Bell (1974) confirm the fact, suggested by intuition, that experimental comparisons in this area are bound to be either very crude or very expensive. The biggest problem is that the performance indices of interest, for instance, the turnaround time of a job, are very sensitive to the work-load existing on the system at the time they are measured, which the investigator in this case can generally neither control nor observe. Bell (1974) found some variability in the elapsed times and also in the CPU times of a synthetic job even if the job was running alone in the system. Of course, this variability increases tremendously when a job is multi-programmed with others. A meaningful approach, under the stationary behavior assumption, would be to take the distribution of turnaround times (or descriptors of it, such as the mean and the variance) as the performance index. However, estimating these descriptors, or even only the mean, by sampling the distribution would in general be too expensive. Approaches which would reduce the variabil-ity due to the rest of the work-load are that of running the synthetic job with the highest possible priority or that of submitting it when the load is likely to be very light. These experiments would not, however, provide the user with the relevant performance information, which consists of the range of turnaround times to be expected under "normal" conditions. Thus, the idea of an accurate performance comparison is in most cases to be abandoned and replaced with more informal plans. A user may gather performance information by experimenting with each system, by interviewing other users, and by studying installation statistics if they are available.

To illustrate how cost comparisons may be performed, we shall present in the following example an approach inspired by the work of Morgan and Camp-bell.

Example 6.3 Two installations A and B are being considered for an application program to be executed a large number of times. The costs of each execution in A and B are to be estimated and compared. First, the job-charging formulas of the two installations are examined. For simplicity, we shall assume that both formulas have the structure

$$C_X = \sum_{i=1}^{n_X} c_{Xi} u_{Xi} \qquad (X = A, B), \tag{6.21}$$

where n_X is the number of resources the users of installation X are charged for, c_{Xi} is the cost of a unit of resource i of X, and u_{Xi} is the number of units of resource i of X consumed by the job. Let installation A charge for the usage of the CPU (unit: 1 s of CPU time), of the primary memory (unit: one word of memory requested by the job), of the disk (unit: one access to the disk), of the tapes (unit: one tape mounted), of the card reader (unit: one card read in), and of the line printer (unit: one line printed out). Also assume that installation B charges only for the usage of the CPU, of the primary memory, of the disk, and of the tapes (with a different unit: one tape access). Therefore, the model of our application program will have to be a scaled-down representation of the program from the viewpoint of the amounts of the above resources consumed in each installation. For example, assume one execution of the program would take 350 s of CPU time on system A and 280 s on system B; then if the reduction factor r is 100, the model should consume 3.5 and 2.8 s of CPU time on A and B, respectively. The same ratio should also exist between memory sizes requested, numbers of disk and tape accesses, numbers of tapes mounted, and numbers of cards read in and of lines printed out. In general, we would like the model to consume u_{Xi}/r units of resource i of system X ($i = 1, 2, \ldots, n_X$) so that its cost will be C_X/r. If this is the case, then an estimate of C_X can be obtained by multiplying this cost by r. Note that it is not necessary that the model be the same for all installations. In principle for each system we might construct a different model, with a different reduction factor. Introducing some differences between models, even in simple cases like the one we are considering, may be required by the different charging formulas used. For example, if the formula for system B contained the term $c_{B12}u_{B1}u_{B2}$ (where u_{B1} is, say, the system's CPU time consumed and u_{B2} is the memory size requested), it would be necessary to make, say, u_{B2} in the model equal to the u_{B2} of the program and not to that value divided by r; otherwise the contribution of this term to the cost of the model's execution on system B would be r times smaller than it should be. Note also that the cost of a job has been assumed to depend only on the total amounts of resources consumed by the job. This may not be exactly true but is often a reasonable assumption, especially if the resources which appear in the charging formula are such that their amounts used by a job are not too sensitive to the behavior of the rest of the work load. In any case, this assumption means that the ordering of resource requests made by the model is immaterial. The only important design requirement for the model is that there be a known ratio between the total amount of each resource consumed by the modeled program and the one consumed by the model.

The system-independence requirement suggests that the program should be characterized by parameters related to logical rather than physical resources (*see* Section 5.2.3). In other words, the model should represent the same program (more precisely, the same information-processing task) for both systems A and B. Thus, it cannot contain parameters

Table 6.9

TYPES OF FORTRAN RESOURCES

Resource type	Important characteristics
1. Arithmetic and logical operation	Statement type (assignment, iteration, branch)
	Data type (integer, real, complex)
	Operation (= , + , − , *, /, .AND., .OR.)
2. Subroutine and function call	Parameters passed
3. Array indexing	Number of indices
4. Run-time routine call	Explicit (SQRT, FLOAT, INT)
	Implicit (data conversions)
5. Input-output operation	Device type
	Characteristics of the file
6. Memory space	Scope (global, local)
	Data type (integer, real, double precision, complex)

Source: Morgan and Campbell (1973).

referring to resources of A which B does not have (for example, the number of words of slow core memory needed by the program, assuming that A is equipped with such a memory and B is not). Also, the model's parameters should not be sensitive to the differences between the ways the resources available in both systems are implemented. For instance, if the two systems have different hardware–software mechanisms for accessing files, this aspect of a job's activity should be characterized by the number (and possibly by the history) of the relevant calls to the operating system instead of by the number and history of disk accesses (which will depend on the system).

The approach proposed by Morgan and Campbell (1973) is intended to satisfy the three requirements of compactness, representativeness, and system independence by constructing a scaled-down picture of a program in terms of its *higher-level language resource demands*. A compiler is viewed as a transformer of higher-level language resource demands into the corresponding demands of the physical resources of each machine or, more precisely, of the system's resources. These demands are then in turn translated into physical resource demands by the operating system. The higher-level language resources (which Morgan and Campbell call *services*) are those known to, and requested by, the programmer. If the language is, say, FORTRAN, we could call them the resources of the FORTRAN machine. Table 6.9 contains a list of these resources and of their main characteristics, which will be used to define suitable resource subtypes. If our application program were the FORTRAN program in Table 6.10, we could analyze it as illustrated in Table 6.11 (which may be viewed as a *FORTRAN resource mix*) and construct the synthetic model of it displayed in Table 6.12. This model reproduces the FORTRAN resource demands of the program in Table 6.10 reduced by a factor of 10. Once it is translated by the FORTRAN compilers of A and B, the model will be executed on both systems, and the costs the program in Table 6.10 would be charged will be estimated by multiplying the model's charges by 10. Experimental results reported by Morgan and

Table 6.10

FORTRAN PROGRAM TO BE MODELED

	Code	Resource types (*see* Table 6.9)	Number of executions
	DIMENSION A(1000)	6	—
	TOT = 0.	1	1
	DO 10 I = 1, 1000	1	1000
	READ (5,500) A(I)	3,5	1000
500	FORMAT (F6.2)	4	1000
10	TOT = TOT + SQRT (A(I))/A(I)	1, 3, 4	1000
	AVG = A(1)/2.0	1, 3	1
	DO 20 I = 2, 1999	1	1998
20	AVG = AVG + (A(I/2 + 1) + A((I + 1)/2))/2.0	1, 3	1998
	WRITE (6,600) TOT, AVG	5	1
600	FORMAT (7HANSWER=,2F10.2)	4	1
	STOP	—	1
	END	—	—

Source: Morgan and Campbell (1973).

Table 6.11

FORTRAN RESOURCES DEMANDED BY THE PROGRAM IN TABLE 6.10

Resource type (*see* Table 6.9)	Resource subtype	Number of times demanded by program	Number of times demanded by model (reduction factor: 10)	Relative frequency [%]
1	a. Real assignment	1 + 1000 + 1 + 1998 = 3000	300	9.68
	b. Iteration	1000 + 1998 = 2998	300	9.67
	c. Real addition	1000 + 1998 + 1998 = 4996	500	16.12
	d. Integer addition	1998 + 1998 = 3996	400	12.89
	e. Real division	1000 + 1 + 1998 = 2999	300	9.67
	f. Integer division	1998 + 1998 = 3996	400	12.89
2	—	—	—	0.00
3	One-dimensional indexing	1000 + 2000 + 1 + 1998 + 1998 = 5997	600	19.35
4	a. Explicit routine (SQRT)	1000	100	3.22
	b. Implicit character-to-real conversion routine	1000	100	3.22
	c. Implicit real-to-character conversion routine	2	0	0.00
5	a. Read (card reader)	1000	100	3.22
	b. Write (line printer)	1	0	0.00
6	a. Local real variables	1002	100	—
	b. Local integer variables	1	0	—

Source: Morgan and Campbell (1973).

Table 6.12

SYNTHETIC MODEL OF THE PROGRAM IN TABLE 6.10 FOR INSTALLATION
COMPARISON

Code	Resource type and subtype (*see* Table 6.11)	Number of executions
DIMENSION A(100)	6a	—
A(1) = 10	1a, 3	1
DO 10 I = 1,100	1b	100
READ (5,500)X	5a	100
500 FORMAT (F6.2)	4b	100
Y = (SQRT(2.0) + 75.0)/63.2	1a, 1c, 1e, 4a	100
DO 20 J = 1, 2	1b	200
20 A(J/2 + 2) = (Y + A(J))/	1a, 1c, 1d, 1e, 1f, 3	200
(Y − A((J + 1)/2))		
10 CONTINUE	—	100
STOP	—	1
END	—	—

Source: Morgan and Campbell (1973).

Campbell for two programs and four systems show that these cost estimates were lower than the actual costs by at most 7%.

There are a few problems with this approach. One is that, with complicated charging formulas, constructing a representative model might be difficult (especially with regard to primary-memory charges, which may require a reproduction of the program's memory occupancy history). Another problem is the amount of work needed to extract the relevant information from large application programs. In most cases, measuring the *program profile*, that is, the number of times each statement is executed in a typical run, will be necessary, since the FORTRAN resources requested by each statement will have to be multiplied by the statement's expected frequency of execution. The analysis of each statement to determine the FORTRAN resources demanded by it is cumbersome, even though the information contained in the profile allows us to exclude from the analysis the infrequently executed statements. This analysis can, of course, be automated by programs similar to a syntax analyzer. However, all of these efforts are likely to be justified in a number of cases of practical interest, especially if and when automatic, relatively inexpensive tools will be available. ∎

6.3.5 System Component Comparisons

The selection of a system component is a problem which arises very often in configuration design studies and sometimes as a consequence of improvement efforts. As discussed in Chapter 8, the design of a configuration involves choices of off-the-shelf hardware components such as CPU's, channels, disk drives, tape drives, printers, terminals, and communications controllers to be interconnected.

Sometimes even software components such as entire operating systems, accounting routines, I/O and communications drivers, and programs which are frequently to be viewed as system components such as translators, editors, and data base systems have to be selected. Improvement studies may indicate the desirability of replacing or adding one or more system components. The new components will then have to be selected among the several alternatives usually available on the market and procured. Both in the design and in the improvement case, the choice will sometimes be restricted to one of the several similar products of the same vendor and sometimes will involve components marketed by different vendors.

Our discussion of the component selection problem in this chapter will be brief. More details can be found in Chapters 7 and 8. Also, the program performance aspects of software component selection are dealt with in Chapter 9.

In general, from a performance viewpoint, the selection of a component requires that the impact of that component's characteristics on the performance of the system be known. If the rest of the system and the work load are completely specified, as is the case of improvement studies, the n candidate components may be compared by analyzing the performances of the n configurations corresponding to the n possible choices. This analysis is done by measurement or, often more conveniently, by simulation. As usual, the selection decision will be based not only on performance but on cost, reliability, maintainability, ease of connection and use, and other (possibly local and contingent) factors. The verification that a component meets certain minimum performance requirements will in many cases be more important to the selection process than the results of a performance comparison study. Sometimes the performance analysis of only one configuration may be necessary, that of the configuration containing the candidate component which an examination of all the other factors has indicated as the most desirable. A design situation is certainly more complex, since the rest of the system as well as the work load may be only sketchily and incompletely specified. We shall discuss this problem in Chapter 8.

It should be noted that the behavior of components, especially that of the hardware components, is often satisfactorily characterizable by parameters which, unlike the indices of system performance used in this book, do not depend on how the component is used and under what input. These parameters are of the same type as the resistance of a linear resistor or the gain of an amplifier. Examples are the access time of a primary memory, the revolution time of a disk or drum, the track-to-track and maximum seek times of a movable-arm disk, the transfer rate of a channel or I/O device, and the memory space occupied by a software component and its minimum and maximum execution times. If, when selecting a component, we are able to specify its desired performance characteristics in terms of values or ranges for these parameters, then the selection process, both in improvement and in design contexts, can be entirely based on the documentation provided by the vendors. However, it will still be useful to verify experimentally before the final acceptance that the selected component's actual performance coincides with the published one. This selection procedure does not make the evaluation study referred to above useless. The only difference is that in this case the study's objective is to obtain the values and ranges of the component's parameters rather than to determine the performance of one or more configurations incorporating the candidate components.

There are at least two system components which cannot be fully characterized by parameters of this type: CPU's and operating systems. We have already seen in Section 5.3.4 how the speeds of different CPU's can be compared. The techniques used are either hand calculations (called *hand timing*) or measurement, and the CPU work load is characterized by an instruction mix or by a set of kernels. A difficult problem in CPU comparisons is the choice of the instruction classes to be included in the mix and the estimation of the frequency of each instruction class. In other words, how can we obtain models of the same work load for CPU's with different instruction sets? This question will be discussed in Section 6.5.

The comparison of different operating systems for the same hardware configuration is an important problem. Syms (1974) has experimentally confirmed what intuition suggests: The operating system can really make a big difference in performance. He compared three interactive operating systems, TSS/360, CP/67, and MTS, managing the same system, an IBM 360/67, in a variety of configurations (one processor or two processors; one, two, or three primary-memory modules; IBM 2311 or 2314 disks; drum or no drum). The comparison of various operating systems presents substantially the same problems as the comparison of different vendor proposals, slightly facilitated in some respects by the fact that they run on the same hardware. The same indices should be selected as comparison criteria. For interactive operating systems, for example, the most important is response time, but also the throughput rate is of concern. The same work-load characterization problems arise, and the same approaches to their solution are generally used. Some of the problems and solutions described by Syms in the work-load characterization area are dealt with in Section 6.5. In terms of both response times and throughput rates for the artificial work loads created by Syms, MTS outperformed TSS with the same hardware configuration by a factor of about 3. CP and TSS had approximately the same performance when CP was running with one processor, one memory module, and slower disks and TSS with two processors, three memory modules, and faster disks.

6.4 EVALUATION TECHNIQUES FOR SELECTION STUDIES

The fact that the various alternatives considered in a selection study usually exist and are accessible makes it possible to compare their performances by measurement techniques. The other techniques can of course be used too, but measurement is the most convenient in almost all cases and therefore the most popular one.

In vendor selection, the measurements which provide a basis for proposal validation and performance comparison are usually performed by each vendor. In principle, the prospective customers could evaluate the performances of the various systems by simulation or analytic modeling. Constructing as many simulators as there are proposals to be validated and compared is likely to be prohibitively expensive. Using a commercial simulator (*see* Section 3.1) is possible and in fact done in a number of selection studies. However, the accuracy of the simulator's results might in certain cases be too low with respect to the requirements of both proposal validation and comparison. Analytic techniques do not seem advanced enough to provide the degree of detail and consequently the accuracy required, especially for comparison studies. The vendors may use conventional measurement tools to gather the necessary data. An essential tool will be a stopwatch, or something equivalent, to measure elapsed times as well as turnaround or response times. Other, perhaps more sophisticated, tools will be required to monitor secondary performance indices during controlled experiments. The fact that the performance data for the study are gathered by different vendors using different measurement tools and techniques may introduce systematic errors of unknown sign and unknown magnitude into the results. Giving clear and unique definitions of indices and operational procedures (*see* Example 6.2) will certainly tend to reduce these errors. Asking the vendors to describe in detail the tools employed and the procedures followed in collecting and reducing the data will also contribute to an increase in the credibility of the results.

Most of the above considerations hold for installation selections. In those studies, measurement techniques seem to be the most convenient ones, also because of the opportunity they offer to a user to evaluate such important aspects of the various installations as ease of use, availability, and programming aids. Neither simulation nor analytic techniques seem to be suitable for this type of selection. The measurement tools required are usually very simple. A time-measuring instrument appropriate to the magnitudes of the times to be measured will be sufficient in most cases.

Component selection is the only area in which simulation may really replace measurement. When the system does not exist, such as in configuration design situations, simulation will in fact be necessary, even though it might be avoided in the simplest cases by using analytic models instead. In CPU selection, instruction mixes and kernels can be hand-timed (which is a form of simulation) or executed. In operating system comparison, measurement is likely to be more convenient if it is feasible.

6.5   WORK-LOAD CHARACTERIZATION FOR SELECTION STUDIES

A number of points related to work-load characterization have been raised and discussed in the previous sections of this chapter. In this section we shall be concerned with two problems which are especially important in vendor selection

and system performance comparisons: the problem of *system-independent characterization* and the problem of *work-load forecasting*.

The need for system-independent work-load models, and some ideas which
may help satisfy it, were discussed both in Chapter 5 (especially in Section 5.2.3)
and this chapter. However, its extreme importance in selection problems calls for
a unified treatment incorporating the illustration of some specific examples.

The problem could be described in general terms as follows. Given n
proposed systems $\mathscr{S}_1, \mathscr{S}_2, \ldots, \mathscr{S}_n$ and a work load W (which is, for example, the
production work load of the current installation), construct n executable artificial
work-load models $W'_1, W'_2, \ldots, W'_n$ such that W'_i is equivalent to W with respect
to system $\mathscr{S}_i$ and the performance indices selected as comparison criteria. Clearly,
this statement would make sense only if the meaning of equivalence between W'_i
and W were defined. W is the work load of $\mathscr{S}$, the system currently installed. Can
W be transported to $\mathscr{S}_i$, and how? If there are nontrivial differences between $\mathscr{S}_i$
and $\mathscr{S}$, any attempt to define equivalence in terms of physical (hardware or
software) resources is bound to fail. Only a characterization of W in terms of
what we called logical resources in Section 5.2.3 can allow us to transfer W to
another system. Ideally, this system-independent characterization should be
based on the information-processing tasks that the installation has to execute, or,
in other words, on the needs of the users. Let us denote this ideal characterization by w. If our knowledge of the user community allowed us to determine the
effects of each proposed system on the behavior of the users, we might be able to
transform w into the work loads $w_1, w_2, \ldots, w_n$ that the same information-
processing tasks would produce on systems $\mathscr{S}_1, \mathscr{S}_2, \ldots, \mathscr{S}_n$, respectively. These
work loads would be characterized by their demands in terms of higher-level
language resources, as illustrated in Fig. 6.7(*a*). These demands could then be
transformed into demands for system resources by the compilers running on each
system. However, our knowledge in this area is far from being sufficient (see the
discussion of this problem in Section 5.2.3). Thus, we have generally to assume
that the output of the user community is invariant with respect to the various
alternatives. The situation will therefore be the one depicted in Fig. 6.7(*b*), where
W is characterized in terms of higher-level language resource demands. That is,
W is thought of as a set of higher-level language programs and of the files these
programs need. We shall assume that, no matter what the outcome of the
selection procedure will be, the language used by the programmers to code a
given problem will not change. Note that we could easily add to the diagrams in
Fig. 6.7 extra levels, introducing the distinction between the operating system and
the hardware level (which are both into level I), or representing, for instance,
virtual machines. However, we have purposely kept the diagrams as simple as
possible.

Under the assumption pictorially represented in Fig. 6.7(*b*), a characterization of W in terms of higher-level language machine resources is system-
independent. An executable model W' of W, consisting of a set of benchmarks
(*see* Example 6.2) or of synthetic jobs based on logical rather than physical

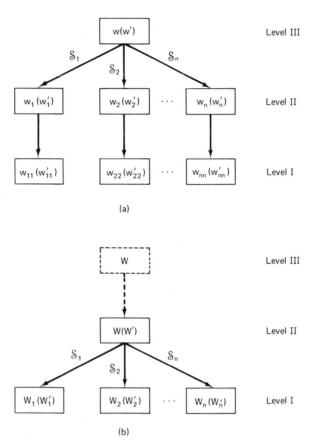

Figure 6.7   Work-load trees for vendor selection problems: (*a*) the ideal solution; (*b*) the practical solution. The symbol representing a model of a work load follows the symbol of that work load in parentheses. Work loads and their models have a lowercase symbol in (*a*) and an uppercase symbol in (*b*). Work-load characterization is in terms of physical resources at level I, of logical resources at level II, and of information-processing needs at level III. The language is machine language at level I, a higher-level language at level II, and a problem description language at level III. Compilers are the transformers between level I and II, program designers and coders are the transformers between levels II and III.

resources (*see* Example 6.3), may therefore be used as the common work load in a performance comparison study. In practice, the programs in such a set are not usually transportable without modifications, because of the differences which always exist between internal data representations, between operating system conventions, and between versions of the same higher-level language implemented for different systems. The problem of adapting benchmarks or synthetic jobs to a system, which in the selection procedure described in Section

6.2.1 is to be solved by each vendor, is frequently a nontrivial one. Baird and Johnson (1974) have listed the characteristics of an ideal set of benchmarks, and we have summarized them in Table 6.13. Automated aids for benchmark conversion, a very expensive and time-consuming task, have been proposed by Baird and Johnson (1974) and other authors.

Table 6.13
CHARACTERISTICS OF IDEAL BENCHMARKS AND BENCHMARK-
HANDLING PROCEDURES

1. Coded in the standard version (if it exists) of a higher-level language in order to minimize source code conversion.
2. Debugged to the extent that results are predictable on all machines being compared.
3. Data files readily acceptable by all systems but also consistent with the architecture of each system so as to avoid unfair comparisons or lack of validity of results.
4. Benchmark conversion by vendors monitorable as in a controlled environment, to gather information on the ease of conversion of the entire work load.
5. Automatic checks of benchmark results.

Source: Baird and Johnson (1974).

These considerations, which have provided a justification for the use of benchmarks or higher-level resource synthetic jobs in system selection procedures, have been predicated on the assumption that there is a set of higher-level languages known to all the systems to be compared. The model W' of work load W [*see* Fig. 6.7(b)] will consist of programs written in languages from this set. There are at least two important cases, however, in which this assumption is not satisfied: the cases of CPU comparison and of interactive system comparison. We shall illustrate them by the following two examples.

Example 6.4   In Example 5.5, we showed how the speeds of two different CPU's A and B can be compared by using an instruction mix and the execution times of the individual instructions. We now ask the question, Does a given instruction mix (for example, the Flynn mix in Table 5.5) represent the same work load for A and B? In general, the answer is no. Identical information-processing tasks will usually be coded in machine-language programs with different proportions of instructions from the same classes for the two CPU's. The same higher-level language programs will be translated by the two compilers into machine language programs in which instructions from the same classes have different frequencies. The fact that different architectures produce different mixes is clearly shown by the two mixes in Table 5.5 if we assume that the two work loads modeled there were not too different statistically from each other. The meaning of the notion of instruction class itself is questionable. For instance, should we put register-to-storage additions (add the contents of register R1 to those of cell X and store the result into R1) in the same class (e.g., the fixed-point add class) as register-to-register additions (add the contents of register R1 to those of register R2 and store the result into R1)? Or should we include the former in the load/store class? Or in both classes?

The only reasonable solution, unless we are solely interested in a first-approximation comparison, is the one of deriving two distinct instruction mixes, one for machine A and one for machine B, from the same higher-level language work load or from a model of it (for example, from a set of kernels). If the two machines, A and B, were those in Table 5.6 and the mix of A were the Gibson mix and the mix of B were the Flynn mix, A would be about 26% slower than B. To make the work load more realistic from the viewpoint of the CPU's, we should include in it all the programs which a CPU would execute if it were selected. This work load should generally contain the operating system, the compilers, and all of the system software which is not run by I/O processors. Unfortunately, however, this may be easier to state than to implement in practice. For example, system programs may not be available at the time of the comparison, or their usage by the user work load may be hard to predict.

The selection of a CPU is often guided by several additional criteria beside speed, such as its potential accuracy (which is directly related to the word length) or the suitability of its instruction set for the intended applications of the system. A rough measure of this suitability may be the minimum number of machine instructions needed to code certain tasks that are thought to represent the application well. The execution times of these tasks are also important, however; otherwise machines with long instruction words would tend to be favored over the others. Perhaps the best criterion would be the programming time required by the various machines for the same tasks, but this is hard to measure. Note that determining the minimum number of instructions needed would eliminate the influence of the programmers or of the code generation phases of the various compilers. However, the minimum is very difficult to determine even for very simple programs, as shown in Table 6.14, in which the "minimum" figures quoted by six vendors and those arrived at by Kernighan et al. (1972) for the inner loop of a simple ALGOL program are reported. This table illustrates, in an extremely simple case, the methodology we have described for comparing CPU's and their instruction sets. We believe that this methodology, based on a higher-level language model of the work load, is conceptually correct. However, the table shows that the results obtained by others, including the vendors, should never be completely trusted—or, perhaps, that vendor results should be trusted more than one would be inclined to do, since the assumption that the vendors know their machines much better than the average user might not always be true.   ∎

In Section 6.3.3, we discussed the performance evaluation aspects of vendor selection procedures, concentrating in particular on the case of a batch-processing installation. There, and at the beginning of this section, we saw that models composed of benchmarks or higher-level synthetic jobs are the best-known ways of representing the work load in these cases. What work-load models should we use in comparisons of interactive systems?

Selecting a work load W at level II as shown in Fig. 6.7(b) is almost always impossible in the case of interactive systems due to the inevitable and macroscopic differences usually existing between interactive command languages. A script prepared for system A in A's command language is not executable by system B. Here, it is necessary to adopt a philosophy close, in some sense, to the one summarized in Fig. 6.7(a). We have to specify the scripts at the information-processing task level (this is model w') and code them in as many different

Table 6.14

SUITABILITIES OF THE MACHINE LANGUAGES OF SIX CPU's
FOR THE INNER LOOP OF AN ALGOL PROGRAM

Program

```
e: = p;
loop: if e ≠ 0 then
begin f: = (t and area (e + 1));
    if f ≠ 0 then area (e + 2): = area (e + 2) + s;
    e: = area (e); goto loop;
end;
```

	Number of instructions required	
Machine	Vendor	Kernighan et al.
DEC PDP-10	4	4
Honeywell–Bull G625	7	5
IBM 360/370	7	5*
Xerox SIGMA 5	6	5
RC 4000	7	7†
UNIVAC 1106	7	6

Source: Kernighan et al. (1972).

* This solution may be slower than some seven-instruction solutions.

†Speed can be increased by using nine instructions.

versions as there are systems (models $w'_1, \ldots, w'_n$). An example of a script specification at level III is the one in Table 5.9. For different systems, this script
specification will have to be translated into completely different sequences of
commands. The work-load models $w'_1, \ldots, w'_n$ will also contain mechanisms to
simulate think times, unless the scripts are submitted by human users during the
experiments. The scripts will invoke the execution of various programs, selected
so as to represent probable usage patterns: editors, compilers, debuggers, application programs. The application programs to be compiled or debugged, the files to
be edited, may be handled by the work-load model designer as though they were
benchmarks or synthetic jobs (and their data) for batch-system comparisons. In
any case, their design or selection should not be based on physical resource
demands but on demands in terms of higher-level language resources. The
following example describes in some detail one of the experimental setups used by
Syms (1974) in his comparison of interactive operating systems (see also Section
6.3.5).

Example 6.5   The systems to be compared were TSS/360, CP/67, and MTS, all running
on an IBM 360/67 configurable in many different ways. The number of active terminals
was kept relatively constant in all measurement sessions and equal to about 24. Each
terminal was assigned a script in each session. The load was changed from session to

session by changing the proportions of the scripts assigned to the terminals. Six scripts
were prepared, three of the compilation type (two PL/I and one FORTRAN), two of the
execution type (one compute-bound and the other paging-I/O-bound), and one of the
editing type. The scripts and their main characteristics are listed in Table 6.15. The load
was in fact changed in a controlled way by varying the ratio between the number of
terminals running the editing script and the number of terminals running the compile and
execute scripts. This ratio was varied from 1:5 to 5:1. Syms observed that the normal
work load corresponded to a ratio of about 2:1.

Table 6.15
SCRIPTS USED TO MODEL THE WORK LOAD IN A COMPARISON OF
INTERACTIVE SYSTEMS

Script number	Name	Description
1	FORTRAN	Causes a 75-card FORTRAN program to be compiled
2	PLILG	Causes a 434-card PL/I program to be compiled
3	PLISM	Causes a 47-card PL/I program to be compiled
4	FORTEX	Causes a compute-bound synthetic job (which performs 1 million additions and prints a line at the terminal) to be executed
5	PAGE	Causes a program which uses a large array and accesses a different page for each operation to be executed
6	EDIT	Performs several editing functions (locates a string in a program, moves the pointer up and down, types some output, and so on)

Source: Syms (1974).

It is interesting to note that Syms was able to express the *load factor* of each system
(*see* Section 5.2.2) as a function of the number of terminals running each script. For
example, if by N_i we denote the number of terminals running the ith script in Table 6.15,
the load factor for CP/67 was

$$L_{\text{CP}} = 4N_1 + 8N_2 + 6N_3 + 4N_4 + 24N_5 + 2N_6, \qquad (6.22)$$

and that for MTS was

$$L_{\text{MTS}} = N_1 + a_2N_2 + 6N_3 + a_4N_4 + 6N_5 + N_6$$

$$(a_i = 8 \quad \text{if } N_i \le 4; \quad a_i = 2.5 \quad \text{if } N_i > 4; \quad i = 2, 4). \qquad (6.23)$$

Table 6.16

WORK LOADS PRODUCING APPROXIMATELY THE SAME PERFORMANCE IN
THE EXPERIMENTS DESCRIBED IN EXAMPLE 6.5 UNDER CP/67

Script number (see Table 6.15)	Number of terminals running each script			
	Workload *a*	Workload *b*	Workload *c*	Workload *d*
1	1	—	3	10
2	3	—	5	—
3	5	1	2	—
4	6	2	4	5
5	—	2	—	1
6	9	19	10	8
Total terminals	24	24	24	24
L_{CP}	100	100	100	100
L_{MTS}	79	53	69.5	36.5

Thus, the combinations of (terminal, script) pairs listed in Table 6.16 produced approximately the same performance under CP. The table also shows the corresponding values of L_{MTS}. As could be expected, an attempt to combine different load factors into a single factor, in order to obtain a common reference against which the values of the performance indices could be plotted and compared, was unsuccessful (*see* Problem 6.16), even though not completely useless. Two work loads under which a system produces the same performance are generally processed with different performances by a different system. As pointed out in Section 5.2.2, there is no conservation of work-load equivalence when moving from one system to another. The only correct comparisons are those in which the systems are driven by models of exactly the same work load.   ■

We shall now briefly discuss the problem of forecasting the work load of an existing installation. We saw in Section 6.3.3 that estimates of future work loads are often considered in selection studies. An important question usually is, Will the candidate systems be able to cope with the increased work load expected to be produced by the installation's users in, say, 2 years from the time the winner will be operational, and at what cost-performance penalties? Of course, similar problems also arise in performance improvement and in configuration design studies.

To predict what the work load will be in the future, we can use techniques based on trend extrapolation. The recent history of the work load at the installation provides data, such as growth rates, from which the work loads to be expected in the near future are computed. In this computation, the assumption is made that the current trends will continue, but corrections are also introduced if additional information is known about new applications, changes in the user community, developments of the global or local economic situation, or other disruptive factors (for example, the probable creation of another installation in the same organization). Of course, the uncertainty of the prediction, as defined, for instance, by the confidence intervals of the estimates of the work-load parameters, will increase with the distance of the projection into the future. As we try to go farther and farther from the present, the confidence intervals become wider, and the probability of unpredictable disruptive factors becomes greater. Beyond a certain point, any estimate should be considered meaningless. It is common opinion that, for typical computer installations, projections cannot extend over a time period of more than 5 years, and sometimes even over a shorter period.

What work-load parameters should we extrapolate? In general, it is reasonable to refer to the work-load characterization selected for the study being performed. If this characterization consists of quantitative parameters (such as CPU time demands, memory space demands, total computer time per month, and so on), we can project into the future the trends exhibited by these parameters in the recent past and obtain in this way models of future work loads of the same type as those used for current work loads. Extrapolating physical resource demands, which are those usually recorded for accounting purposes, is likely to be sufficient when the objective of our study is to determine, for instance, the expected date of saturation of an existing system's capacity. In selection studies, when the existing system is to be replaced by one of the candidates being compared, work-load models which refer to physical resources are inadequate. Thus, a model specified at level III or level II (*see* Fig. 6.7) should also be used for forecasting purposes. In the absence of any indication to the contrary, we can make the assumption that the types of applications processed by the installation are not going to change appreciably. Thus, the only change will be in the total number of jobs submitted within a certain period of time. In other words, the tasks will not change, but the arrival rate of the programs implementing them will. Use of diagrams like the one in Fig. 6.8 for work-load forecasting purposes would be based on this assumption. Note that, for interactive installations, an equivalent assumption is that only the number of active terminals, but not the natures and relative proportions of their activities, will change. Adjusting an executable work-load model, or the way it is used, to take care of this modification is easy. If changes in the nature of the applications are expected, they may not be substantially more difficult than arrival rate changes to introduce into such a model. For example, if the model was constructed using methods like those we called Ac and Ad in Section 5.3.5, it is easy to modify the ratios between the numbers of job models representing the various job classes. If the work-load model is composed of synthetic jobs of the type described in Example 6.3 (*see* Table 6.12), it should not be too difficult to take the expected changes in the applications into account by modifying the fractions of the various higher-level language resources demanded by the model (these are the resource demands listed in the next to last column in Table 6.11). These modifications could be based not only on conjectures but also on extrapolations, if historical records of these demands had been

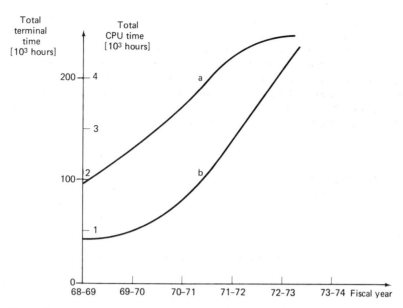

Figure 6.8 Expansion of the work load of the Dartmouth Time-Sharing System produced by on-campus users: (*a*) total terminal time; (*b*) total CPU time. (*Sources*: The Kiewit Computation Center, Dartmouth College, Biennial Reports 1969–1971 and 1971–1973.)

kept for at least the most recent past. Unfortunately, these types of measurements are usually not gathered by an installation, and therefore in work-load forecasts the effects of continuous changes in the applications are either ignored or guessed. Also, the lack of historical data in this area does not allow the estimation of the impact of sudden changes to be based on elements more objective than intuition. One very important and inevitable change of this type is, of course, the installation of the new system. How will the characteristics and the performance of the new system affect the short-term and long-term behavior of the user community? How will this behavior in turn affect the nature and intensity of the work load? As pointed out in Section 5.1, a substantial amount of research is needed before these questions can receive documented, even if only preliminary, answers.

We shall now briefly show, following the approach suggested by Good and Moon (1972), how the work load of a batch-processing university computer center can be projected into the future within the context of a vendor selection study.

Example 6.6 A university is considering the replacement of the system installed at its computer center with a more modern and powerful one. The current installation supports only the batch-processing mode. In the first phase of the study, the assumption is made that this will also be the case of the new system. Since the new system will almost certainly support interactive processing, a sizable portion of the current work load (the one generated by the users who write and debug programs) should be expected to become interactive. Furthermore, a number of new applications, such as document preparation, information retrieval, and computer-aided design, are likely to be encouraged by the presence of the new system and to contribute to an increase in the total work load. Predicting the effects of these work-load changes is, however, the goal of a later phase of the study, not to be dealt with in this example.

Table 6.17

DATA FOR EXAMPLE 6.6

College, i	Undergraduates		Graduates		Annual per capita usage of current system [CPU hr/egs]	
	$u_i(0)$	U_i	$g_i(0)$	G_i	$h_i(0)$	r_i [%]
Sciences	1840	40	316	10	2.71	5
Engineering	1320	35	282	15	10.24	8
Arts and Social Sciences	4240	65	564	25	0.61	7
Agriculture	760	20	156	,5	2.46	4
Business Administration	1400	45	268	20	3.38	7
Medicine	720	15	128	5	5.59	5

Table 6.17 gives the current enrollments in each one of the colleges of the university and the average increases in the enrollments predicted for the next 5 academic years. The table also reports the annual per capita usage of the current system for each college and its expected annual growth rate. The per capita usage of a college has been calculated dividing the total CPU hours of the current system billed to that college by its number of *equivalent graduate students*. This approach is based on the observation that the computing demands (in terms of CPU hours) of 40 undergraduates are approximately equal to the demand of one graduate student and that computer usage by faculty members can be accounted for without appreciable loss of accuracy as if it came from students [*see* Good and Moon (1972)].

What should the ratio between the CPU capacities of the new and of the current system be if the new system had to be able to process without backlogs the work load expected to exist at the end of the 5-year period being considered? That work load, expressed in terms of annual CPU hours for the current system, may be estimated by the formula

$$H(t) = \sum_{i=1}^{6} \text{egs}_i(t) \cdot h_i(t), \tag{6.24}$$

where t is the time in years, with the origin $t = 0$ corresponding to the current academic year; h_i is the annual per capita usage of college i in CPU hours; egs_i is the number of equivalent graduate students in college i; and H is the total annual usage in CPU hours. The values of $egs_i(t)$ and $h_i(t)$ can be computed by the following expressions:

$$egs_i(t) = g_i(t) + \frac{u_i(t)}{40} = g_i(0) + tG_i + \frac{u_i(0) + tU_i}{40}, \tag{6.25}$$

$$h_i(t) = h_i(0)(1 + r_i)^t, \tag{6.26}$$

where g_i and u_i are the numbers of graduate and undergraduate students, respectively, in college i; G_i and U_i are the predicted average increments in the graduate and undergraduate enrollments of college i; and r_i is the annual usage growth rate expected for the typical graduate student in college i. The values of the quantities appearing on the right-hand sides of (6.25) and (6.26) are all given in Table 6.17. Table 6.18 shows the resulting values of $u_i(5)$, $g_i(5)$, $egs_i(5)$, and $h_i(5)$. Applying (6.24) to the results in this table, we have $H(5) = 11,822$ CPU hr. Since a fully utilized computer runs for about

Table 6.18
FIVE-YEAR PROJECTIONS OF ENROLLMENTS AND COMPUTER USAGE FOR EXAMPLE 6.6

College, i	Undergraduates, $u_i(5)$	Graduates, $g_i(5)$	Equivalent graduates, $egs_i(5)$	Annual per capita usage [CPU hr/egs], $h_i(5)$
Sciences	2040	366	417	3.46
Engineering	1495	357	394	15.04
Arts and Social Sciences	4565	689	803	0.85
Agriculture	860	181	202	2.99
Business Administration	1625	368	408	4.74
Medicine	795	153	173	7.13

600 hr every month, and assuming that the load will have to be processed over a period of about 10 months (the much lighter summer load is accounted for by ignoring 2 of the 12 months of the year), we see that a system with twice the CPU capacity of the current system would be needed. Of course, if the new machine is also to be able to process the peak daily loads without backlogs extending into the next day, and if we assume that the highest daily loads will not be greater than twice the average load, then a system with a capacity four times greater than the one of the current system should be procured.

In this example, the work load of the installation has been characterized in terms of the total CPU time demand of the jobs to be processed during an academic year. In using this characterization for forecasting purposes also, we have made the implicit assumption that the nature of the work load will not appreciably change over the next 5 years, so that the proportion of I/O activities and CPU activities will roughly remain the same. Also, when our conclusions about the CPU capacity of the new machine were reached, we made the implicit assumption that the architecture of the new system will be sufficiently "similar" to that of the current one so that ignoring the influence of I/O activities will still be acceptable. In other words, we assumed that the current system is CPU-bound and that this will also be the case of the new system. Simple calculations based on Table 6.17 show that the former assumption is true. If the latter assumption were not satisfied, the work load should be characterized in a different way in order to avoid making grossly wrong decisions. The relative influences of the various resources on the performance of a system are discussed in more detail in Chapter 7. ∎

PROBLEMS

6.1. Propose three indices which you feel would be more appropriate than those listed in Table 6.2 to represent the comparison criteria shown in the same table under the heading "Class." Say how you would measure each one of the three indices in a batch-interactive mode comparison experiment.

6.2. To study the rate of technological progress in the computer field, you may choose a certain value of information processing power, defined, for example, à la Knight, and follow the evolution of the cost of machines having approximately that power over a certain number of years. Table P6.1 lists the costs and birth dates of some

Table P6.1
COSTS OF SOME MINICOMPUTERS HAVING THE SAME POWER

Minicomputer	Date of introduction	Cost [$/hr]
$P \cong 16,000$ instructions/s		
Hewlett-Packard 2114C	January 1968	2.12
TEC Model 520 PCP	June 1969	1.27
Electronic Processors EPI-118	November 1970	0.86
Data General NOVA 1200	December 1971	0.77
$P \cong 24,000$ instructions/s		
Honeywell DDP-516	October 1966	3.46
Interdata Model 4	June 1968	2.30
General Automation SPC-16	May 1970	1.41
Digital Computer Control D-216	August 1971	1.17

Source: Cerveny and Knight (1973).

minicomputers of equal power for two values of power. Use the data in the table to make conjectures about the variations in time of g and K in equation (6.11), assuming that these two parameters are functions only of time and not of P or C.

6.3. Following the simplified approach described in Example 6.1, determine whether the value of N (the number of computers to be installed) corresponding to the minimum

cost C would vary with respect to that in Fig. 6.3 if one of these variations were given to the parameters of the problem:
(a) the total power P required is doubled ($P = 2 \times 10^6$ instructions/s);
(b) the failure probability of each system is divided by 10 ($p_f = 0.01$);
(c) the geographical area over which the users are spread is reduced by a factor of 4; that is, the average distance is divided by a factor of 2.

6.4. Derive an expression for the total cost of the system considered in Example 6.1 assuming that
(a) the cost of service interruptions is proportional to the fraction of facilities which are not working; thus, if $N = 2$, $C_i = K_i(\frac{1}{2}p_f + \frac{2}{2}p_f^2)$; and
(b) the failure probability of a facility is proportional to its power.
If all the parameters have the same values as in Example 6.1 and $p_f(N = 1) = 0.1$, what is the value of N corresponding to the minimum total cost?

6.5. Plot the total information-processing power (in instructions/s) achievable with values of N from 1 through 8 for a given total cost C. Take the approach and the numerical values of the parameters used in Example 6.1. Assume a cost equal to the minimum in Fig. 6.3.

6.6. Do you see any reasons (or any cases in which) one or some of the five methods listed in Table 5.10 for selecting the job models to be included in an executable work-load model should be preferred to the other methods when designing a set of benchmarks or synthetic jobs for a vendor selection problem?

6.7. Would you consider an effort to devise a set of standard work-load models to be used in vendor selections worthwhile? Realistic? Useful? Necessary? Why? What would you think of a large library of standard synthetic jobs from which any customer could assemble a particular work-load model by selecting the jobs and specifying the numbers of their copies as well as the values of their arguments?

6.8. You have to design a set of benchmarks for the selection of one among a number of systems to be proposed by various vendors. The new system will replace an existing one, running in batch-processing mode. The work-load model to be designed is intended to represent the production work load of the present installation. Assume that you have decided to use a method of the Ac type (*see* Table 5.10) to select the job models. Would you partition the jobs in the production work load according to
(a) the languages in which they are written?
(b) the CPU times they consume?
(c) the I/O times they consume?
(d) the ratios between CPU and I/O times?
(e) the ratios between their completion times and their total execution times?
(f) their external priorities?
(g) any other characteristics?
Note that job classes may be defined by more than one of the above parameters and that good arguments can be made in favor of using any of those parameters. Thus, you should discuss these arguments and order the parameters according to your preferences. Is it more reasonable, in your opinion, to classify jobs or job steps? Why do work-load model designers put such an emphasis on the distinction between compilations and executions (*see*, for instance, Example 6.2)?

6.9. The performances of two interactive systems A and B have to be compared. The index selected for the comparison is the mean response time. Design an experiment which will allow you to make this comparison. List the possible sources of variation, and specify how you would experimentally control those which should not contribute to the difference between mean response times. State what statistical tests you would perform to see whether the difference is significant and how the variance of the difference could be analyzed.

6.10. What are the factors which contribute to the differences between the entries in the second row and those in the fourth row of Table 6.8?

6.11. In some operating systems such as GCOS for Honeywell 600 series machines, the usage of all resources by a job is billed in terms of equivalent seconds of CPU time. For example, a job which requires less than $16K$ words of primary memory is billed for an amount of CPU time equal to the CPU time actually consumed, while a job which requires more than $16K$ and less than $32K$ words is billed for twice that amount. Assuming that one of the installations compared in Example 6.3 runs under GCOS, what modifications would you make to the version of the model in Table 6.12 to be executed in that installation?

6.12. You have a batch-type information-processing application which requires a certain power. This power can be obtained either by purchasing a small system or by renting (or buying) a remote job entry station and getting computer time from a large installation. List the arguments in favor and against either alternative, and discuss in detail the method by which you would compare the two solutions from a performance viewpoint.

6.13. The performances of two batch-processing multiprogramming operating systems running on the same hardware are to be compared. Design an experiment having this objective. Specify the factors to be controlled and how you would control them. Would the knowledge of the differences existing between the two systems (e.g., differences in their scheduling policies, memory allocation policies) help you design a better experiment? If so, you can assume that you know these differences and specify them before describing the experiment.

6.14. In a batch-processing installation the operating system currently being used executes only programs which are completely loaded in primary memory. Thus, if the size of a program exceeds the maximum memory space allocatable to it, the programmer must divide it into successive overlays and manage the allotted space by explicit calls to the operating system. An operating system which implements virtual memory by automatically managing a two-level memory hierarchy could be installed without any modifications of the existing hardware. Design an experiment intended to compare the performances of the two operating systems. In particular, select the performance index (or indices) and the criteria you would follow in designing the work-load model. Note that the evaluation of virtual-memory system performance is discussed in detail, but from different viewpoints, in Chapters 7 and 8. The purpose of this problem is to invite you to think about it from a performance comparison viewpoint. You may want to come back to this problem after studying the next chapters. Some inspiration can be obtained by reading the paper by Sayre (1969).

6.15. A popular unit of CPU speed is the so-called MIPS (millions of instructions per second). Is it reasonable, and to what extent, to compare the performances of various CPU's by comparing their speeds in MIPS quoted by the vendors? Why?

6.16. Syms (1974) defined a combined load factor for CP/67 and MTS (*see* Example 6.5 and Table 6.15) as follows:

$$L_{\text{CP-MTS}} = 2N_1 + 8N_2 + 6N_3 + 6N_4 + 10N_5 + N_6.$$

Calculate the values of the other load factors [*see* (6.22) and (6.23)] for the three work loads listed in Table P6.2. Use the results to show that the mean response times of the two systems (which are roughly proportional to the respective load factors) are likely to be multivalued functions of $L_{\text{CP-MTS}}$.

Table P6.2
WORK LOADS CORRESPONDING TO THE SAME COMBINED LOAD
FACTOR ($L_{\text{CP-MTS}} = 100$) FOR THE EXPERIMENT DESCRIBED
IN EXAMPLE 6.5

Script number (*see* Table 6.15)	Number of terminals running each script		
	Workload X	Workload Y	Workload Z
1	4	2	3
2	1	5	4
3	—	6	—
4	4	—	9
5	5	1	—
6	10	10	8
Total terminals	24	24	24

6.17. Which one of the two curves in Fig. 6.8 would you have considered more important if in 1973 you had been requested to forecast the yearly on-campus work load of the Dartmouth Time-Sharing System for the next 2 fiscal years?

6.18. Determine the CPU capacity required in the installation described in Example 6.6 if the system to be installed is to process without backlogs
a. the annual work load expected to be produced by the user community after 3 years of operation of the new system,
b. the peak daily work load, assumed to be about twice the average daily load, also after 3 years.

6.19. Assuming that a system with four times the CPU capacity of the current one is installed as a result of the study outlined in Example 6.6, how would you adjust the predictions about the time the new system will start operating with backlogs if the data collected during the first year of operation showed that the rates r_i were all underestimated and are in fact 50% higher?

7

Performance Evaluation
in Improvement Problems

7.1 IMPROVEMENT PROBLEMS

One of the most important areas of application for performance evaluation techniques is that of improvement. The object of an improvement study, for example, a computer system, is supposed to be working in its production environment at the time of the study but with a level of performance which does not satisfy the manager's or the user's needs or expectations. Of course, even if these needs and expectations are satisfied, it is always convenient to make a system work at a better level of performance, since its value to the users will increase. Financial advantages are very often obtained if a system's performance is improved. For instance, the same work load can be processed in a shorter time, thereby allowing the operations staff to be reduced; better performance attracts more customers; the procurement of a larger, more expensive system may be postponed or avoided because of the increased ability of the current system to cope with an expanded work load; and the addition of a hardware component to the configuration may be made unnecessary by the changes suggested by an improvement study. Such a study may reveal that a hardware component (e.g., an I/O channel) is superfluous, since its removal does not decrease the system's performance appreciably. In this case, we have a *cost improvement* instead of a *performance improvement*. We have seen that many performance improvements result in cost reductions. Moreover, the characteristics and methods of cost

better level
of performance

Financial
short time - same work load

improvement studies are very similar to those of performance improvement studies. Thus, we shall be concerned with both types in this chapter, even though we shall more often refer to studies whose primary objective is the improvement of performance.

The financial and performance benefits of an improvement study should be compared with its cost to see whether the study is worthwhile. Unfortunately, this comparison can only be done a posteriori, when its result is no longer useful. Before the study, we can only (and ought to) estimate the expected benefits and the expected costs, to determine whether we should embark on it or not. Even though only very rough estimates are possible in most practical cases, it is always wiser to consider the question than to blindly start performing an investigation which could turn out to be a waste of resources.

Is it possible to <u>define the *optimum performance*</u> of a computer system? And, if it can be defined, how difficult is it to determine and to achieve? In principle, the optimum performance a certain system can provide in processing a given work load can be defined if the system parameters that may be varied, and the bounds of their variability, are specified. For example, we shall see in Section 7.3.2 that in a multiprogramming virtual-memory system there is usually a value of the degree of multiprogramming that maximizes the mean throughput rate for a given work load. Thus, <u>if the performance index of interest is the mean throughput rate</u> and <u>the only parameter which may be changed is the degree of multiprogram-</u> <u>ming, then clearly there is an</u> <u>optimum performance</u> that the system may produce. Practical situations, however, are seldom so simple. When an improvement study is started, the system parameters that should be considered as candidates for modification are too many to be enumerated. Also, their bounds are difficult to establish. In certain cases, the cost of a change, for instance, of memory expansion, depends on the size of the change, and the bound may be dictated by the maximum amount of money which is available and by the costs of the other possible concomitant changes. Some constraints are not easily quantifiable. These difficulties often make practical situations quite different from cleanly stated mathematical optimization problems. Even when an optimum can be defined, it is extremely difficult to find. The two main reasons for the suboptimal performance of computer systems are the high cost of optimization procedures and the relatively minor incremental benefits which accrue when one tries to increase the performance beyond a certain point. An improvement study is really successful when it results in a substantial increase in performance with relatively little effort. If performance is not too far from the optimum, it will generally be possible to improve it further only by small amounts, and these improvements will normally be quite expensive. Thus, the term *improvement* represents the reality much better than the term *optimization*, and for this reason it has been used in this book instead of the latter.

We stated above that the normal operational condition of a real computer system is a suboptimal one. Why are systems not designed to provide optimum performance for a given cost? Why are improvement studies needed in so many cases and so frequently? There seem to be three main reasons for this situation: the unattractiveness of customized design from industrial and commercial viewpoints; the complexity of computer systems, which our knowledge is not sufficient to master completely; and the variability of a system's environment. The performance of a system depends on the type and magnitude of the work load it has to process and on the operational procedures by which it is managed. Since each installation has a particular work load and particular procedures, an optimum system for a given installation could in principle be designed and built from scratch, but its cost would be prohibitive. Even if this problem could be overcome, it is doubtful that an optimum system could be designed, due to our inadequate understanding of the complex relationships between performance indices and system and work-load parameters. Furthermore, even if our knowledge were sufficient, the dynamic nature of the environment of most systems would still require periodic adjustments to be made and would make the system's performance suboptimal for a large fraction of the system's lifetime.

Thus, computer systems are usually constructed by assembling previously designed hardware components and coordinating their activities by adaptable software (*see* Chapter 8). The relative flexibility and compatibility of hardware and software components is intended to allow a variety of configurations to be obtained by different combinations and specializations of modules from the same pool. The basic assumption is that these configurations can be tailored to the different and ever-changing needs of various installations. Therefore, we may say that improvement studies are not only desirable and often very profitable but also an essential part of the design process.

7.2 IMPROVEMENT METHODOLOGIES

The same lack of knowledge that makes it so difficult to design an optimum performance computer system usually prevents us from determining in a single step whether performance may be improved, by how much, and what should be done to improve it. An improvement procedure is by necessity iterative and in fact contains several cycles at different levels. The activities performed in the main cycle can be broken down into two major phases, for which we shall adopt the medical terms *diagnosis* and *therapy*. These phases are often, but not always, preceded by the appearance of *symptoms* (*see* Fig. 7.1).

An improvement study may be initiated by an installation's manager even in the absence of any symptoms. In these cases, the initial objective is to determine whether there is room for improvement and whether the magnitude of the improvement to be expected would be worth seeking. More frequently, however, the need for a study is generated by observations which suggest that a system is not performing as well as it could or that its performance has become insufficient. These symptoms may come from such sources as daily or monthly statistics, observations made by the operations staff, users' complaints, and data collected

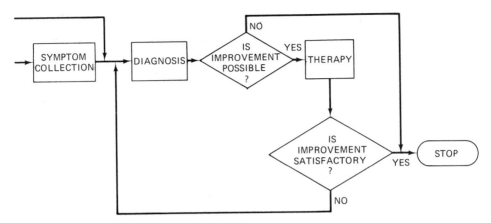

Figure 7.1   Block diagram of an improvement procedure.

1.)   by continuous monitoring instruments. Prompt reporting of symptoms of performance problems is in fact, with accounting, the main purpose of continuous monitoring. The accounting routine is the simplest and ever-present continuous monitoring tool. The data gathered by this routine and the other instruments possibly added to it are to perform this "alarm" function. Typical measurements satisfying this requirement are those of the primary performance indices and of each hardware component's utilization factors. Other useful variables to be monitored may be found among work-load parameters. However, the scope and resolution of continuous-monitoring tools are even more interference-limited than those of other tools, since the performance degradation they may cause is permanent.

2.)   On the other hand, as in the medical practice, diagnosis is mostly based on symptoms (when they exist). If continuous monitoring provided more data than those strictly required to alert the installation's manager, understanding where the problem might be would be easier. However, from a global viewpoint, it is probably more convenient to postpone the collection of further experimental evidence until the diagnostic phase, during which this collection may be limited to the information needed to test certain well-defined hypotheses. In this context, diagnosing a system means determining whether it contains any so-called *performance bug*, where it is, and how it can be removed. A typical diagnosis procedure will consist of formulating a hypothesis, performing a preliminary analysis of its reasonableness, and testing it. If the results of the reasonableness analysis or of the tests are negative, another hypothesis should be formulated and the procedure repeated until positive results are found or until no more hypotheses can be formulated. In the latter case, we must conclude that we are unable to improve the system, and therefore we either learn to live with its current level of performance or replace it by a more powerful one. We should not forget, however, to consider among the hypotheses those implying that improvement may

Diagnosis   1 Formulating a hypothesis
                  until no more hypothesis can be formulated.

be sought by reducing the magnitude or modifying the nature of the work load. The iterative procedure we have just outlined, inspired by the work of Bell et al. (1972), is represented in Fig. 7.2. It should be thought of as being nested inside the improvement procedure depicted in Fig. 7.1, which is also iterative.

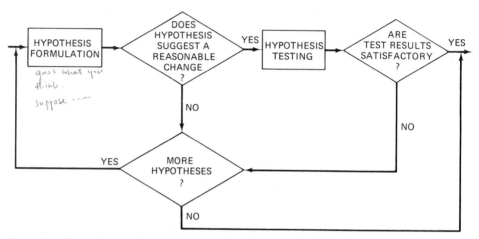

Figure 7.2   Block diagram of the diagnosis phase.

A few comments on the diagram in Fig. 7.2 need to be added here. First, as Bell et al. (1972) point out, hypothesis formulation must be preceded by an information-gathering effort. Investigators cannot be expected to come up with useful hypotheses if they do not have a thorough knowledge of the system; of the installation's work-load, organization, and operational procedures; of the objectives of the management; and of the symptoms or their purposely gathered equivalents. The collection of this information has not been explicitly mentioned in Figs. 7.1 and 7.2 since in some cases the analyst may already be very familiar with the installation. For example, there are installations whose staff includes one or more persons in charge of performance evaluation activities. However, the point that the more the installation is known, the more successful the study is likely to be needs to be stressed in spite of its evident validity, since analysts tend sometimes to rely too heavily on their intuition.

Second, hypotheses are to be formulated about the reasons performance is lower than expected. The symptoms, when they exist, are the effects. The diagnosis phase tries to discover the causes. Sometimes, the causes are hypothesized indirectly. The hypothesis which is formulated is not, say, that the primary memory is too small for the given configuration and work load but that increasing the primary-memory size will be the best investment toward increasing the performance. It is easy to recognize that there is no major conceptual difference between hypotheses about causes and hypotheses about therapies which may be effective in eliminating the unmentioned underlying causes. As we shall see, once a hypothesis about causes is found to be valid, the therapy to be adopted is almost always evident, also because the testing of a hypothesis often consists of predicting the effects of a therapy suggested by it.

It should be noted that the formulation of hypotheses is a difficult and delicate task. Like medical diagnosis, it is an art in which success is generally based on solid foundations of knowledge, understanding, and experience as well as on intuition. The basic type of knowledge required is that of the dependencies of performance indices on work-load and system parameters, that is, of the factors which influence performance. There are no handbooks containing lists of symptoms and corresponding hypotheses, although some partial attempts at providing example lists of this type have appeared in the literature and are quite helpful [see, for example, Bell et al. (1972) and Cockrum and Crockett (1971)]. Bell et al. (1972) have distilled from their experience five general techniques which can help in formulating correct hypotheses. These techniques are listed and briefly commented on in Table 7.1. We shall illustrate the application of some of them in the discussions of examples to be presented later in this chapter.

A third remark on the diagram in Fig. 7.2 must be made about the step following the formulation of a hypothesis. This is a test of the reasonableness of a therapy that the hypothesis suggests. Even before testing the validity of the hypothesis, it is convenient to see whether the possible cures would be cost-effective. The cost of the modifications can usually be estimated with sufficient accuracy at this point. The cost of the remainder of the study is less predictable, but its order of magnitude can probably be determined. The savings and performance benefits which the therapy might produce can only be roughly estimated. However, this test is useful at this point since it may save the investigator the trouble and the expense of testing a hypothesis which would suggest economically unjustifiable changes. Of course, a much more accurate estimation of benefits will be possible after the validity of a hypothesis has been tested. Thus, our tentative conclusion that the suggested change was reasonable should be reassessed before exiting the diagnosis phase, that is, when we ask whether test results are satisfactory. An example of an unreasonable hypothesis is one which would entail hiring an additional operator to speed up the mounting of tapes when this would probably decrease the mean turnaround time by only 5%.

A final comment needs to be made on the hypothesis testing step in Fig. 7.2. This step usually involves the gathering of additional relevant data by a measurement effort. The data collected should provide the analyst with a basis for confirming or rejecting the hypothesis. Ideally, we would like to be able to predict what the performance of the system would be if it were modified according to the suggestions of the hypothesis being tested. A comparison of this performance with the one of the original system would tell us whether our hypothesis is valid (*see* Fig. 7.3). The analysis of performance of the modified system is relatively easy to do using a suitable simulator or analytic model of that system. Doing it by measurement would require the system to be actually

Table 7.1

SOME GENERAL METHODS FOR HYPOTHESIS FORMULATION

Method	Description
1. Identification of similar situations	One's own or somebody else's experience with previous improvement studies is used to generate hypotheses in cases recognized to be similar to the past ones.
2. Discovery of outlying values	Outlying values of performance indices are often interesting symptoms and may lead to valid hypotheses. They should be ignored only after they have been thoroughly explained.
3. Detection of patterns	Interesting patterns in time (cycles, trends) are sought. Graphical techniques are very helpful, but time scales and quantities to be plotted have to be carefully selected.
4. Detection of correlations	Correlations between work-load or system parameters and performance indices may lead to valid hypotheses. However, the existence of correlation is not always due to a cause-effect relationship.
5. Identification and resolution of inconsistencies	The existence of obvious relationships among data collected from different sources, job-related and system-related data, measurements that should be the same, and expected and measured data are checked. The inconsistencies detected are likely to lead to hypotheses.

Source: Bell et al. (1972).

changed. In some cases, when the changes are minor, relatively cheap, and not too disruptive, this can be done. For example, the effects on performance of certain changes to the operating systems may be tested under artificial work-load models, and then under the production work load during special time intervals, before they are incorporated into the production version of the system. In other cases, for instance, when the hypothesis would require an expensive hardware component to be replaced or added, measuring the effects of the change directly before having made the modification decision is impossible. Thus, the validity of the hypothesis will have to be tested either by modeling techniques or by careful

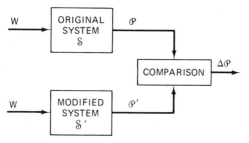

Figure 7.3 Testing an improvement hypothesis by performance analysis and comparison. $\mathscr{S}$ and $\mathscr{S}'$ may be versions of the actual system or models of them. *W* may be a real work load or a model of it.

data collection and interpretation, or by both. Examples of these methods are discussed in Section 7.3. As observed above, the results of this step will be satisfactory if the benefits to be expected from the therapy suggested by the hypothesis clearly dominate its costs.

In diagnosing a system, the chance always exists that none of the hypotheses we formulate is both reasonable and valid (*see* Fig. 7.2). In this case, as shown in Fig. 7.1, the improvement study will terminate with a negative answer, and if the current situation is intolerable, other alternatives (a new, more powerful system or another internal or external installation to absorb part of the work load) will have to be considered. If a hypothesis is found to be valid, then the therapy phase will have to be implemented. This is simply the actual incorporation into the running system of the changes which are expected to be effective because of the predictions of the diagnosis phase. When the testing of the winning hypothesis has been done by modifying the operating system, the therapy phase is generally fast and smooth. If hardware changes are required, this phase is much longer and more complicated. A study for selecting the new components may be needed, various procurement alternatives may have to be examined, and a substantial amount of time may elapse before the selected components are delivered and installed.

The types of changes which an improvement therapy may consist of can be classified in various ways. We shall first make the distinction between *system changes* and *program changes*. The latter category includes the modifications made to all the programs running on a system so as to improve their performance (program performance will be defined and discussed in Chapter 9). For computer systems, Adam Smith's contention that private self-interest contributes to the common good is often valid. That is, improving the performance of individual programs has a beneficial effect on system performance. Among the programs a system executes, some fall within and some without the jurisdiction of the installation's manager. In the former class, we have the operating system (which sometimes, however, cannot be modified for contractual reasons), the compilers, and generally the systems programs; in the latter, we have the programs submitted by users. Installation managers often have control over a nonnegligible fraction of the most frequently executed programs. They can also provide incentive for the improvement of user program performance by severely penalizing "bad" programs. Thus, program changes should always be considered among the possible therapies a manager can use to improve system performance. The specific techniques which can be applied to increase a program's performance are dealt with in Chapter 9. In this chapter, in particular in Section 7.4, we shall concentrate on system changes. The therapies in this category can be further subdivided into *hardware configuration changes* and *operating system changes*. The latter therapies will be referred to as *tuning* therapies, and the former as *upgrading* therapies.

By tuning most people mean the act of tailoring the operating system to the actual work load experienced by a system which has just been installed. We discussed the need for this operation at the end of Section 7.1. Work loads tend to vary in time, their magnitude usually growing and their nature slowly or abruptly changing. Thus, a system will have to be retuned several times during its lifetime. When symptoms of performance degradation are detected, hypotheses which lead to tuning therapies will often be given precedence, since tuning is generally less expensive than upgrading. Unfortunately, when the current hardware configuration is near saturation, tuning is practically useless, and upgrading (or complete replacement) becomes necessary. Sometimes, as noted in Section 7.1, a study may result in the elimination of some hardware component from the configuration. In this case, it is the economical convenience of the system, and not its performance, which is improved.

As observed several times in the previous chapters, any modification which affects the performance of a system will generally cause a change in the behavior of the user community and therefore in the work load. While evaluation studies usually do not take this feedback into account (*see* Section 5.1), some operating system modifications mainly aimed at changing the work load may be successful in improving performance. Most of these modifications do not exploit the feedback mechanism mentioned above. For example, the magnitude of the work load may be decreased by preventing or discouraging certain users from accessing the system or by manually or automatically rejecting jobs when the system is too heavily loaded. The performance/work-load feedback can be used to discourage users responsible for bad system performance from using the system or to encourage them to improve the performance of their programs. A similar type of therapy, which does not rely on the performance/work-load feedback but rather on the cost/work-load feedback, consists of changing the charging policy so as to make the work load more suited to the characteristics of the system. This could to some extent be obtained by increasing the charges for the heavily utilized resources and lowering those for the lightly loaded devices. A pictorial summary of our discussion of the therapy phase is presented in Fig. 7.4.

As illustrated in Fig. 7.1, the implementation of a therapy is to be followed by an assessment of its effects on the performance of the system. Has the predicted improvement been really produced? Because of the approximations made in testing hypotheses or because of the compromises with reality made in

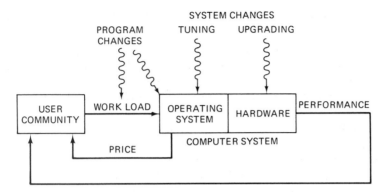

Figure 7.4   Types of improvement therapies.

implementing the therapy, the actual improvement may be quite different from the expected one. If a satisfactory level of performance has not been reached, we shall have to return to the diagnosis phase, or collect symptoms from the modified system, or perhaps start exploring more radical alternatives. Performance comparison is frequently an essential part of this step, too. The characteristics of comparisons in an improvement context, as shown in Fig. 7.3, are quite different from those we encounter in selection problems. The systems to be compared are in fact versions of the same system, which often differ only in very minor (but significant) details. This situation has some important consequences on the evaluation techniques to be used and on the work-load characterization problems to be solved. These consequences are discussed in Sections 7.5 and 7.6.

What is the role of performance evaluation in improvement studies? Unlike the one played in selection procedures, it is an extremely important role. As described in the next sections, and in particular in Section 7.5, all evaluation techniques have their place in these studies. Performance is obviously the main concern of an investigator engaged in an improvement effort. However, as we tried to stress throughout the above discussion, cost considerations should never be overlooked.

7.3 DIAGNOSIS

7.3.1 The Basic Problem

According to the definition given in Section 7.2, the diagnostic phase of an improvement study is the one in which hypotheses about the causes of unsatisfactory performance or, at least, about the most advantageous therapy for improvement are formulated and tested. Implicit in the recognition of the need for a diagnostic phase is the very important observation that different modifications made to a computer system usually have drastically different impacts on its performance. Some changes have no effect in certain situations and a tremendous effect in others. Their influence on performance indices depends on the configuration and on the work load. They may have a strong impact on certain indices and none on others. Thus, the changes which are likely to produce some nontrivial beneficial effect have to be determined case by case. Also, among these changes, that (or those) with the best cost-performance characteristics will have to be chosen.

The phenomena alluded to above are due to the nonlinearities which characterize the behavior of computer systems. More precisely, let $\mathscr{S}$ be a system, P a performance index, and $x_1, x_2, \ldots, x_n$ the n parameters that we consider as modifiable. The x_i's include work-load parameters as well as system parameters. We assume that increases in P correspond to performance improvements. The function $P(x_1, x_2, \ldots, x_n)$ is usually a highly nonlinear function. These non-linearities often take the form of *bottlenecks*. Informally, we say that $\mathscr{S}$ has a bottleneck with respect to P in a certain region of the space of its modifiable parameters if in that region the value of P increases substantially only when one or a few of the parameters are modified. Not even large changes of the other parameters will be able to appreciably improve P, unless they are so large that the boundaries of the region are exceeded. In our informal definition of bottleneck, we have of course assumed that improving P within the region is possible. Thus, we have excluded from our consideration regions centered on local or global maxima of P. The only way to favorably affect P when the system has a bottleneck in the region in which it is working is to diagnose the bottleneck correctly, that is, to discover which ones of the modifiable parameters limit P there. Then, a therapy consisting of changing those parameters in the right direction and by the most convenient amount will be applied.

To understand why bottlenecks are present in computer systems, we have to look at the internal structure and behavior of these systems. Their black-box characterization, represented by the function $P(x_1, x_2, \ldots, x_n)$, is not sufficient for this purpose. A computer system may be viewed as a set of resources which are needed by the jobs running on it. Each job requires certain hardware and software resources and a certain amount of each one of them in order to complete its execution. Resources are in limited supply, and only a very small number of jobs can make use of any given resource at each time instant. For instance, only one job can run on a CPU at any given time. The order in which a job demands the necessary resources is rigid in most cases. Thus, a job requesting a resource which cannot be immediately allocated to it has generally to wait until the resource has been released by all of the jobs with higher priorities for the use of the same resource. If a job is alone in the system, the resources it requests are always free, and there are no queues. In fact, there are no bottlenecks in uniprogramming systems. The bottlenecks arise in multiprogramming systems when resource demands by the jobs which concurrently execute are unbalanced. In this situation, there are resources which are overrequested with respect to the rates at which their service can be provided by the system. Thus, relatively long queues build up for these resources, and as a result other resources tend to remain underutilized. No change in the modifiable parameters will substantially affect performance unless it eases the situation of congestion of the overcommitted resource (or resources). Of course, congestion may be eased by modifying some selected system parameters or work-load parameters, or both.

Multiprogramming was introduced with the objective of increasing the processing power of a computer system. Allowing the operations of various system components to be fully overlapped is a potentially effective way of speeding up the execution of a given work load. However, for the potential benefits of multiprogramming to become real, a situation of uniform loading of these components must be reached. There should be no obstacles to the smooth flow of jobs from one component to another—in other words, no bottlenecks. Note that the ideal condition, from the viewpoint of the rationale behind multiprogramming, would be one in which all of the independent components were 100% utilized. This would mean that the system would be producing its maximum amount of work. However, as mentioned in Section 1.4, maximizing a certain performance index (say, the mean throughput rate) may make another index (say, the mean response time) intolerably inadequate. We shall return to this point later in this section.

An approach to improvement suggested by the discussion above is the one which could be called the *successive removal of bottlenecks*. In fact, a therapy which acts on one or a few parameters does not generally succeed in balancing the system. New bottlenecks, which were previously hidden behind the one just removed, may appear. If further improvement is sought, these bottlenecks are to be diagnosed and cured. Also, sometimes, a therapy may bring the system into another region of its parameter space, where performance is dominated by another bottleneck. The reader with some background in mathematical programming will easily recognize the conceptual similarity between this iterative approach and the method of the gradient applied to the function $P(x_1, x_2, \ldots x_n)$. However, the situation is complicated by the fact that often the set of modifiable parameters includes nonnumerical ones, such as those representing resource management policies.

The concept of bottleneck and the effects of bottlenecks on system performance will now be illustrated by a simple analytic example.

Example 7.1 A batch-processing version of EXOPE including a CPU, a drum, and a movable-arm disk can be approximately modeled by the central-server queuing network in Fig. 7.5 (*see* Section 4.3.5). The system is multiprogrammed among a constant number N of jobs, which reside in primary memory while being processed. A fixed allocation policy is used for the memory. Each job is loaded into a fixed-size partition ($32K$ words) at the beginning of a job step and releases that partition only at the end of that job step. For simplicity, we shall consider the different job steps of a job as distinct jobs. Thus, there will be no difference between jobs and job steps. As in Section 4.3.5, we assume that jobs are statistically identical and that their service time demands are exponentially distributed. We also assume that no partition is ever empty. The performance index to be considered in

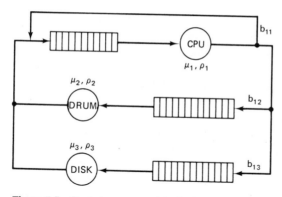

Figure 7.5 Central-server model of the system studied in Examples 7.1, 7.2, 7.3, 7.10, 7.11, 8.1, 8.2, 8.4, 8.5, and 8.6.

Table 7.2

SYSTEM AND WORK-LOAD PARAMETERS
FOR THE MODEL IN FIG. 7.5

Parameter	Description	Value
(a) System parameters		
$\bar{v}_{cpu}$	Mean CPU instruction execution rate	10^6 instructions/s
M	Primary-memory size for user jobs	$160K$ words
m	Memory partition size	$32K$ words
R_{dr}	Drum rotational speed	3000 rpm
t_{wdr}	Drum word transfer time	$3\ \mu s$
R_{ds}	Disk rotational speed	1500 rpm
$\bar{t}_{seek}$	Mean disk seek time	70 ms
t_{wds}	Disk word transfer time	$15\ \mu s$
(b) Work-load parameters		
$\bar{L}$	Mean number of instructions to be executed per job step	240,000 instructions
$\bar{n}_{cpu}$	Mean number of CPU time intervals per job step	20
$\bar{r}_{dr}$	Mean number of words transferred per drum access	2000 words
$\bar{n}_{dr}$	Mean number of drum accesses per job step	15
$\bar{r}_{ds}$	Mean number of words transferred per disk access	2000 words
$\bar{n}_{ds}$	Mean number of disk accesses per job step	4

Table 7.3

MODEL PARAMETERS DERIVED FROM THE PARAMETERS IN
TABLE 7.2

Parameter	Equation	Value
N	$N = M/m$	5
μ_1	$\mu_1 = \bar{v}_{cpu}\bar{n}_{cpu}/\bar{L}$	83.33 s^{-1}
μ_2	$\mu_2 = 1/[(60/2R_{dr}) + t_{wdr}\bar{r}_{dr}]^{\dagger}$	62.5 s^{-1}
μ_3	$\mu_3 = 1/[(60/2R_{ds}) + \bar{i}_{seek} + t_{wds}\bar{r}_{ds}]^{\dagger}$	$8.33 \text{ s}^{-1 \ddagger}$
b_{11}	$b_{11} = 1/\bar{n}_{cpu}$	0.05
b_{12}	$b_{12} = \bar{n}_{dr}/\bar{n}_{cpu}$	0.75
b_{13}	$b_{13} = \bar{n}_{ds}/\bar{n}_{cpu}$	0.2

* This table is used in several examples in Chapters 7 and 8. The parameter
values in the third column differ from one example to another and sometimes
also within an example. These differences are always specified in the text.

† t_{wdr}, t_{wds}, and $\bar{i}_{seek}$ are to be expressed in seconds.

‡ In parts of Examples 7.1 and 7.2, as well as in Examples 7.3, 7.10, and 7.11,
this value is replaced by 16.66 s^{-1}.

this analysis is the mean throughput rate given by (4.103):

$$\bar{T} = b_{11}\mu_1\rho_1. \tag{7.1}$$

In Table 7.3, the values of the model parameters are derived from those of the
relevant system and work-load parameters listed in Table 7.2. The mean throughput rate
can be computed from (7.1) if the CPU utilization ρ_1 is known. The value of ρ_1 for the
central-server model in Fig. 7.5 can be obtained by the method illustrated in Section 4.3.5.
Applying this method and equations (4.108) and (7.1), we have $\rho_1 = 0.475$, $\rho_2 = 0.475$,
$\rho_3 = 0.95$, and $\bar{T} = 1.98$ jobs/s. If the CPU were fully utilized, the mean throughput rate
would be $\bar{T}_{max} = b_{11}\mu_1 = 4.16$ jobs/s.

Table 7.4

MODIFIABLE PARAMETERS FOR EXAMPLE 7.1

Change	Parameters affected	Model parameters affected
(a) Upgrading		
Primary memory size	M	N
CPU speed	$\bar{v}_{cpu}$	μ_1
Drum speed	R_{dr}, t_{wdr}	μ_2
Disk speed	$R_{ds}, t_{wds}, \bar{i}_{seek}$	μ_3
(b) Tuning		
Disk file rearrangement	$\bar{i}_{seek}$	μ_3
File relocation	$\bar{n}_{dr}, \bar{n}_{ds}$	b_{12}, b_{13} *

* Note that $b_{12} + b_{13} = 1 - b_{11} = $ constant.

Now we want to explore the possibility of increasing $\bar{T}$ by changing one or more of the system or work-load parameters which appear in our model. The modifiable parameters are listed in Table 7.4. Note that they do not include all of those displayed in Table 7.2. Using the method described in Section 4.3.5 for computing ρ_1, we can calculate the value of $\bar{T}$ produced by the model of any modified version of our system. The results are plotted in Fig. 7.6. It is evident from this figure that the system has a bottleneck. Increasing the service rate of the CPU (μ_1) or of the drum (μ_2) or the size of the memory (N) does not have any major impact on $\bar{T}$. The only parameters among those listed in Table 7.4 whose modification may cause a substantial improvement in performance are μ_3

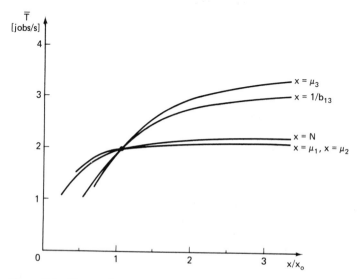

Figure 7.6 Changes in the mean throughput rate of the model in Fig. 7.5 corresponding to changes in various system parameters x. The meaning of x is indicated on each curve; x_0 is the value of x in the unmodified system (*see* Table 7.3).

and b_{13} (or, equivalently, b_{12}). Thus, we conclude that the disk creates a bottleneck and that the only ways to improve $\bar{T}$ are to reduce the load on the disk (by reducing $\bar{i}_{\text{seek}}$ or b_{13}) or to increase the speed of the disk (by increasing R_{ds} and hence reducing t_{wds} or by reducing $\bar{i}_{\text{seek}}$), or both. The former therapy is of the tuning type, and the latter requires upgrading the system, that is, replacing the disk by a faster one. The diagrams in Fig. 7.6 also show that when we change one or more parameters in order to remove a bottleneck, the rate of performance improvement decreases drastically beyond a certain point. At that point, we can say that the bottleneck has been practically removed, and performance is no longer limited by those parameters. Assuming that the bottleneck we have discovered is cured by increasing the service rate of the disk, that point can be seen in Fig. 7.6 to occur at about a disk service rate twice the one in the current system. If we modify the system according to our diagnosis, its model will have the same parameter values as in Table 7.3 except for μ_3, which will now be equal to 16.66 s^{-1}. The utilizations of the three servers in this model are now all identical and equal to 0.714. The mean throughput rate becomes

$\bar{T} = 2.97$ jobs/s. Figure 7.7 presents plots of $\bar{T}$ as a function of the modifiable parameters for the improved system. Note that if in the new system the CPU or the drum are slowed down by a factor of 2, the same $\bar{T}$ as in the original system is obtained. Note also that no evident bottleneck is revealed by the diagrams in Fig. 7.7. We shall return to this problem in Section 7.3.2, after having given an analytic definition of bottleneck. Another interesting remark to be made about Fig. 7.7 is concerned with the shape of the $1/b_{13}$ curve. When only a tuning therapy is allowed, there is an allocation of files which maximizes $\bar{T}$. This is not surprising, since the sum of b_{12} and b_{13} must be constant, and as b_{13} decreases, b_{12} must increase. Thus, the effect of decreasing b_{13} is in some sense equivalent to the one of

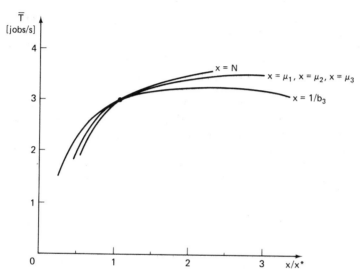

Figure 7.7 Changes in the mean throughput rate of the model in Fig. 7.5 corresponding to changes in various system parameters x. The meaning of x is indicated on each curve; x^* is the value of x listed in Table 7.3 except for μ_3: $\mu_3 = 16.66$ s^{-1}.

increasing the speed of the disk and at the same time decreasing the speed of the drum. At some point, the performance degradation caused by the drum (which tends to become a bottleneck) will more than compensate for the enhancements due to the load reduction on the disk. What may be surprising is the fact that the optimum $\bar{T}$ does not correspond to the point of uniform utilization of all servers. This phenomenon will be investigated in Section 7.3.2. ∎

In Example 7.1, we have been concerned with the effects of variations in the so-called modifiable parameters of a system on the system's mean throughput rate. Our analysis has been based on a central-server model of a simple batch-processing system. We would now like to study the effects of the same changes on other performance indices of interest, in particular on an index of the responsiveness type such as the mean turnaround time $\bar{t}$. The dependencies of utilization factors on parameter changes and their strict relationships with the mean throughput rate will be investigated in Section 7.3.2. We shall now analyze the behavior of $\bar{\imath}$ as a function of the modifiable parameters in the version of EXOPE we considered in Example 7.1.

Example 7.2   Modeling our system again as in Fig. 7.5, we may define $\bar{\imath}$ as the mean real time between the instant a job joins the CPU queue for the first time and the instant it leaves the system along the CPU feedback path. As seen in Section 4.3.5 [equation (4.104)], we have

$$\bar{\imath} = \frac{N}{\bar{T}}. \tag{7.2}$$

Thus, when N, i.e., the memory size M, is constant, $\bar{\imath}$ is inversely proportional to $\bar{T}$. To any improvement of $\bar{T}$ there will correspond an improvement of the system's responsiveness. For example, the parameter values in Table 7.2 will yield $\bar{\imath} = 2.52$ s. If the service rate of the disk is doubled, the mean turnaround time becomes $\bar{\imath} = 1.68$ s. The resources which create bottlenecks with respect to $\bar{T}$ play the same role with respect to $\bar{\imath}$.

However, when the memory size is changed, the above statements are no longer valid. Figure 7.8 displays the diagrams of $\bar{T}$ and $\bar{\imath}$ versus N for the original and the modified system. While the absolute and relative effects of a change of disk service rate grow as N increases, an improvement of $\bar{T}$ is accompanied by a deterioration of $\bar{\imath}$ and vice versa. It can be seen in (7.2) that the product $\bar{\imath}\bar{T}$ increases linearly with N. $\bar{T}$ cannot increase linearly with N because of the bottlenecks created by other resources. Thus, as $\bar{T}$ levels off, $\bar{\imath}$ is bound to increase.

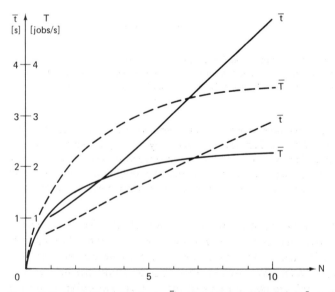

Figure 7.8   Mean throughput rate $\bar{T}$ and mean turnaround time $\bar{\imath}$ vs. the number of jobs N (memory size) for the model in Fig. 7.5 and Table 7.3. Broken curves refer to the case $\mu_3 = 16.66 \text{ s}^{-1}$.

A conclusion we can draw from this example is that productivity and responsiveness can often be improved together but not always. When an improvement therapy is adopted which results in a heavier load on all of the resources, so that all queues may be expected to get longer, productivity is increased at the expense of responsiveness. ■

In this section, we have introduced the concept of bottleneck, which has primary importance in the diagnosis phase of an improvement procedure, have explained why bottlenecks are present in computer systems, and have shown how they manifest themselves in a simple analytic model. A more thorough study of the same model, including a formal definition of bottleneck and providing the basis for a discussion of hypothesis formulation, is contained in the next section. Section 7.3.3 describes the application of these and of other more empirical hypothesis formulation methods to measurement or simulation results. Finally, a statistical diagnosis procedure is presented in Section 7.3.4.

7.3.2 An Analytic Study of Bottlenecks

Our discussion of bottlenecks in Section 7.3.1 and the examination of the results from the model in Fig. 7.5, made in Example 7.1, have raised a number of questions. How can bottlenecks be analytically defined? What are the relationships between the utilizations of system components and the bottlenecks existing in a system? Is the mean throughput rate maximum, and in what sense, when there are no bottlenecks? These important questions will be addressed in the first part of this section, referring to the central-server model of a system such as the one considered in Example 7.1. In the second part, we shall repeat the analysis, using the same model, for a virtual-memory system.

Let us consider a system which can be modeled by a central-server network with s service centers (in Fig. 7.5, $s = 3$). We assume, for the moment, that the primary memory of the system does not create a bottleneck. Thus, the only possible sources of bottlenecks explicitly represented in the model are the servers. Consistently with the observations made in Section 7.3.1, we can say that the resource whose modification has the strongest influence on performance is the one which creates the bottleneck. Following Buzen (1971), we shall therefore define as the source of a bottleneck the resource represented by server Σ_i such that

$$\frac{\partial \bar{T}}{\partial \mu_i} > \frac{\partial \bar{T}}{\partial \mu_j} \qquad (j = 1, 2, \ldots, s; j \neq i). \tag{7.3}$$

Note that this definition does not imply that the bottleneck is to be totally or partially removed by actually increasing the service rate of Σ_i. Tuning actions, for example, an appropriate modification of b_{1i} in our model, may also be used to change the situation.

An immediate consequence of the above definition is that, when

$$\frac{\partial \bar{T}}{\partial \mu_i} = \frac{\partial \bar{T}}{\partial \mu_j} \tag{7.4}$$

for all i and j, there are no bottlenecks in the system. In this case, the system is said to be *balanced*. In a balanced system, a (small) increase in the service rate of one of the components will improve $\bar{T}$ by the same amount no matter which one of the components is involved. In spite of the differences in horizontal scale for the curves in Fig. 7.6, it is evident that our system with the parameter values in Table 7.2 is not balanced and that the disk is the source of a bottleneck.

What is the relationship between a balanced system and a system in which all resources are equally utilized? And a system in which queue lengths at the equilibrium are the same? And a maximum-throughput system?

The conditions of uniform utilization

$$\rho_i = \rho_j \qquad (i, j = 1, 2, \ldots, s) \tag{7.5}$$

become, remembering equations (4.108),

$$b_{1i} = \frac{\mu_i}{\mu_1}, \qquad \frac{b_{1i}}{b_{1j}} = \frac{\mu_i}{\mu_j} \qquad (i, j = 2, \ldots, s). \tag{7.6}$$

Figure 7.7 just refers to this situation for our example system. It can also be shown [*see* Buzen (1971)] that when conditions (7.6), and hence (7.5), are satisfied, the mean queue lengths at the stations are all equal. However, this is not generally a balanced situation, in which we would have, by (7.4) and (4.103),

$$\frac{\partial\rho_1}{\partial\mu_i} = \frac{\partial\rho_1}{\partial\mu_j} = \frac{\rho_1}{\mu_1} + \frac{\partial\rho_1}{\partial\mu_1} \qquad (i, j = 2, \ldots, s). \tag{7.7}$$

Figure 7.7, for example, shows that if we account for the differences in the horizontal scale and start from the point of equal utilizations ($x/x^* = 1$), the improvement in $\bar{T}$ caused by a given increase in the disk service rate is greater than those due to an increase in the service rate of either the CPU or the drum. This is also confirmed by the fact that, starting from the same point, $\bar{T}$ grows as b_{13} is decreased (and b_{12} increased). Thus, a point of balance could be reached by increasing μ_3 further until the derivative of $\bar{T}$ with respect to μ_3 becomes equal to the other partial derivatives, according to condition (7.4). It should be noted, however, that varying only μ_3 will not generally suffice to satisfy (7.4). The other service rates will also have to be adjusted.

A balanced system does not exploit all of its performance potential. The mean throughput rate of a balanced system can usually be improved by tuning it, even though this operation pushes it out of balance. Thus, given a combination of hardware components and a certain work load, the maximum value of the mean throughput rate normally corresponds to an unbalanced situation. Buzen (1971) has found that in this maximum the following relationships hold for all i, $j = 2, \ldots, s$:

$$\frac{b_{1i}}{b_{1j}} = \frac{1 + \bar{N}_i - (\bar{N}_i/\rho_i)}{1 + \bar{N}_j - (\bar{N}_j/\rho_j)}, \tag{7.8}$$

where $\bar{N}_i$ denotes the mean queue length at service center Σ_i (including the job possibly being served), and

$$\frac{\rho_i}{\rho_j} = \frac{\partial \bar{T}/\partial \mu_i}{\partial \bar{T}/\partial \mu_j}. \tag{7.9}$$

Equation (7.8) shows that if Σ_i and Σ_j were equally utilized at the maximum $\bar{T}$, i.e., if $\rho_i = \rho_j$ and $\bar{N}_i = \bar{N}_j$, then we should have $b_{1i} = b_{1j}$. If at the maximum $\bar{T}$ we have $b_{1i} \neq b_{1j}$, then Σ_i and Σ_j cannot be equally utilized there. Thus, by equation (7.9), there must be a bottleneck. More precisely, if $\mu_i > \mu_j$, we have $b_{1i} > b_{1j}$ when T is maximum. Since $b_{1i} > b_{1j}$ and Equation (7.8) imply $\rho_i > \rho_j$, equation (7.9) tells us that Σ_i, the faster server, creates a (relative) bottleneck at that point. The only case in which there are no bottlenecks at the maximum is when all servers are equally utilized [*see* (7.9)]. However, by (7.8), this can happen only if all b's are identical and, by (7.6), if all μ's are identical. Note that the statements made in this paragraph do not apply to the central server. For example, the reader can easily verify, using (4.108), that at the point of maximum $\bar{T}$ in Fig. 7.7 it is $\rho_2 > \rho_1$. That is, the bottleneck is caused by the drum rather than by the CPU, even though the CPU is faster.

The influence of the memory size on performance has so far been ignored. The definition of bottleneck given in (7.3) could be extended to include also the memory resource. However, comparing $\partial \bar{T}/\partial N$ with the other partial derivatives would make little sense, since they are dimensionally different. This problem is discussed from a more pragmatic viewpoint in Section 7.4.3. Here, we shall examine the behavior of $\bar{T}$ and of the utilization factors as functions of N.

From (4.108) we have

$$\frac{\rho_i}{\rho_1} = \frac{\mu_1 b_{1i}}{\mu_i}. \tag{7.10}$$

Since the right-hand side of (7.10) does not depend on N, this is also the case of the ratio ρ_i/ρ_1. Thus, the *relative utilizations* of servers $\Sigma_2, \ldots, \Sigma_s$ remain constant when N varies. As N increases, the mean lengths of the queues will grow, and the servers will be more utilized. By (7.10), utilization factors will grow proportionally, so that their ratios remain unchanged. However, no ρ can ever become greater than 1. Thus, as the highest ρ_i $(1 \leq i \leq s)$ approaches 1 asymptotically, the other ρ's will tend toward lower values. Conditions (7.10) hold also between these asymptotes. Figure 7.9 plots the ρ's versus N for the model discussed in Example 7.1. As ρ_3 (the utilization of the disk which creates the bottleneck) tends toward 1, ρ_1 and ρ_2 tend only toward 0.5. Not surprisingly, changing N does not affect the bottlenecks created by the servers in the system. The only case in which all utilizations can tend to 1 as N increases is when all the servers are equally utilized.

By (4.103), $\bar{T}$ is proportional to ρ_1. Since $\rho_1(N)$ is a monotonically increasing function, $\bar{T}(N)$ is also monotonically increasing with the same shape. As shown in Figs. 7.6, 7.7, and 7.8, $\bar{T}$ tends asymptotically toward $b_{11}\mu_1\rho_1(\infty)$, which

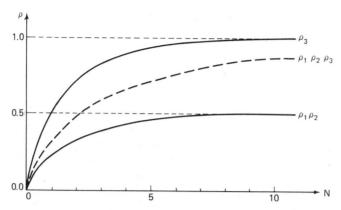

Figure 7.9   Utilization factors of the servers in the model of Fig. 7.5 and Table 7.3 vs. the number of jobs in the system. The broken curve refers to the case $\mu_3 = 16.66\,s^{-1}$.

coincides with b_{11}/μ_1, the absolute maximum throughput rate of the system, only if $\rho_1(\infty) = 1$ (that is, if the CPU is the most utilized resource). The broken $\bar{T}$ line in Fig. 7.8 tends toward the maximum capacity, while the solid $\bar{T}$ line tends toward half this value. The reader may wonder whether the asymptote of the broken line, which corresponds to the condition of equal utilizations, is really the absolute maximum capacity of the system. Earlier in this section, we have seen that the maximum value of $\bar{T}$ is not generally obtained when all ρ's are equal. However, Buzen (1971) has shown that as N increases, the distance between the point of maximum $\bar{T}$ and the point of equal ρ's decreases. For $N \to \infty$, these two points tend to coincide. Thus, the system automatically approaches a tuned condition as the memory size (and the degree of multiprogramming) increases.

Some of the results we have just obtained can also be applied to the study of bottlenecks in virtual-memory systems. To make our considerations simple, we shall analyze in an example a purposely modified central-server model of such a system.

Example 7.3   The system to be studied is a batch-processing, multiprogrammed, virtual-memory version of EXOPE. The system components to be explicitly considered in the model are the same as in Example 7.1: one CPU, one drum (used as a paging device), and one disk (for system and user files). The primary memory contains only parts of the jobs being executed and is automatically managed. The transfers between the memory and the paging drum are not explicitly requested by the jobs but take place whenever the information needed is not found in memory. We assume that virtual memory is implemented by the paging technique (*see* Example 2.7). The memory is divided into *page frames*, each of which contains one *page* of information belonging to a job. Information is transferred between memory and drum by pages. When the page containing a virtual address referenced by the running program is not in memory, a *page fault* is generated, the job is suspended, the CPU is switched to a ready job (if any), and a drum request for the missing page is issued by the operating system. If the memory is full, the missing page will have to replace one of the pages currently in memory. A *replacement algorithm* will choose this page. In this example, we shall assume that the system implements a *fixed allocation strategy*. As in Example 7.1, the memory is divided into a number N of partitions, each of which is assigned to a job. Since in our model jobs are all statistically identical, it is reasonable to make them all the same size $m = M/N$. To vary the degree of multiprogramming N, we can change the number and the size of the partitions for constant M, or vary M for constant m, or vary both M and m so as to change M/m.

The fundamental difference between this system and the one considered in Example 7.1 lies in the fact that a change in the memory space allotted to a job causes its paging activity to vary, in some cases quite drastically. Thus, if we vary the degree of multiprogramming N keeping M constant, b_{12} in our model will be affected—and therefore the other b's. Since the durations of CPU time intervals vary when the page fault rate changes, μ_1 will also be affected (see the equation of μ_1 in Table 7.3, which contains $\bar{n}_{cpu}$). Note that all of these variations occur whenever the drum request rate, i.e., the page fault rate of the programs, varies. Therefore, as will be seen in the sequel, they may be due to changes not only of m but also of the memory management strategy or of the memory referencing behavior of programs.

To study the impact of the degree of multiprogramming on $\bar{T}$ in our model, we shall first assume that N is varied by changing M and that m remains constant. Under these conditions, it is easy to determine the behavior of $\bar{T}$ versus N corresponding to any given drum request rate for each job. Since m and the drum request rate of each job are (in our model) constant when N varies, the model coincides with the one studied in Example 7.1, and $\bar{T}$ grows monotonically with N tending toward a horizontal asymptote, as shown in Figs. 7.6, 7.7, and 7.8. With the parameter values listed in Table 7.3 except for μ_3, which we set equal to 16.66 s^{-1}, $\bar{T}$ would follow curve (a) in Fig. 7.10. This curve coincides with the broken $\bar{T}$ curve in Fig. 7.8. If we now change either the behavior of the programs or the replacement algorithm or both, so that the mean number of drum requests per job becomes $\bar{n}_{dr} = 195$, we have $\bar{n}_{cpu} = 1 + \bar{n}_{dr} + \bar{n}_{ds} = 200$. By the equations in Table 7.3, we obtain $\mu_1 = 833.3 \text{ s}^{-1}$, $b_{11} = 0.005$, $b_{12} = 0.975$, and $b_{13} = 0.02$. With these values of the model parameters, $\bar{T}$ follows curve (b) in Fig. 7.10. The big increment in the paging activity causes the drum to create a bottleneck which severely degrades performance. Note that the page size is assumed to be $1K$ words and that each fault is assumed to require a transfer of $2K$ words, one page in and one out (*see* Table 7.2).

Let us now keep the total memory size M constant and change N by varying m, the space allotted to each job. As m decreases, programs are known to generate an increasing number of page faults. Following Denning and Graham (1975), consider for the moment the following very crude model of program behavior: When one of our programs is given more than 50 pages, its mean number of page faults is $\bar{n}_{dr} = 15$; when it receives less than 50 pages, $\bar{n}_{dr}$ suddenly becomes equal to 195. If this were the case, the mean throughput rate would follow curve (a) in Fig. 7.10 for $N = M/m \leq 3$, while it would follow curve (b) for $N \geq 4$. Thus, the $\bar{T}$ curve would be composed of the solid portions of curves (a) and (b). The mean throughput rate would reach a maximum at a degree of multiprogramming equal to 3 and drop to a very low level for $N \geq 4$. This phenomenon, called *thrashing*, characterizes virtual-memory system performance and is one of the major problems to be solved by the designers and tuners of such systems [*see* Denning (1968b)]. The drop of the $\bar{T}(N)$ curve is usually not so sharp as the one suggested by our rudimentary model. However, thrashing can often be described as a performance collapse. Its cause is easy to derive from our discussion. Due to an increase of the degree of multiprogramming beyond

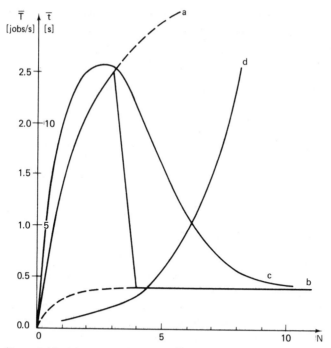

Figure 7.10   Mean throughput rate $\bar{T}$ and mean turnaround time $\bar{t}$ vs. degree of multiprogramming N for the model of a virtual-memory system analyzed in Example 7.3; (a) $\bar{T}$ curve for $m = 32K$ words and $\bar{n}_{dr} = 15$; (b) $\bar{T}$ curve for $m = 32K$ words and $\bar{n}_{dr} = 195$; (c) $\bar{T}$ curve for $M = 160K$ words, $a = 6.25$ pages^{-k}, $\bar{v}_{cpu} = 10^6$ instructions/s, and $k = 2$; (d) $\bar{t}$ curve for the same case as in (c). Note that μ_3 is 16.66 s^{-1}.

a certain point, the space allotted to each job becomes insufficient to contain the essential information needed by the job to execute. Hence, the page fault rates of the jobs suddenly grow and create at the paging device a bottleneck which drastically degrades performance.

A better approximation to the real $\bar{T}$ curve for this system can be obtained by refining a little our model of program behavior. Following Brandwajn et al. (1973), we may use the *lifetime function* proposed by Belady and Kuehner (1969) as an analytic approximation to empirical observations made on a number of real programs. Under a fixed allocation strategy and a given replacement algorithm, the mean CPU time interval between consecutive page faults, $\bar{e}$, was found to be related to m as in Fig. 7.11, curve (a). The curve was called the *lifetime curve* of a program by Belady and Kuehner (1969), who conjectured its shape to be relatively insensitive to the replacement algorithm. The lifetime function

$$\bar{e} = \frac{a}{\bar{v}_{cpu}} m^k, \qquad (7.11)$$

where a and k depend on the properties of the program, is plotted in Fig. 7.11, curve (b), for $a = 6.25$ pages^{-k}, $\bar{v}_{cpu} = 10^6$ instructions/s, and $k = 2$. The exponent k was experi-

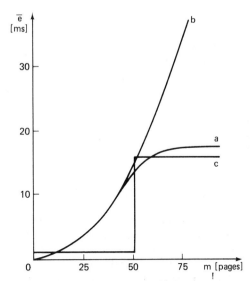

Figure 7.11 Simple models of program behavior: (*a*) a lifetime curve; (*b*) the lifetime function with $a = 6.25$ pages^{-k}, $\bar{v}_{cpu} = 10^6$ instructions/s, and $k = 2$; (*c*) the crude model used in Example 7.3 [see curves (a) and (b) in Fig. 7.10].

mentally found to be between 1.5 and 2.5 for several programs. Since

$$\bar{e} = \frac{\bar{L}}{\bar{v}_{cpu}\bar{n}_{dr}}, \tag{7.12}$$

where the symbols are those of Table 7.2, our previous model of program behavior is represented by a step function in the $(m, \bar{e})$ plane [*see* curve (c) in Fig. 7.11]. The equations in Table 7.3 and (7.11) show that as N increases, m decreases, $\bar{n}_{dr}$ and $\bar{n}_{cpu}$ increase; hence b_{11} and b_{13} decrease, while b_{12} increases. Since the product $\mu_1 b_{11}$ is independent of N, $\bar{T}$ is proportional to ρ_1 by equation (7.1). The method described in Section 4.3.5 to calculate ρ_1 can be applied here, but for each value of N the values of μ_1, b_{11}, b_{12}, and b_{13} differ and have to be recomputed using the equations in Table 7.3, with

$$\bar{n}_{dr} = \frac{\bar{L}}{\bar{v}_{cpu}\bar{e}}, \qquad \bar{n}_{cpu} = 1 + \bar{n}_{dr} + \bar{n}_{ds}, \tag{7.13}$$

and $\bar{e}$ given by (7.11).

The results based on the lifetime function in Fig. 7.11, curve (b), are plotted in Fig. 7.10, curves (c) and (d). Curve (c) is smoother than the one obtained by combining (a) and (b) but still exhibits a maximum for $N = 3$ and a rather sharp decrease of $\bar{T}$ for $N \geq 4$. At $N = 8$, $\bar{T}$ is reduced to only one fourth of the maximum. Curve (d) is the diagram of the mean turnaround time, calculated by (7.2). The reader will notice how steeply it increases beyond the point of maximum $\bar{T}$. The utilization factors in this model do not vary with N as in Fig. 7.9. The diagrams of ρ_1 and ρ_3 have the same shape as the one of T [curve (c) in Fig. 7.10]. Note that ρ_2 is less than ρ_1 for $N \leq 3$ but grows much more rapidly than ρ_1. It becomes greater than ρ_1 at $N = 4$ and tends toward 1 while ρ_1 and ρ_3 decrease. Thus, the relative utilization of the paging device is not independent of N. In fact, ρ_2/ρ_1 grows very rapidly with N.

A virtual-memory system can be prevented from falling into a thrashing situation by controlling its degree of multiprogramming. Note that making N constant is not a good solution since the characteristics of the work load change in time, and therefore also the thrashing curve [curve (c) in Fig. 7.10] is time-variant. Even in our highly simplified model, this curve depends on the values of a and k. A discussion of this control problem will be presented in Section 7.4.2. Evidently, thrashing can also be made more infrequent by broadening the bandwidth of the paging channel and device, that is, by increasing μ_2. The effects of changing μ_2 are the same as in Example 7.1. The increase in $\bar{T}$ due to an increase in μ_2 is much higher when the paging drum creates a bottleneck. When μ_2 decreases, the curve moves downward, especially in the thrashing region, and the maximum toward smaller values of N. The drop of $\bar{T}$ due to the thrashing phenomenon becomes sharper, thereby confirming the observations made by Denning (1968b) that the sensitivity of performance to an overcommitment of memory increases as the traverse time between the paging device and primary-memory increases. When μ_2 is made larger, the curve moves upward everywhere but especially where thrashing occurs. Its maximum also corresponds to a higher value of N. The results of increasing μ_3 are in some sense opposite. The relative increases in $\bar{T}$ will be much greater for low values of N, especially if the disk is a bottleneck there, than for high values of N, where the bottleneck is created by the paging drum. This will also tend to move the maximum of the thrashing curve to the left. Changing $\bar{v}_{cpu}$ has an impact on $\bar{e}$ [see (7.12)] and on μ_1 (see Table 7.3) but not on the b's. Thus, the effects of varying $\bar{v}_{cpu}$ can also be easily predicted. For instance, an increase in $\bar{v}_{cpu}$ always causes $\bar{T}$ to increase, but the amount of the increment depends on whether the CPU creates a bottleneck or not. As N increases, this amount will decrease, since $\bar{T}$ will be limited more and more severely by the paging drum. For low values of N, the increment will of course be smaller if the disk creates a bottleneck than if the CPU does. In any case, an increase in $\bar{v}_{cpu}$ will tend to decrease the optimum degree of multiprogramming. Speeding up one of the other components makes it easier for the paging drum to become the limiting resource as N increases.

What is the influence of program behavior on the performance of a virtual-memory system? And that of the memory management strategy? These questions are discussed in Sections 7.4.1 (see Example 7.10) and 7.4.2. An approximate preliminary answer to both questions can be given here using our model and recognizing that the variations of program behavior and of memory management strategy produce the same result as those of m; that is, they change the page fault rate of each program and hence its drum request rate. The effects of varying $\bar{n}_{dr}$ can be seen in Fig. 7.10 by comparing curve (a) with curve (b). Two more informative and more useful families of curves are plotted in Fig. 7.12. They represent the behavior of performance indices $\bar{T}$ and $\bar{i}$ when the total mean page fault rate $\bar{f}$ varies. The values of the model parameters are those we have assumed throughout this example. Since the mean page fault rate of a program is $1/\bar{e}$, $\bar{f}$ can be computed as [see (7.10) and (7.12)]

$$\bar{f} = N\frac{1}{\bar{e}} = \frac{\bar{v}_{cpu}\bar{n}_{dr}N}{\bar{L}} = \frac{\bar{v}_{cpu}N^{k+1}}{aM^k}. \tag{7.14}$$

It should be noted that the page fault rate of a program is defined above as the number of page requests per unit of CPU time, and not of real time.

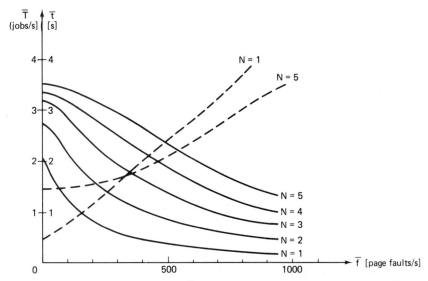

Figure 7.12   Mean throughput rate $\bar{T}$ (solid lines) and mean turnaround time $\bar{t}$ (broken lines) vs. total mean page fault rate $\bar{f}$, with various values of the degree of multiprogramming N, for the virtual-memory system model studied in Example 7.3 ($\mu_3 = 16.66 \text{ s}^{-1}$).

As can be seen in Fig. 7.12, a given value of $\bar{f}$ produces different values of $\bar{T}$ and $\bar{t}$ for different degrees of multiprogramming. If we know the impact of a certain variation of program behavior or of memory management strategy on a and k, we can calculate its influence on $\bar{f}$ from (7.14) and on $\bar{T}$ and $\bar{t}$ from the curves in Fig. 7.12. Of course, the same method can be used to study the effects of changes in M or in N. The reconstruction of curves (c) and (d) in Fig. 7.10 according to this method is left as an exercise for the reader (*see* Problem 7.4).

An example of the application of Fig. 7.12 is the prediction of the effects on $\bar{T}$ and $\bar{t}$ of a change in the size M of the memory for user jobs. Assume that M is increased from 160K to 208K words, that N remains equal to 3, and that a and k have the same values as above. By (7.14), $\bar{f}$ decreases from about 168 to about 100 page faults/s. Thus, from Fig. 7.12, we obtain that $\bar{T}$ is expected to increase from about 2.6 to about 2.9 jobs/s, and $\bar{t}$ to decrease from about 1.2 to about 1 s. If with the bigger memory we want to increase the degree of multiprogramming to 4, (7.14) gives us a total rate of 237 page faults/s, and from Fig. 7.12 we have $\bar{T} \cong 2.8$ jobs/s and $\bar{t} \cong 1.4$ s. ∎

7.3.3 Bottleneck Detection

The concept of bottleneck has been introduced in Section 7.3.1 and analytically defined and investigated in Section 7.3.2. In this section, we shall address the question, How can bottlenecks be detected in a working system?

To detect a bottleneck, we have to formulate a hypothesis about its existence and cause and then verify the validity of the hypothesis. The formulation of hypotheses is greatly helped by symptoms. What are the symptoms of a bottle-neck?

The analytic definition which was given in Section 7.3.2 [*see* (7.3)] is generally not very useful for detection purposes. In a real system it is often hard or impossible to estimate from measurement data the partial derivatives of performance indices with respect to system or work-load parameters. The speed of a processor or the size of a memory cannot usually be increased just for experimental purposes of this type. Sometimes they can be decreased, but normally only by discrete, relatively large amounts. This is, for example, the case of a system with several primary-memory banks or several disks in which one or more of these can be excluded from the system without preventing the system from running. Insofar as the work-load parameters are concerned, they can only be varied in a controlled way when the system is driven by an artificial work-load model. Even though a detection method based on the repeated usage of a set of benchmarks or synthetic jobs can in principle be used (*see* Problem 7.2), the cost of running this work-load model many times often makes it unattractive. Experiments with a controlled work load seem to be much more convenient for hypothesis verification. Note that the discussion in this paragraph does not apply to investigations based on a simulator. The calculation of partial derivatives when a simulator of the system under study is available is a conceptually straightforward task. However, cost considerations may again make another solution appear more attractive.

A solution which is easy to use and works reasonably well, at least as a first step, is the one based on the utilization factors of the various components. The measurement of these factors is, as seen in Chapter 2, relatively easy in most cases. According to the conclusions we have reached in Section 7.3.2, a system with equally utilized hardware components is usually neither balanced nor tuned. However, the three points in which each one of these conditions is satisfied are not generally far from each other. In particular, we observed that the distance between the point of equal utilizations and the one of maximum $\bar{T}$ tends toward zero as the degree of multiprogramming becomes larger. It is more important to note that large differences among utilization factors are a serious symptom of the existence of a bottleneck, especially if the value of one of these factors is close to 1. Thus, while the observed values of the utilization factors do not directly indicate whether the system is balanced or whether it is tuned, they may immediately reveal to the investigator the existence and the source of a severe bottleneck. Examples will be described below.

Another useful symptom of the existence of a bottleneck is the discovery that the system's performance is well below its potential level. Knowing this does not help to find the cause of the bottleneck. However, the ability to estimate the potential performance with which the installation's work load could be processed would not only allow managers to easily detect the existence of performance problems to be cured. It would also provide them with a yardstick against which achieved improvements could be compared and the convenience of possible further improvement efforts evaluated. For instance, when the performance of the system is only a few percent below its estimated maximum it is often not worthwhile undertaking or pursuing an improvement study.

But how do we define the potential performance in this context? What parameters do we consider as modifiable? The work load is assumed to be given and not to change, even though this is very often a false assumption. Let us also assume that our main performance index is the mean throughput rate. Under the very crude assumptions on which the modeling of a multiprogramming system by an exponential central-server queuing network is based, the following expression for capacity can be derived from (7.1) and Table 7.3:

$$\bar{T}_{max} = \frac{\bar{v}_{cpu}}{\bar{L}} \rho_{1\,max}. \qquad (7.15)$$

If all modifications to the configuration are acceptable, except those affecting the processing speed of the CPU, we have $\rho_{1\,max} = 1$ and $\bar{T}_{max} = \bar{v}_{cpu}/\bar{L} = 1/\bar{t}_c$, where $\bar{t}_c$ is the mean CPU time demand of a job and can be easily obtained from the accounting data. Similarly, (7.1), (4.108), and Table 7.3 allow us to express $\bar{T}_{max}$ as a function of μ_2, $\bar{n}_{dr}$, and $\rho_{2\,max}$:

$$\bar{T}_{max} = \frac{\mu_2}{\bar{n}_{dr}} \rho_{2\,max}. \qquad (7.16)$$

If the only unmodifiable parameter is μ_2, then $\rho_{2\,max} = 1$, and $\bar{T}_{max} = \mu_2/\bar{n}_{dr}$. The same considerations repeated for the service rate of the disk give

$$\bar{T}_{max} = \frac{\mu_3}{\bar{n}_{ds}} \rho_{3\,max}, \qquad (7.17)$$

which, for $\rho_{3\,max} = 1$, reduces to $\bar{T}_{max} = \mu_3/\bar{n}_{ds}$. For the system studied in Example 7.1, with the parameter values in Tables 7.2 and 7.3, the capacities given by (7.15), (7.16), and (7.17) are 4.166 jobs/s for the first two and 2.083 jobs/s for the third. Clearly, the lowest of these values coincides with the capacity of the system when the only modification considered is the one of N, the degree of multiprogramming (see, for example, Fig. 7.8).

If the hardware configuration is to remain fixed, and only tuning therapies are allowed, the calculation of the capacity is much more complicated. We shall discuss this problem at the end of Section 7.4.1.

The minimum value of the mean turnaround time can be approximately calculated by (7.2) once $\bar{T}_{max}$ has been obtained. Note that the absolute minimum turnaround time of a job is the time it would spend in the system running in uniprogrammed mode. In Example 7.1, the absolute minimum is 0.96 s, and the minimum when $N = 5$ and the only unmodifiable parameter is μ_1 or μ_2 equals 1.2 s.

The hypotheses discussed so far are of the simplest, most elementary type. The diagnosis phase does not normally stop when the existence and the location of a bottleneck have been discovered. More refined hypotheses must usually be made to identify the cause of the bottleneck, so that the correct therapy may be chosen. For example, suppose we have found that the disk creates a bottleneck. This means that there is a mismatch between the disk service rate and the disk request rate. However, it does not mean that the speed of the disk is insufficient and should be increased; this is just one of the many possible therapies, and indeed an expensive one. Other therapies may be an increase of the buffer size, a decrease of the degree of multiprogramming, a change or a reorganization of the disk contents, an increase of the primary-memory size, or a modification of the job-scheduling algorithm or of the disk-scheduling algorithm. The effectiveness of these therapies depends on the actual cause of the bottleneck. For example, an increase of the buffer size decreases the disk load only if the current size is too small with respect to the needs of the jobs in the work load. It is easy to conceive of situations in which such an increase would be harmful. Referring to the equations in Table 7.3, the decrease in $\bar{n}_{ds}$ might be more than offset by the decrease of μ_3 due to the fact that $\bar{r}_{ds}$ would increase. The formulation of these finer hypotheses is much more system-dependent than that for bottleneck detection. A general and concise treatment of it is extremely difficult, and in any case very strictly related to therapy considerations. We shall give some examples of this formulation in Section 7.4. There are, however, some diagnostic methods whose applicability is quite general and which can help us refine our diagnosis beyond the bottleneck detection stage. They mostly fall into the categories listed by Bell et al. (1972) and reported in Table 7.1. In particular, all the techniques for the interpretation of measurement and simulation results described in Section 2.7 can be used to generate or validate improvement hypotheses. We shall now illustrate how the two methods of graphical presentation illustrated in Section 2.7.1 can serve this purpose.

The *system utilization profile* (*see* Fig. 2.13) is an elementary but often effective technique to display the temporal relationships between the busy and idle intervals of a system's components. It gives us in clearly understandable form some information on the amount of overlap existing between the activities of the components. This information, which cannot be derived from the values of the utilization factors alone, tells us what the other components are doing while one of them is idle. Thus, the system utilization profile often helps us understand why in our system multiprogramming is not so effective as it should be or, in any case, why the performance is lower than could be expected. This diagnostic aid is particularly popular because of the ease with which the necessary data can be gathered by a hardware measurement tool. Similar considerations can be made for *Kiviat graphs*. The use of these two techniques will now be illustrated by three examples inspired by the discussion in Cockrum and Crocket (1971).

Example 7.4 Let us consider a version of EXOPE with one CPU and one I/O channel, and assume that a measurement session has produced the data listed in Table 2.3. Then a system utilization profile can be drawn as in Fig. 2.13 and a corresponding Kiviat graph as in Fig. 2.14. An examination of the utilization factors shows that the system is not seriously unbalanced. The profile shows also that the amount of overlap is reasonable (about 78% of the CPU busy time and about 70% of the channel busy time). To reduce the total processing time of the same work load without modifying the hardware configuration, we have to reduce the system idle time or, perhaps, try to further increase the CPU-I/O overlap. An examination of the Kiviat graph in Fig. 2.14 confirms our feeling that a reduction of the system idle time should be attempted first. Thus, we have to formulate a hypothesis in order to explain why about 20% of the total elapsed time is spent by the system waiting, while no component is doing any work. Three hypotheses, which are by no means mutually exclusive, may plausibly be made:

  a. the system was empty during certain periods of the measurement session;
  b. the system was waiting for operator actions (e.g., tape or disk pack mounting) or for a component which had been disconnected from the system (e.g., for maintenance reasons) to be reinserted;
  c. the system was waiting for disk seeks to complete (note that the I/O channel is not busy during seeks).

Each hypothesis requires further data to be gathered. The profile in Fig. 2.13 does not allow us to decide which ones of the above hypotheses are valid and to what extent. In particular, we should extract from the collected data, from the accounting log of the day of the experiment, and from other installation logs or from new experiments the following information:

  a. the amount of *system idle and input queue empty* time during the session;
  b. the amount of *not ready* time of the various devices during the session;
  c. the amount of *seek only* time during the session.

The longer time (or times) among the ones just listed will point to the area (or areas) where further study might be worthwhile. In that area, new hypotheses will have to be formulated (why are seek only times so long? why are operators so slow in mounting tapes?) until the most reasonable and promising therapy is arrived at. Note that if hypothesis a explains most of the system idle time, the only possible conclusions are that either the session time was not properly chosen or the capacity of the system is not fully utilized.

If we are interested in exploring the possibility of increasing the CPU-I/O overlap, we have to formulate hypotheses about the reasons this overlap is not completely satisfactory in our system. Two of these reasons may be

  a. poor job scheduling: the mix of the jobs in execution is not kept well balanced with respect to the characteristics of the resources; too many I/O-bound jobs together contribute to the *channel only* time, and too many CPU-bound jobs contribute to the *CPU only* time;
  b. inefficient programs: the same problems described above as due to bad scheduling may also be caused by those individual programs which are executed very often in the installation.

Both hypotheses, if confirmed, directly point to areas in which improvement is needed. ■

Example 7.5 Let the system to be improved be the one studied in Example 7.1 (*see* Table 7.2). Since we have extensively analyzed the model of that system depicted in Fig. 7.5, we may wonder what its system utilization profile would be and what hypotheses we could formulate from it. The profile can be obtained by computing the amounts of overlap between the activities of various groups of servers. This computation is straightforward if the equilibrium state probabilities are known. For example, the overlap between the CPU and the drum is proportional to the sum of the probabilities of those states in which both the CPU and the drum have in them a nonzero number of jobs. For the model in Fig. 7.5, the probability of CPU-drum overlap is [from (4.102)]

$$\rho_{12} = \sum_{\substack{\text{all } N \\ \text{with } N_1 > 0 \\ \text{and } N_2 > 0}} p(N_1, N_2, N_3) = y_2 \frac{G(N-2)}{G(N)}, \tag{7.18}$$

where y_2 is given by (4.97). The derivation of (7.18), which can be done following the same type of argument used to obtain the expression of ρ_1 in (4.106), is left as an exercise for the reader.

Similarly, for the other overlap probabilities we have

$$\rho_{13} = y_3 \frac{G(N-2)}{G(N)} = \frac{y_3}{y_2} \rho_{12}, \tag{7.19}$$

$$\rho_{23} = y_2 y_3 \frac{G(N-2)}{G(N)} = y_3 \rho_{12} = y_2 \rho_{13}, \tag{7.20}$$

$$\rho_{123} = y_2 y_3 \frac{G(N-3)}{G(N)}. \tag{7.21}$$

The probabilities that each component is the only one to be busy are given by

$$\rho_{10} = \frac{1}{G(N)} = \rho_1 - \rho_{12} - \rho_{13} + \rho_{123}, \tag{7.22}$$

$$\rho_{20} = \frac{y_2^N}{G(N)} = \rho_2 - \rho_{12} - \rho_{23} + \rho_{123}, \tag{7.23}$$

$$\rho_{30} = \frac{y_3^N}{G(N)} = \rho_3 - \rho_{13} - \rho_{23} + \rho_{123}. \tag{7.24}$$

The derivation of relationships analogous to (7.18)–(7.24) which hold for a central-server model with s servers ($s > 3$) is the subject of Problem 7.6.

Figure 7.13(a) shows the profile obtained from these relationships for the parameter values given in Table 7.3. Note that there cannot be any system idle time in the model. The number of jobs in memory is always N, all servers are always operational, and the disk server is considered as busy during seeks. In this profile, the degree of overlap is not too unsatisfactory, and *CPU only* and *drum only* times are quite short. However, the *disk only* time is more than 25% of the total, and the hypothesis can be formulated that a different distribution of files between drum and disk will increase the overlaps (especially ρ_{123}).

In constructing a Kiviat graph for this two-channel system, many choices of the variables to be reported on the graph are available. We choose the component utilizations ρ_1, ρ_2, ρ_3 and the relative channel overlap $\rho_{23}/\min(\rho_2, \rho_3)$ as the "good" variables. The

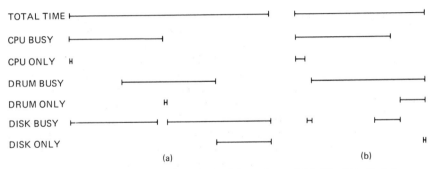

Figure 7.13 System utilization profiles obtained from the model in Fig. 7.5 with (a) the parameter values in Table 7.3 and (b) the same values except $b_{12} = 0.92$ and $b_{13} = 0.03$.

nonoverlapped fractions of these utilizations, ρ_{10}/ρ_1, ρ_{20}/ρ_2, ρ_{30}/ρ_3, and the system idle fraction of the total time are the "bad" variables. This choice is dictated by the desire to avoid variables whose interdependencies are too obvious (for example, ρ_1 and $1 - \rho_1$) as well as by the diagnostic functions we attribute to the graph here. Note that, by (7.1) and (7.2), $\bar{T}$ is proportional to ρ_1 and that $\bar{\imath}$ is inversely proportional to it, since we do not expect to be modifying N, b_{11}, or μ_1. Also, the relative channel overlap and the relative nonoverlapped utilizations have been chosen instead of their absolute counterparts since they are felt to be more meaningful with respect to the diagnostic purposes of the graph. Having made these choices, the Kiviat graph corresponding to the system whose profile is presented in Fig. 7.13(a) is depicted in Fig. 7.14(a). The reader will verify that this graph suggests the same considerations and the same hypothesis as the profile in Fig. 7.13(a).

The profile in Fig. 7.13(b) represents the situation at the point of maximum $\bar{T}$, reached by changing only b_{12} and b_{13} in Table 7.3. The nonoverlapped disk time has practically disappeared. However, *drum only* time is now relatively large (about 20% of

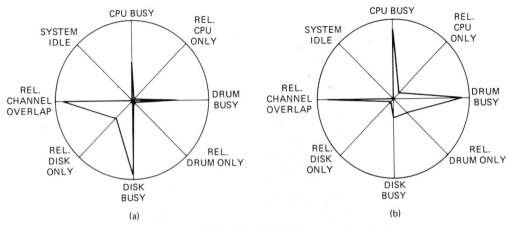

Figure 7.14 Kiviat graphs for the model in Fig. 7.5 with (a) the parameter values in Table 7.3 and (b) the same values except $b_{12} = 0.92$ and $b_{13} = 0.03$.

the total), but the drum is faster than the disk. Also the overlap probabilities $\rho_{13}, \rho_{23}, \rho_{123}$ have decreased, but this can be attributed to the spectacular decrease of ρ_3. In fact, the comparisons between profiles must be made in terms of times and not in terms of utilizations if our performance index is $\bar{T}$. The high values of ρ_1 and of ρ_{12} help justify the improvement in $\bar{T}$ (which is 53% better). However, the profile does not tell us that this is an optimum situation and that no modifications of b_{12} and b_{13} can improve $\bar{T}$ further. The same conclusions can be drawn from examining the corresponding Kiviat graph, plotted in Fig. 7.14(b). While this graph would certainly be considered "better" than the one in Fig. 7.14(a), its ρ_{20}/ρ_2 would be judged too high and its ρ_3 too low by most evaluators. This very simple example should remind us of the difference between a uniformly utilized system and a maximum-$\bar{T}$ system, which has been discussed in Section 7.3.2. We should also not forget that system utilization profiles and Kiviat graphs are diagnostic tools based on the identification of uniform utilization and maximum overlap with maximum performance. We have seen that this identification is possible only as a first approximation. Solving Problem 7.8 will show the reader an example of a system with a "nicer" profile and a "nicer" Kiviat graph outperformed by a system with "uglier" portraits. ∎

Example 7.6   The system to be studied in this example has one CPU, two I/O channels, and eight secondary storage devices (disks), four connected to each channel. Table 7.5 summarizes the results obtained by measuring the system. The corresponding system utilization profile and the Kiviat graph drawn according to the decisions made in Example 7.5 are shown in Fig. 7.15. Both the profile and the graph point to some evident problem areas, most notably the large system idle time, the imbalance between channel utilizations, and the large nonoverlapped portion of each component's activity. The hypotheses that may be formulated to explain the excessive system idle time have been listed and discussed in Example 7.4. The other two major symptoms mentioned above seem to suggest that the

Table 7.5
RESULTS OF MEASUREMENTS ON A COMPUTER SYSTEM

Symbol	Description	Fraction of total time [%]
ρ_1	CPU busy	33.33
ρ_2	Channel 1 busy	25.00
ρ_3	Channel 2 busy	1.65
ρ_{10}	CPU only	24.59
ρ_{23}	Channel overlap	0.41
$1 - \rho_{10} - \rho_2 - \rho_3 + \rho_{23}$	System idle	49.17
δ_1	Device 1 data busy	4.16
δ_2	Device 2 data busy	2.77
δ_3	Device 3 data busy	9.73
δ_4	Device 4 data busy	8.34
δ_5	Device 5 data busy	0.27
δ_6	Device 6 data busy	0.83
δ_7	Device 7 data busy	0.41
δ_8	Device 8 data busy	0.14

Source: Cockrum and Crockett (1971), by permission of AFIPS, Inc.

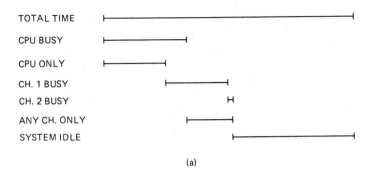

(a)

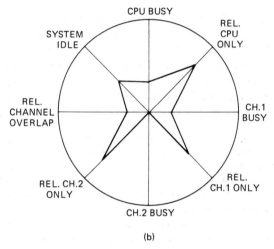

(b)

Figure 7.15 System utilization profile (*a*) and Kiviat graph (*b*) corresponding to the measurement results in Table 7.5. Since the relevant data were not available, the activity of channel 2 has been assumed not to be overlapped with that of the CPU.

placement of the secondary storage devices on the channels has not been done properly. The measurements reported in Table 7.5 confirm this hypothesis. Devices 1 through 4, the most utilized ones, are placed on channel 1, while channel 2 controls the other four devices, whose utilizations are one order of magnitude smaller. A rearrangement of the device connections is therefore expected to appreciably improve the situation. We shall return to this example in Section 7.4.   ■

Once a hypothesis has been formulated, it must be tested. Some hypotheses are relatively easy to test. As in the case of the hypothesis of poor device placement in Example 7.6, testing may sometimes be done by examining additional experimental data. Often, these data are not readily available and must be gathered by a purposely designed experiment but can be obtained at a relatively minor increment in the cost of the improvement study. In other cases, testing a hypothesis by measurement techniques might require much bigger efforts and expenditures. This would, for instance, be the case of those hypotheses which recognize in the insufficient speed of one of the hardware components the primary cause of a bottleneck. Verifying the validity of such a hypothesis directly by increasing the speed of that component (and possibly of some other components, too) is normally unfeasible. However, if the experimenter makes use of an executable artificial model of the work load to drive the system, a less direct but still experimental verification may be possible, especially when the model consists of a set of synthetic jobs. For example, a suitable reduction of the demand for the services of the component believed to create a bottleneck could be interpreted as a change in some sense equivalent to an increase of that component's speed (*see* Problem 7.2).

Hypothesis testing can be done with much more latitude and many fewer constraints if a simulator of the system to be improved is available. All sorts of modifications, including those which are physically unrealizable, can be tried out with a well-designed simulator, the only practical limitation being the cost of simulation runs. An extensive case study in bottleneck detection and removal by simulation has been described by Nielsen (1967). We shall now briefly discuss some aspects of that study.

Example 7.7   The simulated system is an IBM 360/67 time-sharing system. The initial hardware configuration consists of 1 CPU, 3 primary memory modules (256K bytes each), and 6 I/O channels. The channels control the following secondary storage devices: 1 paging drum, 1 eight-module disk unit for paging, another similar unit for file storage, 2 smaller disk units also for file storage, and 31 interactive terminals. Peripherals such as card readers, printers, and tape drives, though part of the configuration, are not simulated. The work-load model consists of interactive tasks selected from 10 classes characterized by a wide spectrum of computational and paging resource demands. No batch or real-time jobs are included, but it is easy to convert some of the interactive tasks to batch tasks by turning off the terminal portions of their interactions. The work-load model can also be varied in many ways, the most straightforward being a change in the number of terminals which run each type of task.

The primary performance index is CPU utilization, which, under certain assumptions (*see* Example 7.1), is proportional to the mean throughput rate. To be more precise, the overhead portion of CPU activity, which is spent allocating resources, handling page faults and interrupts, and performing other system functions, does not directly contribute to $\bar{T}$. Thus, we are in fact interested in the magnitudes of the two components of ρ_1, the user utilization ρ_{1p} and the system utilization ρ_{1s}. Other utilization factors of interest are those of the paging drum (ρ_2), of the paging disk (ρ_3), and of the disks used for file storage (ρ_4). Additional indices such as response time, paging rate (the number of pages transferred per unit time), and mean queue lengths are also observed because of their intrinsic importance and their diagnostic value.

The simulation of the system in its original configuration and with its original work load produces the following results: $\rho_{1p} = 0.12$, $\rho_{1s} = 0.39$, $\rho_2 = 0.07$, $\rho_3 = 0.80$, and $\rho_4 = 0.14\text{--}0.32$. This level of performance is certainly not satisfactory. A concise description of some of the many *hypothesis-test-results* cycles reported by Nielsen (1967) will now be given.

Hypothesis: The large CPU idle time is due to the fact that the load is too light.

Test: Convert the 12 tasks with the highest CPU time demands from interactive to batch.

Results: $\rho_{1p} = 0.14$, $\rho_{1s} = 0.43$, $\rho_2 = 0.10$, $\rho_3 = 0.58$, and $\rho_4 = 0.14$–0.58. The hypothesis must be rejected.

Hypothesis: Performance is degraded by a bottleneck. Since ρ_3 is quite high, the bottleneck is created by the paging disk.

Test: Eliminate the need for the paging disk by reducing the work load to 12 batch, compute-bound jobs with minimal paging requirements.

Results: $\rho_{1p} = 0.43$, $\rho_{1s} = 0.35$, $\rho_2 = 0.08$, $\rho_3 = 0.00$, and $\rho_4 = 0.22$. The hypothesis is valid.

Hypothesis: A satisfactory performance can be obtained by adding three paging disk units, each on a separate channel.

Test: Upgrade the system model and run it under the original work load.

Results: $\rho_{1p} = 0.20$, $\rho_{1s} = 0.46$, $\rho_2 = 0.12$, $\rho_3 = 0.08$–0.12, and $\rho_4 = 0.30$–0.50. The hypothesis is only partially confirmed, since performance is still far from being acceptable.

Hypothesis: There is another bottleneck, this time created by the disks for file storage.

Test: Reduce the access and transfer times of the disks for file storage to zero.

Results: $\rho_{1p} = 0.31$, $\rho_{1s} = 0.69$, $\rho_2 = 0.23$, $\rho_3 = 0.13$–0.17, and $\rho_4 = 0.00$. The hypothesis is valid, but the problem of overhead has become overwhelming.

At this point, the investigators are confronted with two separate questions. One has to do with solving the overhead problem. A careful study of how the operating system works, as well as previous experience or other methods (*see* Table 7.1), will help in formulating hypotheses in this area. Another problem is related to the practical elimination of the bottlenecks which were detected. The approach used to test the last hypothesis, namely, the adoption of infinitely fast disks for file storage, is not realistic. Also, the addition of three channels and three eight-module disk units to remove the paging disk bottleneck is feasible but not economical. Thus, realistic improvement hypotheses will have to be formulated. These include, for example, modifying the disk management algorithms to make them more efficient and replacing the paging disk unit with another paging drum. A suitable simulator may therefore be very helpful also in the planning of the therapy phase of an improvement study. ∎

7.3.4 A Statistical Diagnosis Method

In Section 7.3.1, methods based on the successive removal of bottlenecks were recognized to be useful for performance improvement. Accordingly, bottleneck detection was presented as the main task of the diagnosis phase of an improvement study. The formal definition of bottleneck given in Section 7.3.2 [*see* (7.3)] and the analysis of a simple model of a multiprogramming system showed that, although balancing a system or equalizing the utilizations of its components does not usually maximize its performance, these are very often sound objectives for an improvement effort. The concept on which definition

(7.3) is based can be applied to performance indices different from $\bar{T}$. In Problem 7.3, the reader is asked to extend that definition to the case in which the mean turnaround time $\bar{t}$ is the primary index of performance. However, this is possible only when the index is a single scalar variable. How can we define bottlenecks when the performance index is a statistical distribution or a vector? A possible definition has been implicitly suggested by Beilner (1973) in his proposal for the application to performance improvement problems of the *method of good balance* described in Section 3.3.3.

Let the work load, or an executable model of it, consist of n jobs, and let the vector $(t_1, t_2, \ldots, t_n)$ of their turnaround times be our performance index. Assume that the *desired turnaround time* of each job is somehow known. For example, we may choose as the desired turnaround time t_i^* of the ith job the minimum possible value of t_i, that is, the time the job would spend in the system running in uniprogramming mode. Thus, if we know the vector $(t_1^*, t_2^*, \ldots, t_n^*)$ for any given hardware and software configuration, we can measure the vector $(t_1, t_2, \ldots, t_n)$ and compute the deviation vector $\mathbf{D} = (d_1, d_2, \ldots, d_n)$, with $d_i = t_i - t_i^*$.

Each job in the work load is to be quantitatively characterized by a v-tuple $(w_1, w_2, \ldots, w_v)$ of parameters. For example, these parameters may express the resource demands of each job. We shall assume for simplicity that the w's are all measured in the same units (e.g., in seconds). The deviation $d = t - t^*$, whose values are $d_1, \ldots, d_n$, is a function of these parameters. A definition of bottleneck which can, in some sense, be considered as an extension of (7.3) is the following: A bottleneck is created by the jth resource $(1 \leq j \leq v)$ if, for all h such that $1 \leq h \leq v, h \neq j$,

$$\frac{\partial d}{\partial w_j} > \frac{\partial d}{\partial w_h}. \tag{7.25}$$

Similarly, the system is said to be balanced if, for all j and h,

$$\frac{\partial d}{\partial w_j} = \frac{\partial d}{\partial w_h}. \tag{7.26}$$

However, d is generally a function which exhibits a random-like behavior. Postulating that d can be expressed as the sum of a random component and of a deterministic trend, we can try to approximate this trend by a regression equation. A first-order linear regression equation should suffice for our bottleneck detection purposes. The coefficients a_0 and a_h in the equation

$$d = a_0 + \sum_{h=1}^{v} a_h w_h \tag{7.27}$$

may be obtained from the t, t^*, and w_h of each job, as illustrated in Section 2.7.3. If equation (7.27) is significant, the values of those coefficients a_h which are significant can be used for bottleneck detection as the partial derivatives in definition (7.25). However, the condition of balance (7.26) is to be replaced by the condition that equation (7.27) is nonsignificant. In this case, deviations are balanced, in the sense that no resource demand influences deviations more or less than the others. In other words, the existing deviations can no longer be explained by the shortage of a specific resource but are due to other causes, in particular to the intrinsic queue waits of multiprogramming systems. Thus, the successive-removal-of-bottlenecks method can be applied to this case, the objective here being to obtain a nonsignificant regression equation by successive modifications to the system. These modifications are suggested by the relative values of the significant coefficients in (7.27). The fact that the assumptions on which the validity of the F-test depends are not likely to be satisfied is to be carefully considered (*see* Section 2.7.2). In these cases, it is always advisable to adopt a conservative policy, that is, to choose smaller error probabilities than the desired ones.

7.4 THERAPY

7.4.1 Tuning Therapies

Operating systems are generally designed to be usable in a variety of installations with a number of different hardware configurations and under different work loads. As a result of this fact, which is dictated by evident economical advantages, a satisfactory level of performance can be obtained only if the operating system is adjusted to the characteristics of the installation. While the hardware configuration of an installation is known a priori and is quite stable in time, the actual work load is only approximately and superficially predictable and also time-variant. Thus, the tailoring of the operating system to the work load is to be done on the running system and should generally be repeated several times during the lifetime of the system. This tailoring operation is called *tuning*, a term properly borrowed from the realm of musical instruments. We shall use this term here in a slightly broader sense, to denote all performance improvement therapies which do not involve hardware configuration changes. Modifications of hardware connections which do not entail any hardware addition will also be considered as tuning therapies.

The most important types of changes in the tuning category and some examples of each type are listed in Table 7.6. The table shows how broad is the spectrum of changes which do not involve any modifications to the hardware and may have a nontrivial beneficial influence on performance. Case studies illustrating the implementation and the effects of changes of these types on a variety of systems are reported in a large number of papers. Most of the examples listed in Table 7.6 represent classes of therapies and could be expanded much further.

By looking at Table 7.6, the reader will realize how useful a thorough diagnosis phase may be for system evaluators. Careful diagnosis becomes essential

Table 7.6

MAJOR TYPES OF TUNING THERAPIES

Modifiable entities	Examples
Operating system parameters	Degree of multiprogramming Buffer size Time quantum Definitions of priority classes Page size
Resource management algorithms	Scheduling algorithms (job, CPU, drum, disk scheduling) Addressing algorithms (access methods) Memory management algorithms (allocation, replacement, loading, swapping) Peripheral-device management algorithms Manual procedures (tape or disk pack mounting, manual job scheduling, manual swapping)
Interconnections	Channel-device connections Device-bus connections
Information placement	File placement in the memory hierarchy Resident modules of the operating system
Program performance	Operating system overhead Execution time and memory space demanded by frequently used programs (compilers, editors, data base systems, sorting routines) Memory referencing patterns (locality)
Pricing policies	Usage incentives for light-load periods Penalties for inefficient programs Penalties for the usage of heavily loaded resources
Job acceptance policies	Exclusion of certain types of jobs or users Load limitation

when one considers that many of the types of changes listed in Table 7.6 are or may be quite expensive to make, in spite of the fact that no additional hardware is required. In particular, modifications to automatic resource management algorithms, pricing policies, and program performance usually require existing programs to be modified as well as new programs to be written and interfaced to the existing ones. This is an expensive, time-consuming, and error-prone activity, to be undertaken only when its convenience has been determined with a high degree of confidence. Other changes, such as those of operating system parameters, interconnections, and information placement, require some modifications to be made to the data base of the operating system. Although much cheaper and faster, these operations are to be performed with great care because of the catastrophic effect errors may produce. Also, most of the changes may cause disruptions and unforeseen reactions of the user community. These reactions and disruptions might temporarily or permanently offset the expected improvements. Sometimes the above considerations make it wiser not to implement a tuning therapy that the diagnosis phase has suggested and to take a different course of action. In other cases, we have to choose among several possible therapies.

All of these decisions should be based on a cost-performance criterion. Is the expected improvement worth the cost of the modifications being planned? Which one of the possible therapies is likely to produce the biggest improvement with the lowest cost?

The performance aspect of this criterion requires that relatively simple, inexpensive, and reliable methods be available for the prediction of performance improvements. If a change is easy, quick, and cheap, the best method usually is the experimental one. However, as pointed out above, most of the changes listed in Table 7.6 are not of this type. Thus, if measurement techniques cannot be used for performance analysis, we are left with simulation and analytic techniques. Both of them have advantages and drawbacks, which will be summarized in Section 7.5. Example 7.7 has briefly illustrated an application of simulation to the problem of performance prediction in an improvement context. We shall now present some examples of the use of analytic techniques for the same purpose.

Example 7.8 The analysis of the data in Table 7.5 (*see* Fig. 7.15 and Example 7.6) suggests a change in the device-channel interconnections. In particular, to distribute the total channel load better, we can connect disks 2, 3, 5, and 7 to channel 1 and disks 1, 4, 6, and 8 to channel 2. How can we estimate the performance improvement which will result from this change? An approximate but often sufficiently accurate method, proposed by Cockrum and Crockett (1971), is based on a *system-time equation* derived from the system utilization profile. A system-time equation is an equation which expresses the total time as a sum of component terms. For example, from the profile in Fig. 7.15(*a*) we may write

$$t_{\text{tot}} = t_{\text{cpu busy}} + t_{\text{any channel only}} + t_{\text{system idle}}. \tag{7.28}$$

Using the symbols in Table 7.5, we have

$$t_{\text{cpu busy}} = \rho_1 t_{\text{tot}}, \qquad t_{\text{any channel only}} = [\rho_2 + \rho_3 - \rho_{23} - (\rho_1 - \rho_{10})]t_{\text{tot}},$$
$$t_{\text{system idle}} = (1 + \rho_{10} - \rho_2 - \rho_3 + \rho_{23})t_{\text{tot}}. \qquad (7.29)$$

The reader may verify (7.28) by substituting (7.29) into it.

We now make the assumption that the change in device-channel connections does not affect either $t_{\text{cpu busy}}$ or $t_{\text{system idle}}$. This assumption is very reasonable for $t_{\text{cpu busy}}$ and also, at least as a first approximation, for $t_{\text{system idle}}$. Thus, only the variation of $t_{\text{any channel only}}$ must be determined. The new utilizations of the two channels can be computed from Table 7.5 as $\rho_2' = \delta_2 + \delta_3 + \delta_5 + \delta_7 = 13.18\%$ and $\rho_3' = \delta_1 + \delta_4 + \delta_6 + \delta_8 = 13.47\%$. The new probability of channel overlap, ρ_{23}', is to be estimated by probability theory considerations, since no additional relevant information is available. We note that δ_i is the probability that the ith device was active during the measurement session, and we assume that it will remain the same after the device rearrangement. Assuming that device activities are statistically independent, the overlap probability can be computed as

$$\rho_{23}' = (\delta_2 + \delta_3 + \delta_5 + \delta_7)(\delta_1 + \delta_4 + \delta_6 + \delta_8) = \rho_2'\rho_3' = 1.77\%, \qquad (7.30)$$

and we have, from (7.29),

$$t_{\text{any channel only}}' = [\rho_2' + \rho_3' - \rho_{23}' - (\rho_1 - \rho_{10})]t_{\text{tot}}. \qquad (7.31)$$

Note that the independence assumption is supported by the result of estimating ρ_{23} as $\rho_2\rho_3$, which is equal to 0.415% (*see* Table 7.5). However, the study of a central-server model in Example 7.5 does not support it [*see*, for instance, (7.20)].

The system-time equation (7.28) yields

$$\frac{t_{\text{tot}} - t_{\text{tot}}'}{t_{\text{tot}}} = \rho_2 + \rho_3 - \rho_{23} - \rho_2' - \rho_3' + \rho_{23}' = \rho_{23}' - \rho_{23} = 1.36\%. \qquad (7.32)$$

Thus, the rearrangement of the devices is expected to reduce the total time by 1.36%. This is also approximately the expected improvement in the mean throughput rate. ∎

Example 7.9   The effects on performance of changes in information placement will now be studied by using a central-server model. This improvement study was performed by Hughes and Moe (1973) for a UNIVAC 1108 computer running under the EXEC 8 operating system. The configuration included one CPU (server Σ_1), one high-speed FH432 drum (server Σ_2), one medium-speed FH880 drum (server Σ_3), one slow FASTRAND drum (server Σ_4), and magnetic tape drives (server Σ_5). The system was modeled by a central-server queuing network with five servers. Hughes and Moe defined the throughput rate as the number of CPU-device cycles the N jobs perform per unit time and set $b_{11} = 0$. However, these differences with respect to our previous discussions involving a central-server model are not important here since we shall estimate the effects of the change on the utilization factors of the various servers and not on indices such as $\bar{T}$ or $\bar{i}$.

Table 7.7 shows the utilizations (ρ_i) and the total numbers of requests (n_i) to the five servers represented in the model. These values were measured during an experiment in which the system was driven by a set of benchmarks. Since the utilization of the FASTRAND drum, ρ_4, is much higher than the others, this drum is likely to create a bottleneck. A better distribution of the load among the devices can be obtained by

Table 7.7

ESTIMATION OF THE EFFECTS OF A CHANGE IN INFORMATION
PLACEMENT (SEE EXAMPLE 7.9)

Server number, i	Resource	Utilization before change, ρ_i	Number of requests before change, n_i	Estimated number of requests after change, $\hat{n}_i'$	Estimated utilization after change $\hat{\rho}_i'$	Measured utilization after change, ρ_i'
1	CPU	0.62	67,024	67,024	0.77	0.74
2	FH432 drum	0.26	33,626	33,626	0.32	0.29
3	FH880 drum	0.14	7,351	12,788	0.30	0.27
4	FASTRAND drum	0.90	14,763	9,326	0.71	0.68
5	Magnetic tape	0.18	11,284	11,284	0.22	0.22

Source: Hughes and Moe (1973), by permission of AFIPS, Inc.

transferring part of the FASTRAND requests to the FH880 drum, which is only lightly loaded. A large number of accesses to the FASTRAND drum are due to the fact that this drum is used to buffer information coming from, or going to, slow peripherals such as card readers, punches, and printers. Moving this buffering function to the faster FH880 drum resulted in a decrease of n_4 by 5437 requests. Assuming that we can somehow estimate this decrease without too large an error, we obtain the new numbers of requests $(\hat{n}_i')$ listed in Table 7.7. These numbers have been determined under the assumption that n_1, n_2, and n_5 are not affected by the change, and all the requests which are not made to the FASTRAND go to the FH880 drum. Also the (exponential) distributions of service times and their means $(1/\mu_i)$ will be assumed not to be affected on any of the devices.

A problem with the use of a central-server model in this case comes from the fact that the degree of multiprogramming N is not kept constant by the system. To estimate the mean value of N during the experiment before the change, we may use the model to construct the curve $\rho_1(N)$, which resembles those in Fig. 7.9, and derive N from the measured value of ρ_1 (which in Table 7.7 is 0.62). The points of this curve corresponding to integer values of N can be computed by the method described in Section 4.3.5, observing that the values

$$y_i = \frac{\rho_i}{\rho_1} \quad (i = 2, \ldots, 5) \tag{7.32}$$

are immediately obtainable from Table 7.7. The reader who will construct the $\rho_1(N)$ curve will see by interpolation that $\rho_1 = 0.62$ corresponds to about $N = 4.5$. This is then the value of the mean degree of multiprogramming $\bar{N}$, which we assume to be unaffected by the change.

Note that the request probabilities b_{1i} can be written as

$$b_{1i} = \frac{n_i}{n_1} \quad (i = 2, \ldots, 5) \tag{7.33}$$

and that by equations (4.97) y_i is proportional to b_{1i}. Thus, since n_1, n_2, and n_5 are not affected by the change, after the change we have

$$\hat{y}_1' = y_1, \qquad \hat{y}_2' = y_2, \qquad \hat{y}_3' = \frac{\hat{n}_3'}{n_3}y_3, \qquad \hat{y}_4' = \frac{\hat{n}_4'}{n_4}y_4, \qquad \hat{y}_5' = y_5. \qquad (7.34)$$

The new curve $\hat{\rho}_1'(N)$ can then be computed from (7.34) and $\hat{\rho}_1'$ determined by interpolation for $N = 4.5$. From $\hat{\rho}_1'$, which is found to be about 0.77, we may calculate the values of all the other utilizations using equations (7.32) and (7.34). These utilizations $\hat{\rho}_i'$ are reported in Table 7.7. Their comparison with the measured utilizations after the change shows that a remarkable accuracy may be obtained even by as crude an approach as the one used in this example. ∎

Example 7.10 We shall now study the effects of some changes in the memory management algorithm or in program behavior on the performance of a virtual-memory system. At the end of our discussion of Example 7.3, we concluded that if the changes in the page fault rate caused by these variations can be estimated, then a central-server model can easily be used to approximately determine the corresponding changes in $\bar{T}$ and $\bar{\imath}$ (see, for instance, the curves in Fig. 7.12). In Example 7.3, all jobs were assumed to exhibit the same mean referencing behavior. That is, the values of the coefficient a and of the exponent k in the lifetime function were the same for all jobs. In that situation, it was natural to make the sizes of all memory partitions identical and equal to M/N. However, in practice, programs are all different from each other, and we should expect performance to be improved if a variable-size memory management strategy, whereby each job may be allotted a different amount of space, were adopted. For simplicity, let us assume that all programs have the same k but a different value of a. The space allotted to each job will be kept constant throughout the job's residence in memory, and a departing job will always be replaced by one with the same lifetime function. These are, or course, extremely crude assumptions, but our objective is to illustrate the use of a simple analytic tool in estimating the effects of a memory management change.

In our system, the degree of multiprogramming is constant, and the work load is characterized by the N coefficients $a_1, a_2, \ldots, a_N$ as well as by the value of k. The mean number of page faults generated by the ith job is given by (7.12):

$$\bar{n}_{dri} = \frac{\bar{L}}{\bar{v}_{cpu}\bar{e}_i} = \frac{\bar{L}}{a_i m_i^k}. \qquad (7.35)$$

The condition under which the numbers of page faults produced by all jobs are equal is, evidently, $\bar{e}_i = \bar{e}_j$ for all i, j. This condition can be written as

$$m_j = \frac{a_i^{1/k} m_i}{a_j^{1/k}}, \qquad (7.36)$$

which, taking the constraint

$$\sum_{j=1}^{N} m_j \leq M \qquad (7.37)$$

into account and particularly the equal sign in (7.37), becomes

$$m_j = \frac{M}{\sum_{i=1}^{N} a_i^{-1/k}} a_j^{-1/k}. \qquad (7.38)$$

Thus, if each job is allotted an amount of memory inversely proportional to the $(1/k)$th power of its coefficient a_j, the individual page fault rates are all equal, and the approach of Example 7.3 can be used with no modifications to evaluate $\bar{T}$ and $\bar{t}$. By (7.14) and (7.38), the total mean page fault rate in this case is

$$\bar{f} = \frac{\bar{v}_{cpu}N}{M^k}\left(\sum_{i=1}^{N} a_i^{-1/k}\right)^k. \qquad (7.39)$$

For instance, in the system analyzed in Example 7.3, let $N = 3$, $M = 160$ pages, $k = 2$, $a_1 = 25$, $a_2 = 2.77$, $a_3 = 6.25$ pages^{-k}, and $\bar{v}_{cpu} = 10^6$ instructions/s. From (7.39), we have $\bar{f} = 169$ page faults/s, and from Fig. 7.12, $\bar{T} = 2.58$ jobs/s and $\bar{t} = 1.16$ s.

What happens if the space given to each job does not satisfy condition (7.38)? The mean numbers of page faults $\bar{n}_{dri}$ will differ from each other [see (7.35)], and each job will have a different distribution of CPU times or, at least, a different value of μ_1. In Table 7.3, μ_1 is seen to depend on $\bar{n}_{cpu}$, which is a function of $\bar{n}_{dr}$, as shown by (7.13). Thus, our model is no longer applicable. However, we can still use it to get indicative results, especially if the page fault rates of the programs do not differ too drastically from each other and provided that we do not excessively rely on these results. Suppose that the memory of our system is equally partitioned among the three jobs. Thus,

$$\bar{f} = \bar{v}_{cpu} \sum_{j=1}^{N} \frac{1}{a_j m_j^k} = \bar{v}_{cpu} \frac{N^k}{M^k} \sum_{j=1}^{N} a_j^{-1} \qquad (7.40)$$

yields $\bar{f} = 197$ page faults/s. Equal partitions increase the total mean page fault rate by about 16% in this case. If the central-server model results of Example 7.3 were applicable, we could read from Fig. 7.12 the new values of the performance indices: $\bar{T} = 2.45$ jobs/s, $\bar{t} = 1.22$ s. Therefore, if the equal-size partitioning strategy were replaced by the variable-size one based on (7.38), both $\bar{T}$ and $\bar{t}$ would be expected to improve by about 5% in this case. It is easy to prove that (7.38) is the partitioning which, under the assumptions we have made, minimizes the total mean page fault rate.

The approach we have just illustrated can also be used to estimate the payoffs of program performance improvements. Suppose that in the system described in Example 7.3, with $N = 5$, we improve the referencing behavior of the compiler, for instance, by redesigning and rewriting it. Suppose also that the compiler is so heavily used that it can be assumed to reside permanently in primary memory and that all programs, before the change, produce the same page fault rate. How much is the system going to gain in performance if the page fault rate of the compiler is decreased by 50%?

The total mean page fault rate before the change can be computed from (7.14): $\bar{f} = 781$ page faults/s. The above reduction causes the value of $\bar{f}$ to drop by 10%, down to 703 page faults/s. From Fig. 7.12 we obtain the corresponding values of $\bar{T}$ and $\bar{t}$. $\bar{T}$ increases by about 10% from 1.62 to 1.79, and $\bar{t}$ decreases by about 9% from 3.07 to 2.79. A look at the curves in Fig. 7.12 will convince the reader that the relative improvements due to a given program performance enhancement depend on the initial point, that is, on the values of N and $\bar{f}$. They also obviously depend on the system's situation with respect to bottlenecks. The reader may verify (*see* Problem 7.13) that if the system is unbalanced because of a bottleneck created by the disk, an improvement in program performance or in the memory management strategy has a very minor impact on $\bar{T}$ and $\bar{t}$. The same conclusion is valid if the paging drum is so heavily saturated that our reduction of $\bar{f}$ is not sufficient to take it out of saturation. This is evident in Fig. 7.12 for very high values of $\bar{f}$.   ∎

An important question which arises in connection with tuning therapies is the one about whether, in an improvement effort, they should be considered before or after upgrading therapies. Since upgrading involves selecting and procuring new hardware components, it seems reasonable to state that the possibility of tuning a system should be investigated first. However, as we pointed out earlier in this section, tuning is not necessarily less expensive than upgrading, even though some of the types of changes listed in Table 7.6 are usually quite cheap. Also, the results of measurement experiments may convince the evaluator that the degradation of a tuned system's performance is due to an increase rather than to a shift in the nature of the work load. In these cases, retuning the system should not be expected to contribute substantially to the solution of the problem, and upgrading therapies should be considered immediately. Tuning will, of course, be required after the system has been upgraded.

But how does an evaluator determine when a tuning effort should be terminated or not even undertaken? In this section, we have seen a few simple examples of improvement prediction. If all the feasible changes we consider fail to result in cost-effective predicted improvements, we shall conclude that tuning therapies are useless for our system. This may well happen when the system is at, or close to, the point of optimum performance. How can we determine that this is the case without exhaustively trying all possible changes and estimating or measuring their effects? Of course, this problem would be solved if the optimum values of the performance indices for the given hardware configuration and the given work load were known. We saw at the beginning of Section 7.3.3 that this information may also be extremely useful as a symptom of insufficient performance. However, even for the simplest and most popular indices such as $\bar{T}$, only very rough methods are available. For example, formula (7.15) with $\rho_{1\,max} = 1$ is often used to calculate the capacity of a system. In Chapter 6, the resulting value of $\bar{T}_{max}$ is referred to several times as the *information-processing power*, even though other rudimentary quantitative definitions of the same concept are given in Section 6.3.3.

We shall now show how analytic techniques can be used to estimate the capacity of a given hardware configuration under a given work load. This is only a very primitive step. When a system is modeled as a central-server queuing network, so many details are ignored that, for instance, only a few of the types of changes displayed in Table 7.6 can be represented. For a three-server model, only those tuning changes which can be reflected by variations of m, $\bar{i}_{seek}$, $\bar{L}$, $\bar{n}_{cpu}$, $\bar{r}_{dr}$, $\bar{n}_{dr}$, $\bar{r}_{ds}$, and $\bar{n}_{ds}$ (*see* Table 7.2) may be taken into account. Also, as shown in Example 7.10, it is easy to exceed the boundaries of the domain of validity of the model, at least in the simple version of it used throughout this chapter. Nevertheless, we shall analyze the problem using this simple model in order to illustrate an approach which may prove fruitful, especially if applying it to more complex and accurate models will be feasible.

Our initial observation is that, by (4.101), $G(N)$ is a symmetric function of y_2 and y_3. That is, exchanging y_2 with y_3 does not have any influence on the value of $G(N)$. Thus, by (4.106), ρ_1 is also a symmetric function of y_2 and y_3. This conclusion agrees with the observation that ρ_1 cannot depend on the numbering of the noncentral servers in the network. As a result, the curves corresponding to equal values of ρ_1 in the (y_2, y_3) plane are symmetric with respect to the 45° line in the first quadrant. If we plot them for a given value of N, we obtain a family of curves like the one in Fig. 7.16. The curvature of these lines is smaller than the

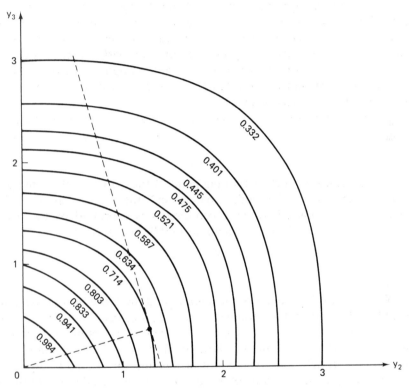

Figure 7.16   Constant-ρ_1 curves for any three-server central-server model with $N = 5$.

one of a circle for high values of ρ_1, that is, near the origin, and becomes greater as ρ_1 decreases. Note also that as N increases the transition between the two types of curvature (i.e., smaller and greater than the one of a circle) takes place at a shorter distance from the origin. To obtain an analytic expression for the system's capacity, various approximations can be made. We shall choose the one which replaces the curves for constant ρ_1 in Fig. 7.16 with arcs of a circle centered in the origin. An arc of radius r will correspond to

$$\rho_1 = \frac{1 + 2x + 3x^2 + \cdots + Nx^{N-1}}{1 + 2x + 3x^2 + \cdots + (N + 1)x^N}, \qquad (7.41)$$

with $x = r/\sqrt{2}$. Note that (7.41) is obtained from (4.106) and (4.101) by setting $s = 3$, $y_2 = y_3 = x$. The error we make by this approximation is zero on the 45° line and maximum on the two axes. It can be shown that the maximum error increases with N and (percentage-wise) with the radius. For example, if $r = 1$, this error is 3% for $N = 5$ and 6% for $N = 10$. If $r = 2$, the error is 11% for $N = 5$ and 25% for $N = 10$. A 25% error is certainly quite high. However, better approximations can be used when a higher accuracy is required. Also, we want to estimate an upper bound for ρ_1, and the approximation considered here has the advantage of producing a value of ρ_1 greater than the real one if the system works in a region where the curvature is greater than that of a circle. Finally, in cases of practical interest, an optimum performance system does not work too far either from the 45° line or from the origin in the (y_2, y_3) plane, and therefore errors should be expected to be always substantially smaller than the maximum values reported above.

With our approximation, the curves for constant ρ_1 in the (y_2, y_3) plane obey the equation

$$y_2^2 + y_3^2 = r^2. \tag{7.42}$$

The coordinates of the operating point of the system in the same plane are, by (4.97), functions of the model's parameters (the μ's and the b's). The only constraint to be satisfied by these coordinates is expressed by the relationship $b_{11} + b_{12} + b_{13} = 1$, which, by equations (4.97), becomes

$$b_{11} + \frac{\mu_2}{\mu_1}y_2 + \frac{\mu_3}{\mu_1}y_3 = 1. \tag{7.43}$$

To maximize $\bar{T}$, N must be maximized, and therefore m must be minimized. When the other modifiable parameters ($\bar{t}_{seek}$, $\bar{L}$, $\bar{n}_{cpu}$, $\bar{r}_{dr}$, $\bar{n}_{dr}$, $\bar{r}_{ds}$, and $\bar{n}_{ds}$) vary, all the coefficients in (7.43) are affected (see Table 7.3). However, for any given values of $\bar{t}_{seek}$, $\bar{L}$, $\bar{n}_{cpu}$, $\bar{r}_{dr}$, and $\bar{r}_{ds}$, these coefficients are constant, and (7.43) is the equation of a straight line. The points of this line correspond to different values of $\bar{n}_{dr}$ and $\bar{n}_{ds}$ (or, equivalently, of b_{12} and b_{13}). However, the sum of these values must be constant. Clearly, the maximum ρ_1 will be the one characterizing the constant-ρ_1 curve to which this straight line is tangent (see Fig. 7.16). The coordinates of the tangency point will define the values of b_{12} and b_{13} which maximize $\bar{T}$. Obviously, the other modifiable parameters must be chosen so as to make this point as close as possible to the origin. Elementary analytic geometry tells us that (7.43) is tangent to (7.42) for

$$r = \frac{(1 - b_{11})\mu_1}{\sqrt{\mu_2^2 + \mu_3^2}}. \tag{7.44}$$

If we minimize r, we achieve the maximum ρ_1. The numerator of the fraction in (7.44) can be written as $(\bar{n}_{cpu} - 1)\bar{v}_{cpu}/\bar{L}$. Since $\bar{v}_{cpu}/\bar{L}$ also appears in $\bar{T}$ [see (7.15)], we cannot conclude that $\bar{L}$ is to be maximized. On the contrary, ρ_1 can be shown to decrease less than proportionally to r as r increases. Thus, $\bar{L}$ must be minimized. From (7.44) and the equation of μ_3 in Table 7.3, we conclude that $\bar{t}_{seek}$ should be minimized (an obvious conclusion). To maximize μ_2 and μ_3, $\bar{r}_{dr}$ and $\bar{r}_{ds}$ should be minimized. However, if we postulate that the volume of information $\bar{n}_{dr}\bar{r}_{dr} + \bar{n}_{ds}\bar{r}_{ds}$ each job transfers from primary to secondary memory and vice versa is to remain constant, reducing $\bar{r}_{dr}$ and $\bar{r}_{ds}$ would increase $\bar{n}_{dr}$ and $\bar{n}_{ds}$. Hence, $\bar{n}_{cpu}$ and the numerator of (7.44) would increase. There are optimum values of these parameters which minimize (7.44) under the constraints that the volume of data transferred by each job is constant and that the results are compatible with the coordinates of the tangency point. Finding these optima is not straightforward. If we assume that μ_2 and μ_3 are dominated by access times and that the feasible modifications of $\bar{r}_{dr}$ and $\bar{r}_{ds}$ cannot have a strong influence on the corresponding service rates, we may keep the original values for $\bar{r}_{dr}$ and $\bar{r}_{ds}$. To simplify the problem even further, let $\bar{r}_{dr} = \bar{r}_{ds}$, as in Table 7.2. Thus, the value of $\bar{n}_{cpu}$ can be derived from the knowledge of the total volume of information transferred by a job, and $\bar{n}_{dr}$ and $\bar{n}_{ds}$ from the coordinates of the tangency point.

As an example, we shall compute the approximate value of $\bar{T}_{max}$ for a system whose model has the parameter values given in Table 7.3, except for μ_3 (which is 16.66 s^{-1}) and for b_{12} and b_{13}, which are the modifiable parameters (this means that we restrict ourselves here to variations in the placement of information). From (7.44), we have $r = 1.22$. Equation (7.41) yields $\rho_1 = 0.781$, and (7.1) gives $\bar{T}_{max} = 3.25$ jobs/s. We also have $b_{12} = 0.88$ and $b_{13} = 0.07$. In Fig. 7.7, $\bar{T}_{max}$ for the same model is equal to about 3.14 jobs/s. The error is therefore about 3%. The optimum values of b_{12} and b_{13} are around 0.85 and 0.1, respectively.

7.4.2 Self-Tuning Mechanisms

Most of the tuning therapies listed in Table 7.6 refer to system characteristics of which, given a configuration and a work load, it is possible to define an optimum choice. As we saw in Section 7.4.1, this is the case of device-channel interconnections and of file placement. It is also, and particularly, the case of some operating system parameters, such as the CPU time quantum in time-sharing systems and the degree of multiprogramming in virtual-memory systems [*see* curve (c) in Fig. 7.10]. Another example is the one of most resource management algorithms. If performance is defined by a single index or figure of merit, every time the choice of one of the several known algorithms has some impact on this index, one of the alternatives produces the best performance. However, the optimum choice of these system characteristics varies with the work load. Therefore, when the work load changes, the system goes "out of tune" and needs to be retuned. As mentioned several times in the previous chapters, a spectral analysis of work-load parameters such as resource demands shows that their frequency spectrum spans many orders of magnitude. Periods range from milliseconds to months and even years. Thus, tuning therapies which can be applied with periods of the order of months cannot take into account higher-frequency variations and will have to refer to averages of work-load parameters over periods of the same order. Device-channel interconnections cannot be changed more often than, say, at most a few times per year. Therefore, this therapy may be used to retune the system when and if the relevant characteristics of the monthly or quarterly work load have substantially drifted away from those which existed at the time the previous tuning was performed.

There are, however, therapies which can be applied more frequently, such as those which consist of adjusting the value of an operating system parameter or of switching from a resource management algorithm to another one. If the tuning process can be automated, these therapies can allow us to tune the system to work-load variations having very short periods. The automation of the tuning process is essential if the system is to follow high-frequency variations of its work load. It is possible to conceive of automatic tuning mechanisms which operate on a much longer time scale, which, for instance, relocate files from one device to another in order to improve the system's performance. In principle, automatic tuning can be performed by an external agent, typically a stored-program hardware measurement tool (*see* Sections 2.3.4 and 2.5). However, a much more popular approach so far has been the one which uses the system itself for this purpose. We shall call such a system a *self-tuning* system.

The diagnosis phase in any automated tuning process consists of the measurement of appropriate quantities and of their interpretation. This requires a continuous-monitoring mechanism and a simple and fast decision algorithm which determines the new values of operating system parameters or the new resource management strategies to be adopted. What quantities should we monitor? As shown in Figs. 7.17(*a*) and (*b*), we may measure work-load parameters (*feed-forward control*) or performance indices (*feedback control*). In general, the former approach would be simpler if the work-load parameters which influence performance were known and their values were available. It would also be more effective since the system would be allowed to prepare itself for the incoming work load. This is seldom the case. However, several self-tuning mechanisms borrow from this approach the idea of relying on the performances of the individual jobs rather than on that of the system to make their decisions. Since those performances are not known a priori, they have to be monitored in real time. Thus, these are *hybrid mechanisms*, having both feedback and feed-forward aspects. They may be schematically represented as in Fig. 7.17(*c*).

Any measurement taken in feedback or hybrid schemes must satisfy an important requirement: There must be a high probability that the measured quantity will remain relatively stable over the period from the instant the tuning decision goes into effect to the earliest instant a new modification can be made. An intrinsic characteristic of feedback control is that regulating decisions are based on measurements of effects whose causes may have disappeared by the time the beneficial consequences of a decision would be felt. If this is the case, the

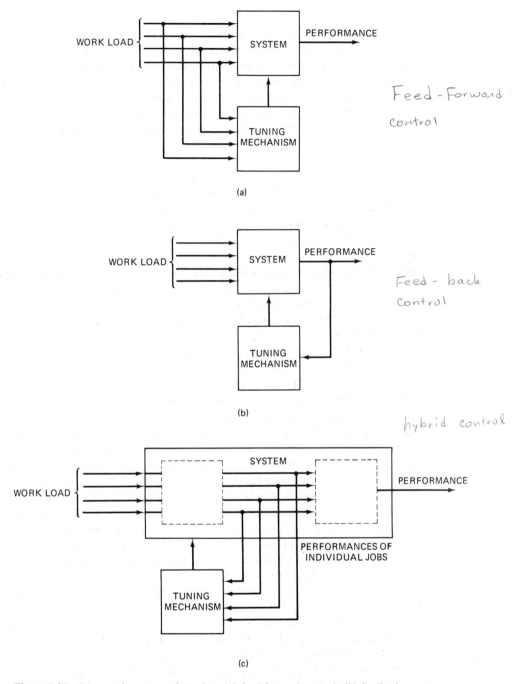

Feed-Forward Control

Feed-back Control

hybrid control

Figure 7.17 Schemes for automatic tuning: (*a*) feed-forward control; (*b*) feedback control; (*c*) hybrid control.

system's performance may be seriously degraded, and instability phenomena may even occur. The above condition requires that the measured data used to select tuning modifications represent the performance of the system or of the individual jobs not only at the time they have been collected but also, with high probability, during the interval in which those modifications will be operational. Immediate corollaries of this requirement are that the diagnosis and therapy phases must be as fast as possible and that tuning decisions should never be based on instantaneous measurements but rather on averages or some more sophisticated predictors of near-future behavior.

Examples of self-tuning mechanisms can be found in many operating systems, especially in the scheduling area. Practical schedulers adopt a variety of techniques to make the system more responsive and, at the same time, better balanced and hence more efficient. Measurements are usually taken at the input (for instance, the time and memory limits declared by the programmers on the job cards) as well as during the processing of the jobs (for example, the system keeps track of the number of time quanta each job has already received). These data are used to assign suitable internal priorities to the jobs, so that the order in which they will receive system resources is, in some sense, optimum. In a batch system, the time and memory limits may be the basis for the assignment of a job to one of several input queues from which the memory manager takes, according to a certain algorithm, the jobs to be loaded into memory. In a time-sharing system, the number of quanta received by a job may be used to determine both the urgency of giving it the next quantum and also, in some cases, a reasonable duration for that quantum. The rationale behind the latter provision is that a job which has already executed for a certain number of quanta is likely to be a long job and, because of the system-wide objective of giving very fast response to trivial requests, should receive longer, less frequent quanta. In reality, the design requirements of a scheduler are so diverse, and its relationships with other resource managers so intricate, that optimizing performance by self-tuning mechanisms incorporated into the scheduler seems still too ambitious a goal. A more appropriate statement is that various self-tuning mechanisms are, often successfully, used in schedulers to improve system performance or some of its aspects. For instance, an important aspect which the scheduler is usually very concerned with is the above-mentioned requirement of providing short turnaround or response times to very short jobs.

Load adjustment is an example of a self-tuning mechanism which may be found in interactive systems [*see* Wilkes (1971)]. In CTSS, for instance, a feedback scheme like the one in Fig. 7.17(*b*) was used. The observed variables were the mean length of all queues and the high-speed drum overflow flag, which is turned on when this drum is full and swapping of user jobs must be directed to the much slower disk [*see* the appendix of Wilkes (1971), written by R. G. Mills]. The controlled variable was the number of users on the system. If this number exceeded the maximum allowable in overload conditions, a user was automatically logged out.

We shall now briefly discuss another important problem in which self-tuning mechanisms can be helpful: the control of the degree of multiprogramming in a virtual-memory system. The objective, as one can immediately understand by looking at curve (c) in Fig. 7.10, is to keep the operating point in the neighborhood of the maximum $\bar{T}$ and to avoid thrashing. Keeping N constant and equal to the value which maximizes $\bar{T}$ would solve the problem if the $\bar{T}(N)$ curve were time-invariant. However, as we may deduce from Fig. 7.12, the fluctuations in the page fault rates of the individual jobs cause the curve to move, and if N is kept constant, the system may well start thrashing as one or more jobs produce so many page faults as to saturate the paging device. We have seen in Section 7.4.1 that variable-space allocation of memory should be expected to alleviate the situation. However, even better results can in principle be obtained if N is allowed to vary. This can be shown by an example.

Let us assume that in the system we analyzed in Example 7.3 all jobs have the same memory referencing behavior characterized by the two parameters $a = 6.25$ pages^{-k} and $k = 2$. We saw in Example 7.3 that the maximum $\bar{T}$ for this system with this work load corresponds to $N = 3$. Figure 7.10, curve (c), tells us that in these conditions $\bar{T} = 2.58$ jobs/s, and Fig. 7.12 tells us that the corresponding total mean page fault rate is about 169 page faults/s. Suppose now that the behavior of the work load suddenly changes, so that this variation can be described as a decrease of a from 6.25 to 2.5 for all jobs. If N remains equal to 3, by (7.14) $\bar{f}$ goes up to about 421 page faults/s, and $\bar{T}$ drops to about 1.5 jobs/s. However, if N is decreased and made equal to 2, $\bar{f}$ drops to 125 page faults/s, and $\bar{T}$ drops only to about 2.08 jobs/s. Thus, the degradation of performance has been reduced from 42% to 19% just by reducing the degree of multiprogramming. This result is easy to check by working graphically on the $\bar{T}$ curves in Fig. 7.12. Note that a self-tuning scheme which would monitor the CPU utilization ρ_1 and try to keep it high by increasing N when ρ_1 goes down would immediately lead to catastrophic thrashing. The reader may see in Fig. 7.12 what would happen, remembering that by (7.14) $\bar{f}$ is proportional to N^{k+1}.

On the other hand, suppose that the work load's behavior improves at some point in time. For example, let a become 2.5 times the original one: $a = 15.625$ pages^{-k}. If $N = 3$, $\bar{f}$ drops to 67.5 page faults/s, and $\bar{T}$ goes up to 2.98 jobs/s. However, if N is increased to 4, we have $\bar{f} = 160$ page faults/s and $\bar{T} = 3.08$ jobs/s. Thus, we obtain an improvement of about 20% instead of 15% by admitting one more job to the primary memory.

It is interesting to see what happens to the page fault rate of each job in the various situations just described. Initially, for $N = 3$, $\bar{f}/N$ is about 56 page faults/s. When a becomes 2.5, $\bar{f}/N$ would go up to 140 if N were kept constant but would become only 62 if N were made equal to 2. When a is 15.625, $\bar{f}/N$ is 22 for $N = 3$ and 40 for $N = 4$. Thus, a control mechanism which tends to keep $\bar{f}/N$ constant (or, at least, to reduce the deviations of $\bar{f}/N$) improves the performance with respect to that of an unregulated system. If the constant reference value of $\bar{f}/N$ is properly chosen, this mechanism prevents thrashing.

Every time $\bar{f}$ increases beyond a certain limit, N is decreased so that $\bar{f}/N$, which by (7.14) is proportional to N^k, remains approximately constant. Figure 7.12 clearly shows that trying to keep $\bar{f}$ constant would be a mistake. Note that the approach of controlling the page fault rate of each individual job allows us to use a hybrid scheme such as that in Fig. 7.17(c). Note also that, as seen in Example 7.10, the condition of identical fault rates is optimum in a variable-space fixed-N environment. And, of course, this is the environment we have here between any two consecutive instants in which N is modified.

How can one keep the page fault rate of a program constant? If the lifetime function represented program behavior adequately, this objective could be reached by allotting the program a space equal to

$$m(a, k) = \left(\frac{\bar{v}_{\text{cpu}}}{a}\bar{e}*\right)^{1/k},$$

(7.45)

where $\bar{e}*$ is the inverse of the page fault rate selected for all programs. Note that in (7.45), as in (7.38), m is proportional to $a^{-1/k}$. As a and k vary, m can be derived from (7.45), and the degree of multiprogramming from $N = M/m$. In practice, the measurement of parameters of a mean-value model, such as a and k, is very difficult. What is especially hard is to satisfy the requirement stated a few paragraphs above. We can, however, try to predict the value of m that will be required in the near future to make the page fault rate of each program approximately equal to the desired one $(1/\bar{e}*)$. Denning (1968a) has suggested that m for each program be estimated by making it equal to the size of the program's working set at the time the estimation is performed.

The *working set* $W(t, \tau)$ of a program at time t, with *window size* τ, is the set of pages referenced by the program during the most recent CPU time interval of length τ. That is, the set of the pages referenced between $t - \tau$ and t. It is very important to keep in mind that this interval is an interval of CPU time actually used by the program (sometimes also called *virtual time*), not an interval of real time.

The *working set strategy* is one of the most successful self-tuning mechanisms ever implemented in computer systems. The space m to be allotted to a program in the near future is estimated at virtual time t as

$$m(t) = w(t, \tau) = |W(t, \tau)|,$$

(7.46)

that is, coincides with the size of the program's working set at that time. N is controlled as a consequence of (7.46). When the sum of all spaces to be allotted to the programs in memory exceeds M, one of the programs is deactivated and swapped out. Vice versa, when this sum is small enough with respect to M that the estimated m (that is, the working set) of another program may fit into primary memory, that program is activated and swapped in. The reader should note that the measurement of $W(t, \tau)$ is not only used to estimate m but also to decide which portion of each program should be kept in memory so that the page fault rate of the program will not differ too much from $1/\bar{e}^*$ in the near future. This portion coincides, in Denning's proposal, with the set of pages $W(t, \tau)$.

Evidently, the choice of τ is crucial. If τ is too large, the space allotted to each program will be too large, and N and $\bar{T}$ will be smaller than would be possible and desirable. If τ is too small, the estimated space requirement for each program will tend to be too small and N too large. Thus, $\bar{T}$ will be degraded by the thrashing phenomenon. In a scheme with constant and uniform window size, the value of τ will have to be chosen by an iterative, manual tuning process and possibly adjusted periodically. However, various proposals of self-tuning mechanisms in which τ is automatically varied [*see* Henderson and Rodriguez-Rosell (1974)] or in which a different value of τ is used for different programs [*see* in Chu and Opderbeck (1972) a scheme with both characteristics] or even for different pages [Prieve (1973)] have been presented. These schemes, capitalizing on the empirical observation that different programs exhibit different behaviors, try to improve the efficiency of the above method in predicting m.

It is also extremely important to note that the working set strategy, as well as its variations, can successfully estimate the space required by each program and hence control the degree of multiprogramming effectively only if the recent-past behavior of a program can be used to predict its near-future behavior. This has indeed been found empirically to be the case for most programs. Referencing patterns are often characterized by the phenomenon of *locality*. Informally, this means that the pages referenced in the recent past have a higher probability of being referenced in the immediate future than the other pages of the program. It is obvious that a very local program, in which the instruction and data references concentrate on a few pages for relatively long periods of time, greatly facilitates a predictive activity like the one of the working set method, which is based on the program's referencing behavior during a backward virtual-time interval. The property of locality and its most interesting aspects will be analyzed in more detail in Chapter 9.

Another self-tuning mechanism to control the degree of multiprogramming in a virtual-memory system has been proposed by Badel et al. (1975). This mechanism is of the feedback type [*see* Fig. 7.17(*b*)]. The measured index is a linear combination of the utilization factors of the various resources during the real-time interval elapsed since the last measurement. Note that measurements are taken at arrivals and departures of jobs or periodically. A biased exponential estimator based on the values of the index measured in the past is then used to make a decision about incrementing, decrementing, or not changing N.

7.4.3 Upgrading Therapies

The modifications of an installation which consist of the replacement or addition of some hardware component have been called *upgrading therapies* in Section 7.2. The term *upgrading* is often employed to denote the replacement of an entire system with a more powerful one, usually from the same manufacturer and frequently from the same family or series of computers. To be consistent with our definitions, we consider this as a case of sole-source procurement, and hence a selection problem, whereas by upgrading we indicate relatively small modifications of the hardware configuration of a given system. These modifications include eliminations of hardware components, in which case a cost-performance improvement is obtained by decreasing cost instead of by increasing performance. Of course, the usual statement about the fuzziness of most of our definitions and their limited ambitions is to be repeated here.

When should an installation manager consider an upgrading instead of a tuning therapy? The conclusion we reached in Section 7.4.1 about this problem was that general rules cannot be established. It is evident that there are cases in which tuning cannot produce any substantial improvements. A system whose resources are uniformly saturated or near saturation is to be upgraded or replaced by a more powerful one unless its work load can be drastically reduced. On the other hand, as mentioned in Section 7.4.1, some tuning therapies may be as expensive as some hardware changes, or even more expensive. When both types of therapies would be possible, the decision is to be made according to a cost-benefit criterion. The future needs of the user community should also be taken into account. Of course, upgrading does not exclude, in fact often requires, tuning (*see* Problem 7.14).

A simple case illustrating the application of a cost-benefit criterion in an upgrading context will now be discussed. In Section 7.3.2, we have formally defined bottlenecks by referring to the partial derivatives of a performance index with respect to the service rates of the various resources. The resource corresponding to the largest derivative was said to create a bottleneck in the system. It is important to realize that the best course of action to improve system performance is not always the one of removing a bottleneck. A bottleneck is certainly to be removed when the system is highly unbalanced. However, if the imbalance is only minor, then it may be more convenient to act on a component which does not create a bottleneck.

Let c_i be the cost of the ith hardware resource, that is, the amount of money invested into it. An increase in the service rate μ_i can generally be obtained by an increment Δc_i of its cost. The two variables μ_i and c_i are usually discrete, and the function $\mu_i(c_i)$ is defined only in a few points corresponding to the models of that type of component available on the market at any given time. Note also that, because of technological progress, $\mu_i(c_i)$ is time-variant. Even if these facts about the function $\mu_i(c_i)$ are ignored, it is perfectly conceivable that, in a mildly unbalanced system in which the jth resource creates a bottleneck, there may be another resource, the ith one, such that

$$\frac{\partial \bar{T}}{\partial c_i} > \frac{\partial \bar{T}}{\partial c_j}. \tag{7.47}$$

In this case, a bigger improvement in performance would be obtained by investing a certain amount of money in the upgrading of the ith resource than the same amount in the upgrading of the jth resource. Note that (7.47) and the statement that the jth resource creates a bottleneck imply that

$$\frac{\partial \mu_i}{\partial c_i} > \frac{\partial \mu_j}{\partial c_j}. \tag{7.48}$$

Based on (7.47), we can formulate a *cost-performance-oriented definition of bottleneck*: The ith resource is said to create a cost-performance bottleneck if (7.47) holds for all $j \neq i$. This definition can be extended to all types of resources, including those whose performance is not characterized by a service rate. For example, it applies to primary-memory space and can be used to decide whether, say, a faster disk or an additional bank of memory should be procured. For all practical purposes, the partial derivatives in the above relationships, due to the difficulty of computing them and to the discrete nature of most of the variables involved, will be replaced by the corresponding incremental ratios.

Example 7.11   The tuned batch version of EXOPE described in several of the previous examples is to be upgraded in order to increase its mean throughput rate $\bar{T}$ by at least 10%, from 3.13 to at least 3.44 jobs/s. The system is the one characterized by the maximum $\bar{T}$ in Fig. 7.7. Its parameters have the values listed in Table 7.3 except for μ_3, which is equal to $16.66\ s^{-1}$, and b_{12}, b_{13}, which are 0.85 and 0.1, respectively. In Section 7.3.2, we saw that the drum, being the faster of the noncentral servers, creates a bottleneck in this situation of maximum $\bar{T}$. However, it would generally be a mistake not to consider any other upgrading possibilities. Table 7.8 summarizes the results of a hypothetical study of the market and our calculations based on the model in Fig. 7.5. The ones included in Table 7.8 are some of the best opportunities available, selected taking into account also the constraints of storage space required and compatibility with the rest of the configuration.

The best mean throughput rate improvements per dollar are offered by memory expansion. If the degradation of the mean turnaround time $\bar{t}$ by 1 s is tolerable, then

Table 7.8

COST-PERFORMANCE ASPECTS OF VARIOUS UPGRADING
THERAPIES EXAMINED IN EXAMPLE 7.11

Component to be upgraded	Amount of upgrading	Cost of upgrading (Δc) [$]	Predicted improvement $(\Delta \bar{T})$ [jobs/s]	Improvement per unit cost $(\Delta \bar{T}/\Delta c)$ [10^3 jobs/$-s]	Predicted variation of $\bar{t}$ [s]
CPU	$\Delta \mu_1 = 53.3\ s^{-1}$	85,000	0.38	0.0044	− 0.17
Drum	$\Delta \mu_2 = 15.3\ s^{-1}$	60,000	0.35	0.0058	− 0.16
Disk	$\Delta \mu_3 = 35.6\ s^{-1}$	35,000	0.09	0.0025	− 0.04
Primary	$\Delta M = 32K$ words	10,000	0.12	0.012	+ 0.24
memory	$\Delta M = 64K$ words	20,000	0.20	0.010	+ 0.50
	$\Delta M = 96K$ words	30,000	0.27	0.009	+ 0.75
	$\Delta M = 128K$ words	40,000	0.32	0.008	+ 1.01

adding $128\,K$ words of primary memory is the cheapest way to achieve the desired performance. The highest improvements of $\bar{T}$ would be obtained by upgrading the drum, which creates a bottleneck. However, replacing the drum would be quite expensive, and this would also be the case of a replacement of the CPU. Of course, it is easy to imagine situations in which upgrading the drum, or even the CPU, would be more convenient than expanding the memory. Good reasons may include the undesirability of a turnaround-time increase and the greater convenience of such a move viewed as the initial step of a much more ambitious upgrading plan. Note also that Table 7.8 does not show the potential of the various solutions with respect to further increases of $\bar{T}$ by tuning. This potential may well be among the considerations for making an upgrading decision. In Problem 7.16, the reader is asked to evaluate it by using the approximate method introduced at the end of Section 7.4.1.   ∎

The methods that can be used to predict the impact of an upgrading therapy on performance are of the same types as those for estimating the effects of tuning modifications. Both simulation and analytic techniques may be applied for this purpose. Since mistakes in upgrading decisions are usually more expensive and harder to correct than mistakes in tuning decisions, the availability of reliable and relatively simple performance prediction methods is even more important in upgrading than in tuning. We shall now extend the discussions of Examples 7.8 and 7.9 to some cases of upgrading therapies.

Example 7.12   The system dealt with in Examples 7.6 and 7.8 (*see* Table 7.5) is to be improved by suitably modifying its hardware configuration. In Example 7.6, our diagnosis, based on the system utilization profile in Fig. 7.15(*a*), recognized in the large system idle time, the channel imbalance, and the insufficient overlaps the three major performance problems of the system. In Example 7.8, we examined the last two problems, in particular channel imbalance, and the effects of some possible cures. A modification which will not increase $\bar{T}$ but might be convenient from a cost-performance viewpoint is suggested by the extremely low utilization of channel 2. What degradation of performance would we have if channel 2 were eliminated and all devices were connected to channel 1? A useful system-time equation for this problem is

$$t_{\text{tot}} = t_{\text{cpu only}} + t_{\text{any channel busy}} + t_{\text{system idle}}, \tag{7.49}$$

with $t_{\text{any channel busy}} = (\rho_2 + \rho_3 - \rho_{23})t_{\text{tot}}$.

Assume that the elimination of channel 2 affects only $t_{\text{any channel busy}}$ which becomes

$$t'_{\text{any channel busy}} = (\rho_2 + \rho_3)t_{\text{tot}}. \tag{7.50}$$

Thus,

$$\frac{t'_{\text{tot}} - t_{\text{tot}}}{t_{\text{tot}}} = \rho_{23} = 0.41\%, \tag{7.51}$$

a very minor decrease of $\bar{T}$, well worth the associated savings.

As mentioned in Example 7.4, a large system idle time may be due to lack of jobs, slow operators, or nonoverlapped disk seeks. A possible upgrading therapy is the replacement of the disks with ones having a higher seek speed. A system-time equation allows us to approximately predict the effect of such a therapy. However, we have to measure the fraction of the total time during which the only system activity is disk seeking. Thus, $t_{\text{system idle}}$ must be broken into the sum of two components: $t_{\text{seek only}}$ and $t_{\text{wait only}}$. The system-time equation is

$$t_{\text{tot}} = t_{\text{cpu only}} + t_{\text{any channel busy}} + t_{\text{seek only}} + t_{\text{wait only}}, \qquad (7.52)$$

and the new equation is

$$t'_{\text{tot}} = t_{\text{cpu only}} + t_{\text{any channel busy}} + \alpha t_{\text{seek only}} + t_{\text{wait only}}, \qquad (7.53)$$

where α is the ratio between the mean seek time of the new disks and the one of the old disks. Hence,

$$\frac{t_{\text{tot}} - t'_{\text{tot}}}{t_{\text{tot}}} = (1 - \alpha)\frac{t_{\text{seek only}}}{t_{\text{tot}}}. \qquad (7.54)$$

If $t_{\text{seek only}}/t_{\text{tot}} = 28\%$ and $\alpha = 0.7$, the improvement given by (7.54) is equal to 8.4%. Note that if devices other than disks (e.g., tapes) were also connected to the channels, the *tape only time* should be isolated from the other components of the system idle time and the improvement factor α applied to the pure *disk seek only time*. ∎

Example 7.13   The UNIVAC 1108 system described in Example 7.9 was measured while being driven by a set of benchmarks prepared by Hughes and Moe (1973). The resulting utilization factors are reported in the ρ_i column of Table 7.9. The reader will notice that they are all quite low. This underutilization of the system components may be due to various causes. If most of it can be explained by system idle time, then the cause is likely to be among those discussed in Example 7.4. However, lack of jobs and slow operators had to be excluded from the possible reasons because of the controlled environment in which the experiment had been performed. Seek only time does not exist in this system but can be replaced by tape search only time among the plausible hypotheses. Another hypothesis which could explain the low utilization of all resources is the one which identifies with the memory the source of a bottleneck. In other words, it is possible that,

Table 7.9
ESTIMATION OF THE EFFECTS OF AN UPGRADING THERAPY:
MEMORY EXPANSION (SEE EXAMPLE 7.13)

Server number i	Resource	Utilization before change ($M = 128K$ words), ρ_i	Estimated utilization after change ($M = 192K$ words), $\hat{\rho}'_i$	Measured utilization after change ρ'_i
1	CPU	0.59	0.79	0.77
2	FH432 drum	0.26	0.35	0.39
3	FH880 drum	0.26	0.35	0.38
4	FASTRAND drum	0.56	0.75	0.74
5	Magnetic tape	0.25	0.33	0.35

Source: Hughes and Moe (1973), by permission of AFIPS, Inc.

due to memory space limitations, the degree of multiprogramming is not sufficiently high so as to keep the system components acceptably busy.

A verification of this hypothesis and an estimation of the improvement that would be obtained by expanding the primary memory can be performed by the approach followed in Example 7.9. A central-server model with $b_{11} = 0$ was used by Hughes and Moe (1973) to derive the curve $\rho_1(N)$. The values of y_2, y_3, y_4, and y_5 needed to calculate ρ_1 for each value of N can be obtained from the measured utilization factors ρ_i [see (7.32)]. From the $\rho_1(N)$ curve, $\bar{N}$ can be derived by interpolation as in Example 7.9. In this case, we have $\bar{N} \cong 2.5$. The memory space that can be allocated to user jobs is $M \cong 64K$ words. The other half of the $128K$-word primary memory is occupied by the EXEC 8 operating system. Note that the measured utilizations also include the operating system overheads, whereas M is the space that may be allotted to the user jobs. However, the assumptions we have to make in order to use a central-server model are so crude that this discrepancy can be accepted or a correction to the measured utilizations may be introduced to account for the overhead.

If M is doubled, we expect $\bar{N} = M/\bar{m}$ to be doubled too. Thus, $\bar{N}' = 5$ for $M' = 128K$ words. The value of $\hat{\rho}_1'$ can be determined from the $\rho_1(N)$ curve assuming that an expansion of memory does not affect either the request probabilities b_{1i} or the service rates of the various components. From $\hat{\rho}_1'$ and the values of y_2, y_3, y_4, and y_5, we can then estimate $\hat{\rho}_2'$, $\hat{\rho}_3'$, $\hat{\rho}_4'$, and $\hat{\rho}_5'$ (see Table 7.9). The measured utilizations, after the upgrading of the memory and under the same set of benchmarks, show a surprisingly good agreement with the predicted values, as can be seen in Table 7.9.

These results also confirm our hypothesis: Doubling the memory size improves $\bar{T}$ (by more than 30%). Note, however, that a central-server model is never completely idle. Therefore, it cannot be used to estimate the effects of modifications which reduce the system idle time. ■

7.5   EVALUATION TECHNIQUES IN IMPROVEMENT STUDIES

Much attention has been given in the previous sections of this chapter to the evaluation techniques used in improvement efforts. In this section, we shall briefly summarize the most important considerations we have made on this topic.

An essential role is played by performance analysis in improvement methodologies. Both to test hypotheses formulated in the diagnosis phase and to predict the consequences of proposed therapies, analyzing with sufficient accuracy the performance of a modified version of the system to be improved is necessary.

Since the system to be improved, by definition, does exist, measurement techniques can be applied to it. However, only seldom are these techniques convenient for analyzing the effects of modifications, since changes to both the hardware and the software of a system are often expensive and risky. Measurement is useful to gather symptoms on a permanent basis (by continuous monitoring) or on an ad hoc basis (for instance, when further evidence is needed to support a hypothesis). It is often not suitable for predictive purposes, even though some limited applications of measurement techniques in this area can be envisaged. Some system modifications can, for example, be simulated by approp-riate work-load modifications, which are relatively easy to introduce if the system is driven by an executable artificial work-load model, especially a set of synthetic jobs. Another application of measurement techniques in this area is the one based on extrapolation. For instance, the effect of adding one memory module may be approximately estimated by excluding one of the memory modules from the system and comparing the new with the original performance. Because of the nonlinearities which exist in the behavior of computer systems, the results of these extrapolations should always be used with great caution.

The prediction of the effects of system modifications is therefore to be made, in most cases, by simulation or analytic techniques. Several examples of the usage of these techniques, especially of the analytic ones, have been discussed in detail in Sections 7.3 and 7.4. The values of the parameters for these models and their calibration can be based on the results of the unmodified system's measurement. As observed in Section 6.4, the relative accuracy of a model is generally more important than its absolute accuracy. In other words, a model which estimates, say, index $\bar{T}$ with a 20% confidence interval but deviations $\Delta\bar{T}$ with a maximum error of 1% may be preferable to a model whose $\bar{T}$ and $\Delta\bar{T}$ have a 5% confidence interval. However, very often what really matters is the order of magnitude of $\Delta\bar{T}$ and a uniform accuracy in the prediction of $\Delta\bar{T}$'s due to different modifications. The considerations made in Sections 6.3.1 and 6.4 on performance comparison and its influence on the choice of the evaluation techniques to be used can be repeated for improvement studies. In these studies, however, most of the problems are made much simpler than they are in selection studies by the the fact that the systems to be compared are quite similar to each other.

7.6   WORK-LOAD CHARACTERIZATION IN IMPROVEMENT STUDIES

The observations that improvement studies require performance compari-sons to be made and that these comparisons raise simpler problems than those for selection purposes are valid also for the work-load characterization aspects of improvement investigations.

The comparison of the unmodified system with a modified version of it requires that the work-load model under which the study is performed be transportable from the original to the modified system. Thus, the work-load model must be *modification-independent*. This requirement is usually much easier to satisfy in improvement than in selection studies. The changes considered in improvement studies are minor with respect to the often radical differences between the alternatives to be compared for selection. A lower-level characteri-zation, even one in terms of physical resources, will generally suffice, provided that the changes to be considered do not affect the work-load parameters. For example, if we do not rule out the possibility of changing the CPU, our work-load model should not represent the computational demands of the jobs by their CPU times. A less CPU-dependent characterization, such as an instruction mix or, even better, a statement mix, should be preferred.

The main reason of this requirement is that, as discussed in Section 6.3.1, the comparison of two versions of a system is to be performed under the same work loads so as to eliminate an important source of undesired variation. This objective should be achieved by making the two work loads identical at the level of the information-processing needs of the users (*see* Section 6.5). If we were able to predict the effects of a change on the user community, this approach would normally produce two different work-load models at lower levels. However, since obtaining this is still beyond the state of the art, work-load models which are identical at a lower level are used. If the system modifications whose effects have to be examined are not too drastic, the two lower-level models we have just mentioned would probably be only slightly different from each other, and the assumption that they are identical is not likely to have a big impact on the results in most cases. It can be argued that the approximations usually made, especially when using analytic techniques, are so crude that ignoring the reactions of the user community to a change in the system is perfectly legitimate. In fact, the surprising agreement with experimental results obtained by very gross analytic models (see, for instance, Examples 7.9 and 7.13) would tend to support this view. These reactions cannot, however, be ignored when the modification of the system is intended to influence the work load through them.

The arguments which justify the use of lower-level (e.g., physical-resource-oriented) work-load models in conjunction with simulators or analytic models of the system apply also to the work-load models to be used in measurement experiments. In particular, sets of synthetic jobs are well suited to most of the measurement aspects of improvement studies. The flexibility of synthetic jobs may be useful when system modifications require that the work-load model be modified or when, as mentioned in Section 7.5, changes in the work-load model are used to simulate system changes. What was said above about the choice of the level at which the jobs will be characterized should be kept in mind also when designing an executable work-load model, and not only an analytic or simulation model, for an improvement study.

PROBLEMS

7.1. Study the shape of the function $\bar{T}(\mu_1, \mu_2)$ for a two-server central-server model with $b_{11} = 0.1$, $b_{12} = 0.9$, and $N = 3$. Draw some of its contour lines in the (μ_1, μ_2) plane, and show the regions of the plane in which μ_1 causes a bottleneck, those in which μ_2 causes a bottleneck, and those in which the model is balanced. Given a value of μ_1, is there a value of μ_2 which optimizes $\bar{T}$?

7.2. You are given a system whose hardware configuration is composed of a CPU, a primary memory, one disk controller and drive, one tape controller and drive, and one I/O controller driving a card reader and a printer. You are also given a set of synthetic jobs which constitutes a good model of the installation's work load. The synthetic jobs are physical-resource-oriented; that is, they have been constructed as described in Example 5.8. Design a series of measurement experiments, based on the use of the work-load model, intended to identify the resource or resources which create bottlenecks and to improve the system's mean throughput rate by the successive removal of the bottlenecks detected.

7.3. Following the conceptual approach illustrated in Section 7.3.2, define bottlenecks for an open-network model of a computer system. Take as the primary performance index $\bar{t}$, the mean turnaround time whose formula, in the exponential case, is given in (4.86). Assume that the system includes a CPU, a drum, and a disk, having parameter values as in Table 7.2, and an I/O server with $\mu_4 = 5\,\mathrm{s}^{-1}$. Also, assume that the mean arrival rate is $\lambda = 2$ jobs/s and that jobs can terminate only after receiving service from the disk (i.e., $b_{21} = 1$). Using the model in Fig. 4.16, determine which one of the servers causes a bottleneck in the system. Compare your results with the findings of Example 7.1, where a similar system was modeled by a closed queuing network.

7.4. Using the curves in Fig. 7.12 and the parameter values for which they were drawn (*see* Example 7.3), construct point by point the corresponding $\bar{T}(N)$ and $\bar{t}(N)$ curves. Show that these coincide with curves (c) and (d) in Fig. 7.10.

7.5. Perform an analytic study of the open-network model constructed in Problem 7.3 to see whether the following conclusions we arrived at in Section 7.3.2 hold:
(a) when all utilization factors are identical, the system is generally not balanced, and vice versa;
(b) if only b_{12} and b_{13} are modifiable, the performance has an optimum corresponding to a particular pair of values of these parameters;
(c) the point of optimum performance, if it exists, does not generally coincide either with the point of balance or with the point of uniform utilization.

7.6. Generalize the results of Example 7.5 regarding the amounts of overlap between pairs and triples of resources in a central-server model [equations (7.18) through (7.24)] to the case of a model with s servers. Try to express the overlap probabilities $\rho_{ij...k}$ as functions of utilizations $\rho_i, \rho_j, \ldots, \rho_k$, lower-order overlap probabilities $\rho_{ij}, \ldots, \rho_{hk}, \rho_{ijh}, \ldots$, and the normalization function $G(N)$.

7.7. Construct a Kiviat graph for the system studied in Problem 7.3. Decide the variables to be reported on the axes (whose number is not necessarily restricted to 8) so as to facilitate the diagnosis of the system, in particular the detection of bottlenecks. Formulate improvement hypotheses based on the Kiviat graph you have constructed. State whether additional analyses would be required to confirm the validity of the hypotheses and, if so, what data would be needed for this verification.

7.8. Draw the Kiviat graph of the uniform utilization system whose parameters have the values in Table 7.3 except for μ_3, which is equal to $16.66\,\mathrm{s}^{-1}$. Report on the axes the same variables as in Fig. 7.14. Using these conventions, draw the Kiviat graph of the same system at the point of optimum $\bar{T}$, i.e., for $b_{12} = 0.85$ and $b_{13} = 0.1$. Compare the two graphs, and comment on the usefulness of Kiviat graphs as tools for coarse improvement and for fine improvement.

7.9. Using a system utilization profile like those in Fig. 7.13, formulate improvement hypotheses for the virtual-memory system described in Example 7.3 (note that $\mu_3 = 16.66 \text{ s}^{-1}$) with $N = 5$. Predict from a suitable system-time equation the impact on $\bar{T}$ of a 20% increment of the paging drum's rotational speed (which increases R_{dr} and decreases t_{wdr}).

7.10. Repeat Problem 7.9 assuming $N = 2$.

7.11. Analyze the conceptual relationship between the two definitions of bottleneck given in (7.3) and (7.25) in the case of the model in Fig. 7.5. Assume that the job parameters $w_1, \ldots, w_v$ referred to in definition (7.25) represent the global demands of CPU time, drum time, and disk time of each job. Also, instead of $\bar{T}$, make the mean job turnaround time $\bar{t}$ appear as the performance index in (7.3), and replace d and w_i in (7.25) by their averages over all the jobs.

7.12. Our calculations in Example 7.10 showed that an improvement of about 5% is expected to result from replacing the equal-size memory partitioning strategy in the model of Example 7.3 with a variable-size strategy based on (7.38) for $N = 3$. What would be the expected improvement for $N = 5$?

7.13. Repeat Problem 7.12 assuming $\mu_3 = 8.33 \text{ s}^{-1}$ as in Table 7.3. Calculate also the expected improvements in $\bar{T}$ and $\bar{t}$ for this value of μ_3 and $N = 3$ as in Example 7.10.

7.14. A multiprogramming system contains one CPU, one drum, and one disk. The parameters of a central-server model of the system are $\mu_1 = 100 \text{ s}^{-1}$, $\mu_2 = 50 \text{ s}^{-1}$, $\mu_3 = 20 \text{ s}^{-1}$, $b_{12} = 0.6$, $b_{13} = 0.3$, and $N = 5$. The performance of the system, represented by its $\bar{T}$, is to be improved. In the improvement effort, at most $50,000 can be spent. For simplicity, assume that b_{12} and b_{13} can be varied at no cost (keeping their sum constant) and that μ_1, μ_2, and μ_3 can be given continuous increments with the following unit costs: $\Delta c_1/\Delta \mu_1 = 1400 \text{ \$-s}$, $\Delta c_2/\Delta \mu_2 = 3200 \text{ \$-s}$, and $\Delta c_3/\Delta \mu_3 = 1000 \text{ \$-s}$. Also, assume that the memory size is not a modifiable parameter. Using the curves in Fig. 7.16, or an equivalent analytic approach, determine the amounts you would spend in increasing μ_1, μ_2, and μ_3. Does the final value of $\bar{T}$ depend on whether the modifications of the μ_i's are determined before or after those of b_{12} and b_{13}? Would it make sense to optimize $\bar{T}$ acting on b_{12} and b_{13} first, then increase the μ_i's, and then optimize again?

7.15. How would you estimate the capacity of a system of which you know only the utilization profile? Assume that the profile in Fig. 7.13(a) is given. Getting inspiration from the profile in Fig. 7.13(b), which corresponds to the maximum value of $\bar{T}$ obtainable by varying b_{12} and b_{13} only, try to determine an approach to approximately estimate the capacity. Test your ideas on the profile in Fig. 7.15 (a) and the data in Table 7.5.

7.16. Referring to the upgrading problem discussed in Example 7.11, determine whether increasing the size of the memory by $128K$ words would be more or less convenient than replacing the drum by a faster one from the viewpoint of the potential further increases of $\bar{T}$ by tuning. Use the approximations introduced at the end of Section 7.4.1 for computing the capacity. Comment on the magnitude of the errors you expect from the use of these approximations in the calculations required by this problem.

7.17. Construct a system utilization profile for the system studied in Example 7.11, and calculate, using an appropriate system-time equation, the improvements in $\bar{T}$ which would be produced by the increments of μ_1, μ_2, and μ_3 listed in Table 7.8. Compare these improvements with those given in Table 7.8, which were calculated by a central-server model, and discuss the reasons for any major discrepancies you may find.

7.18. What would you think of a self-tuning mechanism which would base its control of the degree of multiprogramming in a virtual-memory system on periodic measurements of the lengths of the paging-drum queues? Assume that the paging drum has eight sectors and one queue for each sector. The mechanism determines periodically the sum of the queue lengths and selects the value of N for the next time interval according to the value of this sum. Devise reasonable policies for
   (a) making the selection of N (would you consider associating a value of N to each range of queue lengths, or allowing N to be incremented or decremented at most by 1 at each decision point, or adopting some other policy?);
   (b) selecting the job (or jobs) to be deactivated when N is to be decreased;
   (c) distributing a freed region of the primary memory among the jobs which are still active when N is decreased;
   (d) determining a good sampling period.

7.19. In Examples 7.3 and 7.10, we considered a paging drum of the same type as the drum used in the batch version of EXOPE discussed, for instance, in Example 7.1, that is, a drum with a single queue of requests to be serviced according to the FCFS policy. In practice, a paging drum is usually organized in a different manner because of the speed requirements a virtual-memory system imposes on the second level of its memory hierarchy. The drum is divided into sectors, and a page can be transferred in or out during the time a single sector takes to pass under the magnetic heads. A separate queue is maintained for each sector, so that one page transfer may take place during each sector time interval. State what effects on the thrashing curve of the system you would expect to result from the replacement of the FCFS drum with a paging drum like the one just described. Could the central-server model used in Examples 7.3 and 7.10 be employed to predict these effects quantitatively? Would the modifications to be made to the model still allow us to obtain a closed-form solution?

8

Performance Evaluation in Design Problems

8.1 DESIGN PROBLEMS

The third category of problems to which performance evaluation techniques are applied, among those listed in Section 1.5, is the one of design problems. The boundaries of this category are as vague as those of the others. The definition given in Section 1.5 encompasses the problems which are encountered when one tries to determine how a computer system capable of satisfactorily handling certain information-processing tasks can be constructed. The fundamental feature which characterizes design with respect to selection is the creativity required. Selection is restricted to what is available on a certain marketplace at a particular moment, whereas design consists of creating a system which did not exist before in order to meet some needs not satisfied by what is available. Of course, designing a system does not usually mean that the system is to be created from nothing. Normally, the designer will make proper use of preexisting components, which will be combined in a new fashion to meet new requirements, or old requirements in a more satisfactory way. These components will have to be selected among those available. If no component exists which can perform a certain function according to the designer's desires, a new component will have to be designed and implemented using, if possible, available components.

Improvement problems, like selection problems, deal with finished products. However, the process of modifying a system in order to improve it is conceptually

396

close to the one of designing the system. After all, optimization is an important aspect of design, and designing systems to be tailored later to a particular environment is common practice in computer systems engineering (*see* Sections 7.2 and 7.4.1). Not only are design studies often accompanied by selection and improvement studies, but sometimes the need for a design study arises from the results of improvement or selection efforts. For instance, an organization may decide to directly design the configuration for its installation if a competitive selection study has failed to produce acceptable results, or to design a new operating system for an existing configuration if an improvement study has indicated the convenience of such a decision.

All design problems can ideally be stated as follows: Produce an *implementable description* of a system which satisfies the given *design specifications*. The output of a design study is a description which can be understood by a group of implementors and used by them to actually construct the system. This description is obtained by the designers from the design specifications, which may be formulated by the designers themselves or by some "customer" or by both. In the case of computer systems, as for all engineering products, there are three types of specifications: *functional specifications*, *performance specifications*, and *cost specifications*. In general, as seen in Section 1.4, functional specifications refer to what the system is supposed to be able to do (for example, to correctly process the information entering the system through certain media, to store it, to output results in a certain form, to interact with its users in specified ways, to protect the privacy and the integrity of their information, and so on). Performance specifications prescribe how well the functions defined by functional specifications should be performed (for example, how rapidly, how efficiently, how cost-effectively). Finally, cost specifications usually consist of the requirement that the total cost of the system be minimized under the constraints imposed by the other types of specifications. It should be noted that the total cost includes the costs of the hardware and software components as well as those of the design and production of the system. If the system is designed for in-house use, the total cost should also include the running and maintenance costs.

The very broad meaning that the term *performance* may be given has already been commented on in Section 1.1. We repeat here that as performance specifications we shall consider only those expressible in terms of our restricted definition of performance, that is, of the types of indices introduced in Section 1.4. Thus, when referring to performance specifications, we shall mean statements such as the following: The mean instruction execution rate of the system must be greater than a certain minimum; the mean throughput rate produced while processing a specified work load must be at least equal to a given value and must not be degraded by more than a certain percentage under a defined peak work load; the mean response time to editing commands and its standard deviation must not be greater than certain maximum values; the number of active editing terminals which the system can support with a given mean response time must be greater than a given minimum; and so on.

These performance specifications closely resemble those included in the requests for proposals which are prepared for the vendors in competitive selections (*see* Section 6.2.1). Actually, a request for proposals is the basis for the design study performed by each vendor in order to satisfy the prospective customer's needs. This is an example of a design study undertaken for a specific installation. As we saw in Chapter 6, the work load of that installation may be known in more or less detail but is always relatively well known with respect to the work loads for which systems are to be designed in a number of other cases. Often, the work load which a system will have to process is so vaguely known at design time that it cannot be specified much beyond the stages of its intended broad field of application (e.g., scientific computation, business data processing) and of the required "size" or "power" of the system (characterized by such adjectives as "large," "medium," or "small"). In these cases, quantitative performance specifications like those mentioned in the previous paragraph, which must explicitly refer to a given work load to be meaningful, either cannot be used or have to be defined with respect to some fictitious work load believed by the designers to represent the system's spectrum of applications.

The situation just described arises when a system is to be designed not for a single, specific installation or for a family of similar installations but for a large number of applications whose maximum common set of properties can only be characterized by such generic descriptors as "large scientific and engineering calculations." To be more specific would require knowing each individual installation where the system will be running or, at least, restricting quite drastically the class of installations for which the system is being designed. This would mean that a much greater number of much more specialized computers should be designed and constructed, an obviously inconvenient course of action for a manufacturer. On the other hand, the design of a system, whose replicas are supposed to behave satisfactorily in many installations with completely different characteristics, cannot be based on such a vague and superficial definition of its work load. Actually, a system which is all things to all users is not even conceivable.

A way out of this dilemma is what we could call, simplifying the complexities of the real world as we often do, the *three-stage approach* (*see* Fig. 8.1). In the first stage, manufacturers do not design systems but rather *families of components*. These include one or more CPU's, various primary- and secondary-memory device types, communications equipment, I/O channels, device controllers, and so

Figure 8.1   Three-stage approach to computer system design. The knowledge of the particular work load to be processed by the system increases substantially as one proceeds from the first to the third stage.

on. Some of these components may even be purchased from other manufacturers instead of being designed, developed, and implemented in house. The purposes of a family of components are not usually stated very precisely. In fact, these components are the building blocks to be used in the second stage, the one of _customization._ The second stage is characterized by a much more detailed knowledge of the work load, due to the fact that a system is now to be assembled for a specific installation. Thus, performance indices can be defined and the satisfaction of performance requirements can be among the objectives of the design study. This study is performed either by the customer or by the vendor and usually results in the selection of hardware and software components for the system. However, the insufficient specification of the work load and the inadequacy of design methods make the third stage necessary. This stage, which is called _system tuning_ (*see* Section 7.4.1), is performed under the real work load after the system has been installed.

The three-stage approach, which was adopted rather early in the history of computers and is still the predominant one, affects the design of system software as well as that of hardware components and configurations. For the reasons mentioned above, an operating system is often not designed for a single, specific installation but for a large class of installations. Some operating systems support various processing modes, and most of them are capable of managing a number of different configurations which can be built by combining components from a given family. The required flexibility is often obtained at the expense of efficiency. The objective of generality makes an operating system bigger; more expensive to design, write, and debug; more resource-consuming; and less reliable than one tailored to a particular configuration and application. On the other hand, its possible use in a large number of installations, allowing its cost to be distributed over these installations, economically justifies this practice.

In this chapter, we shall for the most part be concerned with the second stage of the three-stage approach. The first stage encompasses the design of hardware components, a topic which is very interesting from technological and engineering viewpoints but not one of central concern in this book. The performance characteristics of the components are supposed to satisfy, compatibly with the existing economical and technological constraints, the desires of the system designers. These designers often play an important role in component design. They not only use the available components as building blocks but stimulate with their requirements the development of new and more convenient pieces of equipment. Among the hardware components, CPU's are those which need the attention of system designers the most because of their role in the execution of the programs which constitute both the work load and the operating system. However, in spite of its impact on a system's performance, CPU design will not be dealt with here. We shall be concerned only with the applications of performance evaluation to the problems of combining various components together and organizing their activities so as to meet some given performance specifications of the types encountered in the second stage. Our considerations will include some performance aspects of operating system design, even though this activity should be considered as being carried out during the first stage. Tuning will not be treated, since it is discussed in Section 7.4.1.

8.2 DESIGN METHODOLOGIES

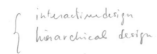

In Section 8.1, we outlined the three-stage approach which is frequently taken to design and implement computer systems. Rather than creating systems for specific installations from scratch, computer manufacturers assemble kits of components which are then used by them or sometimes by the customers to construct systems with characteristics suitable for each particular environment. The opposite approach, which consists of designing the components after a system has been specified in detail for an individual installation, is followed only in special cases. It is for the most part restricted to some components (such as pieces of system software or of equipment which cannot be found on the market) and to research environments or one-of-a-kind applications.

In any case, independently of whether the three-stage approach is adopted or not, there are two basically different philosophies with which design problems can be attacked. Various terms can be used to define these philosophies. The first can be called *bottom-up*, or *horizontal*, or *inside out*, or *iterative* design, and the second, *top-down, or vertical*, or *outside in*, or *hierarchical* design. None of these terms is completely satisfactory, but, since a choice is to be made, we shall choose the adjectives iterative and hierarchical. Design methodologies are based on one of these two philosophies or, more often, on both mixed together in various proportions.

Iterative design consists of generating an initial solution to the design problem and of transforming it into an acceptable one by iterative modifications. Thus, design is viewed as a trial-and-error process, which produces by successive approximations a system satisfying the given specifications. The design cycle is represented in Fig. 8.2. This figure raises some questions which we shall briefly discuss, emphasizing the performance viewpoint.

First, how does one design the initial system? The design specifications summarize what is needed. The knowledge of the characteristics of the available components, or technologies, and of the solutions adopted in similar installations will usually be exploited by the designer in this phase. As we shall see in Section 8.3.1, analytic models, even if they are extremely simple, may be very helpful. What is wanted is, first of all, a reasonable approximation to an acceptable configuration. The choice of the initial solution often has a profound influence on the outcome of the design process and may even make it impossible or very expensive. Thus, it is important that this choice be made with great care and that the available techniques and tools be used to increase the probability of success. When the initial configuration is specified, the operating system for it must be selected or designed. The initial hardware–software system is to be determined

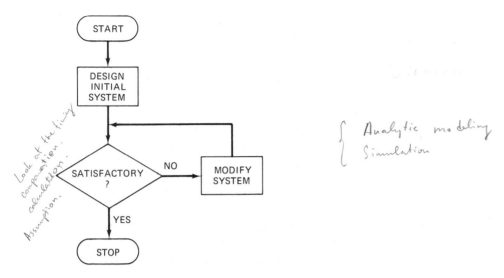

Figure 8.2   Flowchart of the iterative design methodology.

with enough detail to make iterative performance analyses possible and meaningful.

Second, <u>how</u> can we determine whether the system we have arrived at is satisfactory? This verification must be made for all specifications, including the functional and economical ones. From the viewpoint of performance, the design is to be tested by some performance analysis technique. Until the system is implemented in some form, measurement techniques cannot be used. Analytic modeling or simulation will therefore have to be employed. The work-load model or models by which the system model will be driven, as well as the performance indices of interest, should be derived from the performance specifications. Simulation will often be preferred to analytic techniques, in spite of its higher cost, because of the greater degree of detail and flexibility it offers. Perhaps only a computer manufacturer has the resources needed to do performance analysis by measurement techniques since the earliest stages of a design study. In the case of a manufacturer, all components are usually available and can be connected together with relative ease; measurement tools and data reduction facilities are ready or their procurement or construction is easy to justify; work-load models, in the form of sets of benchmarks prepared by the customers or even in the form of executable traces, gathered by the designers themselves, are also generally available. The next sections, and in particular Section 8.5, will contain some more details on the use of the various evaluation techniques in system design.

Third, how can we determine the modifications to be made to a design which does not satisfy the specifications? The reader has certainly noticed the conceptual similarity between iterative design and iterative improvement (compare, for example, Fig. 8.2 with Fig. 7.1). If we consider only performance requirements, we can say that the iterative design process consists of the improvement of an initial version of the system by successive modifications, made with the objective of satisfying the given specifications. Thus, most of our discussion of improvement methodologies in Chapter 7, including the approaches to diagnosis and therapy, applies to this phase of iterative design. The basic philosophy is still the one of a guided exploration, in the space of design parameters, of the hypersurfaces representing performance indices, with optimization (or at least improvement) purposes. Improvement hypotheses are formulated and tested. The results of the tests often provide guidance for the formulation of future hypotheses. The study by Nielsen (1967), partially described in Example 7.7 as an application of simulation to an improvement problem, was in fact an iterative design study, since its purpose was to design the configuration of a time-sharing system to be installed.

Hierarchical design is based on the opposite philosophy. The structure of the system and the characteristics of its components are derived directly from the design specifications, so that the result is guaranteed to be functionally correct as well as performance-wise and cost-wise satisfactory. In its pure form, hierarchical design does not require any verifications, except perhaps those which may be necessary to eliminate possible doubts about the correct application of the design procedures. From a performance viewpoint, this philosophy would in principle require the application of performance synthesis methods (*see* Section 1.4). Unfortunately, these methods, which would allow system configuration and parameters to be derived directly, though possibly in several steps, from performance specifications, are not well developed, except for extremely simple cases. However, hierarchical design methods are being studied and proposed with the main objective of ensuring the correctness of the designs of complex systems. It may therefore be possible to introduce performance considerations into these methods, and in any case the study of their performance aspects is important.

The methods being proposed consist of the gradual specification of the system to be designed through a hierarchy of *levels of abstraction*. As discussed in more detail in Section 8.4, each level of abstraction corresponds to a description of the system characterized by a certain degree of abstraction from reality. That is, certain real features (e.g., implementation constraints, external influences) are ignored at a level in order to explore some design issues on which the neglected aspects are not expected to have an appreciable influence. These features will then be introduced gradually at lower levels, so that their effects may be properly taken into account and the design may proceed to stages of further refinement. In going from a higher to a lower level of abstraction, the degree of detail of the system's description increases, and often (but not always) the various modules constituting a description at the higher level are decomposed into interconnected submodules at the lower level. Ideally, at the end of the process, the lowest level should yield a description which can immediately be translated into an implementation. This description should be in terms of hardware components which exist or can be designed by equipment designers and of software components which can be coded by systems programmers.

Note that the distinction between hardware and software is introduced as late as possible in a hierarchical design procedure. This is consistent with the philosophy that holds this distinction to be conceptually unimportant, as demonstrated by the fact that the boundaries between the domains of hardware and software are very sensitive to technological progress and therefore constantly changing. In iterative designs, the hardware–software distinction is already present in the initial system, although some latitude for change is in principle offered by the modification phase of the design cycle, especially before the implementation of the prototype. We should realize that in both iterative and hierarchical designs, this flexibility is always limited if only the available equipment can be used. However, as shown in Section 8.3.3, the investigation of hardware–software trade-offs may be very fruitful even under these rather severe constraints. The time of *total system design*, that is, of a purely hierarchical procedure with no component constraints, has certainly not come yet. On the other hand, the time in which the hardware was designed first, with no concern for the software, and the software was "added" to it later has hopefully gone forever.

We said in Section 8.1 that there are three types of specifications: functional, performance, and cost specifications. What is the role of performance evaluation in the two design methodologies we have summarized in this section? This question will be investigated from various points of view in the rest of this chapter. However, we can repeat here the general observations made in Section 6.2.2 about the role of performance evaluation in selection problems. That is, performance in our restricted sense is a very important factor but by no means the only one to be taken into account when designing a system. The impact of the system on the organization in which it will have to be installed cannot usually be reduced to the system's throughput rate or response time. The image it will present to the users (languages, interfaces, ease of use, availability, security), the changes in the organization's procedures it will bring about, and even the prestige which may derive from installing it have to be considered, sometimes as seriously as the values of performance indices and sometimes even more.

8.3 PERFORMANCE CONSIDERATIONS IN ITERATIVE DESIGN

8.3.1 Analytic Techniques for the Design of an Initial Configuration

Starting with a good initial system enhances the probability of success of an iterative design procedure. It also reduces the number of cycles required and therefore the cost and the duration of the effort. However, the design of the initial system should not be too expensive or time-consuming; otherwise the advantages we gain in the iterative part of the procedure might be offset, or perhaps even more than offset, by the increased complexity of the initial phase. It is clear that a reasonable compromise must be found between the two conflicting requirements that the initial design be "good" and that it be relatively quick and cheap to perform. How can we achieve both goals?

There are no complete and widely accepted procedures to produce a first-approximation design of a general-purpose computer system. What would be required is a sequence of steps, involving relatively simple calculations, which could be followed to derive values of system parameters and, possibly, suggestions about various organizational aspects of the system (for example, the topology of the hardware configuration, the placement and organization of files, the schemes for resource management). In other, more established fields of engineering, approximate methods of this type exist, and designers make widespread use of them. In computer engineering, only for those types of systems whose work load is easy to characterize have these methods been devised and successfully introduced. In such systems, most notably those dedicated to real-time applications such as airline reservations, the work load, consisting of a single or very few types of transactions, is statistically stable and relatively predictable. The analytic design procedures which have been proposed for them make a complete study of various design trade-offs and the optimization of cost-performance indices possible [*see*, for instance, Martin (1967) and Stimler (1969)]. A conclusion easily drawn from the observation that systematic design methods exist only for such systems is that, even in the area of design, the major problem yet to be solved is the one of work-load characterization.

For all other types of systems, there are some partial methods, which deal with only some of the aspects of the system to be designed, and a large variety of analytic models, whose solutions provide designers with useful formulas or diagrams. Most of these models are applicable to components or parts of the system, or they encompass only some of the system's features. Until global system models are introduced, or at least coherent sets of existing models are put together, performance synthesis methods will not be available. An important step in this direction is represented by hierarchical modeling techniques [*see* Browne et al. (1975)]. However, the partial models we have mentioned, especially the simplest ones, can be used to design the initial configuration, as we shall show by a few examples in this section. Unfortunately, as stated above, complete systematic procedures are missing even for initial system design. Thus, our examples will discuss some particular, though important, problems. The emphasis will as usual be on the use of performance evaluation techniques, in this case analytic techniques.

Example 8.1 A multiprogramming EXOPE system, to be used in fast-turnaround batch mode in medium-small installations, is to be designed. We assume that the designers have already decided that the initial configuration will include one CPU, one drum or head-per-track disk (for the nonresident portion of the operating system, the compilers and utility programs, and temporary user files), one movable-arm disk (for buffering input and output information and storing permanent user files), one card reader, and one line printer. The drum and the disk are to be interfaced to the memory via two independent controllers. In this example we are concerned with determining the approximate values of the component parameters. These values should provide some guidance in the selection of the equipment and in the design or selection of the system software. The problem we are considering here is sometimes called, for evident reasons, a *sizing problem*.

A first-approximation sizing of the CPU, primary memory, and secondary storage devices for a multiprogramming system may be made by using a simple system model such as a central-server queuing network. Since this is a closed network, only the jobs which are loaded in primary memory at any given time, and the resources they are using or waiting for, can be modeled. In our case, the model will consist of three servers (*see* Fig. 7.5). The degree of multiprogramming N, assumed to be constant, is directly related to the primary memory size, as shown in Table 7.3. The servers are characterized by their service rates μ_i, which, as may be seen in Table 7.3, depend on the devices' performance parameters (but also on some work-load parameters).

Table 8.1
WORK-LOAD PARAMETERS AND
PERFORMANCE SPECIFICATIONS FOR
THE DESIGN IN EXAMPLE 8.1

	Value
Work-load parameters[*]	
$\bar{L}$	0.9×10^6 instructions
$\bar{n}_{cpu}$	10
$\bar{r}_{dr}$	8000 words
$\bar{n}_{dr}$	6
$\bar{r}_{ds}$	12,000 words
$\bar{n}_{ds}$	3
Performance specifications	
$\bar{T}_{min}$	1 job/s
$\bar{t}_{max}$	6 s

[*] For symbol definitions, see Tables 7.2 and 7.3.

An analysis of the user needs and of the expected work load should give us the information displayed in Table 8.1. The table contains values assumed to have resulted from such an analysis. The usual assumptions about the work load (statistically identical jobs, exponential distributions) will, of course, be made. The performance specifications for that portion of the system represented in the model are also included in Table 8.1. The two performance indices $\bar{T}$ and $\bar{t}$ are not those of the whole system but those which characterize this portion. For instance, $\bar{t}$ is the mean residence time of a job (more properly, of a job step) in primary memory. Note that the model's performance is specified by the inequalities

$$\bar{T} \geq \bar{T}_{min}, \qquad \bar{t} \leq \bar{t}_{max} \tag{8.1}$$

and that the values of $\bar{T}_{min}$ and $\bar{t}_{max}$ are given in Table 8.1. Our present objective is the one of determining reasonable values for μ_1, μ_2, μ_3, and N (that is, the primary memory size M) so that the performance specifications are satisfied and the cost is minimum. To solve the problem, at least two courses of action are open to us. One is to consider a number of available alternatives for each component being considered and to calculate performance and cost of all possible combinations of these alternatives. The optimum solution will be the cheapest one among those which satisfy the performance requirements. The other approach consists of assuming a cost model and determining the values of the parameters which minimize the total cost without worrying about the availability of pieces of equipment characterized by those values. Then, once the optimum solution has been found, we try to approximate it by considering only available components.

Since applying the first approach is conceptually straightforward, we briefly illustrate how one might proceed with the second. As a simple cost model, we shall take the one expressed by Grosch's law (6.11) for the servers, that is,

$$\mu_i = K_i C_i^2 \quad (i = 1, 2, 3), \tag{8.2}$$

and a proportional relationship for memory:

$$C_M = K_M M = K_N N. \tag{8.3}$$

The most serious justification for these models is their simplicity. However, economies of scale have been found to exist for the processing speeds of CPU's (to which μ_1 is proportional) and for mean access and transfer times of drums [see Sharpe (1969)]. In particular, in a regression study performed by Sharpe the cost of fixed-head rotating devices was found to be proportional to $\bar{\imath}_a^{-0.655} t_{wdr}^{-0.089}$, where $\bar{\imath}_a$ is the mean access time. On the other hand, the economies of scale for memory size are much smaller and have been neglected in (8.3). Note that since μ_i also depends on the work load, so does K_i.

The total cost of the equipment for the modeled portion of the system is

$$C = h_1\sqrt{\mu_1} + h_2\sqrt{\mu_2} + h_3\sqrt{\mu_3} + h_N N. \tag{8.4}$$

Cost C is to be minimized. The coefficients in (8.4) should be computed from the costs and the characteristics of suitable commercial components as well as from the work-load parameters in Table 8.1. We shall choose $h_1 = h_2 = h_3 = 10,000$ dollars-s$^{1/2}$ and $h_N = 5000$ dollars (on the basis of partitions of 16K words, 32 bits/word).

From the data in Table 8.1, the equations in Table 7.3, and (7.2), we have $b_{11} = 0.1$, $b_{12} = 0.6$, $b_{13} = 0.3$, and

$$N_{max} = \bar{\imath}_{max} \bar{T}. \tag{8.5}$$

For $\bar{T} = \bar{T}_{min}$ (we intend to increase $\bar{T}$ over this minimum by iterative modifications), (8.5) yields $N_{max} = 6$.

To simplify our task further, we eliminate one of the unknowns by making $\rho_2 = \rho_3$. Even though we have learned in Section 7.3.2 that the optimum $\bar{T}$ corresponds to a situation in which the faster noncentral servers are more utilized than slower ones, we choose to leave the search for the optimum $\bar{T}$ to the iterative part of the design and to the tuning phase. After all, the approximations we have made in estimating the values in Table 8.1 are so crude that a more accurate optimization method would probably be useless. We could also take into account what we know about maximum-$\bar{T}$ situations by choosing for the ρ_2/ρ_3 ratio a value greater than 1.

From $\rho_2 = \rho_3$, (4.97), and (4.108), we have

$$\mu_3 = \frac{b_{13}}{b_{12}}\mu_2, \qquad y_3 = y_2 = b_{12}\frac{\mu_1}{\mu_2}. \tag{8.6}$$

For any given value of μ_1/μ_2 and of N, we can calculate ρ_1 by the method described in Section 4.3.5. From each value of ρ_1 and the given $\bar{T}_{min}$, we obtain

$$\mu_1 = \frac{\bar{T}_{min}}{b_{11}\rho_1}; \tag{8.7}$$

μ_2 is derived from the value of μ_1/μ_2 used to calculate ρ_1, and μ_3 from (8.6). Cost C can now be computed by (8.4). Note that we have reduced the problem to one with only two independent variables, N and μ_1. If we plot for each value of N between 1 and N_{max} [see (8.5)] the curve $C(\mu_1)$, we obtain curves which are concave upward like those in Fig. 8.3.

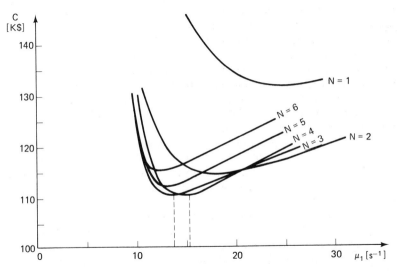

Figure 8.3   Total cost of the system designed in Example 8.1 as a function of μ_1 and N.

There are two minima whose costs are practically identical. The first is for $N = 3$ and $\mu_1 = 15.57\,\text{s}^{-1}$, and the second for $N = 4$ and $\mu_1 = 14\,\text{s}^{-1}$. Both correspond to $\mu_1/\mu_2 = 1.5$. To determine more precisely which one should be chosen and to analyze intermediate cases like that for $N = 3.5$ is probably pointless. Thus, we shall arbitrarily choose the second, for which we have $\mu_2 = 9.33\,\text{s}^{-1}$, $\mu_3 = 4.66\,\text{s}^{-1}$, and $M = 64K$ words. We also have $\rho_1 = 0.713$, $\rho_2 = \rho_3 = 0.641$. The total cost, given by (8.5), is $C = 109,500$ dollars, of which the CPU takes 37,400, the drum controller and drive 30,500, the disk controller and drive 21,500, and the primary memory 20,000. From the work-load parameters in Table 8.1 and the equations in Table 7.3, we see that the following component characteristics would be consistent with our results: $\bar{v}_{cpu} = 1.26 \times 10^6$ instructions/s, $R_{dr} = R_{ds} = 1500$ rpm, $t_{wdr} = 10\,\mu\text{s}/\text{word}$, $t_{wds} = 13\,\mu\text{s}/\text{word}$, and $\bar{t}_{seek} = 38$ ms.

The reader has certainly noticed that the curves in Fig. 8.3 are rather flat. Over the range of values of μ_1 which is considered for each one of them, the total cost always varies less than 20% with respect to the minimum. The variation is even smaller over the range of the values of N for each given value of μ_1/μ_2. Thus, the choice of the solution is not very critical, and this confirms our feeling that a study more sophisticated than the one we have done is probably not justified.

The problem we have investigated in this example could have been formulated in a different manner. Instead of assigning performance bounds such as $\bar{T}_{\min}$ and $\bar{i}_{\max}$, a maximum cost $C_{\max}$ could have been given, and the system with the highest $\bar{T}$ or the lowest $\bar{i}$ among those which satisfy the cost constraint sought. The reader can find an exercise of this type in Problem 8.2. ∎

We shall now see how the same model we have used in Example 8.1 can be applied to the initial design of a virtual-memory system.

Example 8.2 The hardware configuration of the virtual-memory EXOPE system to be designed has the same components as the system dealt with in Example 8.1. Thus, a three-server central-server model can be used as in Example 7.3, in which the behavior of a virtual-memory system was investigated. We shall assume that the performance specifications for this system are those given in Table 8.1. The work load will be characterized by the values of parameters $\bar{L}$, $\bar{r}_{ds}$, and $\bar{n}_{ds}$ reported in Table 8.1; $\bar{r}_{dr}$ will have to be made equal to the page size, which we assume to be $1K$ words. Note that the page size should also be determined by the design procedure but will be considered, for the moment, among the data of the problem. The parameters $\bar{n}_{dr}$ and $\bar{n}_{cpu}$ are unknowns to be determined. Adopting the lifetime function as our mean-value model of program behavior and assuming that this behavior is the same for all programs, we must also specify a and k [see (7.11) in Example 7.3]. We shall let $k = 2$ and $a = 140$ pages^{-2}. Alternatively, and more realistically, we may measure the lifetime curves of programs which we believe are typical of the applications of the system, as described in Section 9.3.1, and construct a "typical" lifetime curve from them.

The cost model must differ from the one summarized in (8.4). An examination of the equations in Table 7.3 will convince the reader that, since $\bar{n}_{cpu}$ is no longer a given constant, the cost of the CPU cannot be proportional to $\sqrt{\mu_1}$. The same assumptions about economies of scale made in Example 8.1 lead here to a cost proportional to $\sqrt{\bar{v}_{cpu}}$. Also, the value of h_2 will have to be changed in order to account for the fact that now information is transferred between drum and memory in pages, whose size differs from the previous value of $\bar{r}_{dr}$. The cost of a secondary-memory device depends very much on its size. In this and the previous example, we assume that the sizes of the drum and the disk are known and constant. The problem of choosing these sizes is discussed in Section 8.3.2. Since M and N are no longer proportional to each other, the cost of the memory will have to be made proportional to M. Thus, the new cost model will be

$$C = h_1'\sqrt{\bar{v}_{cpu}} + h_2'\sqrt{\mu_2} + h_3'\sqrt{\mu_3} + h_M M. \tag{8.8}$$

We shall choose the following values for the coefficients in (8.8): $h_1' = 35$ dollars-s$^{1/2}$, $h_2' = 3000$ dollars-s$^{1/2}$, $h_3' = 10{,}000$ dollars-s$^{1/2}$, and $h_M = 312.5$ dollars/page (about 0.95 cents/bit for 32-bit words). A convenient way of organizing the computations consists of selecting a certain number of values of y_2 and y_3 [as defined in (4.97)]. The same arguments by which we justified the arbitrary decision of making $\rho_2 = \rho_3$ in Example 8.1

can be used to explain why here we make $\rho_1 = \rho_3$, and hence $y_3 = 1$. For each value of y_2, we let N vary between 1 and $N_{\max}$, and, by applying the method illustrated in Section 4.3.5, we compute the corresponding values of ρ_1. Taking for each y_2 the maximum value of ρ_1, we compute [by (4.108), (7.1), (7.13), and Table 7.3]

$$\bar{v}_{cpu} = \frac{\bar{L}\bar{T}_{\min}}{\rho_1}, \tag{8.9}$$

$$\mu_3 = \frac{b_{13}\mu_1}{y_3} = \frac{\bar{n}_{ds}\bar{v}_{cpu}}{y_3\bar{L}}. \tag{8.10}$$

We then consider a number of values for M. For each (y_2, M) pair, and the value of N which maximizes ρ_1 for the given value of y_2, we calculate $\bar{e}$ using (7.11). From (4.97), (7.12), and Table 7.3 we have

$$\mu_2 = \frac{1}{\bar{e}y_2}. \tag{8.11}$$

At this point, using (8.8), the total cost C can be calculated. We report the results of our calculations in Fig. 8.4. The curves there show C as a function of N (the degree of multiprogramming which maximizes ρ_1 for each value of y_2 considered) and of M. The minimum cost corresponds to $N = 3$ and $M = 64K$ words. Its value is 98,600 dollars. The parameters which define the configuration are $\mu_2 = 27.4\,s^{-1}$, $\bar{v}_{cpu} = 1.4 \times 10^6$ instructions/s, and $\mu_3 = 4.66\,s^{-1}$. The other parameters of interest have the following values: $\bar{n}_{dr} = 14$, $\bar{n}_{cpu} = 18$, $\mu_1 = 28\,s^{-1}$, $\rho_1 = \rho_3 = 0.639$, and $\rho_2 = 0.511$. To the total cost the CPU contributes 41,400 dollars, the paging drum 15,700, the disk 21,500, and the primary memory 20,000. The disk characteristics quoted at the end of Example 8.1 are also acceptable here. The CPU has to have a slightly higher mean processing speed. For

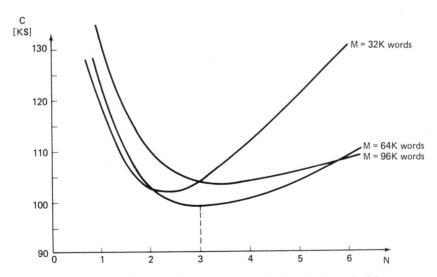

Figure 8.4 Total cost of the virtual-memory system designed in Example 8.2 as a function of N (the degree of multiprogramming which maximizes $\bar{T}$) and M.

the drum, a possible choice of the characteristics would be $R_{dr} = 1500$ rpm and $t_{war} = 16 \mu s/\text{word}$.

No conclusions should ever be drawn from studies full of crude, unvalidated approximations such as those presented in this example and in Example 8.1. However, the observation can be made, for what it is worth under these conditions, that our model of a virtual-memory system has about the same cost and the same performance as the model of the system designed in Example 8.1. In the, virtual-memory version of the system, programmers do not have to either fit their programs into a partition (16K words in Example 8.1) or "fold" them into successive overlays not bigger than a partition. They have a much larger address space at their disposal. However, the statement that the two models have about the same performance is based on the assumption that the automatic management of memory in the virtual-memory system is efficient. Our design has selected for each condition the value of N which maximizes $\bar{T}$. If this assumption is not satisfied, the additional freedom gained with the much larger address space may have to be paid for with poorer performance or a more expensive system, or even with both.   ∎

The models we have used in Examples 8.1 and 8.2 are not suitable, in that form, for designing the initial configuration of an interactive system. The use of an extremely simple model in the design of such a system will now be illustrated.

Example 8.3   The work-load parameters and performance specifications of an interactive system to be designed can be found in Table 8.2. If we assume that the random variables L and t_t are independent and exponentially distributed, we can apply the closed queuing model in Fig. 4.20. With the degree of detail that our characterization of the work load has, the only unknown is $\bar{v}_{cpu}$, the mean processing speed of the CPU. Note that in order to make use of the results obtained in Example 4.10 for the model in Fig. 4.20, we must assume that the CPU, the only system component explicitly represented, is allocated to the running processes according to the processor-sharing discipline.

✓ **Table 8.2**

WORK-LOAD PARAMETERS AND PERFORMANCE SPECIFICATIONS
FOR THE DESIGN IN EXAMPLE 8.3

	Symbol	Value
Work-load parameters		
Mean number of instructions to be executed per interaction	$\bar{L}$	500,000 instructions
Mean think time of users	$\bar{t}_t$	20 s
Number of active consoles to be supported	N	25
Performance specifications		
Maximum value of mean response time	$\bar{t}_{max}$	1 s
Minimum value of mean throughput rate	$\bar{T}_{min}$	1 interaction/s

From (4.120) and (4.118) we have

$$\frac{N}{\bar{T}} - \bar{\iota}_t \leq \bar{\iota}_{max}, \tag{8.12}$$

$$\frac{N}{\bar{\iota} + \bar{\iota}_t} \geq \bar{T}_{min}. \tag{8.13}$$

Since we do not want the system to be saturated, we have to make $N < N^*$ [*see* (4.122)]. To quickly calculate the value of μ_s, we may use approximation (4.123), which yields

$$\mu_s \cong \frac{N-1}{\bar{\iota}_t} + \frac{1}{\bar{\iota}}. \tag{8.14}$$

Thus, setting $\bar{\iota} = \bar{\iota}_{max}$ in (8.14), we have $\mu_s \cong 2.2 \text{ s}^{-1}$. Since $\mu_s = \bar{v}_{cpu}/\bar{L}$, we have $\bar{v}_{cpu} \cong 1.1 \times 10^6$ instructions/s.

If we accept the approximation made in (4.123), we can assume that $\bar{\iota}$ is really equal to 1 s and can calculate $\bar{T}$ from (4.120) and (4.118). We obtain $\bar{T} = 1.19$ interactions/s and $\rho_s = 0.54$. The validity of the approximation may then be verified by calculating ρ_s from (4.117). The saturation, as defined by Kleinrock (1968), would be reached for a number of terminals $N^* = 45$.

By considering more complex models, for instance, by replacing the single-server representation of the system with a queuing network, other component characteristics could be determined. A hierarchical modeling approach (*see* Section 8.4) could be used to gradually increase the degree of detail of our model. The value of $\bar{v}_{cpu}$ calculated here could serve as a basis for the calculation of other system parameters. Alternatively, the rest of the configuration could be selected by some other method (for instance, from the knowledge of the configurations of similar systems) and modified by an iterative design procedure. In any case, a much more detailed characterization of the work load than the one in Table 8.2 will have to be introduced. ∎

8.3.2 The Design of the Memory Hierarchy

A crucial problem in computer system design is the one of configuring the memory hierarchy. In Examples 8.1 and 8.2 we considered only a particular aspect of this problem. We shall return to those designs in Examples 8.4 and 8.5 in order to extend our discussion, after giving a brief summary of the reasons which make memory hierarchies necessary.

The presence, in practically all computer systems, of several types of storage devices, based on different memory technologies, is due to a compromise between size, performance, and cost requirements. Since the beginning of the computer era, and presumably for a long time in the future, this compromise has been and will be the only reasonable solution to the problem created by these conflicting requirements. In a few words, the problem can be stated as follows. A certain total storage size M_{tot} is needed in a system to store user and system programs and data. The performance of the system is directly related to v_{cpu}, the processing speed of the CPU (or CPU's). However, the CPU can run at full speed only if the storage system can keep up with the CPU's referencing frequency. More precisely, the access time and the transfer rate of the storage system with respect to the CPU must have the same order of magnitude as $1/v_{cpu}$ and v_{cpu}, respectively. Since for performance reasons the CPU requires a random-access memory, the access time is of the same order as the inverse of the transfer rate. Therefore, we shall restrict our considerations to access times. Memory technologies cannot provide access times $t_a \approx 1/v_{cpu}$ with costs per bit $c(t_a)$ such that the total cost of the storage system,

$$C_{tot} = c(t_a)M_{tot}, \tag{8.15}$$

is not prohibitive. In Fig. 8.5(a), let $M_{tot} = 10^9$ bits and $v_{cpu} = 10^6$ instructions/s. Thus, $t_a \approx 1\,\mu s$. From the diagram in Fig. 8.6, we have $c(1\,\mu s) \cong 1$ cent/bit. From (8.15), we have $C_{tot} = 10^7$ dollars. Note that the diagram in Fig. 8.6 approximately represents the trend of what should in fact be displayed as a cloud of points. The cloud moves downward and to the left as time progresses. However, and because of this, the storage space demands by computer users also increase in time.

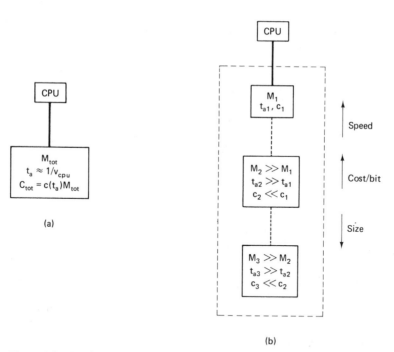

(a)

(b)

Figure 8.5 Two implementations of the same storage system: (a) the single-level solution; (b) a three-level memory hierarchy.

The compromise alluded to above consists of implementing the storage system as a hierarchy of different types of memories. Figure 8.5(b) shows a

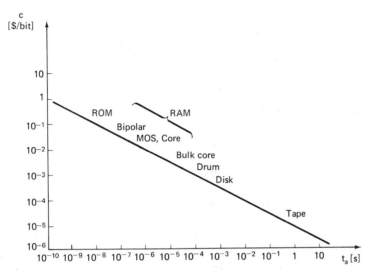

Figure 8.6   Approximate relationship between cost per bit c and access time t_a of memory tehnologies.

storage system composed of three levels. Each level i ($i = 1, 2, \ldots$) is characterized by a different size M_i, a different access time t_{ai}, and therefore a different cost per bit $c_i = c(t_{ai})$. Level 1 is the primary memory, the only part of the storage system which can be directly accessed by the CPU. Thus, only t_{a1} must have the order of magnitude of $1/v_{cpu}$. Higher levels may have longer access times and therefore substantially lower costs per bit (*see* Fig. 8.6). Thus, they are made larger and larger, as their unit cost decreases. For example, if the storage system mentioned above is implemented as in Fig. 8.5(*b*) with $M_1 = 10^7$ bits, $M_2 = 10^8$ bits, $M_3 = 0.9 \times 10^9$ bits, $t_{a1} = 1 \mu s$, $t_{a2} = 10$ ms, and $t_{a3} = 100$ ms, we have

$$M_{tot} = M_1 + M_2 + M_3 \cong 10^9 \text{ bits} \tag{8.16}$$

and

$$C_{tot} = c_1 M_1 + c_2 M_2 + c_3 M_3 \cong 2.9 \times 10^5 \text{ dollars}, \tag{8.17}$$

since $c_1 \cong 10^{-2}$ dollar/bit, $c_2 \cong 10^{-3}$ dollars/bit, and $c_3 \cong 10^{-4}$ dollar/bit. Thus, the total cost given by (8.17) is almost two orders of magnitude lower than the one previously computed for the single-level storage system. Note that in our discussion we have ignored an important physical constraint. The access time of a high-speed memory is influenced by the size of the memory. Thus, even if the economical factors could be forgotten, there would still be technical reasons for limiting the size of primary memory, and the maximum size would decrease as the

speed of the CPU increases. However, the economical limitation usually inter-
venes before the physical one.

We therefore conclude that a hierarchical implementation can drastically
reduce the total cost of a storage system and make it tolerable.   But is it always
equivalent to the single-level solution in terms of performance? For the answer to
this question to be affirmative, the following condition ought to be satisfied: The
CPU always finds in the primary memory the information it needs at the time the
need for it arises. In other words, the hierarchical storage system should make the
CPU believe that the storage consists of a single level with size M_{tot} and, ideally,
access time t_{a1}. If no reference to level 1 were successful and all information had
to be retrieved, for example, from level 2, the access time of the storage system,
as seen from the CPU, would be about t_{a2}, and the system's performance would
be catastrophically degraded. We may say that a memory hierarchy presents an
equivalent access time t_{ae} to the CPU. To make t_{ae} as close to t_{a1} as possible is
the main task of the memory management policy. This policy, which may be
manual or automatic, is concerned with determining where the various pieces of
information the system must contain should be stored as well as when and how
they should be moved to other levels of the hierarchy. Note that the use of
rotating storage devices or, more generally, of bulk-transfer devices at all levels of
a hierarchy except the primary level is made possible by the property of locality
that programs more or less exhibit (*see* Sections 7.4.2 and 9.2.2). Indeed, the
transfer of a block of words for each access effectively distributes the penalty of
the very long access times of these devices over many words, but only because of
the fact that most of these words will be referenced, due to the locality property,
in the near future. It should also be observed that the dotted connections
between the levels of the hierarchy in Fig. 8.5(*b*) only represent pictorially the
hierarchical structure of the storage system. They do not imply that, for instance,
information can be moved between level 1 and level 3 only via level 2.
Topological connections will be represented by solid lines.

The design of the memory hierarchy is a fundamental part of computer
system design. It involves, besides the specification of the memory management
policy, the choice of the number of levels and of the topology of the connections
between levels as well as that of the technology, size, and performance characteristics of each level. We shall now briefly return to the initial-configuration
designs described in Examples 8.1 and 8.2 and discuss them from a memory
hierarchy design viewpoint.

Example 8.4   In the batch-processing EXOPE system of Example 8.1, it was decided
since the beginning that the storage system would be composed of three levels: a
random-access primary memory, a drum, and a disk. Both rotating devices would be
connected to the primary memory and transfer blocks of information to and from it when
requested by the operating system. Thus, the technologies to be employed at the three
levels were more or less selected initially. The memory management policy was also
chosen without examining any other alternative. Each program, when loaded in primary
memory, is allocated a fixed-size partition. The management of this space is done by the

programmers by inserting in their card decks appropriate job control cards or higher-level language statements which the compiler translates into calls to its storage allocation routines or to the operating system. Programs will need to access the drum and the disk during their execution, since not all of the information they have to process or that they produce can usually fit into a partition of memory. This information may include parts of their code, input data, output results, files and library routines they have to access, and nonresident modules of the operating system. Since the drum has a shorter access time than the disk, we shall tend to store on drum information having a higher frequency of usage. On the other hand, because of its higher cost per bit, the drum will be made smaller than the disk.

Our design procedure, based on a central-server model, has determined explicitly the size M of primary memory [which, to be consistent with the symbols in Fig. 8.5(b), should be called M_1] and the speeds of the drum and the disk. More precisely, we have computed μ_2 and μ_3, which are functions of the access time and transfer rate of the two rotating devices. How can we determine the sizes M_2 and M_3 and the speed of the primary memory? What role do these parameters play in the design?

The order of magnitude for t_{a1}, the access time of the primary memory, is given by $1/\bar{v}_{cpu}$ and that of its transfer rate by $\bar{v}_{cpu}$. Better estimates of these memory parameters can be obtained if the total memory request rate is known. This requires knowledge of the architecture of the CPU, of the instruction mix, and of the transfer rates of the drum and the disk. More details on these points will be given at the end of this section (*see* Example 8.7). Of course, also the particular technology to be employed (destructive-readout core or non-destructive-readout semiconductor) is to be known.

In an iterative design procedure, the value of $\bar{v}_{cpu}$ determined in Example 8.1 may be used to estimate initial values for primary-memory parameters. These values will then represent primary-memory performance in the iterative phases of the procedure and will be modified if necessary to satisfy the design requirements. Alternatively, they will be the basis for selecting an existing primary memory, whose parameters will be used (and possibly changed into those of another existing memory) in the iterative analyses of performance and cost. In a hierarchical design method, corrections to the initial values of primary-memory parameters will be made as lower levels of abstraction are reached, that is, as more details are introduced about the architecture of the CPU, the instruction mix, and the request rates of the rotating devices and their connections to the memory.

It is important to observe that $\bar{v}_{cpu}$ has been obtained assuming the cost model (8.3) with a certain value for the coefficient h_N, which is proportional to the cost per bit. However, the cost per bit is related to the access time, which depends on $\bar{v}_{cpu}$. Thus, if the value of $\bar{v}_{cpu}$ dictates a value of t_{a1} which is not consistent with the cost per bit assumed in our cost model, the design should be repeated after suitably modifying h_N. In the case of an initial design like ours, however, it is generally not worthwhile to make these adjustments at such a crude level of approximation. It is usually more fruitful to proceed immediately to the iterative phases, where the global and more detailed model of the system, and, from a certain point on, the prototype system itself, is operated upon.

The sizes of the drum and of the disk should be determined by deciding how the information to be stored will be partitioned between them and by estimating the volumes of each portion of the total. In doing this, the number and the needs of the users, the performance and cost requirements, and the presumable expansion of the installation will somehow have to be taken into account. This investigation should also provide estimates of the mean numbers of drum and disk requests per job, $\bar{n}_{dr}$ and $\bar{n}_{ds}$. Once the sizes of the drum and of the disk have been selected, the coefficients h_2 and h_3 in the cost model (8.4) can be determined. For fixed-head rotating devices, Sharpe (1969) found the cost to be roughly proportional to the square root of the size. Thus, even h_2 in (8.4) will be proportional to $\sqrt{M_2}$. If M_2 and M_3 are modified, the system should in principle be redesigned for two reasons: because of the changes in h_2 and h_3, and because of those in $\bar{n}_{dr}$ and $\bar{n}_{ds}$.   ■

Example 8.5   Most of the discussion in Example 8.4 about the design of the memory hierarchy for the batch EXOPE of Example 8.1 is valid also for the virtual-memory version of the same system designed in Example 8.2. The main differences between the two memory hierarchies are in the memory management policy (which is automatic here for the primary-memory/drum hierarchy) and in the tasks assigned to the rotating devices. In our virtual-memory system, the drum is used only for paging. This means that all the jobs which are partially loaded in primary memory must have the totality of their code and data (in other words, their virtual-address spaces) on drum, so that any referenced page not found in memory can be fetched from the drum. The disk will store all the rest of the information, which the active jobs will occasionally need. If the information coming from the disk is loaded into a job's virtual-address space, then it may be paged out, if necessary, to the drum. Otherwise, it will be rewritten to the disk or destroyed when no longer needed. In any event, the drum should in principle be large enough to be able to contain the virtual-address spaces of all the active jobs. Capitalizing on the fact that only rarely is a virtual space full, especially in machines with long virtual addresses, this size may be substantially reduced. However, the above calculation will always provide an indication of the order of magnitude of the space required. Therefore, the value of h_2' in (8.8) should be considered proportional to $\sqrt{N}$, since it is proportional to $\sqrt{M_2}$ and M_2 is proportional to N. The introduction of this correction into the results obtained in Example 8.2 will be left as an exercise for the reader (*see* Problem 8.6).

It should be noted that the value of $\bar{v}_{cpu}$ determined in Example 8.2 requires a primary-memory access time which is probably too short with respect to the cost per bit assumed in applying (8.8). We shall discuss this problem in Example 8.6.   ■

Both in Example 8.4 and Example 8.5, we discussed the design of three-level memory hierarchies. However, the management of the hierarchy in the former was entirely nonautomatic, whereas a two-level automatically managed hierarchy was included in the latter. Multilevel hierarchies in which automatic management is extended to all levels have been incorporated into several machines and are probably going to be even more popular in the future. This trend follows a long tradition of innovations introduced into computer systems with the objective of freeing the user from the burden of dealing directly with the hardware and its peculiarities. The list of these innovations includes operating systems and higher-level languages.

To illustrate how an automatic multilevel memory hierarchy can be evaluated and designed, we shall study an example of a three-level hierarchy of this type. This hierarchy will be obtained by inserting one more automatically managed level between the CPU and the primary memory in the system designed in Example 8.2. Note, however, that the approach to be described can be applied to other memory hierarchies having the same structure, organization, and management policies.

As with all memory hierarchies, the advantage to be expected from the introduction of a *cache memory* (or *high-speed buffer*) between CPU and primary memory is that of a cost-performance improvement. A cache memory allows a fast CPU to process instructions at full speed while at the same time most of the primary-memory space needed is implemented in a slower and therefore cheaper technology. We shall see in Example 8.6 that the addition of a cache memory level to the system we have designed in Example 8.2 will be very beneficial, since that system requires a CPU processing rate which is substantially higher than the primary-memory rate we have assumed. Incidentally, we note that the cache is, in the hierarchy in Fig. 8.7, the memory level which satisfies the definition of primary memory, that is, the level directly referenced by the CPU. However, our terminology and symbology will not be modified as a consequence of this observation (*see* Fig. 8.7).

There are various organizations for cache memories. We shall adopt for our discussion the one which is most consistent with the way the other levels are managed. Information is moved on demand between primary memory and cache in blocks whose size is generally an integral submultiple of the page size. We shall call these blocks *subpages* and divide the cache into *subpage frames*. The ratio

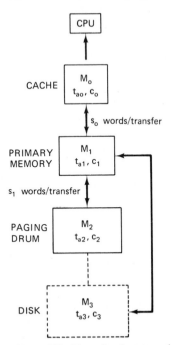

Figure 8.7 Three-level automatically managed memory hierarchy designed in Example 8.6. The disk, connected to the primary-memory level, is not automatically managed.

between page size s_1 and subpage size s_0 is usually a power of 2. When a word which is not in the cache is referenced by the CPU, the subpage which contains it is transferred from primary memory to the cache. If the page including the referenced subpage is not in primary memory, it must be fetched from the drum and loaded into memory before the desired subpage is moved to the cache. In some systems, the transfer of the referenced subpage to the cache may begin as soon as that subpage has been loaded in primary memory. Similarly, the referenced word may be sent to the CPU as soon as it appears in the cache. We shall, however, make the simpler assumption that a transfer must be completed before another transfer involving the same information or a portion of it can be initiated.

The drum is assumed to contain all of the information which constitutes an active job. Every subpage in the cache has its parent page in primary memory. Thus, at any given instant and for any active job, the information stored in the cache is a subset of that in the primary memory, which in turn is a subset of that stored on the drum. When a transfer cannot be made without replacing a page or subpage, the replaced block of information will be written back to the level where the new block comes from. If no modifications were made to the replaced block since it was last loaded into the level it is now leaving, this write operation is not required. However, in the sequel, we shall not make any distinction between these two types of replacement (this distinction *is* to be made in Problem 8.9). The replacement policies may be different at the different levels of the hierarchy. Since the evaluation of a memory hierarchy is easier if they are the same [*see*, for example, Mattson et al. (1970)], we shall assume that both cache and primary memory are managed according to the *least recently used* (LRU) policy, which is perhaps the most popular replacement algorithm. Under LRU, it is the least recently referenced page or subpage to be replaced when necessary. If the allocation of both the cache and the primary memory is fixed, this page or subpage is the least recently used among those belonging to the running job. This policy which we shall adopt for our discussion, is called *local LRU replacement.* In a *global replacement* policy, on the other hand, all pages or subpages stored at the level being considered are possible candidates for replacement [*see* Denning (1970)]. Even though we allow subpages of all active jobs to coexist in the cache, we shall not switch the CPU to another job if a subpage fault can be satisfied by the primary memory. The CPU will be switched only when the referenced information must be retrieved from the drum, that is, when we have a page fault (or, of course, when a disk operation is requested by the running job).

Example 8.6   The initial design procedure illustrated in Example 8.2 resulted in a system in which the mean processing speed of the CPU is to be equal to 1.4×10^6 instructions/s. Applying the considerations made in Example 8.4 on how the initial values of the primary-memory characteristics can be determined, we see that this speed is likely to require a memory with an access time of a few hundred nanoseconds. Let us assume $t_{a1} = 300$ ns. Remembering that the design was based on a memory cost of about 1 cent/bit, Fig. 8.6 tells us that we underestimated this cost. Let the current cost for a technology with $t_{a1} = 300$ ns be 4 cents/bit. If the value of h_M in (8.8) is modified accordingly, the curves in Fig. 8.4 change. For instance, the new minimum-cost solution among the configurations examined corresponds to $N = 2$ and $M = 32K$ words. The total cost of this solution is now 132,600 dollars and that of the previous optimum is 158,600 dollars. Note also that, unfortunately, the new solution would require an even higher $\bar{v}_{cpu}$ (1.8×10^6 instructions/s).

We want to design a three-level memory hierarchy including a cache so that the system satisfies the performance requirements in Table 8.1. Our objective is to reduce the total cost of the system with respect to those just quoted above. Since there are many design parameters to be specified, we shall not seek a minimum-cost solution. Consistently with our initial-design philosophy, we shall perform only a few local optimizations whose results can be effectively used to reduce the number of different configurations to be considered in a more accurate, though still preliminary, design procedure. Our approach will be to take the design of Example 8.2 and add a cache memory to it without affecting its performance. The cache access time will have to be of the order of 300 ns so as to match $\bar{v}_{cpu}$.

It is easy to realize that if μ_2, N, and $\bar{e}$ are equal to the ones in the solution of Example 8.2 ($\mu_2 = 27.4 \text{ s}^{-1}$, $N = 3$, $\bar{e} = 45.5$ ms) and if the work-load and performance specifications are the same, then our design procedure produces the same values for the characteristics of the remaining components. Thus, we shall replace the primary memory by a two-level storage system which, with $N = 3$, causes each job to have a mean execution interval longer than or equal to 45.5 ms.

Of the automatic hierarchy parameters listed in Fig. 8.7, the values of s_1, t_{a2}, c_2, and M_2 have already been selected (note that $s_1 = \bar{r}_{dr} = 1K$ words). Thus, the design parameters to be determined are M_0, s_0, t_{a0}, M_1, t_{a1}, c_0, and c_1. The parameters t_{a0} and c_0, t_{a1} and c_1 are related to each other as shown in Fig. 8.6. The first five can be used to express analytically the equivalent access time of the memory hierarchy and the mean execution interval $\bar{e}$, as described below.

For a given program and a given replacement algorithm, the lifetime curve usually varies with the size of the frames in the first level of the hierarchy. Thus, if there were no cache (and the primary memory had the speed of the cache), the mean execution interval would be $\bar{e}(m_1, s_1)$, with $m_1 = M_1/N$. To obtain $\bar{e}$ when the cache is there, we have to add to $\bar{e}(m_1, s_1)$ the transfer time of a subpage, $s_0 t_{a1}$, multiplied by the mean number of cache-memory transfers between consecutive page faults, which is $[\bar{e}(m_1, s_1)/\bar{e}(m_0, s_0)] - 1$ if $\bar{e}(m_0, s_0)$ denotes the mean interval between subpage faults (*see* Fig. 8.8). Using $\bar{e}_i$ as a

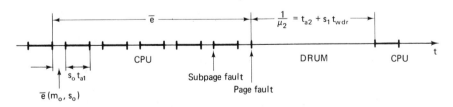

Figure 8.8   Timing diagram for the automatic three-level hierarchy in Fig. 8.7. The diagram refers to the average job assumed to run in uniprogramming mode (no queues). Heavy segments represent memory-to-cache transfers.

shorthand notation for $\bar{e}(m_i, s_i)$, we have

$$\bar{e} = \bar{e}_1 + \left(\frac{\bar{e}_1}{\bar{e}_0} - 1\right) s_0 t_{a1}. \tag{8.18}$$

Note that we have written the transfer time of a subpage as $s_0 t_{a1}$ since we assume that level 1 is a random-access memory with transfer rate $1/t_{a1}$. If it were a core memory with cycle time t_{cycle}, the transfer time would be $s_0 t_{cycle}$. If it were, say, a drum, the transfer time would be $\bar{t}_{a1} + s_0 t_{wdr} = 1/\mu_1$, denoting by μ_1 the drum's mean service rate.

In Fig. 8.8, we can see that during one entire CPU-drum cycle, the average program makes $(\bar{e}_0/t_{a0})(\bar{e}_1/\bar{e}_0) = \bar{e}_1/t_{a0}$ references to the memory hierarchy. The total duration of this cycle, including the subpage transfer which follows a page transfer, is, in a uniprogramming environment, $\bar{e} + 1/\mu_2 + s_0 t_{a1}$. Thus, the equivalent access time of the hierarchy with respect to a single program is [by (8.18)]

$$t_{ae} = \frac{t_{a0}}{\bar{e}_1}\left(\bar{e} + \frac{1}{\mu_2} + s_0 t_{a1}\right) = t_{a0}\left(1 + \frac{s_0}{\bar{e}_0}t_{a1} + \frac{1}{\bar{e}_1}\frac{1}{\mu_2}\right). \tag{8.19}$$

During page transfers, the CPU may be switched to other programs. Thus, it is the equivalent access time during the intervals marked "CPU" in Fig. 8.8 that should match the value of $\bar{v}_{cpu}$ determined in Example 8.2. This time, denoted by t_{ae}^*, is not equal to t_{ae} but can be easily obtained from the discussion regarding (8.19):

$$t_{ae}^* = t_{a0}\left(1 + \frac{s_0}{\bar{e}_0}t_{a1}\right). \tag{8.20}$$

For any given program, the family of lifetime curves $\bar{e}(m, s)$ can be constructed for various values of s (see, for instance, Fig. P8.1). If one or a few programs likely to represent the typical applications of the system being designed can be identified, these curves will provide the data required to evaluate (8.18), (8.19), and (8.20) for a variety of possible configurations. Thus, an iterative design procedure may be utilized to perform a guided exploration of the parameter space, with the objective of obtaining a satisfactory design. Analytic formulas which may help in this search can be derived by introducing a simple mathematical characterization of the family of lifetime curves for the average program. Following Gelenbe (1973), we shall assume that $\bar{e}(m, s)$ does not depend on s and shall approximate it by the exponential lifetime function $(a/\bar{v}_{cpu})m^k$.

The cost of the system's components considered in Example 8.2, except that of the primary memory, does not change if $\bar{e}$ is kept constant. Thus, we shall be interested in the cost of the cache-primary-memory system, which is given by

$$C_{01} = c_0 M_0 + c_1 M_1. \tag{8.21}$$

Let us assume that all of the design parameters have been selected except for M_0 and M_1. Examining (8.20) and (8.21), the reader will realize that when M_0 and M_1 decrease, C_{01} decreases but t_{ae}^* increases. We shall therefore seek a locally optimum cost-performance by trying to minimize the product $C_{01}t_{ae}^*$. We introduce the ratio $\alpha = M_1/M_0$ and express the product $C_{01}t_{ae}^*$ as a function of α. From (8.20) and (8.21) we have

$$C_{01}t_{ae}^* = t_{a0}M_1\left(\frac{c_0}{\alpha} + c_1\right)\left(1 + \frac{s_0 t_{a1}N^k\bar{v}_{cpu}}{aM_1^k}\alpha^k\right), \tag{8.22}$$

and from (8.18),

$$M_1 = \left[\frac{N^k \bar{v}_{\text{cpu}}}{a}(\bar{e} - s_0 t_{a1} - s_0 t_{a1} \alpha^k)\right]^{1/k}. \tag{8.23}$$

Substituting (8.23) into (8.22), we have an expression of $C_{01} t_{ae}^*$ in which the only independent variable is α. Calculating the derivative of this expression with respect to α and setting it equal to 0, we obtain the following equation:

$$\alpha^{k+1} + \frac{c_0}{c_1}\frac{k}{k-1}\alpha^k - \frac{c_0}{c_1(k-1)}\left(1 + \frac{\bar{e}}{s_0 t_{a1}}\right) = 0. \tag{8.24}$$

Note that this equation contains neither a nor t_{a0} nor N. If we choose $k = 2$, $c_0/c_1 = 5$, $s_0 = 64$ words, and $t_{a1} = 1\,\mu s$, the solution is $\alpha \cong 12.5$. From (8.23) we have $M_1 = 57{,}849$ words and $M_0 = M_1/\alpha = 4627$ words. Assuming $t_{a0} = 0.25\,\mu s$, (8.20) yields $t_{ae}^* = 320$ ns. The cost C_{01} given by (8.21) with $c_1 = 1$ cent/bit and $c_0 = 5$ cents/bit is about 25,900 dollars. If we choose more reasonable sizes for the cache and the primary memory, such as $M_0 = 4K$ words and $M_1 = 64K$ words, the above values become $t_{ae}^* = 340$ ns and $C_{01} = 27{,}500$ dollars. Thus, the total cost of the system is only 106,100 instead of 158,600 dollars, as computed at the begining of this example for a two-level hierarchy. Note that (8.18) gives $\bar{e} = 55.4$ ms instead of 45.5 ms. Thus, we should also have a slight increase in performance caused by our new choice of M_0 and M_1. ∎

In the design of a hierarchy that we performed in Example 8.6, the procedure was decomposed into two successive stages. The first stage (described in Example 8.2) assumed no cache and produced values for the characteristics of all system components. The cost of the resulting system was, however, quite high due to the primary-memory speed required. Thus, in the second stage, the primary memory was replaced by a two-level hierarchy without modifying the other components, so that the system's performance would not be affected. By this approach, which can be considered as a limited example of hierarchical design (*see* Sections 8.2 and 8.4), the total cost of the system was substantially reduced.

Several other approaches can be followed to design a system of the same type. For instance, one can start with a configuration already containing a three-level hierarchy, assign reasonable values to the parameters of the cache and of the primary memory, determine $\bar{e}$ for various values of N by equation (8.18) or from the appropriate lifetime curves $\bar{e}(m, s_0)$ and $\bar{e}(m, s_1)$, and proceed with the design as shown in Example 8.2, making sure that the resulting $\bar{v}_{\text{cpu}}$ matches the value of t_{ae}^* given by (8.20). Another possible use of the same basic set of analytic and empirical tools is described by Traiger and Mattson (1972), who choose values for all of the system parameters except M_0, M_1, s_0, and s_1. For each primary-memory technology, characterized by the pair (t_{a1}, c_1), they determine the values of M_0, M_1, s_0, s_1 which optimize a cost-performance index, the total rental cost per instruction executed. Comparing the values of this index given by different memory technologies allows system designers to choose the most appropriate technology for their system and to evaluate new technologies. Furthermore, memory designers can apply the same approach to determine the most effective ways of improving a certain type of memory, for example, whether it is better to decrease its unit cost or to increase its speed.

So far the estimation of the primary-memory speed required was made in a very crude fashion (*see* Examples 8.4 and 8.6). A more detailed calculation should include the effects of the various devices which access the primary memory directly. These effects will now be briefly discussed for two systems, those designed in Examples 8.1 and 8.6. The results of these calculations constitute the starting point of the detailed design of the primary memory, which will not be dealt with in this book.

Example 8.7   Figure 8.9 displays a block diagram of the system designed in Example 8.1. The diagram emphasizes the viewpoint we shall adopt here. That is, the primary memory is considered as the center of the system and may be accessed through DMA (direct memory access) ports by a number of processors. In our example, there are three processors: the CPU, the drum controller or channel, and the disk controller or channel.

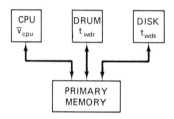

Figure 8.9   Block diagram of the system designed in Example 8.1.

We are, of course, ignoring the I/O processor (or processors) responsible for the transfers of I/O data from the card reader or other input equipment to the disk and from the disk to the printer or other output equipment. During these transfers, data are usually buffered in primary memory. Ignoring the request rates of I/O processors is legitimate if, as is often the case, they are several orders of magnitude lower than those of the other processors.

What is the maximum memory request rate we may have in the system in Fig. 8.9? To answer this question, we must calculate the request rates of the three processors in it and add them together. The CPU should process $\bar{v}_{cpu}$ instructions/s. How many memory references will they require? Consider an instruction mix which represents satisfactorily the composition of the programs to be processed by our system. If instruction i has relative frequency f_i and requires g_i references to primary memory, the mean memory request rate of the CPU is

$$\bar{f}_{cpu} = \bar{v}_{cpu} \sum_i f_i g_i. \tag{8.25}$$

Table 8.3 summarizes the information needed to calculate $\bar{f}_{cpu}$. This information can be derived from a normal instruction mix in an obvious way. Assuming $\bar{v}_{cpu} = 1.26 \times 10^6$ instructions/s, as determined in Example 8.1, (8.25) yields $\bar{f}_{cpu} = 2.4 \times 10^6$ references/s. Note that this approach cannot be used when the CPU is pipelined. Simulation or a much more sophisticated analysis is required in that case.

Table 8.3

INSTRUCTION MIX FOR EXAMPLE 8.7

Number of references per instruction	Relative frequency [%]
1	22
2	67
3	9
4	2

The drum processor, when transferring data, makes memory requests at a rate

$$f_{\text{drum}} = \frac{1}{t_{wdr}}, \tag{8.26}$$

and the disk processor at a rate

$$f_{\text{disk}} = \frac{1}{t_{wds}}. \tag{8.27}$$

The request rates of the drum and of the disk are constant, whereas that of the CPU is time-variant. For our system, $f_{\text{drum}} = 10^5$ references/s and $f_{\text{disk}} = 0.77 \times 10^5$ references/s. The total memory request rate when all three processors are active is

$$f_{\text{tot}} = \bar{f}_{\text{cpu}} + f_{\text{drum}} + f_{\text{disk}}. \tag{8.28}$$

In our system, $f_{\text{tot}} = 2.577 \times 10^6$ references/s. When the disk or the drum processor or both are accessing memory, they have higher priority than the CPU, which will therefore be slowed down whenever an access conflict with any of the other processors arises. If we want our memory to be able to accommodate the rate f_{tot} without causing, over relatively long intervals, $\bar{v}_{\text{cpu}}$ to be less than the one we have computed, we must make the memory transfer rate, or *bandwidth*, greater than or equal to f_{tot}. Of course, this is in some sense a worst-case viewpoint, since we assume concurrent activity of all processors. On the other hand, we make the optimistic assumption that the CPU is able to utilize all memory cycles. If core technology is chosen, the cycle time will have to be at most equal to $1/f_{\text{tot}} = 388$ ns. Implementing a single-module core memory with this bandwidth, which corresponds to an access time of less than 200 ns, is quite expensive. Thus, modularization will be employed to obtain the required bandwidth from an inherently slower technology. Also, techniques well known in memory design such as interleaving and cycle staggering may be applied to further increase the speed of a multimodule memory. Access-path widening can enhance the performance of both single-module and multimodule memories [for a description of these techniques, *see*, for example, Watson (1970)]. In the case of semiconductor technology, the cycle time approximately coincides with the access time, and access times of about 400 ns are not too difficult or expensive to obtain. However, the techniques mentioned above may be employed to broaden the bandwidth of these memories also.

In the virtual-memory system designed in Example 8.6, the CPU does not communicate directly with the primary memory. The CPU in Fig. 8.9 should be replaced by the cache, which is characterized, when it is transfering data to or from the primary memory, by a constant request rate $f_{cache} = 1/t_{a0}$. If t_{a0} is 250 ns, as in Example 8.6, $f_{cache} = 4 \times 10^6$ references/s. To accommodate this request rate, the bandwidth of the primary memory as seen from the cache is to be broadened by a factor of 4 (since $t_{a1} = 1 \mu s$). Widening the access path by transferring 4 words at a time is a popular method for achieving this result. To satisfy the requirements of the CPU, the maximum transfer rate of the cache must be greater than or equal to $\bar{f}_{cpu}$. In our virtual-memory system, assuming the instruction mix in Table 8.3 and taking $\bar{v}_{cpu} = 1.4 \times 10^6$ instructions/s as dictated by the design procedure in Example 8.2, we have, from (8.25), $\bar{f}_{cpu} = 2.67 \times 10^6$ references/s and a maximum value for t_{a0} of $1/\bar{f}_{cpu} = 374$ ns.   ∎

8.3.3   Exploring Design Trade-offs

A designer is usually confronted with a number of trade-offs, each involving a choice to be made between the conflicting requirements of cost and value. Let a feature supposed to increase the value of the system to its users be under consideration for incorporation into the design. Is the expected increase in value worth the cost of the feature and the inconveniences caused by its possible side effects? Several examples of cost-performance and hardware-hardware trade-offs have been described both in Chapter 7 and in Sections 8.3.1 and 8.3.2. An example of a hardware-hardware trade-off is the one between primary-memory size and paging drum speed in a virtual-memory system. Other trade-offs to be considered in system design are those between hardware and software. These present themselves naturally when system components have to be designed or when among the available hardware components some implement certain functions and some do not (so that if one of the latter is chosen, these functions will have to be implemented in software).

In the past, the cost and inflexibility of hardware considerably restricted the freedom of a designer. The optimum boundary between the domains of hardware and software was constantly moving following the evolution of technology, but the margin for alternative solutions in the vicinity of the boundary was relatively narrow. The advent of microprogramming and large-scale integration has opened new perspectives and has remarkably widened the designer's field of choices. It has become feasible to implement parts of the operating system in firmware and even in hardware (or in a hardware–firmware combination). Which one of the possible alternatives is the best? Which one will be the best a year from now?

Answering these questions does not require only a performance evaluation study. Economical and functional issues will have to be seriously examined as well as the nonquantifiable effects of each alternative on the installations and their user communities. However, the performance side of hardware-software trade-offs is obviously important. A study performed by Foley (1971) on the optimum design of computer graphics systems will be described as an example of how the cost-performance aspects of hardware–hardware and hardware–software trade-offs may be evaluated.

Example 8.8 The configuration of the interactive computer graphics system to be designed is shown in Fig. 8.10(*a*). A model of the system is depicted in Fig. 8.10(*b*). The model describes the possible paths of user requests through the system. A request made by a user may be for a service provided by the central computer CC or for a local service. In the former case, the request will have to be preprocessed by the local computer LC [block 6 in Fig. 8.10(*b*)], shipped over the data link DL (block 7), and processed by CC (block 8),

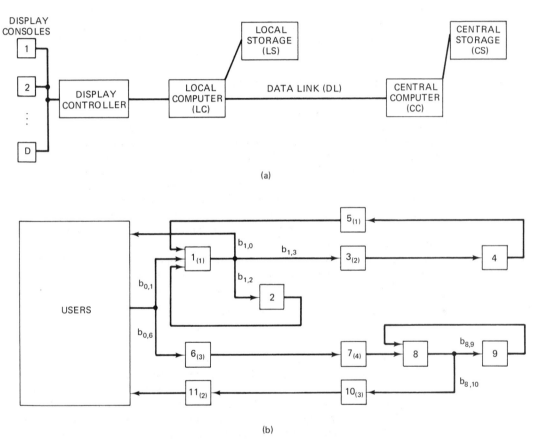

(a)

(b)

Figure 8.10 Computer graphics system (*a*) and model (*b*) considered by Foley (1971). Blocks in (*b*) represent different functions to be performed by the corresponding physical devices in (*a*). The priorities of these functions, when necessary, are indicated in parentheses inside each block.

perhaps involving accesses to the central computer's bulk storage CS (block 9). Then the results will be shipped back over DL (block 10), postprocessed by LC (block 11), and finally output to the user. A command requesting a locally satisfiable service is processed by LC (block 1). Sometimes such a command may involve one or more accesses to the local bulk storage LS (block 2) or to the central bulk storage CS (blocks 3, 4, and 5). The blocks in the model represent separate service centers which are in some cases implemented by the same physical device. In these cases, service will be given by the device according to the fixed priorities reported in Fig. 8.10(*b*) in parentheses inside the blocks involved.

A number of simplifying assumptions are implied by the model's structure. The absence of a loop around block 6 means that preprocessing must be completed by LC before the relevant messages are shipped over DL. Also, LC cannot access LS while preprocessing or postprocessing a request. When CS is accessed to satisfy a service request being processed locally by LC (block 4), the intervention of CC is assumed not to be needed. CC is not, of course, dedicated to the graphics system, but the additional load on it is not explicitly represented in the model. It is, instead, implicitly taken into account by a suitable reduction of the CC's mean execution rate $\bar{v}_{CC}$. CS is assumed to consist of multiple disk drives. Thus, the probability of conflicting CS accesses (blocks 4 and 9) is so low that specifying priorities for these two blocks may be avoided.

Clearly, the design of a system like the one in Fig. 8.10(*a*) does not consist only of determining the hardware and software characteristics of the components. A number of function-allocation problems and hardware–hardware and hardware–software trade-offs need to be explored. A typical function-allocation problem is the one of determining which tasks should be processed on the local computer and which on the central computer. Examples of hardware–hardware trade-offs are the subdivision of computing power between the local and the central site and the sizing of the local and central bulk storages. An example of hardware–software trade-off is the possible implementation of a number of display functions in the hardware of the display controller or by programs to be executed by the local computer. The implementation in hardware is generally faster but more expensive and harder to modify than the one in software.

A cost-performance criterion will be chosen to compare various possible solutions to the design problem. The figure of merit to be maximized will be the mean throughput rate per unit cost, measured in interactions per second per dollar:

$$\frac{\bar{T}}{C} = \frac{D}{\bar{t} + \bar{t}_t} \frac{1}{C}, \tag{8.29}$$

where D is the number of display consoles supported by the system, $\bar{t}$ is the mean response time, $\bar{t}_t$ is the mean user think time, and C is the total cost. Since $\bar{t}_t$ is given [*see* Table 8.4], D is known, and C may be estimated from the prices of the components, the only quantity to be calculated in (8.29) is $\bar{t}$. The closed queuing network model in Fig. 8.10(*b*) allows us to derive $\bar{t}$ analytically under the assumptions of constant branching probabilities and exponential service-time distributions at all service centers. A simulator of the model, in which these assumptions were not satisfied, gave results differing in a variety of cases by at most 7% from those obtained analytically with the same mean values of both the branching probabilities and the service times.

Table 8.4 lists the hardware and application parameters from which branching probabilities and mean service times are to be computed. A number of assumptions are implicitly or explicitly present in the choice and definitions of these parameters. The unit of memory space is the *record*, equal to 12,000 bits. All graphics applications are assumed to be composed of *display macroinstructions*. Examples of these primitives, which may in some sense be considered as units of work load to be processed, are initialize display, pentracking, rotation, line blink, change intensity, convert integer to ASCII, obtain current position, and so on. Display *applications* are classified into various types, for instance, text

Table 8.4

HARDWARE AND APPLICATION PARAMETERS OF THE GRAPHICS
SYSTEM IN FIG. 8.10(a)

Symbol	Definition
$\bar{t}_t$	Mean user think time [s]
$\bar{v}_{LC}$	Mean display macroinstruction execution rate of LC [macroinstructions/s]
M_{LC}	Primary memory size of LC [records]
$\bar{t}_{LS}$	Mean service time of LS [s/record]
M_{LS}	Size of LS [records]
v_{DL}	Transmission rate of DL [bits/s]
$\bar{v}_{CC}$	Mean display macroinstruction execution rate of CC [macroinstructions/s]
$\bar{t}_{CS}$	Mean service time of CS [s/record]
G	Number of service request types
L_i	Number of display macroinstructions needed for type i service ($i = 1, 2, \ldots, G$)
p_i	Probability of a service request of type i ($i = 1, 2, \ldots, G$)
n_i^{BS}	Number of accesses to bulk storage required by a type i request processed by LC, given one record of primary memory for program ($i = 1, \ldots, G$)
n_i^{CS}	Number of accesses to CS required by a type i request processed by CC ($i = 1, 2, \ldots, G$)
L_{pp}	Number of display macroinstructions to be executed by LC for preprocessing or postprocessing (blocks 6 and 11)
F	Maximum size of an application's program and data base [records]
a_j	Probability of accessing record j of a file ($j = 1, 2, \ldots, F$); file records are numbered in order of decreasing probability of access
E	Minimum size of primary memory of LC needed to implement a display application [records]
L_m	Length of a message sent over DL [bits]

Source: Foley (1971).

editing, two-dimensional drawing, and network analysis. Each type of application is characterized by a sequence of *interactions* (or *service requests*). For example, the network analysis application will include interactions such as the following: move element into place, identify an element with light-pen, delete identified element, connect ports of identified elements, delete connection, and so on. Each interaction is in turn characterized by the number L_i of display macroinstructions needed to execute it, its probability p_i, the number of accesses n_i^{BS} to bulk storage (LS or CS or both) it requires if processed by LC, and the number n_i^{CS} of accesses to CS if processed by CC. The number of display macroinstructions for each interaction is sufficient to represent its computational requirements since a macroinstruction mix is assumed to be given for each application. The mean macroinstruction execution rate can be calculated from the mix [*see* (5.9)] both for LC ($\bar{v}_{LC}$) and CC ($\bar{v}_{CC}$). As mentioned above, rate $\bar{v}_{CC}$ must be reduced to account for the effects of the additional load on CC.

The total information needed by an application has a maximum size of F records. The records of an application's files are numbered in order of decreasing access probability a_j. Thus, if E is the minimum amount of primary memory of LC in which the display functions not provided by the hardware and required by a given application can be implemented, the first $M_{LC} - E$ records of the file will be in the primary memory, the next M_{LS} will be in LS, and the remaining $F - M_{LS} - M_{LC} + E$ records will have to be stored in CS. Note that we assume all consoles to be working on the same application. Most of the parameters in Table 8.4 vary with the application. Thus, letting

$$A(k) = \sum_{j=1}^{k} a_j \qquad (k = 1, \ldots, F), \tag{8.30}$$

the probabilities that a referenced record is in the primary memory of LC, in LS, and in CS, respectively, are

$$p_{LC} = A(M_{LC} - E),$$
$$p_{LS} = A(M_{LS} + M_{LC} - E) - p_{LC}, \tag{8.31}$$
$$p_{CS} = 1 - p_{LC} - p_{LS}.$$

The processing tasks of an application will be distributed between LC and CC according to a minimum-response-time criterion. Let Λ be the set of indices of the interactions assigned to LC and Γ that of the interactions assigned to CC. Thus, the probability $b_{0,1}$ of a user issuing a local service request is

$$b_{0,1} = \sum_{i \in \Lambda} p_i. \tag{8.32}$$

The probability of a service request for CC is

$$b_{0,6} = 1 - b_{0,1} = \sum_{i \in \Gamma} p_i. \tag{8.33}$$

The mean number of accesses to bulk storage per interaction made by LC, if it is used and if only one record in the memory of LC is available as program area, is

$$\bar{n}^{BS} = \sum_{i \in \Lambda} \frac{p_i}{b_{0,1}} n_i^{BS}, \tag{8.34}$$

and the one made by CC, if it is used, is

$$\bar{n}^{CS} = \sum_{i \in \Gamma} \frac{p_i}{b_{0,6}} n_i^{CS}. \tag{8.35}$$

When $M_{LC} - E$ records of memory are available in LC, the mean number of accesses to bulk storage (either LS or CS) will approximately become $(1 - p_{LC})\bar{n}^{BS}$. The mean number of visits to block 1 is $1 + (1 - p_{LC})\bar{n}^{BS}$, and the last visit is followed by a return to block 0. Therefore,

$$b_{1,0} = \frac{1}{1 + (1 - p_{LC})\bar{n}^{BS}}, \tag{8.36}$$

and similarly

$$b_{1,2} = \frac{p_{LS}\bar{n}^{BS}}{1 + (1 - p_{LC})\bar{n}^{BS}}, \tag{8.37}$$

$$b_{1,3} = \frac{p_{CS}\bar{n}^{BS}}{1 + (1 - p_{LC})\bar{n}^{BS}} = 1 - b_{1,0} - b_{1,2}. \tag{8.38}$$

The mean CPU time needed by an interaction requesting local service is given by

$$\bar{t}_{1\,\text{tot}} = \sum_{i \in A} \frac{p_i}{b_{0,1}} \frac{L_i}{\bar{v}_{\text{LC}}}, \tag{8.39}$$

and that for an interaction involving CC is

$$\bar{t}_{8\,\text{tot}} = \sum_{i \in \Gamma} \frac{p_i}{b_{0,6}} \frac{L_i}{\bar{v}_{\text{CC}}} \tag{8.40}$$

Since the number of passes through server 1 during a local interaction is $1/b_{1,0}$ and that through server 8 is similarly $1/b_{8,10}$ during a central interaction, the mean service times $\bar{t}_1$ and $\bar{t}_8$ can be computed as in Table 8.5. This table summarizes the equations which express the branching probabilities and the mean service times of the model in Fig. 8.10(*b*) as functions of the parameters in Table 8.4 or of those we have just derived from them.

Table 8.5
BRANCH PROBABILITIES AND MEAN SERVICE TIMES
FOR THE MODEL IN FIG. 8.10(*b*)

$b_{0,1} = \sum_{i \in A} p_i^{\,*}$	$\bar{t}_1 = b_{1,0}\bar{t}_{1\,\text{tot}}{}^{\S}$
$b_{0,6} = 1 - b_{0,1}$	$\bar{t}_2 = \bar{t}_{\text{LS}}$
$b_{1,0} = \dfrac{1}{1 + (1 - p_{\text{LC}})\bar{n}^{\text{BS}}}{}^{\dagger}$	$\bar{t}_3 = \bar{t}_5 = \bar{t}_7 = \bar{t}_{10} = \dfrac{L_m}{v_{\text{DL}}}$
$b_{1,2} = \dfrac{p_{\text{LS}}\bar{n}^{\text{BS}}}{1 + (1 - p_{\text{LC}})\bar{n}^{\text{BS}}}{}^{\dagger}$	$\bar{t}_4 = \bar{t}_9 = \bar{t}_{\text{CS}}$
$b_{1,3} = 1 - b_{1,0} - b_{1,2}$	$\bar{t}_6 = \bar{t}_{11} = \dfrac{L_{pp}}{\bar{v}_{\text{LC}}}$
$b_{8,9} = \dfrac{\bar{n}^{\text{CS}}}{\bar{n}^{\text{CS}} + 1}{}^{\ddagger}$	$\bar{t}_8 = b_{8,10}\bar{t}_{8\,\text{tot}}{}^{\P}$
$b_{8,10} = 1 - b_{8,9}$	

Source: Foley (1971).
* *See* (8.32).
† *See* (8.31) and (8.34).
‡ *See* (8.35).
§ *See* (8.39).
¶ *See* (8.40).

The mean time $\bar{t}_h'$ spent by a service request at service center h every time that center is gone through will be

$$\bar{t}_h' = \bar{t}_h + \bar{t}_{wh} \qquad (h = 1, 2, \ldots, 11), \tag{8.41}$$

where $\bar{t}_{wh}$ is the mean waiting time in the center's queue. Times $\bar{t}_h'$ can be calculated by analytic techniques. To compute the mean response time, we note that the mean time spent by a request in a loop like the one formed by service centers 8 and 9 in Fig. 8.10(b) is

$$\bar{i}'_{89} = \frac{\bar{i}'_8}{b_{8,10}} + \left(\frac{1}{b_{8,10}} - 1\right)\bar{i}'_9 = \frac{\bar{i}'_8 + b_{8,9}\bar{i}'_9}{b_{8,10}}, \tag{8.42}$$

since on the average a request goes $1/b_{8,10}$ times through block 8 and one less time through block 9 before exiting. Applying the same approach to the loop composed of blocks 1, 2, and (3, 4, 5), we can write

$$\bar{i} = b_{0,1}\frac{\bar{i}'_1 + b_{1,2}\bar{i}'_2 + b_{1,3}(\bar{i}'_3 + \bar{i}'_4 + \bar{i}'_5)}{b_{1,0}} + b_{0,6}\left(\bar{i}'_6 + \bar{i}'_7 + \frac{\bar{i}'_8 + b_{8,9}\bar{i}'_9}{b_{8,10}} + \bar{i}'_{10} + \bar{i}'_{11}\right). \tag{8.43}$$

Note that the number of requests in the queuing network in Fig. 8.10(b) is equal at any given time to the number of active consoles, which can never be greater than D. If, in particular, there is only one active console, $\bar{i}_{wh} = 0$ for all h in (8.41), and no queuing analysis is needed to compute $\bar{i}$, since all the variables in (8.43) can be obtained from the equations in Table 8.5.

How are the design trade-offs and function-allocation problems reflected in the approach we have just described? Those which were called hardware–hardware trade-offs are obviously incorporated into the choices for the hardware component parameters in Table 8.4. For example, we may trade M_{LS} with v_{DL}. That is, an increase of M_{LS} might allow us to decrease v_{DL} so as to keep the cost constant and to improve the performance with respect to a certain design. Hardware–software trade-offs are for the most part represented by E, the memory space needed in LC to implement in software those display functions which are not implemented in hardware, and by the execution times of display macroinstructions, from which the processing speeds $\bar{v}_{LC}$ and $\bar{v}_{CC}$ are derived. The macroinstructions which are implemented in the hardware of the display controller will not contribute to the calculations of mean macroinstruction execution times, leading to higher values of $\bar{v}_{LC}$ and $\bar{v}_{CC}$. The effects of these higher values on service times can be seen in (8.39), (8.40), and Table 8.5. Also, since E will be smaller than it would be if they had to be implemented in software, p_{LC} will be larger, and p_{LS} and p_{CS} will be smaller [see (8.31)]. This will increase $b_{1,0}$ [see (8.36)], while $b_{1,2}$ and $b_{1,3}$ will decrease [see (8.37) and (8.38)]. It is evident from (8.43) that $\bar{i}$ will decrease as a consequence of implementing some macroinstructions in hardware, but the cost will generally increase. An alternative solution would consist of trading hardware with hardware. Instead of incorporating extra hardware into the display controller, one could increase the primary memory size of LC so that $M_{LC} - E$ would not change. In this case, there would be no effects on $b_{1,0}$, $b_{1,2}$, and $b_{1,3}$, but those on $\bar{v}_{LC}$ and $\bar{v}_{CC}$ would still be there and would tend to increase $\bar{i}$. However, the cost of the two solutions may well be different, and the difference would probably be in favor of the software implementation even in this case.

Function allocation influences the composition of sets Λ and Γ. Thus, by (8.32) and (8.33), it affects $b_{0,1}$ and $b_{0,6}$ and by (8.34) and (8.35), $\bar{n}^{BS}$ and $\bar{n}^{CS}$. Table 8.5 shows that all branching probabilities, $\bar{i}_1$, and $\bar{i}_8$ in fact depend on function allocation. We should therefore expect $\bar{i}$ to be quite sensitive to our decisions in this area and make these decisions with the objective of minimizing $\bar{i}$, since under the assumptions of Foley's study they do not have any appreciable impact on the total cost.

The trade-offs we have just discussed can be exploited to minimize $\bar{T}/C$. The approach followed by Foley consists of considering the configurations which can result from combining in all permissible ways existing components. In particular, if among the components in Fig. 8.10(*a*) CC and CS are assumed to be given, a configuration is obtained by choosing one of the available LC/display-controller pairs, one of the possible primary-memory sizes for LC, one of the possible sizes for LS (assuming the same speed for all LS implementations), and one of the available transmission rates for DL. Foley collected a data base, containing data on available components, which allowed 12,480 distinct configurations to be obtained. An iterative optimization procedure which performed a guided search through the space of possible designs so as to avoid examining most of the configurations was used to find the optimum solutions for various values of *D*, various monthly costs, and various types of display applications. The values of the parameters in Table 8.4, which should have been measured, had instead to be estimated since no measurement data were available. The reader will notice that, in spite of the numerous and rather drastic assumptions made to simplify the model, and in particular the work-load model, the values of work-load parameters such as L_i, p_i, n_i^{BS}, n_i^{CS}, L_{pp}, F, and a_j and the relative frequencies of display macroinstructions in application mixes may be very hard to find or to determine. Only an intimate knowledge of an application can allow a designer to produce reasonable estimates for these parameters. Thus, we see here that the work-load characterization problem is not completely solved unless methods are devised for reliably estimating or measuring the work-load parameters or unless extensive work-load measurements, whose results are relatively transportable to different environments, are undertaken.

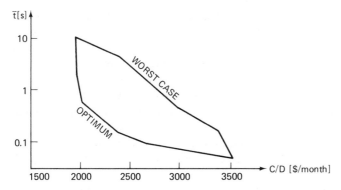

Figure 8.11   Mean response time vs. monthly cost per console for optimum and worst designs [*Source*: Foley (1971), by permission of ACM, Inc.]

Some of Foley's results are presented in Fig. 8.11, which shows the cost-performance advantages of optimum designs. According to this diagram, for a monthly cost per console of 2500 dollars the mean response time can be made as low as 0.1 s. However, the worst configuration among those considered would result in a mean response time of about 2 s. To achieve a response time of 0.1 s, the worst design would require about 3400 dollars per console per month.   ∎

8.4 PERFORMANCE CONSIDERATIONS IN HIERARCHICAL DESIGN

The iterative design philosophy introduced in Section 8.2 and discussed in some of its performance aspects in Section 8.3 is still the one being used in most computer system designs. A hierarchical philosophy, which was also briefly introduced in Section 8.2, has been proposed as a better alternative. The bases of this philosophy are essentially the same as those of the analytic approaches to the design of an initial system described in Section 8.3.1. A pure iterative design approach consists of building a system (in reality or in model form) out of experience and intuition, verifying a posteriori whether and how it works, and modifying it until it becomes acceptable from functional, economical, and performance viewpoints. In Section 8.3.1, we tried instead to derive component specifications and sizing information from the performance requirements and from crude models of the system and of the work load. The component specifications were then to be used as guidelines for selecting or designing the hardware and software components of the initial system. Iterative modifications of the initial system would finally lead us to an acceptable system. Note that in our simple examples the given models were never changed, and the original configuration was considered to be fixed. In a real design procedure, a designer will construct several models corresponding to different configurations containing, for instance, multiple disks or drums, various types of channels, and several CPU's, and compare their cost-performance characteristics in order to get useful advice on the choice of the configuration.

The philosophy of deriving system characteristics from design specifications could be extended to cover the whole design process if we had the knowledge required for such an approach. This philosophy is well known and quite successfully applied by designers in several fields of engineering, in which the systems to be designed are sufficiently understood. This does not seem yet to be the case for computer engineering. Only a few types of systems, primarily those whose work load is relatively well specifiable, can be designed according to a hierarchical approach. However, this type of approach, or much more probably a combination of the iterative and hierarchical methods, is likely to become increasingly popular as a deeper knowledge of computer systems, computer users, and applications is acquired.

A purely hierarchical approach proceeds, as mentioned in Section 8.2, by successively lowering the level of abstraction of the system's specification. At each level of abstraction, a specification of the whole system exists, having the degree of detail corresponding to that level. The specification which is obtained at the lowest level is to serve as the basis for the system's implementation. Thus, a hierarchical approach produces a number of models of the whole system, one for each level. It is generally possible to define the functional and performance characteristics of each model, which will have to be compatible with those required for the system. At a given level of abstraction, the model will consist of parts or *modules*. The model at the next level may be obtained by decomposing [*see* Parnas (1972)] these modules into interconnected submodules, whose functions and performance must be specified before proceeding. However, as pointed out by Parnas (1969), a lower level of abstraction may also be reached by identifying submodules which are shared by other modules, and not disjoint as suggested by the concept of decomposition, or by introducing further details into a module, for example, some external influences or interactions with other modules which had been ignored at the higher level. When a new level is specified, the designers should verify that the functional and performance requirements stated at the beginning of the procedure, and which were used to define the first level, are still satisfied, unless, of course, the methods employed to derive the new level from the previous one guarantee that this objective is automatically achieved.

A concept which should not be confused with the one of hierarchical design is that of *hierarchically structured system*. Such a system is organized into *layers*, all of which coexist. The first layer (layer 1) generally corresponds to what the users see. In other words, it is the user-machine interface. All the details which are hidden from the users are implemented in the underlying layers. This principle may be extended to all layers. Layer i will only be known directly by layer $i - 1$ and know directly only $i + 1$. A module on layer i will be expressed in terms of the modules on layer $i + 1$, and not (at least explicitly) of those on layers $i + 2, i + 3, \ldots$. The same principle may be be concisely stated by saying that layers are *not transparent*. On the last layer, we have the *primitives*, which are the real hardware components. A layered system may be viewed as a *hierarchy of virtual machines*. Each layer is a virtual machine implemented in terms of the underlying machine, that is, by using the functions provided by the layer immediately below it. The final machine in the hierarchy must of course be the physical one.

A hierarchical structure can to some extent be identified in all systems. It usually consists of at least the hardware layer, the operating system layer, and the layer of programming and job control languages. Dijkstra (1968) found a hierarchical structure to be very convenient also within the operating system, especially from the viewpoints of system implementation, testing, and modification. Note that these findings agree with some of the most important claims of structured programming techniques (*see* Section 9.4.3). Top-down program design procedures have been recommended in order to obtain a hierarchically structured program. However, especially in computer system design, it is convenient to keep the two concepts separate. A hierarchical procedure may be used to design a nonlayered system. Also, a layered system may be designed by a nonhierarchical approach. We must recognize, however, that it is natural to attack the design of a layered system in a hierarchical manner and that hierarchical methods naturally tend to produce hierarchically structured systems, even though the correspondence between layers and levels of abstraction may not be one-to-one.

As is the case with layered programs, little is known about the performance aspects of layered systems. Ideally, the performance specifications for the modules of layer $i + 1$ should be directly derived from the specifications for the modules of layer i. The latter should also contribute to the choice of an organization for the underlying modules. The state of the art has not yet reached the point where this would be feasible. However, several models already exist which can be used for these purposes at various stages in the design procedure, and many more are expected to result from the fast rate of development of the modeling area. It should also be noted that excessive modularization may lead to inefficiencies due to the overheads introduced by module scheduling and inter-module communications.

As Lynch (1972) pointed out, hierarchical system design will be possible also from a performance viewpoint only when total system models can be constructed. These models will have to be initially so simple as to be solvable. They will also, however, have to be expandable into more and more sophisticated and detailed submodels, corresponding to lower and lower layers of the system. Methods should then be available to relate the performances of the submodels to that of the model on the next higher layer. Unfortunately, nonlinearities and complicated intermodule interactions make the decomposition of a model into submodels very difficult. Some promising avenues for further investigation can be derived from the papers by Courtois (1975) and Browne et al. (1975). Courtois has studied the applicability of decomposition techniques used in econometrics to stochastic models of computer systems. Browne et al. have constructed a hierarchical queuing model of a complex system, analyzed its various parts separately, and then combined the results of these analyses to obtain a solution for the model of the whole system. Some rules, inspired by performance considerations, have also been proposed for the design of a layered system. An example is the rule, mentioned by Lynch (1972), that the time constants of the functions of a certain layer be much larger than the time constants of the functions of the next layer below it. In other words, for a layered system to be efficient, each module of layer $i + 1$ must be made to respond, when invoked by a module of layer i, much more rapidly than is required of the latter module when invoked by a module of layer $i - 1$.

We have seen that analytic techniques do not allow us yet to devise complete hierarchical design procedures. Simulation techniques, on the other hand, can provide substantial help if properly employed. An example will now be discussed, emphasizing the performance aspects, in which the hierarchical approach proposed by Zurcher and Randell (1968) is applied to the first levels in the design of a multiprocessor system. The example is drawn from Randell (1968).

Example 8.9   A multiprocessor system is to be designed. Its functional, performance, and cost specifications will not be explicitly given but are assumed to exist. The design methodology consists of developing a simulator which at each point in time represents the state of progress of the design and, in particular, contains the decisions made up to that point. Such a simulation model, besides being a vehicle for the orderly evolution and documentation of the design effort, allows the designers to verify the functional correctness and to evaluate the performance of the system while it is being specified in greater and greater detail. The approach is hierarchical and proceeds from the highest to lower levels of abstraction.

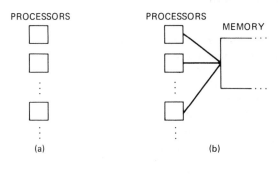

PROCESSORS

(a)

PROCESSORS   MEMORY

(b)

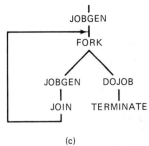

JOBGEN

FORK

JOBGEN   DOJOB

JOIN   TERMINATE

(c)

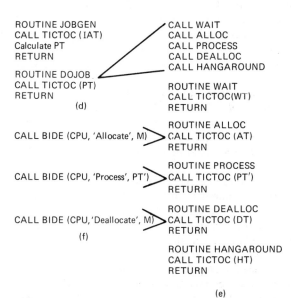

ROUTINE JOBGEN
CALL TICTOC (IAT)
Calculate PT
RETURN

ROUTINE DOJOB
CALL TICTOC (PT)
RETURN
                    (d)

CALL WAIT
CALL ALLOC
CALL PROCESS
CALL DEALLOC
CALL HANGAROUND

ROUTINE WAIT
CALL TICTOC(WT)
RETURN

ROUTINE ALLOC
CALL BIDE (CPU, 'Allocate', M)   CALL TICTOC (AT)
                    RETURN

ROUTINE PROCESS
CALL BIDE (CPU, 'Process', PT')   CALL TICTOC (PT')
                    RETURN

ROUTINE DEALLOC
CALL BIDE (CPU, 'Deallocate', M)   CALL TICTOC (DT)
                    RETURN
            (f)

ROUTINE HANGAROUND
CALL TICTOC (HT)
RETURN

(e)

Figure 8.12   Level-0 model of a multiprocessor system: (a) block diagram of step 0;
(b) block diagram of step 1; (c) the structure of the simulator; (d) the simulator
routines at step 0; (e) modifications and additions to (d) in order to obtain the
simulator at step 1; (f) modifications to (e) needed when level 1 is added. [*Source*:
Randell (1968).]

435

Figure 8.12(*a*) is a block diagram of the system at the highest level of abstraction. Jobs, each characterized by its arrival time (derivable from the distribution of interarrival times IAT) and by its processing time PT, arrive, are executed by one of the processors and leave. There is no restriction on the number of processors, and no other details such as memory, channels, and secondary storage are taken into account. To simulate our system (which, for the moment, is still extremely simple), the process-interaction organization for the simulator (*see* Section 3.2.3) is the most convenient one. A process-oriented extension-modification of FORTRAN was used by Zurcher and Randell since no simulation language of this type (e.g., SIMULA) was available to them. We shall adopt in our own description the same language, which incorporates features allowing parallel processes to be specified. For instance, Fig. 8.12(*c*) displays a flowchart of the simulator at the highest level of abstraction. After calling the routine JOBGEN, which generates the first job, FORK causes the two routines JOBGEN and DOJOB to be executed in parallel, or, more precisely, as if they were called and processed simultaneously. This reflects the fact that jobs are assumed to be independent, and hence executable in parallel without constraints. While JOBGEN, having generated a new job, returns by a JOIN operation to the point where FORK is invoked again, DOJOB is shared by all the jobs which are being executed concurrently on the simulated system.

The functions of JOBGEN and DOJOB are detailed in Fig. 8.12(*d*). Both call TICTOC, a routine which simulates the passage of time by incrementing the simulated system's clock by the amount specified in TICTOC's argument.

Evidently, at this level of abstraction, the only performance questions which can be examined are those having to do with the number of jobs present in the system at any given instant and with the time spent by a job in the system. Job turnaround times and the number of jobs completed during a certain interval (i.e., the mean throughput rate over that interval) can be calculated. At this point, the values of these indices given by the model are of course optimistic, since no restrictions are imposed on the availability of system resources.

By a simple functional decomposition, we can introduce more detail into this model (which will be called the *step-0 model*). For example, we can expand the job model by replacing a job's single state (the processing state) with five states: wait, allocate, process, deallocate, and hangaround. By so doing, we have introduced the memory, a resource which must be allocated to a job before it can be executed and deallocated before it can depart from the system. However, as shown in Fig. 8.12(*b*), the memory is assumed to be infinite. Any job entering the system can be allocated as much memory as its needs. The modifications to the step-0 model required in order to obtain the step-1 model can be deduced from Figs. 8.12(*d*) and (*e*). The call to TICTOC in DOJOB is replaced by a sequence of five calls, and the five routines to be added simply consist of a call to TICTOC with the duration of the corresponding state as the argument.

Two remarks are to be made here. First, the job characterization necessary in step 1 is more detailed than the one needed in step 0, since the durations of the five states must be specified for each job. Second, the increased degree of detail allows us to investigate, by using the model, questions such as, How many jobs are being allocated memory at a certain instant or on the average? What is the maximum number of jobs in the allocate state at the same time? By transforming the step-0 model into the step-1 model, we have increased the number of the variables which describe the instantaneous state of the system. These variables are listed, together with the performance indices mentioned above, in Table 8.6 under the "Level 0" heading.

Table 8.6

STATE VARIABLES AND PERFORMANCE INDICES
AT THE VARIOUS LEVELS OF A
HIERARCHICAL MULTIPROCESSOR-SYSTEM MODEL

Configuration: 4 CPU's, 8 channels, $512K$ bytes
Work load: mean CPU time: 1 s; mean size: $16K$ bytes;
             exponential distributions

	At $t = 30$ s	
	Mean	Maximum
Level 0[*]		
Number of jobs:		
In the system	23.25	40
In wait state	0.19	2
In allocate state	16.23	31
In process state	6.40	17
In deallocate state	0.28	2
In hangaround state	0.14	3
Completed	83	83
Job turnaround time [s]	6.37	13.79
Level 1[†]		
Number of jobs in the pool to be:		
Allocated	0.46	5
Processed	0.57	6
Deallocated	0.28	2
Number of jobs in:		
Allocate queue	8.06	29
Process queue	2.35	13
Deallocate queue	0.0	2
Number of jobs on:		
CPU's	3.17	4
Channels	5.33	8
Memory utilization [bytes]	344,572.75	520,944
CPU utilization	0.7915	—
Level 2[‡]		
Number of jobs in channel pool	2.38	18
Number of jobs on interrupted CPU's	0.31	3
Channel utilization	0.6659	—

Source: Randell (1968).
[*] *See* Fig. 8.12.
[†] *See* Fig. 8.13.
[‡] *See* Fig. 8.14.

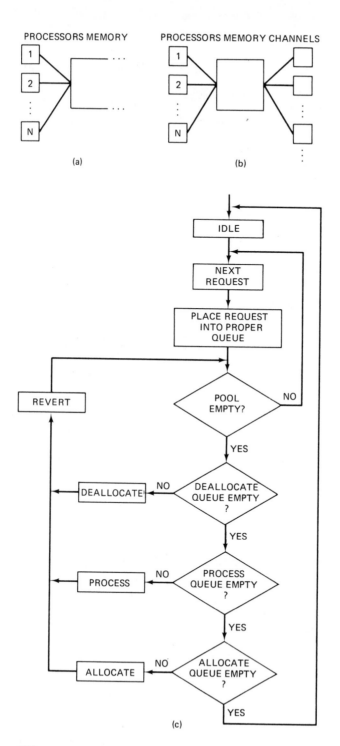

(a)

(b)

(c)

438

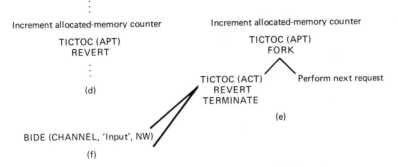

$\vdots$

Increment allocated-memory counter

TICTOC (APT)
REVERT

$\vdots$

(d)

Increment allocated-memory counter

TICTOC (APT)
FORK

TICTOC (ACT) Perform next request
REVERT
TERMINATE

(e)

BIDE (CHANNEL, 'Input', NW)

(f)

Figure 8.13 Level-1 model of a multiprocessor system: (*a*) block diagram of step 0; (*b*) block diagram of step 1; (*c*) flowchart of the CPU process; (*d*) the ALLOCATE part of (*c*) at step 0; (*e*) the ALLOCATE part of (*c*) at step 1; (*f*) modification to (*e*) needed when level 2 is added. [*Source*: Randell (1968).]

It is not easy to introduce into the model we have obtained a restriction like that of a finite number of processors. Modifying it may not present unsurmountable difficulties in this particularly simple case, but in general any modification to a large simulator can be very expensive and risky. And, of course, designers should be expected to change their minds several times during a design. Instead of trying to modify the model, we shall create another model of the more complex system. The new model will not supersede the old one but will be connected to it and coexist with it. All requests to the processors (for allocation, processing, and deallocation) will be placed into a buffer, called the *CPU pool*. To have the old model do so we must only replace the calls to TICTOC in the ALLOC, PROCESS, and DEALLOC routines by calls to BIDE, as shown in Fig. 8.12(*f*). BIDE is a routine which places requests into a pool. Its arguments are the name of the pool, the type of the request, and the desired amount of the requested resource (e.g., the memory space M for allocation and deallocation, the processing time PT for execution). The model in Figs. 8.12(*d*) and (*e*), modified as illustrated in Fig. 8.12(*f*), will be called the *level-0 model*.

Below it, a set of concurrently executing CPU processes will be implemented by the FORK mechanism. The flowchart of a CPU process is as shown in Fig. 8.13(*c*). This process is idle until a request appears in the CPU pool. This event causes the CPU process to add the request to the appropriate queue. Note that the restriction on the number of CPU's requires that queues be introduced. The three queues that will be considered are the allocate queue, the process queue, and the deallocate queue. When the pool is empty, the CPU process examines these queues and simulates the execution of one of the waiting requests according to the priorities deducible from Fig. 8.13(*c*). A CPU process (and the corresponding CPU) goes back to the idle state only when the CPU pool and the three queues are empty. The execution of a request is simulated as described in Fig. 8.13(*d*), which shows the flowchart of the execution of an allocate request. The counter which records the total amount of memory occupied is incremented, TICTOC is called with the CPU time (APT) needed for an allocation operation as its argument, and finally the REVERT routine is invoked.

Again the degree of detail can be increased without changing the level of abstraction. We may add channels to the model as in Fig. 8.13(*b*). Initially, the number of channels will be unconstrained. The channel times needed to load a job into memory (ACT) and to unload it (DCT) will be calculated from the channel speed and the size of the job. Only a minor modification to the allocate and the deallocate part of the CPU process will be required. Figure 8.13(e) shows such a modification for the allocate part. The FORK mechanism allows the CPU process to go on servicing further requests while the invoked channel performs the desired transfer.

A job which is in the allocate state at level 0 is in one of four states at level 1: in the pool, or in the allocate queue, or being allocated by a CPU, or being loaded by a channel. Similar considerations, with some obvious modifications, may be made for the process state and for the deallocate state. The programs at level 1 operate on state variables which are less abstract than those at level 0. The interconnections between the two levels are such that the level-0 variables reflect those at level 1. For instance, the duration of the allocate state for a job is directly related to the durations of the four states into which this state has been decomposed at level 1. The state variables at level 1 are listed in Table 8.6 with the performance indices which can be calculated at this level. Having introduced limitations on the number of processors and on the memory size, questions about CPU and memory utilization can be meaningfully answered here. It is also evident that the presence of level 1 will influence the performance indices which are measured at level 0, namely, turnaround time and throughput rate.

As noted by Randell (1968), the introduction of another real-life constraint such as the one on the number of channels could be handled at level 1. However, it is more convenient to create one more level. A *channel pool* which works like the CPU pool described above may be set up. The FORK routine will be used to create *n channel processes*, if *n* is the number of channels [see Fig. 8.14(a)]. A channel process may have the flowchart presented in Fig. 8.14(b). The only modifications required in the model at level 1 are those shown in Fig. 8.13(f). One of the TICTOC calls in the activate and deactivate parts of each CPU process [see Fig. 8.13(e)] will be replaced by a call to BIDE, which puts a transfer request into the channel pool. With these modifications, we obtain the *level-1 model*. At level 2, an additional performance index, channel utilization, can be defined and computed by the model. Some new job states are also added, as shown in Table 8.6. This process of successive functional decomposition and creation of lower levels of abstraction may be continued until the primitives (the routines at the lowest level, those not containing any calls to routines other than the elementary ones such as TICTOC) are implementable by physical hardware, software, or firmware mechanisms.

Among the advantages of this approach, the flexibility of the resulting simulator is particularly important in a design environment. For instance, suppose that we make the jobs to be processed tasks of the same large job and that, therefore, they are no longer independent of each other. The nature of the communication mechanisms between levels is such that only level 0 will have to be changed. The underlying levels, if they are coded correctly, correctly handle any request pattern. The same conclusion holds if we want to model interactions with terminals. To do this, it is sufficient to replace the process state on level 0 with a sequence of process and wait states. Such a modification obviously requires more information about job and user behavior to be input into the simulator, but no changes have to be made to the models at the lower levels.   ■

Hierarchical approaches to system design are interesting and promising. However, several obstacles still exist and make them difficult to use in their pure form. Among the obstacles summarized by Parnas and Siewiorek (1975), some of

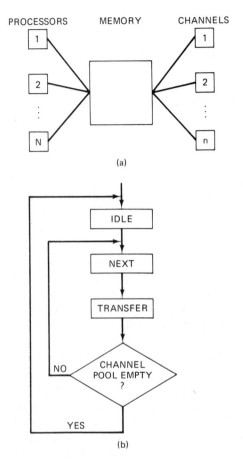

Figure 8.14 Level-2 model of a multiprocessor system: (*a*) block diagram; (*b*) flowchart of the channel process. [*Source*: Randell (1968).]

which have already been mentioned, we have the following:

a. Design requirements are difficult to determine in general and to describe accurately without implying decisions which should be made only during the design.

b. The set of possible designs which satisfy the specifications is usually too large and must be restricted by adding internal specifications, for example, about the available hardware.

c. Often the primitives (e.g., the hardware configuration) are known at the outset and cannot be changed.

d. The system which results may easily turn out to be too inflexible, or some of its mechanisms may be difficult to implement.

Thus, design procedures which properly mix the iterative and hierarchical approaches together, alternating *outside in* phases with *inside out* phases, are probably more convenient than the pure versions of both approaches. The problem then is choosing a good mixture, so that the advantages of both can be retained and their drawbacks eliminated or reduced.

design — modeling Tech.
implement — intractable p

8.5 EVALUATION TECHNIQUES FOR DESIGN STUDIES

In this section, we shall summarize the observations we have made throughout the previous sections of this chapter on the role of the various performance evaluation techniques in system design.

We have seen that modeling techniques predominate during the early phases of design over measurement techniques due to the fact that, often, a system being designed is not available and therefore cannot be measured. The only exception to this statement is also a practically important one, because of the unfortunate manner in which most systems were designed in the past and several are still designed today. The approach we are referring to is that of implementing an initial system, making it run somehow by ad hoc trial-and-error methods, and then trying to improve it by an iterative procedure. This is, of course, one of the two ways in which a system may be iteratively designed, and the worse. The other one, which we always tried to refer to in Sections 8.2 and 8.3, consists of applying the same philosophy to a model of the system. The latter method is better since it gives designers much more flexibility, allows them to postpone the freezing of design decisions into expensive and more rigid hardware and software structures, and has therefore the potential for producing better systems. However, at some point, working on the model becomes inconvenient. If an analytic model is used, this point is reached fairly soon. The amount of details that may be introduced into such a model is usually modest and does not allow one to go much beyond what we have called the initial-design phase. A simulation model is clearly much more powerful from this viewpoint. However, a simulator may well become as complex and as inflexible as the system being designed. When this happens, it is probably more convenient to implement the system and to switch to measurement techniques. This point will be probably reached sooner in design studies performed by vendors than in those performed by customers. Thus, the difference between the two iterative design methods just described lies in the time at which the implementation of the prototype is started. By stating that the latter method is the better, we expressed the opinion that the implementation should be started as late as possible, and that modeling techniques, even at the present stage of their development, can provide designers with the information required to make most of the fundamental design decisions.

In the context of an iterative design procedure, all types of measurement and all sorts of tools may be useful when the first version of the system starts running. Tools which monitor the system in order to gather symptoms of performance bugs are to be accompanied by tools which help explain some unexplained phenomenon and by tools which verify the performance predictions of the models. Thus, meters and tracing tools, hardware and software instruments, and logs and checkpoints may all have useful applications in design. Of course, the internal tools should be incorporated into the system at the earliest stages of its conception, and their harmonious cooperation with each other and with the rest of the system should be of continuous concern to the designer (*see* Section 2.5). Most of these tools, if not all, will not only be used in the last phases of the design procedure. Some of them will continuously monitor the system's operation; others will be left in the system for any measurement needs that may arise, most notably for the tuning of the system as it is installed and for its periodic retuning (*see* Section 7.4.1).

As pointed out in Chapters 3 and 4, measurement techniques will also serve the purposes of calibrating and validating the models and of providing values for the work-load parameters. Measuring these parameters requires that the work load exist and be accessible. Since this is not generally the case during the first phases of a design project, a similar work load to measure must be found. We shall come back to this problem in Section 8.6.

Simulation was described above as the most convenient technique to be employed when iteratively transforming an initial design into the design or a prototype to be implemented. The initial design, obtained from an analytic model, or from intuition, or from previous experiences, will be simulated, and the simulator will be iteratively modified until it satisfies the design requirements at a reasonably deep but still manageable degree of detail. Clearly, instead of immediately constructing a large and complex simulator to represent the initial system, one could adopt a hierarchical procedure like the one described in Example 8.9. Thus, the first part of the design would be mainly hierarchical, and the second part mostly iterative. Alternatively, the two approaches could be more finely intermixed. An advantage of the hierarchical approach would be, as pointed out in Example 8.9, the greater flexibility of the simulator. It should be evident that flexibility is the most important property of a simulator to be used in a design project.

Another very important requirement for a simulator, especially in the first, exploratory phases of design, is that it be as efficient (i.e., as fast) as possible. This will make searches in the parameter space faster and less expensive. Unfortunately, efficiency is in conflict with accuracy and resolution. Thus, also, this requirement seems to suggest an initially simple and fast simulator whose degree of detail is then gradually increased as more design decisions are made and more aspects of the system's configuration and organization are specified. A complex, detailed simulator can be immediately constructed if a number of decisions have already been made, so that, as in the case described by Nielsen (1967), the space of acceptable designs is much more restricted than when one starts from zero. And, even in these cases, building a large simulator to begin with may be harmful, as reported by Campbell and Heffner (1968). It may take longer than implementing the system, it may be more expensive, and the system may even turn out to be easier to understand and to modify than the simulator. A technique which is promising for both improvement and design studies is that proposed by Kimbleton (1975). A simulator built according to this technique uses the known solution of an approximate analytic model to calculate the contribution to performance of each time interval between two consecutive events of the job-arrival or job-departure type. This approach speeds up the simulation considerably without apparently affecting too drastically the accuracy of such results as the system-residence time of a job.

Both analytic and simulation models have another function in design studies. They may be used "on demand" to answer particular questions which arise during the study. If a global system model is available, most of these questions should be answerable by it. If it is not, a specific model, which addresses only the particular problem being examined, is set up and used to obtain an answer that will help the designers make a decision. Thus, the design study is in some sense broken up into a number of substudies which may be relatively easy to perform by analytic or simulation techniques. In the past, good justifications for not using global models were the inadequacies of analytic models and the complexity and inflexibility of general-purpose global simulators. The introduction of hierarchical model-building procedures in both fields might change the situation. Also, the main problem with piecemeal modeling should always be kept in mind when applying it: The nonlinearities and complex interactions between various parts of the system may make this type of modeling either as complicated as global modeling or too crude to be trusted. As our knowledge of systems increases, it may become feasible to decompose a system into modules with very weak or well-understood interactions among them, so that the substudies mentioned above can be performed independently of each other and their results easily combined together. This is expected [*see* Lynch (1972)] to be much easier in hierarchically structured systems if performance interactions among modules and among layers become as well defined and as restricted as functional interactions must be in structured programs.

The role of modeling techniques, especially simulation, in hierarchical design has been illustrated in Section 8.4. Insofar as measurement is concerned, its primary use will be, according to Lynch's prediction, for the purpose of quality control. Thus, measurements of design parameters and performance indices should be much more important than the collection of detailed traces, to be used only to understand unexpected phenomena if and when they are detected. The functions of measurement techniques as the best sources for model parameter values and the most reliable methods for model calibration and validation remain, of course, at least as important as they are in iterative design.

8.6 WORK-LOAD CHARACTERIZATION FOR DESIGN STUDIES

The problem of specifying the work load which the system will have to process is a crucial one in computer system design. The reader will at this point recognize without hesitation the reasons such a specification is absolutely necessary. In fact, it is sufficient to remember that the values of the indices in terms of which the performance requirements are expressed are meaningless if the work-load conditions under which they must be satisfied are not precisely stated. On the other hand, determining realistic work-load conditions for a system to be designed is extremely difficult. Of the three classes of problems examined in this book (selection, improvement, and design), design is the one in which work-load specification may be the most difficult. This is the case when a system is being designed not for a particular installation or at least for a well-defined application but for a large class of installations and applications.

In fact, when the installation is known, the problem is conceptually not more complicated than it is in a selection context (*see* Section 6.5). User needs have to be analyzed and their evolution in the near future predicted. These are certainly nontrivial problems. However, they are much simpler than those which designers encounter when trying to design a system supposed to satisfy the needs of a number of installations. As the size of the population of prospective customers increases, the knowledge of the actual work loads that the various incarnations of the system will experience becomes fuzzier. Since the quality of the design is, roughly speaking, directly related to the quantity of work-load information available to the designers, this quality will tend to deteriorate. Yet, if the system is being designed for a well-defined application (such as the control of a certain type of industrial process, airline or hotel reservations, information retrieval), it is still possible to reliably estimate, perhaps in a parametric way, the most important characteristics of the work load. Thus, systems are designable which will work efficiently in a number of installations after having gone through a few, well-understood modifications to be tailored to the peculiarities of their environment.

An even more difficult task is the one of designing a *general-purpose* system. This term usually indicates that almost nothing is known about the work load to be expected. Designing in these conditions of ignorance seems to be nearly impossible. A pessimist would comment that this explains why so many commercial general-purpose systems are so bad. An optimist, on the other hand, would find it amazing that systems designed in such desperate conditions are after all capable of producing reasonable performance.

Of course, both sides would be right and wrong. As the knowledge of the work load decreases, the design of specific, finished systems becomes more difficult and less successful. A system which is purposely designed and tuned for a certain installation may be excellent for that installation and those few others which are very similar to it. However, it is likely to perform poorly in most of the other environments. The only convenient solution seems to be the establishment of a connection between the degree of specification of the work load and that of the system. For a work load which is defined only as being "general-purpose," the design effort will have as its first goal the one of creating not a single system but a "general-purpose" family of systems. As we saw in Section 8.1, a family can be viewed as a kit of hardware and software components which may be combined in a number of ways so as to cover somehow the field of possible applications and the requirements of the class of installations for which the family is intended. Thus, if we do not consider the tuning stage, the design process consists of the two successive stages of computer family design and customization. The second stage is performed only when more detailed and precise work-load information becomes available. In this way, a reasonable performance can often be achieved, in agreement with the optimist's viewpoint. However, the pessimist would probably be right arguing that a satisfactory result is often achieved at the expense of a waste of resources, due to the constraints inevitably introduced into the customization stage by the family's components and to the lack of systematic methods for performing the customization.

In those phases of a design procedure which make use of a modeling technique, the characterization to be considered for the work load will be dictated by the system model, which in turn will be determined by the work-load information available. The quality of the results produced by a model cannot be better than that of the input data. The values of the work-load parameters should be carefully estimated or, more conveniently, measured. However, measurements cannot be performed on the real work load until the system is installed and delivered to its users. This is the time of the tuning phase, when all of the previous phases have been completed. Therefore, the values of the work-load parameters will have to be derived from measurements of other work loads whose characteristics are assumed to be close to those of the unknown work load that the system will have to process. The designers of a computer family often use input traces recorded in installations where systems of the predecessor family of the same type are running. A new generation of computers is designed assuming that it will have to process the work loads of the previous generation. As certain design decisions are taken, some changes in the input traces or in the parameters derived from them may have to be made as a consequence of those decisions. For instance, when the instruction sets of the CPU's in a new family are specified, the instruction traces should be converted to reflect the new instruction sets. Another example of the use of alien work loads in design may be found in the simulation of virtual-memory mechanisms to study and compare various memory management policies. The work load is in this case usually represented by memory reference strings generated by programs not written for the system being designed but for another (hopefully virtual-memory) machine. Here, as in the previous example, the assumption is made that the work load will be different from that being used only in some minor and therefore not very relevant aspects. Often this assumption, especially in the latter example, is not too unrealistic. For instance, it may be argued that most of the programs the new system will execute are likely to be different from the ones running on an old system but that the differences in their memory referencing patterns would not influence the choice of the memory management policy if they could be taken into account. In arguing this, we implicitly neglect, among other things, the effect of the policy on the users.

The situation of ignorance about the work load that we have described is by no means hopeless. It can be substantially improved by undertaking systematic studies of user behavior. These studies should not only be system-oriented but also, and especially, user-oriented. Designers must know more about the work load to be expected if better systems are to be designed. This additional knowledge can come only from technical and psychological investigations of user needs, reactions, habits, and expectations.

PROBLEMS

8.1. Design by an iterative approach an initial configuration for a small batch-processing system. Assume that the configuration will include a CPU, a head-per-track disk, and a movable-arm disk and that the work load can be characterized with respect to this configuration as in Table 8.1. The performance specifications for the system to be designed are $\bar{T}_{min} = 1.5$ jobs/s and $\bar{t}_{max} = 3$ s. Take as the starting configuration the one which has resulted from the investigation in Example 8.1 and modify it iteratively, analyzing the model after each change to determine whether the given performance requirements are satisfied. Try to consider also the economical aspects in making your modifications, assuming the cost model (8.4).

8.2. Devise a procedure which can be used to design a system like the one dealt with in Example 8.1 assuming that cost requirements are assigned instead of performance specifications. Let the work-load parameters be those given in Table 8.1, and let the maximum system cost, computed according to (8.4), be $C_{max} = 80,000$ dollars. Your goal is to design a system with maximum or nearly maximum $\bar{T}$ which satisfies the constraint $C \leq C_{max}$. Consider both the case of unconstrained $\bar{t}$ and the case in which it must be $\bar{t} \leq \bar{t}_{max}$.

8.3. Repeat the initial-configuration design of Example 8.1 using the open-network model in Fig. 4.16. Assume that the mean job arrival rate is $\lambda = 1$ job/s and that jobs can terminate only after receiving service from the disk (i.e., $b_{21} = 1$). Assume also that the mean service rate of Σ_4 has already been determined and is $\mu_4 = 3$ s^{-1}. The only performance specification in this case is $\bar{t}_{max} = 6$ s. Compare your results (in particular the values of μ_1, μ_2, and μ_3) with those obtained in Example 8.1, and discuss the reasons of any sizable differences you may notice.

8.4. The design procedure illustrated in Example 8.1 determines the required characteristics of the components for a given configuration. However, the composition of the configuration is usually among the unknowns of the problem. Attack the same design as in Example 8.1 considering a different configuration. For instance, you may try with two independent and identical drums or disks, assuming that their access probabilities are half of those considered for the single component in Example 8.1. In other words, you may assume that the two drums or disks are equally loaded. Do you expect the total cost, computed by (8.4), to increase or decrease because of the addition of another device?

8.5. Solve Problem 8.2 for the virtual-memory system dealt with in Example 8.2.

8.6. Repeat the design procedure described in Example 8.2 assuming that the drum cost coefficient h'_2 in (8.8) is given by

$$h'_2 = h'_{21}\sqrt{N}$$

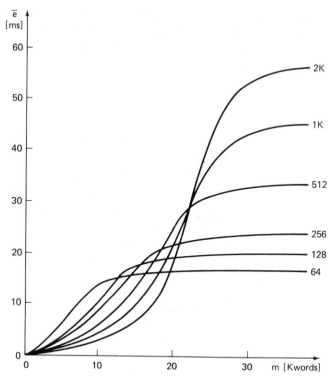

Figure P8.1   Family of lifetime curves for Problem 8.7. Each curve corresponds to a different page size, reported (in words) on the curve.

with $h'_{21} = 2000$ dollars-s$^{1/2}$. This correction was suggested by the discussion at the end of Example 8.5.

8.7. You are given the family of lifetime curves depicted in Fig. P8.1. Describe how you would use them to design a memory hierarchy like the one illustrated in Fig. 8.7 and discussed in Example 8.6. As an exercise which would have to be repeated many times during such design, calculate the performance of the three-level virtual-memory system which resulted from Examples 8.2 and 8.6, assuming that the average program running on that system behaves as in Fig. P8.1.

8.8. Design the instrumentation required to experimentally verify that the memory hierarchy specified in Example 8.6 performs according to the assumptions and predictions of its designers. Discuss also the actual implementation of the tools, the problems you would expect (interference, storage, resolution, prereduction, etc.), and how you would try to solve them.

8.9. In Example 8.6 it was assumed that none of the pages or subpages to be replaced has to be written back to the paging drum or to the primary memory, respectively. This is equivalent to the assumption that the CPU never executes any instruction which stores a word into the cache. You are now asked to redesign the same memory hierarchy for the system specified in Example 8.2 after having removed this assumption. To simplify the study, the probability that a page or subpage to be removed is to be written back may be considered constant and not very sensitive to relatively small variations of the subpage or page size. For subpages, let this probability be 0.6, and for pages, 0.75.

8.10. Determine the approximate total memory bandwidth required in a system with two CPU's, each having a mean memory request rate equal to 2×10^6 references/s; two channels, each controlling a drum having a transfer rate of 0.5×10^6 words/s; two channels, each controlling four disks having each a transfer rate of 0.3×10^6 words/s; one channel controlling six tape drives, each having a transfer rate of 10^5 words/s; and one display processor with a transfer rate of 10^6 words/s. Repeat the calculation under several assumptions about the values of the probabilities of overlap between the active periods of the various components of the system. The worst-case design corresponds to the requirement that the memory be able to satisfy the simultaneous requests of all the devices connected to it without causing any appreciable performance degradation. How would you implement a worst-case memory for this system by a semiconductor technology characterized by read times of 300 ns and write times of the same magnitude?

8.11. In the system described in Problem 8.10, each CPU is connected to the memory by an independent bus. Three additional buses are used to connect to memory the drum channels, the disk channels, and the tape-display pair, respectively. Determine the bandwidths required for these five buses.

8.12. Modify the model of a computer graphics system in Fig. 8.10(*b*) to account for possible accesses to the local storage LS during the preprocessing and postprocessing operations (blocks 6 and 11) and for the use of the central computer CC required when accesses are made to the central storage CS during the local processing of a service request (block 4). How would these modifications be reflected in the list of parameters displayed in Table 8.4 and in the analytic treatment of Example 8.8 [equations (8.30)–(8.43) and Table 8.5]?

8.13. A large information-processing system consisting of a central computer and *n* satellite computers distributed over an entire region is being designed for a banking application. The satellite computers are connected to the central computer via telephone lines according to a star topology, as shown in Fig. P8.2. Each one of them is expected to provide local service to up to *h* interactive terminals. During daytime, the system is to be mainly used to process transactions which require retrieving a record from an on-line data base making some modifications to it, and restoring it into the data base. The whole data base is stored in the secondary memory of the central computer, which extracts a number of daily reports from it every night. However, since the probability that the transactions requested at a certain location involve a small portion of the data base is generally high, the response time of the system would probably decrease if that portion of the data base were also stored in the secondary memory of each satellite computer. In this case, when a needed record is not found in the local data base, a message is sent to the central computer. This computer knows on which satellite computer the up-to-date version of that record is, asks it to ship the record, and routes the record to the requesting location, where the record is updated and shipped back to its source. By so doing, the centralized data base may be updated only once a day and serves as a

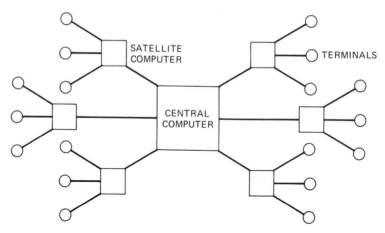

Figure P8.2   Block diagram of the system dealt with in Problem 8.13.

backup to the distributed one. Let the probability of requesting a missing record be $e^{-M_2/A}$, where e is the base of natural logarithms, M_2 is the size of the local secondary memory in bytes, and A is $1M$ byte. The problem to be investigated is the choice of M_2. Getting inspiration from Example 8.8 and possibly also from Example 6.1, construct a model which can be used to evaluate the cost-performance trade-off related to this choice, and describe its use for the intended purpose. Take the mean response time as the primary performance index of interest, and introduce all the assumptions you consider necessary (or desirable) and reasonable.

8.14. A microprogrammable CPU can perform an operation in hardware, firmware, or software. The decision, to be made at design time, depends on the expected costs of the three implementations and on their performance characteristics (weighted according to the expected frequency of execution of the operation). Assuming that a minimal microinstruction set has already been specified for a CPU being designed, describe in detail the procedure you would follow to determine whether a given operation not included in the microinstruction set should be added to it, or to the machine language by microprogramming it, or to the library of utility programs by programming it. Examples of operations that might be considered are the calculation of the square roots, the search operation (fetch an operand, compare it with the contents of a register, and increment a counter or raise a flag if certain specified conditions are satisfied), and the floating-point divide.

8.15. Specify how you would instrument the hierarchical simulation model described in Example 8.9 so that the data listed in Table 8.6 can be collected.

8.16. Modify the model illustrated in Fig. 8.12 [excluding the changes shown in Fig. 8.12(*f*)] so as to introduce limitations on the number of processors and on the size of the memory [Figs. 8.13(*a*) and (*b*)] without creating a new level of abstraction. Compare the characteristics of your solution (ease of construction, understandability, flexibility) with those of the model represented in Figs. 8.12 and 8.13.

9

The Evaluation
of Program Performance

9.1 INTRODUCTION

Devoting a separate chapter to a discussion of program performance evaluation may seem in contradiction with the principle we stated several times
throughout the book, namely, that there is no conceptual difference between
hardware and software and that computer systems should be considered from the
performance evaluation viewpoint as hardware–software complexes. On the other
hand, an even greater emphasis has been put on the distinction between the
system and its work load. And the work load consists of information-processing
tasks which present themselves to the system as programs to be executed. This
distinction corresponds quite well to two basically different and extremely important points of view: that of the persons who are responsible for the whole system
and its performance (an installation's manager and staff) and that of the programmers (the users), who are responsible only for their programs and are interested
only in the performance with which the system executes these programs. Note
that there is at least one category of persons whose viewpoint is a combination of
both: the systems programmers. They use a system like any other programmer,
but their programs have the task of managing the resources of the same or of
another system. When these programs are debugged and running, they cease to
be part of a work load and become part of a system.

451

Thus, we see at least two reasons, which seem to be sufficiently good, for dealing with program performance evaluation in a book on computer system performance evaluation. One is that the work load, whose study is so essential to the definition and the analysis of system performance, consists of programs. The other reason is that nearly all of the algorithms which constitute an operating system are implemented in the form of programs, whose efficiency as programs generally has a nontrivial impact on the system's performance.

In spite of the fact that we have often considered user-oriented system performance indices such as mean turnaround or response times, very seldom did our optics coincide with that, at least equally important, of an individual user (the only example is perhaps in Section 6.3.4). This optics focuses the attention of the evaluator on the program. It is the program which is to be designed, selected, or modified. The system appears, in some sense, only in the background, as an unmodifiable part of the program's environment. It establishes, so to speak, the rules of the game. It influences heavily, sometimes unpredictably, the program's performance. By executing the program, it provides a service to the user, who normally has to pay for it. Often, the system and its characteristics must be specified and explicitly taken into account in evaluating programs. In other cases, as we shall see, the performance of a program can be defined and evaluated in a system-independent way.

The objects of our study in this chapter will be programs. There are many important characteristics according to which programs are evaluated: first, correctness, accuracy, and reliability; then maintainability, readability, understandability, testability, expandibility, design cost, running cost, and so on. We shall concentrate on the performance or efficiency of programs, that is, roughly speaking, on *how well* they perform their information-processing tasks. However, we should always keep in mind that the value of a program depends on a number of characteristics which, in certain situations, are more important than performance as we shall define it in Section 9.2. Various relationships exist among these characteristics, and several trade-off decisions have to be made when a program is designed and implemented.

We have explained the main reasons for devoting this chapter to the topic of program performance evaluation. This subject is such an important part of software engineering, and more generally computer engineering, that it would certainly deserve a whole book. We shall therefore limit ourselves to an introductory discussion of its most important aspects and to the simplest types of programs and of systems. Only sequential, non-recursive programs written for conventional machines will be considered. The virtual-memory systems to be referred to will have the most straightforward organization. As will be explained in more detail later, the allocation of virtual space will be static. Also, a paging technique and a demand-paging strategy will be assumed throughout the chapter. To illustrate the basic notions presented in this chapter, we shall use FORTRAN, which is still the most widely known and popular language for scientific and technical applications. These decisions have been made in the interest of brevity and clarity. It was felt that getting involved in too many details would tend to obscure the concepts. Once they have been assimilated, the concepts can be relatively easily extended to cover the practical cases arising with more complex, or just different, types of programs, languages, and machines.

This chapter's structure mirrors the one of the rest of the book. In Section 9.2 we shall define programs from our viewpoint and discuss the major indices which can be used to quantitatively assess their performance, both in a nonvirtual (Section 9.2.1) and in a virtual (Section 9.2.2) memory environment. The main techniques and tools which can be used to evaluate these indices are presented in Section 9.3. In Section 9.3.1 we shall be concerned with measurement, and modeling (both analytic and simulation) is dealt with in Section 9.3.2. The three major classes of evaluation problems are examined in Section 9.4 to show how the evaluation techniques illustrated in Section 9.3 can be applied in program selection studies (Section 9.4.1), program improvement studies (Section 9.4.2), and program design studies (Section 9.4.3).

9.2 PROGRAM PERFORMANCE INDICES

9.2.1 Time and Space

What is a program? Knuth (1968) has given the following definition: "An expression of a computational method in a computer language is called a *program*." The two key terms in this definition are *computational method* and *computer language*. A *computational method* is a procedure having all the characteristics of an algorithm except possibly finiteness, that is, the property of terminating after a finite number of steps. An algorithm is, as our readers know, a finite set of rules which precisely specify a sequence of operations or steps to be executed in order to solve a problem. The fact that a program is written in a computer language means that it can be executed by any computer which "understands" that language. Of course, any human being who knows the language can also execute the program, for example, by pencil and paper.

When it is executed (by a person or by a computer), a program transforms certain input information into output data, usually called the *results*. For instance, a program which computes the square root of a positive number x has the value of x as its input data and $\sqrt{x}$ (or an acceptable approximation of $\sqrt{x}$) as its result. This view corresponds to the black-box representation reported in Fig. 9.1(a).

Some of the most interesting questions which may be asked about a program relate to the *difficulty* of its execution. This difficulty will of course depend on various factors, among which are the complexity of the computational method (whose study is the task of the theory of computational complexity) and the *skills* of the executor. The first answer we would give to the question "How difficult was it to calculate $\sqrt{x}$ by pencil and paper using this program?" would probably be as follows: "For $x = 19.35$ and an error smaller than 10^{-3}, it took about 3

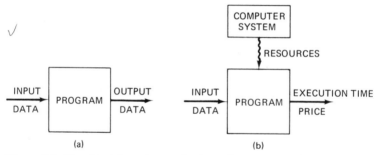

Figure 9.1 Two black-box characterizations of a program: (*a*) the input-output characterization; (*b*) the input-performance-price characterization.

minutes." This seems to indicate that the *execution time* of a program is a useful, though approximate, way of describing its difficulty. Of course, the dialogue reported above implies that the person who asked the question has some knowledge of our computational ability and of the calculating tools (slide rule, abacus, pocket calculator) we had at our disposal when we executed the program. Another possible way of characterizing the difficulty of the program would be to quote the cost of its execution, which is the sum of the costs of the resources we consumed (our mental energy, our time, the pencil, the paper, and so on). Even the cost would generally depend on the input data, as we felt was the case of the execution time when we specified that our answer was valid "for $x = 19.35$ and an error smaller than 10^{-3}."

The black-box program characterization which represents our viewpoint in this chapter is the one in Fig. 9.1(*b*). We are not interested here in the results of a program but, assuming that they are correct, in the time it takes to obtain them and in the price we have to pay for the resources the program consumes. We shall see that these two indices are strictly, though not always simply, related to each other.

While the price is primarily an economical index, the execution time has all the characteristics of a performance index. If it is accepted as a measure of difficulty, it may be used to compare two programs which express the same computational method or two programs which express two different computational methods to obtain the same results. The faster will be the better.

Execution time will be considered here as the main program performance index, but we should never forget that other indices may be more important in certain situations or environments. The popularity of execution time is also due to its relationships with the price of executing a program. However, conflicts sometimes arise between the two indices. In these cases, the choice should be made according to a minimum-global-cost criterion. An optimum trade-off between programmer time and computer time should be sought, of course taking their respective costs into account.

An observation which has already been made but deserves being repeated is that, even though we shall refer for brevity to the performance, the execution time, and the execution price of a program, we should never forget that these in fact characterize (*program, input*) *pairs*. Only for those programs whose performance is relatively insensitive to input data variations can we speak of program performance without specifying the values of the input data.

Another important remark is that our answer ("about 3 minutes") to the question on the difficulty of computing $\sqrt{x}$ implicitly meant "3 minutes without interruptions." Clearly, one cannot characterize the difficulty of execution of a program by the duration of a time period during which other activities not related to the execution of that program were performed. Ideally, a program performance index should not depend on anything but the behavior of the program. A dependence on the values of some system parameters such as the speed of the CPU may be tolerable, but a dependence on such time-variant, unpredictable quantities as the parameters of the system's work load is not. Thus, as we concluded in Section 6.3.4, the execution time of a program in a multiprogramming environment cannot be taken as a viable index. If the program is processed with given input data in uniprogramming mode, the variability of its execution time is not equal to zero [*see*, for example, Bell (1974)] but is often sufficiently small so as to make this time an acceptable index of the program's performance. Note also that the uniprogramming execution time of a program running on a certain system is the lower bound of that program's execution times when the same system is operated in multiprogramming mode.

We shall see in Example 9.1 that there are various definitions of the uniprogramming execution time, with different degrees of system dependence. In any case, however, we must bear in mind that generally the uniprogramming execution time is a system-dependent performance index. There is in principle no guarantee that the result of a performance comparison between two comparable programs can be transported to systems different from the one on which the comparison has been performed. In other words, it is perfectly conceivable that, given two programs which compute $\sqrt{x}$, the one which is the faster on system A be the slower on system B. Of course, we must assume that both programs can run on both machines. The problem of a system-independent characterization of programs, which is very important in system evaluation studies and particularly in system selection, has been discussed in Sections 5.2.3 and 6.5 and will come up again throughout this chapter.

Even though we have identified an acceptable performance index for programs (at least for those written to be executed by a given system), we are still far from having reached our goals. We want to learn how the value of this index may be influenced so that performance specifications can be satisfied in program design and the performance of a given program can be improved. To do this, the black-box characterization we have used to define our performance and economical indices must be abandoned. A more detailed analysis of the program's structure and behavior is now needed.

disjoint states

The basic question of program performance analysis is, How does a program spend its execution time? To answer this question, it is useful to define a set of disjoint states in which the program can be found during its execution. If $S = (S_1, S_2, \ldots, S_n)$ is such a set, the behavior of the program can be described by the sequence of the states visited during execution and by the time spent in each state. Formally, this characterization may be represented as a sequence $\{i_j(t_j)\}$ [$j = 1, 2, \ldots, ;$ $i_j \in (1, 2, \ldots, n)$], where t_j is the duration of the jth interval of execution, which is spent in state S_{i_j}. If we define, for all j and for $k = 1, 2, \ldots, n$,

$$t_j(k) = t_j \quad \text{when } k = i_j,$$
$$t_j(k) = 0 \quad \text{when } k \neq i_j, \tag{9.1}$$

then the total time spent in state S_i during the execution of the program is

$$t(i) = \sum_{j=1}^{r} t_j(i), \tag{9.2}$$

where r is the number of intervals in which the execution time (assumed to be finite) has been subdivided. The execution time is given by

$$t = \sum_{i=1}^{n} t(i). \tag{9.3}$$

An example of this decomposition is the one in which the program states correspond to various hardware resources whose mutually exclusive services are obtained by the running program. If we assume that the system consists of the CPU, a tape drive, and a terminal and does not allow programs to overlap their computations with their secondary storage and I/O transfers, we may define three states: the CPU state, the tape state, and the terminal state. The behavior of a program can therefore be represented as in Fig. 9.2(a) or, equivalently, Fig. 9.2(b). Note that during the tape or the terminal state the CPU may be active controlling the transfers, but we assume that it is not doing any directly useful computation for the user. This decomposition of our main performance index t into components which may be viewed as partial performance indices leads us to a characterization of program performance in terms of *resource demand patterns* (e.g., the sequences of CPU, tape, and terminal intervals or *bursts*) and of *global resource demands* such as $t(1)$, $t(2)$, and $t(3)$ in Fig. 9.2(b). Such characterization is very close to that on which the computation of the price of a program's execution is normally based. In most cases, the usage of resources which can only be consumed by one program at a time is charged according to the total duration of such usage. If a resource is used by a program together with another resource, then we may take this into account when the program's states are defined. For instance, if CPU and tape activities can be overlapped by performing tape-memory transfers via the direct memory access (DMA) mechanism, the following four states may be defined: CPU only, tape only, CPU-tape, and terminal.

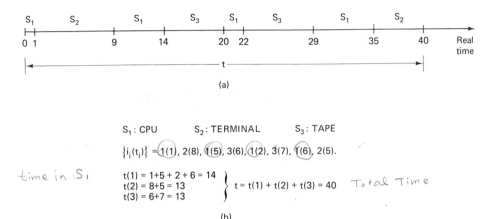

S$_1$: CPU   S$_2$: TERMINAL   S$_3$: TAPE

$\{i_j(t_j)\}$ = 1(1), 2(8), 1(5), 3(6), 1(2), 3(7), 1(6), 2(5).

time in S$_1$

$t(1) = 1+5 + 2 + 6 = 14$
$t(2) = 8+5 = 13$ $t = t(1) + t(2) + t(3) = 40$ Total Time
$t(3) = 6+7 = 13$

(b)

Figure 9.2   Decomposition of the uniprogramming execution time of a program with given input data: (*a*) timing diagram of the execution; (*b*) the states of the program, their sequence, and their durations.

Storage resources, in particular primary memory, are not only charged according to the time they are used but also according to the amount of space occupied. Thus, both the mean or maximum *space* and the *space-time product* (defined as the integral of primary-memory space over uniprogramming time) are employed to characterize a program's memory space demand. In nonvirtual-memory systems, the dependence of the uniprogramming execution time on the memory space needed is relatively weak. It would be zero if loading and unloading times were not taken into account and if overlays were excluded from our consideration. However, the space needed always influences the price to be paid and the multiprogramming execution time (when the loading of large jobs tends to be delayed). The situation is completely different in virtual-memory systems, as will be seen in Section 9.2.2.

Other types of decomposition, leading to different performance indices, are obviously possible. For example, the information which constitutes a program may be divided into pieces which will be called *blocks.* At any given instant of its execution, the program will be accessing one of these blocks. During any interval of time, only a subset of the blocks will usually be accessed. Referencing a block or a distinct subset of blocks may be viewed as a state of the program, and the execution time may be decomposed into the intervals spent in each one of these states. A block may consist of a single word or character (an instruction or a datum), a group of words, a subroutine, an array, a record, a file, an operating system module called by the program, an overlay, and so on. It may be useful to group into the same block all of the information which is bulk-transferred between the primary memory and any other device, so that the device's access and transfer times can be viewed as spent by the program in accessing that block. The sequence of the states defined by the blocks is a description of the *referencing pattern* produced by the program when processing the given input data. We shall return to this description in Section 9.2.2.

The decomposition may also be restricted to, or made much more detailed in, certain portions of the total execution time. For instance, we may be interested in analyzing how a program spends its CPU time. That is, what types of instructions does the program execute most frequently? What fractions of the total CPU time are absorbed by the various types of instructions or statements? What variables, arrays, and data structures account for most of the CPU time? Answers to all of these questions can be provided if a distinct state is associated to each instruction (or statement) in the program and the CPU time intervals of the program's execution are decomposed into the intervals spent in each one of these states. The sequence $\{i_j(t_j)\}$ that we obtain this way will be called a *program trace*. Practically all of the questions regarding the behavior of a program during execution can be given an answer if the trace and the listing of the program are known. This derivation is illustrated for some useful program characterizations in the following example.

Example 9.1 The executable statements of a small FORTRAN program are listed in Table 9.1. To simplify our discussion, we assume that the program is executed by a FORTRAN machine (for instance, a machine consisting of a computer system with a FORTRAN interpreter running on it).

A black-box characterization like that in Fig. 9.1(*a*) can be obtained by listing all the input variables (XO, YO, H, JNT, IENT) and all the output variables [H, XO, YO, X, A(I)] in the program's text. To define our main performance index, the execution time, we have to specify the criteria according to which the beginning and the end of execution are determined.

There are at least two reasonable definitions of execution time in our present context. One adopts the external-world viewpoint: The execution time is the time between the instant the card reader starts reading the first card of the program and the instant the printer prints out the last line of results. This, which would more or less correspond to the definition of turnaround time in a uniprogrammed batch system, includes in the execution time the durations of several operations which perhaps depend more on the system than on the program, such as the transfers from card reader to tape and from tape to printer, the code conversions, and the loading and unloading operations. The other definition refers to the "pure" execution. The program is assumed to be loaded in memory, and its execution time is the interval between the beginning of the first instruction and the completion of the STOP instruction. This definition, although less directly related to the programmer's waiting time than the former, has the advantage of being less system-dependent and therefore of giving more emphasis to the instrinsic behavior of the program. We shall, in this example and throughout the chapter, take the latter as our definition of execution time. Note that there are other ways to define execution times even in a batch-processing environment like the one assumed here. Of course, different definitions have to be devised when dealing with other types of systems (*see*, for example, Problem 9.1).

Going back to our program, the "pure" execution time just defined will be the sum of those times required to process each one of the ν input cards preceding the card with IENT = 0. Therefore, we could interpret a program run as the concatenation of ν

Table 9.1

LISTING AND PROFILE OF A SMALL FORTRAN PROGRAM

Statement number	Statement	Frequency count	Time	S
1	10 READ(5, 1) XO,YO,H,JNT,IENT	2	100	1
2	IF(IENT) 20,40,20	2	4	2
3	20 WRITE(6,2) H,XO,YO	1	50	3
4	CALL RK2(FUN,H,XO,YO,JNT,IENT,A)	1	2	4
5	STEP = FLOAT(JNT)*H	1	11	5
6	X = XO	1	1	6
7	DO 30 I = 1,IENT	1	2	7
8	X = X + STEP	1	2	8
9	30 WRITE(6,3) X,A(I)	1	51	9
10	GO TO 10	1	1	10
11	40 STOP	1	1	11
	END	—	—	
12	FUNCTION FUN(X,Y)	8	120	12
13	FUN = 1./X	8	64	13
14	RETURN	8	40	14
	END	—	—	
15	SUBROUTINE RK2(FUN,H,XI,YI,K,N,VEC)	1	15	15
16	H2 = H/2.	1	8	16
17	Y = YI	1	1	17
18	X = XI	1	1	18
19	DO 2 II = 1,N	1	2	19
20	DO 1 J = 1,K	1	2	20
21	T1 = H*FUN(X,Y)	2	18	21
22	T2 = H*FUN(X + H2,Y + T1/2.)	2	36	22
23	T3 = H*FUN(X + H2,Y + T2/2.)	2	36	23
24	T4 = H*FUN(X + H,Y + T3)	2	22	24
25	Y = Y + (T1 + 2.*T2 + 2.*T3 + T4)/6.	2	46	25
26	1 X = X + H	2	6	26
27	2 VEC(II) = Y	1	3	27
28	RETURN	1	5	28
	END	—	—	

Source: Knuth (1971), by permission of John Wiley & Sons Ltd.

separate runs, each with different values of the five input variables listed above. Each run will begin and end with the execution of the READ statement. The $(\nu + 1)$st run will stop immediately after the READ statement and the subsequent IF test. Dividing the total execution time by ν, we would have the mean execution time of each run. If the sample of input data being considered were large enough and could be viewed as "typical," the inverse of this mean time could be defined as the *mean processing rate* of one input data set, an index of program productivity often used for certain programs (measured, for example, in payrolls computed per minute, invoices prepared per minute, mailing addresses printed per hour, reports generated per hour, and so on).

Since we postulate the existence of a FORTRAN machine by which the program is executed and whose physical implementation has been left unspecified, no program states corresponding to physical resources can be defined. (In fact, when the object code resulting from the program's compilation runs on a tape-oriented batch-processing system, its execution consists of an alternation of CPU and tape intervals. The tape intervals occur when READ and WRITE statements are executed.) However, states corresponding to *FORTRAN machine resources* can be defined, as we did in Section 6.3.4, Example 6.3. Tables 6.10 and 6.11 illustrate the analysis of another FORTRAN program performed according to the FORTRAN resources listed by Morgan and Campbell (1973) (*see* Table 6.9). The same analysis for the program in Table 9.1 is proposed in Problem 9.3 as an exercise for the reader.

Alternatively, we may identify the program states with the various blocks into which we subdivide the program's address space. A simple example of such a subdivision is presented in Figs. 9.3(a) and (b). There are three instruction blocks (the main routine, the function FUN, the subroutine RK2) and four data blocks (S_4 is the state in which no data are referenced). Figure 9.3(c) shows a possible sequence of instruction block states. The

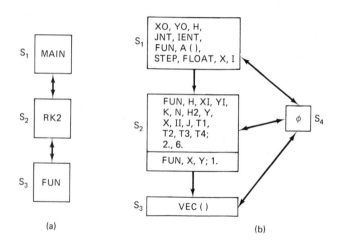

(a)

(b)

$\{i_j (t_j)\}$ = 1(104), 2(31), 3(28), 2(18), 3(28), 2(18), 3(28), 2(11), 3(28), 2(41), 1(121).

(c)

$\{i_j (t_j)\}$ = 1(104), 2(54), 4(5), 2(41), 4(5), 2(41), 4(5), 2(34), 4(5), 2(33), 3(3), 4(5), 1(67), 4(1), 1(52), 4(1).

(d)

Figure 9.3 Program states and their durations for the program in Table 9.1: (*a*) instruction block states; (*b*) data block states; (*c*) sequence of instruction block states visited during a sample execution; (*d*) sequence of data block states visited during the same execution.

total times spent in each block may, for example, suggest that the execution time could be reduced by a nontrivial amount if FUN, which accounts for 34.4% of the time, were speeded up (*see* Section 9.4.2). Similarly, Fig. 9.3(*d*) displays the corresponding sequence of data block states.

Refining the subdivision of the program into instruction blocks, we arrive at the program trace characterization. Each executable statement now defines a distinct state. The trace tells us the order in which these states are visited and the time spent in each one of them. ●A possible trace, obtained when the first input card has IENT = 1, JNT = 2 and the second IENT = 0, is reported in Table 9.2. From the knowledge of the trace, answers to practically all performance-related questions can be derived. A few examples follow.

Table 9.2

A TRACE FOR THE PROGRAM IN TABLE 9.1

MAIN	RK2	FUN	MAIN	RK2	FUN
1(50)				21(2)	
2(2)					12(15)
3(50)					13(8)
4(2)					14(5)
104	15(15)			21(7)	*28*
	16(8)			22(11)	
	17(1)			*18*	12(15)
	18(1)				13(8)
	19(2)				14(5)
	20(2)			22(7)	*28*
	21(2)			23(11)	
	3			*18*	12(15)
		12(15)			13(8)
		13(8)			14(5)
	21(7)	14(5)		23(7)	*28*
	22(11)	*28*		24(4)	
	18			*11*	12(15)
		12(15)			13(8)
		13(8)			14(5)
	22(7)	14(5)		24(7)	
	23(11)	*28*		25(23)	*28*
	18			26(3)	
		12(15)		27(3)	
		13(8)		28(5)	
	23(7)	14(5)	5(11)	*4*	
	24(4)	*28*	6(1)		
	11		7(2)		
		12(15)	8(2)		
		13(8)	9(51)		
	24(7)	14(5)	10(1)		
	25(23)	*28*	1(50)		
	26(3)		2(2)		
			11(1)		
			121		

How many I/O operations are performed by the program? This question, which in physical terms corresponds to asking the number of tape accesses made, can be answered by counting the number of times READ and WRITE statements are executed. In the trace of Table 9.2, this number is 4. A similar approach can be followed to determine, for instance, the number of times RK2 is called (1 in Table 9.2); the number of times variable XO is accessed, that is, read or written (5 in Table 9.2); and the time spent executing the function FUN (224 time units in Table 9.2). All of these questions are easy to answer if the *frequency counts* of each statement, defined as the total number of times the statement has been executed, are known. The collection of the frequency counts of all the statements in a program has been called a *program profile* by Knuth (1971). The profile of a program changes when the values of its input data change. Thus, like all the performance indices we have introduced, it characterizes a (program, input) pair rather than a program. Table 9.1 reports the profile derived from the trace in Table 9.2. Note that statements such as 21, which contain function calls, appear in the program trace twice for each of their executions.

A program profile can also be used to derive the *dynamic statement mix* of a program (*see* Section 5.3.4). Each statement is classified as belonging to one (or sometimes more than one) class, and the sum of the frequency counts of the statements in each class yields the relative frequency of that class. The last column in Table 6.10 represents a statement mix for the program in the same table.

Other questions cannot be answered if we know only the profile, which characterizes the execution of a program in a concise way at the expense of a substantial loss of information. For instance, how long are the time intervals between consecutive I/O operations? This question requires knowledge of the execution sequence, which a trace contains but which a profile and a mix do not. For the trace in Table 9.2, the answer would be 2 time units between statements 1 (READ) and 3 (WRITE), 443 time units between 3 and 9 (WRITE), and 1 time unit between 9 and 1.

As a final observation, note that a profile or a mix can be used to compute the total execution time only if the execution times of each statement or class of statements are known. Of course, a statement or a class which takes longer to execute than another may have a heavier influence on performance even if its frequency count is lower. For example, in Table 9.1, statement 3 has more influence than 14 even though their frequency counts are 1 and 8, respectively. This can be seen in the last column of Table 9.1, which reports the total times spent executing each statement. The sum of these times is equal to the total execution time.   ∎

9.2.2 Indices of Program Behavior

Address pattern
Locality
Instruction mixed.

In a virtual-memory environment, the performance of a program and the price to be paid for running it depend on some behavioral aspects of the program which are practically irrelevant in non-virtual-memory systems. The execution time is much more sensitive to the space needed by the program than in the type of environment we have considered in Section 9.2.1. However, it is not the total space demand that matters; what does matter is the minimum amount of physical memory space required by the program to work "efficiently." To clarify this notion, let us perform a simple conceptual experiment. During the execution of a given program on a multiprogrammed virtual-memory system, we record the amount of memory which is allotted to the program at each instant it receives the attention of the CPU. Then we execute the same program on the same system but in uniprogramming mode, giving it at each instant of its CPU time the same amount of primary memory it had in multiprogramming mode. The execution time we measure in these conditions is our performance index for the program. The relationships among this time, its components, and the price of a run are practically the same as those mentioned in Section 9.2.1. Note that if the memory policy decisions depend on the global load, the value of our index will be influenced by the load even in the context of our uniprogramming experiment. Bard (1973) has proposed a single-parameter characterization of the effects of the load which allows the behavior of a program under certain global policies to be approximately predicted. However, to simplify our discussion further, the memory policy will be assumed to assign the space to a program independently of the other active programs. For example, the amount of space may be fixed and constant (fixed-allocation strategy) or coincide at any time with the working set size of the program at that time (*see* Section 7.4.2). We shall also assume, again for simplicity, that virtual memory is implemented by the paging technique outlined in Examples 2.7 and 7.3.

In a characterization of the program's execution in terms of resource usage intervals as in Fig. 9.2, a new state which does not exist in nonvirtual-memory systems appears: the *page wait* state (*see* Fig. 9.4). The total time spent in the

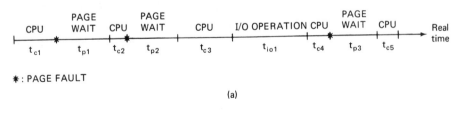

	PAGE		PAGE				PAGE		
CPU	WAIT	CPU	WAIT	CPU	I/O OPERATION	CPU	WAIT	CPU	Real time
t_{c1}	t_{p1}	t_{c2}	t_{p2}	t_{c3}	t_{io1}	t_{c4}	t_{p3}	t_{c5}	

✳ : PAGE FAULT

(a)

n_f: NUMBER OF PAGE FAULTS

n_{io}: NUMBER OF I/O OPERATIONS

$t_c = \sum\limits_{j=1}^{n_f + n_{io} + 1} t_{cj}$: CPU (OR VIRTUAL) TIME

$t_p = \sum\limits_{j=1}^{n_f} t_{pj}$: PAGE WAIT TIME

$t_{io} = \sum\limits_{j=1}^{n_{io}} t_{ioj}$: I/O TIME

$t = t_c + t_p + t_{io}$: EXECUTION TIME

$t_{nv} = t_c + t_{io}$: NONVIRTUAL-MEMORY EXECUTION TIME

MEAN PAGE FAULT RATES:

$$\bar{f}_c = \frac{n_f}{t_c}$$

$$\bar{f}_{nv} = \frac{n_f}{t_{nv}}$$

$$\bar{f} = \frac{n_f}{t}$$

(b)

Figure 9.4 Execution of a program in a uniprogrammed virtual-memory system; (*a*) timing diagram; (*b*) possible definitions of the page fault rate.

page wait state is equal to the product of the mean page waiting time and the total number of page faults generated by the program during its execution.

The mean page waiting time is a system parameter, equal to the sum of two characteristics of the paging channel-device complex, the mean access time and the page transfer time. However, the number of page faults depends both on the system and on the program. The system influences it through the memory management strategy, which determines how much memory space a program must be given and which portion of the program will reside there at any instant of its execution. The program influences the number of page faults by its way of referencing the information stored in its virtual-address space. In other words, the number of page faults depends also on the program's *referencing behavior*.

As observed in Section 8.3.2, the goal of an algorithm for the automatic management of a memory hierarchy is to prepare in primary memory the information needed by the CPU just before the CPU references it. If this goal could be perfectly achieved, a program's execution would have to be suspended only for the I/O operations explicitly requested by the program, just as in a non-virtual-memory environment. To approach this objective, the management algorithm must try to predict the referencing behavior of the running program. Looking at the same problem from the opposite viewpoint, we may say that, given a management algorithm, a program should try to adapt its behavior to that expected by the algorithm, so as to make the algorithm's predictions as successful as possible. This remark suggests that the referencing performance of a program could be quantified by an index expressing how close the program's behavior is to the one postulated by a particular management algorithm. If predictions were perfect, the pages to be needed in the near future could be preloaded, thereby eliminating all page faults. Thus, the *number of page faults* (or the *mean fault rate*) generated by a program under a given algorithm could be taken as a measure of the "distance" between this and the perfect program. Let programs P_1 and P_2, when executed on the same system with the same memory management strategy, generate two mean fault rates $\bar{f}_1$ and $\bar{f}_2$, with $\bar{f}_1 > \bar{f}_2$. Then we would say that P_2 has a better (referencing) behavior than P_1 under the given strategy. Note that P_1 and P_2 are assumed to run under the conditions of the conceptual experiment described in the first paragraph of this section. Also, mean fault rates may be defined with respect to the CPU time rather than to the non-virtual-memory execution time or to the total execution time of each program. These different definitions of mean fault are illustrated in Fig. 9.4, where $\bar{f}_c$ appears to be the least system-dependent one.

Yet, even having taken such great care, the strong dependence on the strategy often makes the fault rate unsatisfactory as a program performance index, because what "the same strategy" means in this context is not clear. For example, assuming that a fixed-allocation strategy is selected, does this mean that P_1 and P_2 are to be executed in memory partitions of the same size, besides being under the same loading and replacement policies? If the answer is no, how are the partition sizes determined? If yes, is it reasonable to compare the behaviors of different programs, obliging them to run into the same amount of physical space? This is acceptable when comparing two different versions of the same program (*see* Section 9.4.2). In general, however, an index reflecting only the intrinsic referencing behavior of the program would be preferable. Knowledge of this index for a program, combined with knowledge of the memory management strategy under which it will run, should ideally enable one to calculate the program's fault rate and hence its execution time.

For most applications, a complete characterization of the referencing behavior of a program [more precisely, of a (program, input) pair] is given by its *address trace* or *reference string*. This trace can be derived from the program trace introduced in Section 9.2.1 (*see* Table 9.2) and provides answers to all questions which may be asked about the program's behavior. Let us assume, as we shall always do in this chapter, that virtual memory is statistically allocated to programs. In other words, each information item has a distinct virtual address which remains the same throughout the program's lifetime and is not shared with any other information item. Then there is a one-to-one correspondence between the words of the program and the virtual addresses. The reference string is defined as the chronological sequence of the virtual addresses a_j referenced by the program, each with the indication of the CPU (or virtual) time t_j to the next reference:

$$\{a_j(t_j)\} \qquad (j = 1, 2, \ldots, r), \tag{9.4}$$

where r is the total number of references generated by the program. Thus, the reference string is one of the many possible decompositions of the execution time, or, more precisely, of the CPU time of a program. The states which define this decomposition correspond to the distinct addresses in the virtual-address space occupied by the program. Note that this characterization, being at the level of virtual space and virtual time, is completely independent of the memory management strategy.

As done in Section 9.2.1 with the program trace, several other characterizations can be derived from a reference string. For example, we may group virtual addresses into blocks. Given a set of blocks $B = (b_1, b_2, \ldots, b_n)$, we may define a many-to-one mapping from the set A of virtual addresses to B, so that each a_j is associated to one and only one block b_i. This mapping, applied to each element of the address trace (9.4), transforms it into the *block trace* or *block reference string*

$$\{i_j(t_j)\} \qquad (j = 1, 2, \ldots, r) \tag{9.5}$$

where b_{i_j} has been replaced by i_j for the sake of brevity.

Since the practical reason for considering blocks is our interest in treating them as single entitities during transfers and for allocation purposes, each block usually consists of information items having contiguous addresses in virtual space. Particular types of blocks are the *segment*, which is generally a variable-size, logically and functionally well-defined block, and the *page*, a fixed-size block. Thus, depending on the type of block we are considering, (9.5) may be called the *segment trace* or the *page trace*. These traces are still strategy-independent and, as we shall see in Example 9.2, may be made slightly more compact than the address trace.

But how much can we reduce the amount of information needed to represent program behavior without losing essential information? Can we characterize program behavior by a histogram like a program profile or a mix? The answer, of course, depends on the objective of the study. As the dependence of the program behavior model on the strategy increases, the amount of information needed to characterize the performance of a program decreases. At one extreme, when everything is known, the index may be a scalar, for instance, the number of page faults. At the other extreme, when no information on the strategy is to be present in the characterization, the chronological order of the references must be preserved, and there seems to be no completely satisfactory index not having the form of a sequence. Some relatively compact models which approximately represent program behavior for certain purposes or for given classes of strategies will be described in Section 9.3.2. An example which allows us to introduce the fundamental notion of locality will now be discussed.

Example 9.2   We shall derive from the program trace in Table 9.2 a block reference string which represents the referencing behavior of the program in Table 9.1. Let us assume that the first input card has IENT = 1, JNT = 1 and the second IENT = 0. Thus, the trace to be considered consists of the first 10 elements of the first column in Table 9.2 followed by the whole second column, for a total of 43 elements and 456 time units. We arbitrarily subdivide the virtual space occupied by the program into variable-size blocks. The mapping of program statements and data into blocks is shown in Table 9.3.

The reader may verify that, knowing this mapping and the program listing in Table 9.1, the block reference string in Table 9.4(a) is derivable from our 43-element subtrace of the trace in Table 9.2. The string has been constructed for an execution of the program on

Table 9.3

DECOMPOSITION INTO BLOCKS OF THE PROGRAM IN TABLE 9.1

Block number	Block contents	
	Statements	Data
1	MAIN(1–11), FLOAT	—
2	—	XO, YO, H, JNT, IENT, FUN, X, I, STEP, A(I)
3	FUN(12–14)	—
4	—	X, Y, FUN, 1.0
5	RK2(15–28)	—
6	—	H, XI, YI, K, N, H2, Y, X, FUN, II, J, T1, T2, T3, T4, VEC(II), 2.0, 6.0
7	READ	—
8	WRITE	—

Table 9.4

BLOCK REFERENCE STRING GENERATED BY THE PROGRAM IN
TABLE 9.1

(a) Block reference string

i_j: $\dfrac{172}{50}$ $\dfrac{12}{2}$ $\dfrac{128}{50}$ $\dfrac{12}{2}$ $\dfrac{56}{15}$ $\dfrac{56}{8}$ $\dfrac{56}{1}$ $\dfrac{56}{1}$ $\dfrac{56}{2}$ $\dfrac{56}{2}$ $\dfrac{56}{2}$ $\dfrac{34}{15}$ $\dfrac{34}{8}$ $\dfrac{3}{5}$ $\dfrac{56}{7}$

i_j: $\dfrac{56}{11}$ $\dfrac{34}{15}$ $\dfrac{34}{8}$ $\dfrac{3}{5}$ $\dfrac{56}{7}$ $\dfrac{56}{11}$ $\dfrac{34}{15}$ $\dfrac{34}{8}$ $\dfrac{3}{5}$ $\dfrac{56}{7}$ $\dfrac{56}{4}$ $\dfrac{34}{15}$ $\dfrac{34}{8}$ $\dfrac{3}{5}$ $\dfrac{56}{7}$ $\dfrac{56}{23}$

i_j: $\dfrac{56}{3}$ $\dfrac{56}{3}$ $\dfrac{5}{5}$ $\dfrac{12}{11}$ $\dfrac{12}{1}$ $\dfrac{12}{2}$ $\dfrac{12}{2}$ $\dfrac{128}{51}$ $\dfrac{1}{1}$ $\dfrac{172}{50}$ $\dfrac{12}{2}$ $\dfrac{1}{1}$

(b) String of block reference sets (one set every 25 time units)

(1, 2, 7)(2, 7)(1, 2, 8)(1, 2, 8)(1, 2, 5, 6)(3, 4, 5, 6)(3, 4, 5, 6)(3, 4, 5, 6)(3, 4, 5, 6)
(3, 4)(3, 4, 5, 6)(3, 4, 5, 6)(5, 6)(1, 2, 5, 6)(1, 2, 8)(1, 2, 8)(1, 2, 7)(1, 2, 7)

a FORTRAN machine rather than on a hardware machine. Each statement is fetched from memory and entirely decoded. Then a reference to all the necessary data is made, and the statement is executed by the FORTRAN processor without any further references. The only concession to reality is the assumption that READ and WRITE are implemented by two I/O routines, stored in blocks 7 and 8. Note that the string generated by the compiled program running on a hardware CPU would be much longer, with much shorter intervals between consecutive references. These shorter intervals are so short with respect to those of interest in program performance evaluation (e.g., the times between page faults or the page waiting times) that their mean length is often considered, thereby ignoring the differences among them. With some strategies such as local LRU or FIFO replacement, as we shall see in Section 9.3.1 (for example, in Table 9.8), reference times do not influence the number of page faults and may therefore be omitted in the trace. Note that the accuracy of the string in Table 9.4(a) is adequate for several practical purposes. For instance, the first 50 time units of it, instead of 1 7 2, would· in the object program's string contain a much longer sequence of intermixed 1's, 7's, and 2's.

Another form for a reference string is the one in terms of *reference sets*, shown in Table 9.4(b). To construct it, virtual time is divided into constant-length intervals. The set of blocks referenced during each interval is the block reference set for that interval. A reference set string is less accurate but much more compact than a normal reference string. Some applications of it will be shown in the sequel.

The reader will easily realize that transforming the reference string in Table 9.4(a) or (b) into a string in terms of other blocks is straightforward if a many-to-one mapping of the blocks in Table 9.3 into the new blocks exists. However, this transformation is impossible (at least when perfect accuracy is required) in all other cases. If the program is divided into four pages $\pi_1 = (b_1, b_3)$, $\pi_2 = (b_5)$, $\pi_3 = (b_7, b_8)$, and $\pi_4 = (b_2, b_4, b_6)$, then the page reference string corresponding to either string in Table 9.4 can be obtained immediately by replacing each block number by the corresponding page number (for example, 1 7 2 becomes 1 3 4). However, if the mapping is many to many, knowledge of the original address trace is required, or an imprecise result must be acceptable. For instance, if part of block 2 were in page π_4 and part in a new page π_5, 1 7 2 could be transformed into 1 3 4 or 1 3 5 or 1 3 4 5, depending on the data in block 2 actually referenced by the program at that point.

Table 9.5

BLOCK REFERENCE DENSITIES IN THE STRING OF TABLE 9.4(a)

Block number	References in the whole string (block profile)	References in the last 20 elements	References between the 11th and the 50th element
1	13	9	0
2	11	7	0
3	12	0	9
4	8	0	6
5	18	1	13
6	17	1	12
7	2	1	0
8	2	1	0

Let us now analyze in detail the string in Table 9.4(a). The *block profile* of the program for this run, presented in Table 9.5, shows that blocks, like statements, are not referenced uniformly. The differences in the reference densities may be even bigger for shorter substrings, as shown in Table 9.5. During any given time interval we may choose, the program is likely to restrict its references to a subset of its blocks. This can be clearly seen in Fig. 9.5, which displays what we shall call a *portrait* of the program [more precisely, of the (program, input) pair]. During the first 100 time units, only blocks 1, 2, 7, and 8 are referenced, and the next 30 time units involve only blocks 5 and 6, a subset of the set of blocks which is totally disjoint from the previous one. The transitions between these subsets, which are called *localities*, may be less neat than in this case, since the new locality may have some blocks in common with the old one, but are frequently quite abrupt in the time domain. The program, during its execution, stays in each locality l_j for a time t_j, which may be viewed as the *lifetime* of l_j. Its behavior could be characterized by the sequence $\{l_j(t_j)\}$ of its localities and their lifetimes. Thus, when a program's dynamic behavior is to be represented, localities appear as a natural and convenient choice for the program's states. However, the identification of localities in a block reference string is not unique. It depends on the time scale which is adopted. For example, the two sequences of localities in Table 9.6 are equally legitimate characterizations of the behavior of our program as described in Table 9.4(a) and in Fig. 9.5. The problem of precisely defining localities will be discussed in Section 9.3.2.

The property of concentrating references into a relatively small region of the whole virtual space over relatively long intervals of virtual time is called the *property of locality*. What are the causes of locality? In our program, the reader will easily recognize that

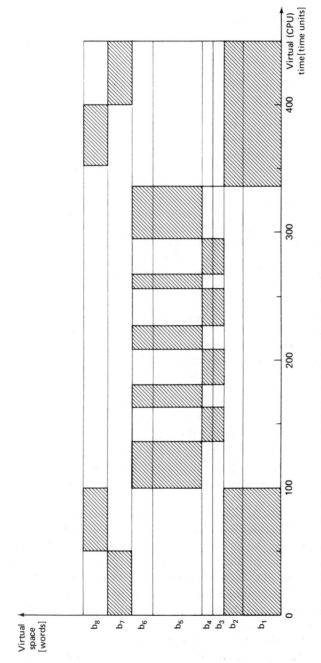

Figure 9.5 Portrait of the program in Table 9.1 derived from the block reference string in Table 9.4(a).

469

Table 9.6

TWO DIFFERENT CHOICES OF LOCALITIES FOR THE BLOCK
REFERENCE STRING IN TABLE 9.4

$\{l_j(t_i)\}$ = (1, 2, 7, 8)(104), (3, 4, 5, 6)(231), (1, 2, 7, 8)(121)

$\{l_j(t_i)\}$ = (1, 2, 7)(54), (1, 2, 8)(50), (5, 6)(31), (3, 4)(28), (5, 6)(18), (3, 4)(28), (5, 6)(18), (3, 4)(28),
         (5, 6)(11), (3, 4)(28), (5, 6)(41), (1, 2)(19), (1, 8)(50), (1, 2, 7)(52)

---

locality is due to the structure of the code and to the way the program's information has
been partitioned into blocks. Since the flow of control often tends to proceed sequentially
through the program and only a small subset of the data is referenced even during
relatively long intervals, grouping adjacent statements and their data into blocks causes the
block reference string to exhibit some locality phenomena. These phenomena are
strengthened by loops (which do not appear in our string since no loop is executed more
than once) and arrays or other data structures on which the program operates for long
periods of time. Locality transitions evidently occur in our string when control is transferred from one block to another (e.g., from the MAIN routine in block 1 to the RK2
subroutine in block 5 or vice versa) or data accesses switch from a subset to another subset
of data blocks. In the behavior of our program we can find a reflection of the mental
structure and abilities of its author. The human mind cannot devote its attention to too
many processes simultaneously, especially in activities in which a high reliability of the
results is desirable or essential. Thus, the mental processes of a programmer are to be
made serial or nearly serial. Their serialization is usually favored by the structure of
programming languages and is the ultimate cause of locality.   ■

What has just been said of our program of course applies to practically all
programs. Experiments have shown that programs generally exhibit some degree
of locality, but the question is whether this degree can be quantified by a scalar
index independent of the memory management strategy. This question, which has
not yet received a satisfactory answer, is a very important one because of the
special exploitation of program locality made in the organization of virtual-
memory systems.

Virtual memory is usually implemented by an automatically managed memory hierarchy, in which, as we saw in Section 8.3.2, the access time increases
substantially as we go from the first to the second level. If we transferred a word
from secondary to primary memory only when this word is referenced by the
running program, each word's access time would be dominated by the access time
of the second level. Transferring a large number of words at each secondary-
memory access drastically decreases the mean access time per word. However,
since all of these words except the referenced one are in fact preloaded into
primary memory (that is, they are transferred before being referenced), they must
be chosen so that their probability of reference in the near future is high.
Otherwise, bulk transfer would be useless or harmful instead of being advantageous. Furthermore, the fact that in most cases the second level of a hierarchy is not

a random-access memory makes bulk transfers convenient only if the words involved are stored in consecutive locations. This is highly desirable also in the case of a random-access memory because of the simplicity of sequential-access mechanisms. For all of the above remarks, it is easy to understand why program locality is a basic assumption without which the current approaches to virtual-memory implementation would produce an unacceptable performance. In a paging system, for instance, a reference to a word not in primary memory causes the page which contains that word to be fetched from the paging device. Preloading of the other words belonging to the fetched page would be a catastrophic mistake if the probability that most of them were to be referenced soon were zero or very low. Only the fact that programs exhibit locality makes the mechanism we have described work with acceptable levels of efficiency.

From another viewpoint, we can say that the time penalties due to secondary-memory accesses are reduced to tolerable levels if the whole current locality can be kept in primary memory. However, if the current locality always included all the pages of the program, we would end up with a non-virtual-memory system or with a constantly thrashing virtual-memory system. Thus, program locality is an essential property for the success of virtual-memory systems, whose efficiency in fact increases as locality is improved (*see* Example 7.10).

The above discussion also helps us understand why locality is exploited by memory management strategies in making their predictions. Each strategy tries to estimate the composition of the current locality and to keep as much of it as possible in primary memory. The evident assumption is that the program will stay in its current locality (whose size should be substantially smaller than that of the program) for a relatively long time and therefore also in the near future. In other words, the assumption is that the program has a good degree of locality. Different strategies, however, define locality in different ways. For example, fixed partitioning with LRU replacement assumes that the page reference probability at any given time is maximum for the most recently referenced page and minimum for the least recently referenced one, so that keeping in primary memory the m most recently used pages is likely to minimize the number of page faults. Thus, for this strategy, the locality of a program gets better as its behavior approaches the one assumed by the LRU algorithm. It is also natural to expect that a program's performance for a given allotted space m will be as good as the fit of its behavior to that of the ideal model just described. Similarly, working set strategies estimate the size and composition of the current locality by equating them to those of the working set, defined in Section 7.4.2. Therefore, the degree of locality of a program (and its performance) in a working set environment is directly related to how well the program's working set approximates its current locality. The approximation will be bad when an abrupt locality transition takes place. Not only with a working set strategy but also with LRU and the other strategies, which base their predictions on the property of locality, a dramatic increase in paging activity will correspond to such a transition.

In summary, we have identified with locality the property which, roughly speaking, determines the performance of programs in a virtual-memory environment. A satisfactory, concise, strategy-independent quantification of locality has not been proposed yet. While all memory management strategies exploit locality, their definitions of locality differ to some extent from each other. Thus, strategy-dependent indices may be hard to replace or may have to be preferred in a number of applications to strategy-independent characterizations of locality. In any case, designing local programs and improving the locality of the existing ones should be expected to provide better program and system performance, especially if the definition of locality which is adopted coincides with that of the memory management strategy under which the program is to run (*see* Section 9.4.2).

9.3 PROGRAM EVALUATION TECHNIQUES

Timer. — detect execution time bygin/end

9.3.1 Program Measurement

The indices of program performance which were introduced in Section 9.2 would not have any meaning if they were not experimentally measurable. But how can they be measured?

The measurement of the execution time of a program requires a clock and the ability to detect the beginning and the end of the run. Once a precise definition of this index has been given for the specific environment and the study to be performed, the experiment can be designed in all its details. For example, if the definition coincides with that of the uniprogramming turnaround time, one can start a stopwatch when the program begins to be read in and stop it when the results are completely printed out. Alternatively, the operating system can be properly instrumented to perform the equivalents of these operations. In most cases, the accounting routine reports this time, or an approximation of it, to the user. If the pure execution time of the program's code is of interest, two instructions which read the internal clock of the system may be inserted into the program, one at the beginning and one at the end. Example 9.3 will illustrate some applications of this elementary technique, which can obviously be used also to measure the time spent in any portion of a program.

The main problems in these time measurements usually come from the inaccuracy and inaccessibility of the clock and from the difficulty of verifying that the measured quantity coincides with the desired one. Real-time clocks which are only readable by a privileged instruction, that is, by the operating system, are often unsatisfactory for measuring program times. The overhead caused by frequent clock accesses, and especially the inaccuracies due to their interference with the measured program, may be intolerable in certain studies and for certain programs. Also, the resolution of a clock must be adequate to the experiment. A program (or a subroutine, or a loop) whose execution time is around 10 ms should not be timed with a clock whose period is $\frac{1}{60}$ s. The use of a real-time clock has

inaccuracy, inaccessibility of clock
Interference - due to multiprogramming.
resolution.

the drawback that no distinction is possible between times spent in actually executing the program and times spent, for instance, in servicing interrupts. Thus, even if great care is taken to avoid interferences from other user processes, there is always a chance that the collected data are nonnegligibly distorted by unpredicted and undetected events. Virtual-time clocks, which are interval timers incremented only during the execution of an individual process, are certainly more reliable, although they usually measure only CPU times. In any case, as pointed out also in Section 2.3.2, the experimenter should very carefully study the characteristics of the clock available in the system before instrumenting a program and designing an experiment. From the viewpoint of user program measurement, the existence in a system of a high-resolution clock accessible by a nonprivileged machine instruction and of mechanisms by which the operating system could keep track of the durations of certain types of interventions during specified intervals would be very desirable.

The space occupied by a program, in the simple case of static allocation, is measured and usually reported to the programmer by the loader, a component of the operating system. Thus, the main global performance indices introduced in Section 9.2.1 are measurable at the operating system or at the code level, where software measurement tools are better suited than hardware tools. This remark is quite generally applicable to all program measurements. Hardware tools can in some cases be used, but their resolution is unnecessarily high, and their lack of direct contact with the program to be measured (whose electrical effects only may be detected) often makes them unsuitable. As mentioned in Section 2.3.3, the situation is somewhat different with microprograms. For these, however, the best tools are often of the firmware type—hence conceptually similar to software tools (*see* Section 2.4.1). Thus, we shall limit our discussion to an illustration of the use of software tools in program measurement.

We have already alluded to the use of *checkpoints* in the measurement of execution times. In this case, the checkpoints simply detect the beginning and the completion of the run, read the clock, and record their reading in a memory location reserved for that purpose. The checkpointing technique can be used in all program measurements in which each event to be detected can be unambiguously associated with the execution of an instruction or of a statement. Since this evidently includes the possibility of tracing a program, the conclusion reached in Section 9.2.1 for a program trace means that checkpoints allow us to give answers to practically any performance-related question. As we shall see in Example 9.3, the more direct the correspondence between the event to be detected and the execution of an instruction, the easier and cheaper the measurement. Accesses to individual data items or data structures, which can be made by several instructions and from several routines or procedures, are more difficult and expensive to measure than a specific subroutine call. Similarly, the number of times a certain statement is executed is more easily measurable than the number of additions performed. The difficulties we refer to here are not conceptual ones. For example, if the profile of the program is generated, determining the number of

program profile - frequency count of each statements.

additions or the number of accesses to a certain variable is not conceptually more complicated than determining the number of executions of a given statement, as we saw in Example 9.1. However, if the whole profile is not needed and not available, instrumenting a program in order to gather the former quantities requires a very careful scanning of the program's text and a much greater number of checkpoints. The cost of installing checkpoints and the corresponding measurement routines into a program for a given purpose can be considered roughly proportional to the number of checkpoints to be inserted. This is also an acceptable first approximation when tools designed to facilitate the insertion of checkpoints, such as the Informer and the SMT (*see* Section 2.4.2), are employed. Therefore, even though in principle checkpointing would allow us to obtain a complete, detailed history of a run, that is, a program trace, this is normally done only when absolutely necessary. In practice, the minimum, or a near-minimum, number of checkpoints will be installed. If a profile is needed, the program will not be traced. If the number of executions of a few statements is desired, a profile is superfluous and therefore will not generally be measured. As Example 9.3 shows, even the tracing of a program does not require one checkpoint per instruction or per statement.

Example 9.3   We shall describe the use of checkpoints to instrument the program in Table 9.1 so that various performance-related questions about a given (program, input) pair can be answered experimentally. In Chapter 2, we learned that a conceptual model of the system to be measured underlies any measurement experiment and that this model helps the evaluator design the experiment and interpret its results. In the case of a program measured by the checkpointing technique, *graph models* derived from the program's flowchart are the most obvious candidates for such a role [*see*, for example, Russell and Estrin (1969)]. A flowchart of the program in Table 9.1 is given in Fig. 9.6(*a*). Fig. 9.6(*b*) shows one of the many different graph models which may be drawn from this flowchart. To construct this directed graph, a vertex was initially created for each statement. Statements such as 5 or 21, which include function calls, must be represented by a number of vertices equal to the number of functions they call plus 1. For example, statement 5 was split into two vertices: the first represents the actions taking place before the calling of FLOAT, and the second the actions to be performed after returning from FLOAT. Then the vertices were connected to each other by arcs corresponding to the possible transfers of control. The graphs representing RK2 and FUN were incorporated into the one of the MAIN routine, so that a single connected graph would be obtained. Finally, all the vertices in series with each other were collapsed into the same vertex. Vertices n_i and n_j are said to be *in series* if there is an arc from n_i to n_j and this is the only outcoming arc for n_i and the only incoming arc for n_j. The rationale of this reduction is very simple and very important: Two vertices in series are always executed the same number of times, unless the program is suspended and aborted during the execution of the first because of a failure, an error, or an action of the operator. The notion of series connection can be extended to subgraphs, as the readers familiar with graph models of electric circuits and with Kirchhoff's laws certainly know. If a connected subgraph has only one vertex with incoming arcs from the rest of the graph and only one vertex (not necessarily distinct) with outcoming arcs to the rest of the graph, then the subgraph can be replaced by a single vertex, and if this vertex is

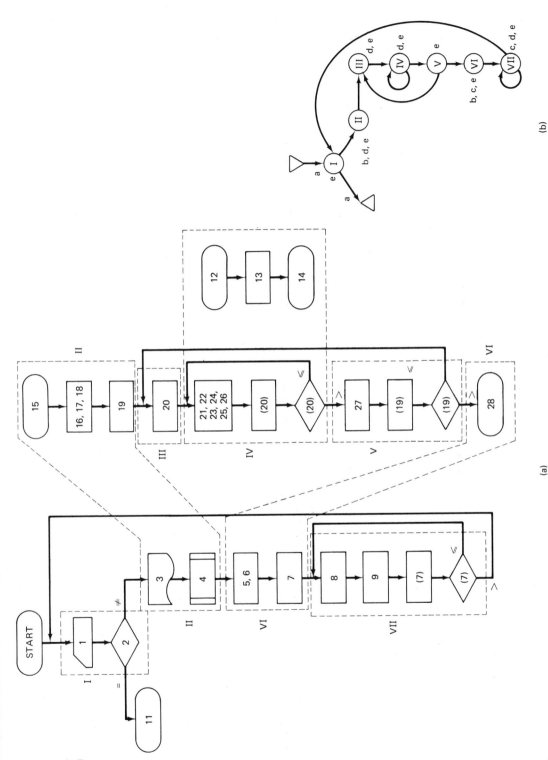

475

Figure 9.6 Flowchart (*a*) of the program in Table 9.1 and a graph model (*b*) derived from it.

(a)

(b)

Table 9.7

MODIFICATIONS FOR INSTRUMENTATION PURPOSES TO BE
MADE TO THE PROGRAM IN TABLE 9.1

Statement number		New statement
(a) Measurement of execution time		
1		CALL ITIME(INIT)
1′	10	READ(5,1) XO,YO,H,JNT,IENT
11	40	CALL ITIME(IFIN)
11′		KTIME = IFIN − INIT
11″		WRITE(6,4) KTIME
11‴		STOP
(b) Measurement of the time spent in RK2		
1′		KTRK2 = 0
4		CALL RK2(FUN,H,XO,YO,JNT,IENT,A,KTRK2)
11	40	WRITE(6,5) KTRK2
11′		STOP
15		SUBROUTINE RK2(FUN,H,XI,YI,K,N,VEC,KTRK2)
15′		CALL ITIME(INIT)
28		CALL ITIME(IFIN)
29		KTRK2 = KTRK2 + IFIN − INIT
30		RETURN
(c) Measurement of the number of times STEP is accessed		
1		N58 = 0
1′	10	READ(5,1) XO,YO,H,JNT,IENT
5′		N58 = N58 + 1
8′		N58 = N58 + 1
11	40	WRITE(6,6) N58
11′		STOP
(d) Measurement of the program profile		
1		NII = 0
1′		NIII = 0
1″		NIV = 0
1‴		NVII = 0
1^{iv}	10	READ(5,1) XO,YO,H,JNT,IENT
3′		NII = NII + 1
7′		NVII = NVII + 1
11	40	WRITE(6,7) NII,NIII,NIV,NVII
11′		STOP
19′		NIII = NIII + 1
20′		NIV = NIV + 1
(e) Measurement of the program trace		
1		CALL TRACE(0)
1′	10	CALL TRACE(1)
1″		READ(5,1) XO,YO,H,JNT,IENT
3	20	CALL TRACE(2)
3′		WRITE(6,2) H,XO,YO
7′		CALL TRACE(7)
19′		CALL TRACE(3)
20′		CALL TRACE(4)
26′		CALL TRACE(5)
27′		CALL TRACE(6)

Table 9.7—*cont.*

Statement number	New statement
Measurement routine	
29	SUBROUTINE TRACE(J)
30	IF (J .EQ. 0) L = 0
31	L = L + 1
32	LTRAC(L) = J
33	CALL ITIME(K)
34	LTIME(L) = K
35	RETURN
	END

in series with others, they may be collapsed. For instance, the subgraph consisting of vertex VII and is self-loop in Fig. 9.6(*b*) satisfies the above condition. If we replace it with a single vertex, we see that this vertex is in series with vertex VI. These two vertices are always executed the same number of times. Similarly, we conclude that III and V are executed the same number of times and that the number of executions of vertex I is equal to that of II and VI plus 1. However, it is important to note that the reductions of a graph model must be chosen according to the problem at hand. Those which resulted in the graph model in Fig. 9.6(*b*) are adequate for our purposes, as we shall see below. The additional reductions described above, while helpful in decreasing the number of check-points required in some of the problems, may render the model unable to guide us in the measurement of, for example, the number of WRITE operations issued by the program, since the number of times vertex VII is executed ceases to be measurable as its self-loop disappears.

The instrumentation which would enable us to answer some specific questions about our program's performance will now be examined in detail.

a. What is the execution time? Two checkpoints must be inserted into the program, on the arcs labeled a in Fig. 9.6(*b*). The corresponding code modifications, which assume the existence of a FORTRAN-library routine ITIME(K), are reported in Table 9.7(a). ITIME, when called, returns the current value of the real-time clock as an integer. If the program to be measured has multiple exits, it may be convenient to transform it into a single-exit program before inserting the checkpoints.

b. How much time is spent in subroutine RK2? The instrumentation required is similar to that needed in the previous case except for the fact that a subroutine may be executed several times during a run [*see* Table 9.7(b) and the b labels in Fig. 9.6(*b*)]. Note that we have assumed the time spent in FUN to be part of the time we want to measure. Problem 9.6 asks the reader to instrument the program so as to keep these two times separate.

c. How many times is the variable STEP accessed? This variable is mentioned in statements 5 and 8, once in each. Thus, the problem is equivalent to the one of determining the number of times 5 and 8 are executed. Two checkpoints, acting as counters, inserted where the c labels in Fig. 9.6(*b*) are, will suffice. The modifications required are shown in Table 9.7(c).

d. What is the profile of the program? Because of the way the graph model in Fig. 9.6(*b*) has been constructed, we know that the statements to which each vertex corresponds are always executed the same number of times. This is the case, for example, of statements 3, 4, 15, 16, 17, 18, and 19, which will be executed NII times. The only exceptions are statements 12, 13, and 14, each of which is executed $4 \cdot$ NIV times. An examination of the graph model also shows that, as we found earlier in this example, the following relationships hold between the numbers of executions of its seven vertices:

$$\text{NII} = \text{NVI}, \qquad \text{NIII} = \text{NV}, \qquad \text{NI} = \text{NII} + 1. \tag{9.6}$$

Only four of these numbers (for instance, NII, NIII, NIV, and NVII) are independent, and the whole profile may be gathered by only four checkpoints [*see* Table 9.7(d)]. Note that since the profile is also a powerful debugging tool, the insertion of redundant checkpoints may be useful to make program tests more thorough and reliable. Sometimes, especially with large programs, it may be more convenient to organize the counters in a vector and make each checkpoint a subprogram call which increments one element of that vector.

e. What was the path followed by the flow of control? A trace of the program in terms of the vertices of the graph model in Fig. 9.6(*b*) can be obtained by inserting one checkpoint of the tracing type in each vertex. Again, we could reduce the total number of checkpoints by capitalizing, for instance, on the fact that vertex VI is always to be executed in order to reach VII from V. Thus, vertex VI need not be traced. The same considerations show that not even I and II have to be traced. Therefore, only four checkpoints would be sufficient, but the processing of the nonredundant trace would be longer and more expensive, while its recording would be cheaper and the interference lower. Also, when the program is traced for debugging purposes, using more checkpoints than the bare minimum may be wiser. Table 9.7(e) presents the seven checkpoints needed to gather a full trace and the text of the TRACE measurement routine. An additional checkpoint to be executed only once, CALL TRACE(0), is used to initialize the pointer to the LTRAC buffer in the routine. The code of TRACE includes the reading and recording of the time (statements 33 and 34). This may not be necessary and is likely to consume substantial additional time and contribute to the interference of the tracing mechanism. To reduce this interference to a minimum, checkpoints which increment the pointer L and record the block number in LTRAC(L) locally, without calling any subroutine, should be used. Clock readings, if necessary, should be added as machine instructions, provided the CPU's repertoire includes such a feature. The vectors LTRAC and LTIME should be kept in a COMMON area. For brevity, the text of TRACE in Table 9.7(e) does not include the handling of the buffer overflow problem.   ■

Another software measurement technique, which was introduced in Section 2.4.3, is the one based on *sampling.* This technique can be applied to program performance measurement, particularly to gather approximate relative frequencies of execution of various parts of a program. As is the case with the measurement of operating systems, its main advantages over checkpointing are the generally lower interference and the fact that sampling does not require the measured program to be modified. The latter characteristic is extremely important, especially for large and complex programs. On the other hand, sampling is less powerful, since no tracing type of measurement can be performed, and less accurate.

If the program runs in a uniprogramming environment, we can sample its activity by having the real-time clock, or an interval timer, interrupt the CPU periodically and cause a measurement routine to be called. This routine must have access to the program status information to be recorded on some storage medium. When it is reduced (preferably later, in order to minimize the interference at data collection time), this information will allow us to determine what the program was doing at that time. If it was running on the CPU, from the instruction being pointed to by the program counter the reduction program will deduce the region of code which was being executed. To be more precise, if that instruction belongs to a subprogram which is called from several points in the program, it will generally be difficult or impossible to determine which point it was called from, and the region of activity will have to be restricted to the boundaries of the subprogram itself. This is also the case of interruptable operating system modules, whose activity should be kept distinct from that of the program since the programmer does not have any control over the operating system. Note that the existence of uninterruptable modules in the operating system is one of the sources of error which may affect the results obtained by sampling.

If the program was found to be waiting, the status information recorded will enable the data reduction program to determine the reason for the wait. In a multiprogramming environment, a program may be waiting for a resource it needs to become available rather than for the completion of an I/O operation it has explicitly requested. These two types of wait will have to be accounted for separately, since the programmer can to some extent influence the latter but not the former. If the measurement routine has access to the operating system's data base, this information is available and can be recorded. To be allowed to do that, the routine must run in privileged mode and actually be part of the operating system. If the sampling tool is to run as a user job and not require any modification of the operating system, this problem is usually a very difficult one and may even be unsolvable. In the Problem Program Evaluator (PPE), a sampling tool designed by Boole and Babbage Inc. for programs running on IBM/360 and 370 systems, this obstacle could be overcome for CPU waits (that is, ready times) only by exploiting some unused bits in the program status vector [*see* Holtwick (1971)]. The queue waits for other resources, however, could not be separated from the times those resources are actually used. The user is given the total time spent in each resource, which PPE properly defines in logical rather than physical terms, that is, in terms of data sets rather than of pieces of equipment. Ideally, programs should not be sampled in real time but in virtual (CPU) time, if their profile is desired, or on the basis of uniprogramming execution time, if their I/O performance is also of interest.

In systems with dynamic relocation or virtual memory, sampling cannot be performed at the physical memory level, since absolute addresses point to different information items at different times. However, a sampling tool which is part of the operating system has access to all of the information required to operate at the virtual level. Checkpoints work in these environments as they do in any other type of system. The only problem which may arise with an instrumented program running a virtual-memory system is that it may be difficult to estimate the influence of the instrumentation (checkpoints, measurement routines, data buffers) on the program's dynamic behavior. In some types of measurements, the interference may turn out to be unexpectedly high, and reducing it may be quite difficult.

The measurement of the strategy-dependent indices of program behavior which were discussed in Section 9.2.2 can usually be performed only by the operating system. For example, no checkpoint in a user program can detect page faults. An alternative way of performing these measurements is by simulating the memory management strategy and inputting into the simulator the address trace generated by the program in one of its runs [*see*, for example, Belady (1966)]. This type of trace-driven simulator is easy to design and implement. Table 9.8

Table 9.8
ALGORITHM FOR SIMULATING THE LOCAL LRU REPLACEMENT STRATEGY

Inputs: l = length of the page reference string to be examined

u = number of pages in the program

m = memory space allotted to the program

$\{i_j\}$ = page reference string (reference times can be ignored)

Output: nf = number of page faults generated

Algorithm:

1. (Initialize LRU stack, pointer to current reference, and number of page faults.) Set $s_h \leftarrow 0$ for $h = 1, \ldots, u$, $j \leftarrow 0$, $nf \leftarrow 0$.
2. (Move to next page referenced and to the top of the stack.) Set $j \leftarrow j + 1$, $k \leftarrow 1$.
3. (Search stack for current reference.) If $s_k = 0$, set $\delta \leftarrow \infty$ and go to 4. If $s_k = i_j$, set $\delta \leftarrow k$ and go to 4. Otherwise, set $k \leftarrow k + 1$ and repeat this step.
4. (Determine whether page fault is generated.) If $\delta > m$, set $nf \leftarrow nf + 1$.
5. (Update stack.) Set $s_h \leftarrow s_{h-1}$ for $h = k, k - 1, \ldots, 2, s_1 \leftarrow i_j$.
6. (Test termination condition.) If $j < l$, go to 2. Otherwise, stop.

---

shows an algorithm for determining the number of page faults generated by a page reference string under LRU replacement. In Table 9.9, an algorithm for the computation of the number of page faults and of the mean working set size of a program under a pure working set strategy is displayed. Those readers who have never done it are urged to simulate these two strategies manually by applying the algorithms in Tables 9.8 and 9.9 to a short string, for example, the one in Table 9.4(a) (*see* Problems 9.8 and 9.9).

In Table 9.8 it is easy to see that a page fault is generated when δ, the distance of the current reference from the top of the LRU stack, is greater than

program behavior indices — Address pattern.
Locality of Ref. Characteristic
Instruction mix

Table 9.9

ALGORITHM FOR SIMULATING THE PURE WORKING SET
STRATEGY

Inputs: l = length of the page reference string to be examined

u = number of pages in the program

$\{i_j\}$ = page reference string (references are assumed to be issued at regular intervals; hence their times are ignored)

τ = window size (in number of references)

Outputs: nf = number of page faults generated

$\bar{w}$ = mean working set size

Algorithm:

1. (Initialize sum of working set sizes, pointer to current reference, pointer to least recent reference in window, number of page faults, and counters of the pages in window.) Set $sw \leftarrow 1$, $j \leftarrow 1$, $k \leftarrow 1$, $nf \leftarrow 1$, $c_h \leftarrow 0$ for $h = 1, \ldots, u$, $c_{i_1} \leftarrow 1$.
2. (Move to next reference and determine whether page fault is generated.) Set $j \leftarrow j + 1$. If $c_{i_j} = 0$, set $nf \leftarrow nf + 1$.
3. (Update counters and, if necessary, window.) Set $c_{i_j} \leftarrow c_{i_j} + 1$. If $j - k + 1 > \tau$, set $k \leftarrow k + 1$, $c_{i_k} \leftarrow c_{i_k} - 1$.
4. (Compute working set size and update sum.) Set $s \leftarrow 0$. For $h = 1, \ldots, u$, if $c_h > 0$, set $s \leftarrow s + 1$. Set $sw \leftarrow sw + s$.
5. (Test termination condition.) If $j < l$, go to 2.
6. (Compute mean working set size.) Set $\bar{w} \leftarrow sw/l$. Stop.

---

m, the allotted space. Also, the LRU stack is independent of m, since it contains all pages referenced in the past, no matter how much space has been allotted to the program in memory. If, instead of specifying m, we keep u counters, one per stack position, and we increment at each reference examined all those corresponding to stack positions $h < \delta$, at each instant the hth counter contains the number of page faults that would be generated up to that instant if m were equal to h pages. This observation, which is the basis of the *stack-processing technique* [*see* Mattson et al. (1970)], allows one to construct the lifetime curve of a (program, input) pair under LRU in just one pass over the reference string (*see* Problem 9.8). Note also that reference times can be ignored, since the number of page faults does not depend on them.

Even if only part of an address trace is to be examined, the measurement of the indices mentioned above is meaningless if the trace is too short. An examination of the literature in this field shows that the length of a trace used in this type of simulation is normally of the order of 10^6 references, which correspond to a CPU time of the order of 1 s (of course, this depends on the speed of the CPU and on the primary-memory bandwidth). These simulations tend to be quite expensive, unless the type of strategy or the accuracy requirements of the study allow the experimenter to reduce the degree of detail of the trace. For example, when dealing with certain working set strategies, a string of reference sets [*see* Table 9.4(b)] is often sufficiently accurate, as we shall see below. It is worth noting that simulation allows us to measure program behavior indices in a perfectly controlled environment, whereas direct measurement of the same indices is often influenced by factors such as the instantaneous load on the system and the behaviors of the other programs. Thus, when program evaluation is the objective, simulation is to be preferred. In strategy evaluation problems, direct measurement, or at least the simulation of a multiprogramming environment with multiple traces, should be chosen.

How can we measure an address trace? As we saw in Section 9.2.2, an address trace, which is a complete characterization of the behavior of a (program, input) pair, can be derived from a program trace at the machine language level if the virtual address of each instruction and of each datum in the program is known and if the mechanisms for accessing them (e.g., indirect addressing, indexing) are specified. However, the amount of information with which we must supplement a program trace in order to derive the corresponding address trace is so large that this approach is seldom convenient, unless an approximate trace obtained by making some simplifying assumptions is sufficient for the purposes of the study.

A more straightforward, even though quite expensive, approach to the measurement of an exact address trace is the one based on the *interpretive execution* of the program. This consists of inputting the program in machine language form into a properly instrumented interpreter which executes it simulating the real system. The interpreter is instrumented in order to record all the references to memory made by the program and also, if necessary, the (simulated) times at which they are issued. It should be noted that the essential purpose of interactive execution is to slow down the processing of the program so that the referenced addresses may be recorded. After all, the program's instructions during normal execution are interpreted by the hardware or firmware of the CPU's control unit. Thus, a hardware or firmware tool could be designed to capture addresses as they are generated by the CPU, buffer them, and store them periodically on some secondary storage medium. In fact, some of the stored-program hardware tools described in Section 2.3.4 could be used for address trace collection in real time. Purposely built wired-program tools can also be conceived that would serve this purpose. However, the unavailability or the price of these tools has made interpretive execution the most popular technique for this type of measurement, in spite of its cost in terms of interpreter design and computer time (real to simulated time ratios of several orders of magnitude are not uncommon).

9.3.2   Program Modeling

Many types of models have been proposed and are used to represent computer programs. Different applications often require different types of program models. We have already introduced some examples. In Chapter 5, we saw that in system evaluation studies programs are often represented by their resource demands and that there are various levels of resources. The instruction or statement mix described in Section 5.3.4 and the higher-level language resource model used in Section 6.3.4 are just two types of models in this class. In Section 9.3.1, graph models were found to be the most appropriate conceptual representations of programs for measurement purposes. Many more models have been devised for problems not directly related to performance evaluation: correctness verification, parallelism detection, program translation, and others.

In this section we shall restrict our discussion to a few types of models which may be used for program performance analysis, that is, for estimating the values of some of the indices introduced in Sections 9.2.1 and 9.2.2. In particular, in the first part of the section we shall be concerned with the estimation of the execution time and of the profile of a program both by analytic methods and by simulation, and in the second with some simple models of program behavior.

The first to be considered is a *Markov model* proposed by Beizer (1970) for the purpose of analytically determining the execution time of a program. As we shall also see later in this section, Markov processes have been and are quite popular in program modeling [*see*, for example, Ramamoorthy (1965)]. Beizer's model is a directed graph in which each arc is characterized by a triple (p, u, v), where p is the conditional probability that the flow of control, if it reaches the source vertex of the arc, will go through the arc; u is the mean execution time of the arc; and v is the variance of this time. The distribution of each arc's execution times is arbitrary, the only condition being that its mean and variance exist. Beizer's method will be illustrated by applying it to the program in Table 9.1.

Example 9.4   The graph model of our sample program shown in Fig. 9.6(*b*) can be transformed into the one in Fig. 9.7(*a*) by using vertices to represent junctions and decision points and arcs to represent blocks of statements which are in series with each other (see the definition of series connection in Example 9.3). Thus, in this model, all processing is concentrated in the arcs, whereas in the one of Fig. 9.6(*b*) it is all in the vertices. Each arc has a label, which in Fig. 9.7(*a*) is enclosed in a rectangle. The label consists of the triple (p, u, v) introduced above. The values of the mean execution times of the arcs have been derived from those reported in Table 9.2. Their variances have all been assumed to be zero. In fact, the variability of the execution times of most instructions on most machines is so small that it can be ignored. This will not generally be the case of arcs such as *gh*, *hi*, and *gr*, which include READ or WRITE statements. However, for simplicity, we have also assumed the variance of their execution times to be zero. The estimation of the probabilities is usually the hardest problem. These are the probabilities of transition from a vertex to another. They are assumed to be constant, that is, independent of time and of the path followed by the flow of control to reach the source vertex. The latter assumption, which makes this a Markov model, is particularly unrealistic, since it is certainly not true for most of the conditional branch instructions in practical programs. Beizer (1970) classifies conditional branches into the following four categories:

    a. Those branches whose condition, or *predicate*, depends only on the input data. If the values of the input data are known, the transition probabilities can be easily

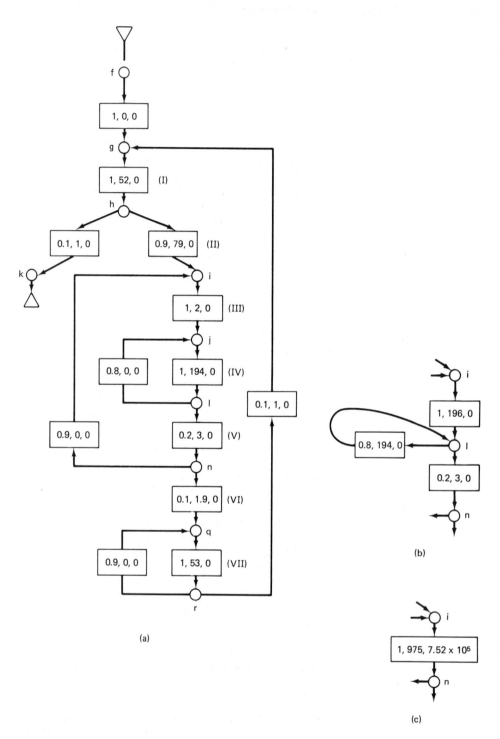

(a)

(b)

(c)

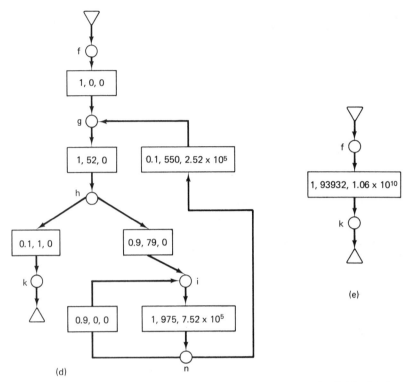

Figure 9.7 Calculation of the execution time of the program in Table 9.1 by successive vertex elimination according to the method proposed by Beizer (1970).

computed from these values. For example, if statement 2 of our program is written as IF (IENT.EQ.0) GO TO 40, its predicate is evidently (IENT = 0). Estimating p_{hk} and p_{hi} is therefore equivalent to estimating the mean number of significant input cards per run, i.e., of cards with IENT $\neq$ 0. If this number is 10, then $p_{hk} = 0.1$ and $p_{hi} = 0.9$.

b. Those branches whose predicate depends on the structure of the program but whose probabilities are easy to estimate due to the simplicity of the structure and of the dependence. An example is the branch at the end of a DO loop, say the loop consisting of statements 7, 8, and 9. Its predicate is (I $\leq$ IENT), and an examination of the DO statement is sufficient to conclude that if IENT $\geq$ 1, $p_{rg} = 1/\text{IENT}$ and $p_{rq} = (\text{IENT}-1)/\text{IENT}$. Thus, if we expect IENT to be around 10, we obtain the values reported in Fig. 9.7(*a*) for these two probabilities and for those of the same type.

c. Those branches whose probabilities are noncritical with respect to the computation of the execution time. For example, if the mean execution times of two parallel branches are approximately the same, the resulting equivalent execution time does not appreciably depend on their individual probabilities (see the equation of u'_{ab} for the parallel transformation in Table 9.10).

Table 9.10

EQUATIONS FOR NODE ELIMINATION IN A MARKOV MODEL
OF A PROGRAM

Series transformation: $a \to b \to c \Rightarrow a \to c$

$$p'_{ac} = p_{ab}p_{bc}$$

$$u'_{ac} = u_{ab} + u_{bc}$$

$$v'_{ac} = v_{ab} + v_{bc}$$

Parallel transformation: $a \overset{\circ}{\underset{\circ\circ}{\rightrightarrows}} b \Rightarrow a \to b$

$$p'_{ab} = p^{\circ}_{ab} + p^{\circ\circ}_{ab}$$

$$u'_{ab} = (p^{\circ}_{ab}u^{\circ}_{ab} + p^{\circ\circ}_{ab}u^{\circ\circ}_{ab})/(p^{\circ}_{ab} + p^{\circ\circ}_{ab})$$

$$v'_{ab} = (p^{\circ}_{ab}v^{\circ}_{ab} + p^{\circ\circ}_{ab}v^{\circ\circ}_{ab})/(p^{\circ}_{ab} + p^{\circ\circ}_{ab}) + [(u^{\circ 2}_{ab}p^{\circ}_{ab} + u^{\circ\circ 2}_{ab}p^{\circ\circ}_{ab})/(p^{\circ}_{ab} + p^{\circ\circ}_{ab})] - u'^{2}_{ab}$$

Loop transformation: $\overset{\curvearrowleft}{a} \to b \Rightarrow a \to b$

$$p'_{ab} = p_{ab}/(1 - p_{aa})$$

$$u'_{ab} = u_{ab} + p_{aa}u_{aa}/(1 - p_{aa})$$

$$v'_{ab} = v_{ab} + [v_{aa}p_{aa}/(1 - p_{aa})] + u^{2}_{aa}p_{aa}/(1 - p_{aa})^{2}$$

Source: Beizer (1970).

d. Those branches whose probabilities are difficult to estimate, mostly because of their predicate's complex dependence on the structure of the program or of the complexity of the structure, or of both.

Beizer claims that only 5% of the branches belong to category d and that the speed of his technique, which is mechanizable, allows one to investigate the sensitivity of the total execution time to the values of their probabilities by varying them and repeating the analysis. In this way, one might be able to reduce or even eliminate the need for the cumbersome analysis which would be required to estimate the probabilities of these branches.

Once the graph model is constructed, the estimation of execution time can be performed by the *star-mesh transformation* method, which is well known in electric circuit theory. The method consists of the following steps.

Step 1. Choose a vertex, which is neither an entry nor an exit, to be eliminated. For example, let this be vertex j in Fig. 9.7(*a*).

Step 2. Split the chosen vertex into replicas so that its outcoming arcs are in series with its incoming arcs. For instance, j is split into two vertices j' and j'' such that arcs lj' and $j'l$ are in series, and so are ij'' and $j''l$. The new arcs $j'l$ and $j''l$ have the same label as jl.

Step 3. Apply the serial-transformation equations in Table 9.10 to the newly created series connections, so as to eliminate the new vertices. In our example, we obtain the two arcs il and ll, whose triples are given by the serial-transformation equations [*see* Fig. 9.7(*b*)].

Step 4. If parallel connections have appeared in the graph, eliminate them by applying the parallel-transformation equations in Table 9.10. In our case, no parallel links have been created.

Step 5. If self-loops have appeared, eliminate them by using the loop-transformation equations in Table 9.10. The removal of vertex *j* has created the self-loop *ll*, which is eliminated by modifying the label of arc *ln* as dictated by the loop-transformation equations. At this point, arcs *il* and *ln* are in series and can be combined together, thereby eliminating vertex *l* [*see* Fig. 9.7(*c*)]. When no further eliminations are possible, return to step 1.

These five steps should be repeated until the graph is reduced to only the entry and the exit vertices. The label of an arc connecting an entry to an exit vertex contains the probability of leaving from that exit having entered the program at that entry point as well as the mean and variance of the execution time between those two vertices. An application of the above procedure, with vertices *j*, *q*, *i*, *g* successively selected for removal in step 1, is illustrated in Fig. 9.7. The result in Fig. 9.7(*e*) tells us that the mean execution time is 93,932 time units and the standard deviation has the same order of magnitude, in spite of the zero-variance assumption for all arcs. The sensitivity of these figures to the accuracy of probability estimates is obviously crucial. The readers are invited to get some insights into its magnitude by varying the three distinct probabilities involved (p_{hi}. p_{lj}, and $p_{ni} = p_{rq}$) and applying the procedure to the modified models (*see* Problem 9.10). ■

A model like the one described in Example 9.4 is easy to simulate. However, its simulation does not seem to have any particular advantage over its analytic solution except perhaps the fact that a simulator can more readily provide information on where most of the execution time of the program is spent. On the other hand, simulation is certainly more expensive in terms of computer time than the analytic technique we have described and is probably a convenient choice only if a more complicated model (for instance, a non-Markovian one) is to be used.

In the realm of deterministic models of programs, simulation would seem to be definitely superior to analytic techniques, or, more precisely, to have no alternatives. Decisions, in a deterministic model, are not based on given branching probabilities but on the values of the actual predicates. Thus, a model of this type must explicitly include all the predicates. Knowing the values of the predicates at each instant during the program's execution will be sufficient to determine the path followed by the flow of control. Let us call *control variables* those program variables which appear in at least one predicate and *control state* a set of possible values of the control variables. A model, in order to be complete, must specify how each block of serial statements influences the control state of the program. In the program in Table 9.1, the predicates (after the appropriate substitutions of subroutine arguments) are (IENT = 0), (I ≤ IENT), (J ≤ JNT), and (II ≤ IENT). The control state of the program at a certain instant is given by the value of the vector (IENT, JNT, I, J, II) at that instant. The block consisting of statements 1 and 2 sets IENT and JNT to values read in from an input card but does not modify the other control variables. The block composed of statements 21 through 26 does not have any influence on the control state of the program. Note that there may be indirect influences which must also be represented in the model. If there were a statement 6' such as IENT = IENT + INT(H), all blocks including statements which set or modify H (in our example, only the block of statement 1) and their influence on H should be specified in the model, even though H is not a control variable.

In summary, a deterministic model of a program may be built as a graph model like, for example, the one in Fig. 9.6(*b*). To determine the execution time and the program trace (hence, also the profile and other performance indices), it is necessary and sufficient to specify the execution time of each vertex, its direct or indirect influence on the control state, and the predicate which may exist at its exit.

We shall now show that, when we are interested in a program's profile, it is possible to write equations in the frequency counts of the various blocks and, for relatively simple program structures, solve them analytically. The solutions express frequency counts as functions of the input data and allow one to determine the program profile and a number of important program performance indices (including the execution time) for any given set of values of the input data. In those cases in which solving the *profile equations* is very difficult or impossible, approximations should be sought or simulation applied. In a large program, analytic formulas of this type could be derived for parts of the program and used to speed up its simulation (*see* Problem 9.14).

The limitations of this analytic approach and the approximations which may be employed to overcome them have not yet been explored completely. We shall describe the method by applying it to the simple program in Table 9.1. However, to apply it, we have to transform the program so that its flowchart becomes a *D-chart*. A D-chart [so-named after Dijkstra (1972), who first introduced it] is a flowchart whose only formation rules are represented by the three constructs in Fig. 9.8: *composition*, *alternation*, and *iteration*. More precisely, a D-chart is a directed graph with five types of vertices: rectangular boxes, which are used to represent blocks of statements in series or any more complicated D-chart (for instance, boxes Z in Fig. 9.8); diamond-shaped vertices, which represent decisions; circular vertices, which represent junctions; and the two triangular types of vertices, representing entry and exit points. If X and Y are D-charts, then the three constructs in Fig. 9.8, each one of which may be represented by a single rectangular box Z, are D-charts. These constructs will be called *elementary D-charts*. The language constructs corresponding to the elementary D-charts are the three pillars of GOTO-less programming: the normal sequencing of statements $(X; Y)$, the conditional statement **if** q_z **then** X **else** Y, and the loop **while** q_z **do** X. Note that, in Fig. 9.8 and in the sequel of our discussion, a predicate is considered as a Boolean variable whose value is 1 if the predicate is true and 0 if it is false. Note also that all elementary D-charts in Fig. 9.8 have one input and one output only.

Once a graph model of the program in D-chart form is constructed, the profile equations may be written by iteratively replacing each elementary D-chart with a single-input/single-output box and applying the corresponding equations in

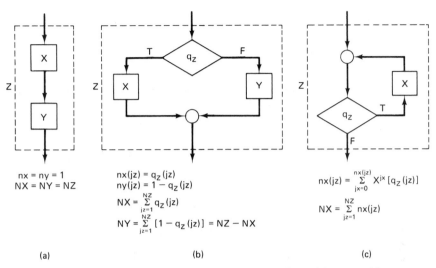

$$nx = ny = 1$$
$$NX = NY = NZ$$

$$nx(jz) = q_z(jz)$$
$$ny(jz) = 1 - q_z(jz)$$
$$NX = \sum_{jz=1}^{NZ} q_z(jz)$$
$$NY = \sum_{jz=1}^{NZ} [1 - q_z(jz)] = NZ - NX$$

$$nx(jz) = \sum_{jx=0}^{nx(jz)} X^{jx}[q_z(jz)]$$
$$NX = \sum_{jz=1}^{NZ} nx(jz)$$

(a)   (b)   (c)

Figure 9.8   Elementary D-charts and their profile equations: (*a*) composition; (*b*) alternation; (*c*) iteration.

Fig. 9.8. The symbols used in these equations will now be explained. Let X be a rectangular box and Z another rectangular box which replaces an elementary D-chart containing X in the iterative procedure mentioned above. We denote by nx the number of times X is executed every time Z is entered and by NX the total number of times X is executed during the execution of the program. In other words, NX is the frequency count of X. Since Z is entered in total NZ times and each time we may have a different value of nx, we indicate these values by $nx(jz)$, with $jz = 1, 2, \ldots, NZ$. Obviously, we have

$$NX = \sum_{jz=1}^{NZ} nx(jz). \tag{9.7}$$

Note that jz, the index counting the number of times box Z is entered, is assumed to be incremented as the flow of control enters Z and to be initially equal to zero. We shall call jz the *execution index* of Z.

The equation of $nx(jz)$ in Fig. 9.8(c) requires some additional explanations. By $q_z(jz)$ we denote the value of predicate q_z when box Z is entered for the jzth time. $X(q_z(jz))$ is the value of $q_z(jz)$ after box X has been executed once. The value of $q_z(jz)$ after jx executions of X is denoted by $X^{jx}[q_z(jz)]$, and we set $X^0[q_z(jz)] = q_z(jz)$. Thus, the equation of $nx(jz)$ in Fig. 9.8(c) simply expresses the fact that if we apply X $nx(jz)$ times to $q_z(jz)$, we make this predicate false for the first time since box Z was entered. That is, at the $nx(jz)$th application of function X, $q_z(jz)$ becomes 0. A closed-form expression of $nx(jz)$ may be obtained only when q_z and X are specified. For example, in a simple DO loop, where the index I goes from the initial value INIT to the limit LIM in increments of 1, if $q_z = (I < LIM)$, then we have

$$nx(jz) = (INIT < LIM) + (INIT + 1 < LIM) + \cdots + (INIT + nx(jz) < LIM),$$
(9.8)

where the last predicate, and only it, must be false. Then, if $INIT < LIM$,

$$INIT + nx(jz) = LIM,$$
(9.9)

hence

$$nx(jz) = LIM - INIT.$$
(9.10)

If on the other hand $INIT \geq LIM$, then

$$nx(jz) = 0.$$
(9.11)

Equations (9.10) and (9.11) can be written in a more compact form as

$$nx(jz) = (LIM - INIT)(LIM \geq INIT),$$
(9.12)

where $(LIM \geq INIT)$ is 1 if the enclosed inequality is satisfied and 0 if it is false. Similarly, if the predicate q_z is $(I \leq LIM)$, (9.12) becomes

$$nx(jz) = (LIM - INIT + 1)(LIM \geq INIT).$$
(9.13)

Note that the number of times a FORTRAN DO loop is executed equals $nx(jz) + 1$, where $nx(jz)$ is given by (9.10) or (9.11). This discrepancy is due to the difference between the structure of the iteration in FORTRAN and that of the elementary D-chart in Fig. 9.8(c). Note also that $nx(jz)$ in (9.10) depends on jz if LIM or INIT depend on jz.

The Z boxes in Fig. 9.8 may in turn be part of a bigger D-chart which, in the iterative replacement procedure to be illustrated in Example 9.5, is to be replaced by a larger box, say W. Every time W is entered, Z is executed $nz(jw)$ times, where $nz(jw)$ is analogous to the $nx(jz)$ of the same elementary D-chart in Fig. 9.8. For each execution of W, index jz runs from 1 to $nz(jw)$ and is reset to 0 every time the flow of control leaves W. Thus, X is executed a number of times equal to

$$nx(jw) = \sum_{jz=1}^{nz(jw)} nx(jz, jw),$$
(9.14)

and the total number of executions of X (unless or until W is in turn replaced by a larger box) will be

$$NX = \sum_{jw=1}^{NW} \sum_{jz=1}^{nz(jw)} nx(jz, jw).$$
(9.15)

If W is enclosed into a box V, NX and NW in (9.15) will have to become $nx(jv)$ and $nw(jv)$. Furthermore, $nx(jz, jw)$ and $jz(jw)$ will be replaced by $nx(jz, jw, jv)$ and $nz(jw, jv)$, respectively.

Example 9.5   The program in Table 9.1 is not in a form suitable for a D-chart representation but is easily transformable for this purpose. Figure 9.9(a) shows the D-chart of a program equivalent to the original one. The reader will not have much difficulty in understanding how the transformation was performed and what its effects would be on the program's text. Beside each rectangular box, in parentheses, the numbers of the statements represented by that box are reported. Note that the structural discrepancies between FORTRAN and D-chart-oriented languages, like the difference between iterations mentioned a few paragraphs above, require that some statements appear in more than one box. However, this does not create any problems, except a slight increase in the complexity of the D-chart. Of course, we must remember this when computing the number of times a certain statement, say 21, is executed. Since 21 is executed once every time B or C or E or F is executed, then $N21 = NB + NC + NE + NF$. Table 9.11(d) gives the relationships between the frequency counts in the D-chart of Fig. 9.9(a) and those in the

Table 9.11

CORRESPONDENCE BETWEEN THE D-CHART IN FIG. 9.9(a) AND
THE FLOWCHART AND GRAPH MODEL IN FIG. 9.6

(a) *Definitions of higher-level boxes at the various steps of the iterative replacement procedure* (solid line = composition, broken line = iteration)

Step 0	1	2	3	4	5	6

$$C ---- N \begin{array}{c} B \\ \\ D \end{array} \quad R$$

$$F ---- P \begin{array}{c} E \\ \\ G \end{array} S ----U \quad V ---- W \quad X$$

$$K ---- Q \begin{array}{c} H \\ \\ L \end{array} T$$

with A and M at step 5 connecting to X.

(b) *Predicates*

$q_N = (J < JNT)$
$q_P = (J < JNT)$
$q_U = (II \leq IENT)$
$q_O = (I < IENT)$
$q_W = (IENT \neq 0)$

(c) *Control variables*	Set by	Incremented by
IENT	A, L	—
JNT	A, L	—
J	B, E	C, F
II	B	D, G
I	H	K

(d) *Relationships between frequency counts*

$NI = NA + NL$
$NII = NB$
$NIII = NB + NE$
$NIV = NB + NC + NE + NF$
$NV = ND + NG$
$NVI = NH$
$NVII = NH + NK$

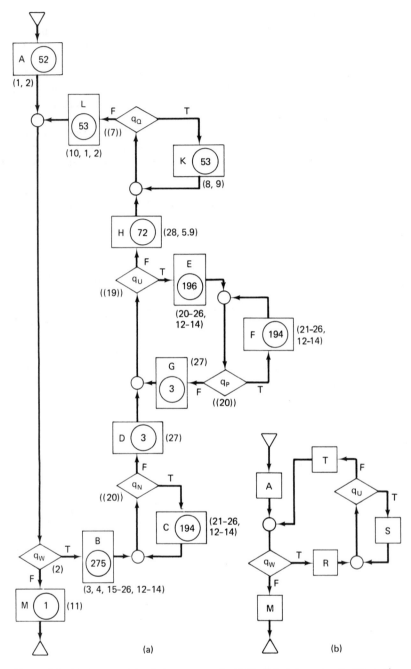

Figure 9.9 D-chart models of the program in Table 9.1: (*a*) at step 0; (*b*) during step 3 of the iterative replacement procedure [*see* Table 9.11(*a*)].

graph model of Fig. 9.6(*b*), in which each statement belongs to only one vertex. In the circle inside each rectangular box in Fig. 9.9(*a*) we report the execution time of the box, corresponding to that given in Table 9.2. Note that decisions and junctions are assumed to be executed in zero time.

Table 9.11 [(b) and (c)] contains the information which must accompany the D-chart in order for our problem to be solvable. In (b), the five predicates which appear in Fig. 9.9(*a*) are specified, and in (c) a characterization of the boxes of the D-chart is given in terms of their influence on the control state of the program. The reasons for the predicate names (q_N, q_P, ...) will be clear if the reader follows the iterative replacement procedure summarized in Table 9.11(a). At each step, all possible replacements of elementary D-charts by higher-level boxes are made. For example, in the D-chart in Fig. 9.9(*a*) there are three iteration loops like the one in Fig. 9.8(*c*). That involving box *C* and decision q_N will be replaced by box *N*, and similarly *F* and q_P by *P* and *K* and q_Q by *Q*. Then boxes *R*, *S*, and *T* will be obtained by applying composition and so on until the entire D-chart is reduced to a single box, *X*. Figure 9.9(*b*) depicts the D-chart just after the introduction of *R*, *S*, and *T*.

At this point, having constructed the hierarchy of D-charts in a bottom-up fashion, the profile equations may be written. To do so, it is convenient to proceed in the top-down direction, starting from *X* and moving toward the leaves of the tree, as shown in Table 9.12. The equations in this table are obtained from those in Fig. 9.8 and from equations (9.12)–(9.15).

A few remarks must be made on the derivation of the profile equations.

First, these equations contain as many lowercase variables as there are iterations and as many execution indices as there are predicates. The five boxes inside iteration D-charts are *V*, *S*, *C*, *F*, and *K*, and the corresponding lowercase variables are *nv*, *ns*, *nc*, *nf*, and *nk*. The five predicates are q_W, q_U, q_N, q_P, and q_Q, and the corresponding execution indices are *jw*, *ju*, *jn*, *jp*, and *jq*.

Second, boxes with a composition interrelationship not only have the same final frequency counts but also the same instantaneous frequency counts, provided that these are observed at the exit of the smallest box which encloses them all. For instance, there is a composition relation among *V*, *U*, *N*, and *Q* [they are all connected by solid links in the tree in Table 9.11(a)]. Thus, we have not only $NV = NU = NN = NQ$ but also $nv = nu = nn = nq$. Since *nv* is the number of times *V* is executed when *W* is entered, we expect it to be a function of the execution index of *W*, *jw* and therefore write $nv(jw) = nu(jw) = nn(jw) = nq(jw)$.

Third, *W* is an iteration but not a DO loop; q_W tests IENT, which is set by *A* the first time and then by *L* every time *V* is executed. Thus, it is convenient to denote the sequence $IENT_1$, $IENT_2$, ... of the values of IENT by a two-dimensional quantity such as IENT(*jw*, *jv*). Since *jv* is incremented as *V* is entered and reset to zero every time *W* is exited, inside *V* IENT(1, 1) will denote the first value of IENT (i.e., $IENT_1$), IENT(1, 2) will correspond to the second ($IENT_2$), IENT(1, *nv*(1)) to $IENT_{nv(1)}$, IENT(2, 1) to $IENT_{nv(1)+1}$, and so on. Similarly, inside *U* the current value of IENT, the one just tested by q_W, will be denotable by IENT(*jw*, *ju*) and inside *Q* by IENT(*jw*, *jq*), and the same notation will be applicable to JNT.

Fourth, the number of consecutive input cards with IENT $\neq$ 0 is a datum of the problem and has been indicated by ν in Table 9.12.

Solving the profile equations of this simple program is straightforward. A solution for $NX = 1$, $IENT_i \geq 1$, and $JNT_i \geq 1$ ($i = 1, \ldots, \nu$) is presented in Table 9.13. The

Table 9.12

PROFILE EQUATIONS FOR THE D-CHART IN FIG. 9.9(a)

Equation	Step	Type
$NA = NW = NM = NX$	5	Composition
$NV = \sum\limits_{jw=1}^{NW} nv(jw)$	4	Iteration
$NR = NU = NT = NV$	3	Composition
$NS = \sum\limits_{jw=1}^{NW} \sum\limits_{ju=1}^{nu(jw)} ns(jw, ju)$	2	Iteration
$NB = NN = ND = NR$	1	Composition
$NE = NP = NG = NS$	1	Composition
$NH = NQ = NL = NT$	1	Composition
$NC = \sum\limits_{jw=1}^{NW} \sum\limits_{jn=1}^{nn(jw)} nc(jw, jn)$	0	Iteration
$NF = \sum\limits_{jw=1}^{NW} \sum\limits_{ju=1}^{nu(jw)} \sum\limits_{jp=1}^{np(jw, ju)} nf(jw, ju, jp)$	0	Iteration
$NK = \sum\limits_{jw=1}^{NW} \sum\limits_{jq=1}^{nq(jw)} nk(jw, jq)$	0	Iteration

$$nv(jw) = nu(jw) = nn(jw) = nq(jw) = \#\,(\text{IENT}_i \neq 0) = \nu$$
$$ns(jw, ju) = np(jw, ju) = [\text{IENT}(jw, ju) - 1][\text{IENT}(jw, ju) \geq 1]$$
$$nc(jw, jn) = [\text{JNT}(jw, jn) - 1][\text{JNT}(jw, jn) \geq 1]$$
$$nf(jw, ju, jp) = [\text{JNT}(jw, ju) - 1][\text{JNT}(jw, ju) \geq 1]$$
$$nk(jw, jq) = [\text{IENT}(jw, jq) - 1][\text{IENT}(jw, jq) \geq 1]$$

same table shows the expressions of NI through NVII derived from those of NA through NK in the same table and from the equations in Table 9.11(d). These formulas allow us to calculate the same frequency counts that we would measure by the instrumentation in Table 9.7(d), from which we can construct the program profile as defined in Section 9.2.1. Knowing the execution time TJ of each box J in the full-blown D-chart [see Fig. 9.9(a)], we can therefore compute very rapidly the amount of time which is spent in J for any set of input data values. The sum of all these times is the execution time of the program, for which we give in Table 9.13 a formula computed from the values of the statement times appearing in Table 9.2. Using this formula, the reader may verify that the execution time for $\text{IENT}_1 = 1$, $\text{JNT}_1 = 2$, $\text{IENT}_2 = 0$ is the one resulting from the trace in Table 9.2 ($t = 650$ time units). Also, for $\text{IENT}_i = 10$, $\text{JNT}_i = 5$ ($i = 1, \ldots, 9$), the formula provides an execution time of 93,932 time units, which coincides with the mean execution time found in Example 9.4 [see Fig. 9.7(e)].

Table 9.13
SOLUTIONS OF THE PROFILE EQUATIONS IN TABLE 9.12 FOR
$NX = 1$, $IENT_i \geq 1$, $JNT_i \geq 1$ $(i = 1, 2, \ldots, v)$

$NA = NW = NM = 1$

$NV = nv(1) = v$

$NR = NU = NT = v$

$NS = \sum\limits_{ju=1}^{v} IENT(1, ju) - v$

$NB = NN = ND = v$

$NE = NP = NG = \sum\limits_{ju=1}^{v} IENT(1, ju) - v$

$NH = NQ = NL = v$

$NC = \sum\limits_{jn=1}^{v} JNT(1, jn) - v$

$NF = \sum\limits_{ju=1}^{v} \sum\limits_{ip=1}^{IENT(1,ju)-1} [JNT(1, ju) - 1] = \sum\limits_{ju=1}^{v} [IENT(1, ju) - 1][JNT(1, ju) - 1]$

$NK = \sum\limits_{jq=1}^{v} IENT(1, jq) - v$

$NI = 1 + v$

$NII = v$

$NIII = \sum\limits_{ju=1}^{v} IENT(1, ju)$

$NIV = \sum\limits_{ju=1}^{v} IENT(1, ju) \cdot JNT(1, ju)$

$NV = \sum\limits_{ju=1}^{v} IENT(1, ju)$

$NVI = v$

$NVII = \sum\limits_{jq=1}^{v} IENT(1, jq)$

$t = NA \cdot TA + NB \cdot TB + \cdots + NM \cdot TM$

$= 194 \sum\limits_{ju=1}^{v} IENT(1, ju) \cdot JNT(1, ju) + 58 \sum\limits_{ju=1}^{v} IENT(1, ju) + 151v + 53$

The application of the approach to a somewhat more complicated program is illustrated in Table 9.14. The new program is identical to the one we have analyzed except for statement 20, which is now DO 1 J = II, K. The initial value of the DO loop index J is set to 1 in *B* and incremented in *D* and *G*. Thus, nothing changes for box *C*, but with

Table 9.14

MODIFICATIONS TO BE MADE TO TABLES 9.12 AND 9.13 IF
STATEMENT 20 IS CHANGED TO DO 1 J = II,K

To Table 9.12

$$nf(jw, ju, jp) = [\text{JNT}(jw, ju) - jp - 1][\text{JNT}(jw, ju) \geq (jp + 1)]$$

To Table 9.13

$$NF = \sum_{ju=1}^{\nu} \sum_{jp=1}^{\text{IENT}(1,ju)-1} [\text{JNT}(1, ju) - jp - 1][\text{JNT}(1, ju) \geq (jp + 1)]$$

$$= \sum_{ju=1}^{\nu} (\{\text{IENT}(1, ju)[\text{JNT}(1, ju) - \tfrac{1}{2}\text{IENT}(1, ju) - \tfrac{1}{2}] - \text{JNT}(1, ju) + 1\}$$

$$\cdot [\text{JNT}(1, ju) \geq \text{IENT}(1, ju)]$$

$$+ \{\tfrac{1}{2}[\text{JNT}(1, ju) - 2][\text{JNT}(1, ju) - 1]\}[\text{JNT}(1, ju) < \text{IENT}(1, ju)])$$

$$NIV = \sum_{ju=1}^{\nu} \text{IENT}(1, ju)[\text{JNT}(1, ju) - \tfrac{1}{2}\text{IENT}(1, ju) + \tfrac{1}{2}] \qquad \text{if} \quad \text{JNT}(1, ju) \geq \text{IENT}(1, ju)$$

$$= \sum_{ju=1}^{\nu} \{\text{IENT}(1, ju) + \tfrac{1}{2}\text{JNT}(1, ju)[\text{JNT}(1, ju) - 1]\} \qquad \text{if} \quad \text{JNT}(1, ju) < \text{IENT}(1, ju)$$

$$t = 194 \sum_{ju=1}^{\nu} \text{IENT}(1, ju) \cdot \text{JNT}(1, ju) - 97 \sum_{ju=1}^{\nu} [\text{IENT}(1, ju)]^2 + 155 \sum_{ju=1}^{\nu} \text{IENT}(1, ju)$$

$$+ 151\nu + 53 \qquad \text{if JNT}(1, ju) \geq \text{IENT}(1, ju) \quad \text{for all } ju$$

$$= 252 \sum_{ju=1}^{\nu} \text{IENT}(1, ju) + 97 \sum_{ju=1}^{\nu} [\text{JNT}(1, ju)]^2 - 97 \sum_{ju=1}^{\nu} \text{JNT}(1, ju) + 151\nu + 53$$

$$\text{if JNT}(1, ju) < \text{IENT}(1, ju) \quad \text{for all } ju$$

---

respect to P we have

$$\text{II}(jp) = jp + 1, \tag{9.16}$$

since II equals 2 when the flow of control enters U (hence also P) and is incremented by 1
in G. The equation of nf in Table 9.14 is drawn from (9.12). The formulas of NF, NIV,
and t can be derived with some manipulation from that of nf and from the previous
formulas in Table 9.13. The solutions have been obtained under the same assumptions
made in Table 9.13.

The formulas which the method yields are certainly useful in a variety of contexts. It
is evident, however, that for larger programs the analysis should be automated or at least
substantially aided by a computer and that suitable approximation methods should be
introduced for those cases in which exact solutions are too difficult to obtain. ∎

Our discussion of program behavior indices in Section 9.2.2 showed the
existence of a number of different characterizations for the referencing behavior
of programs. These characterizations span a wide spectrum of degrees of detail

and of dependencies on memory management strategies. At one extreme, we have the reference string, which is an extremely detailed and strategy-independent model of program behavior. At the other, we have single scalar indices such as the number of page faults, whose values do not really characterize a (program, input) pair but rather the combination of a program, its input data, and the particular strategy under which the program is run. The concept of locality is strategy-independent but is also very difficult to quantify in a strategy-independent way.

The only performance analysis technique in which a program's reference string can be used is trace-driven simulation. Both for other types of simulation and for analytic techniques, a more concise model of program behavior is needed. Retaining all of the relevant information which a string contains while substantially reducing its size seems to be impossible if the strategy is to be left totally unspecified. Thus, work on program behavior models has to proceed along the two directions of specialization and approximation.

Specialized models are those which are constructed for a given class of strategies. They may be exact, in the sense that all of the relevant information is present in them. In other words, they may yield exact results when used to compute certain program performance indices. However, it is not possible, or appropriate, to apply them to different problems or with strategies not belonging to that class.

A simple example of such a model is the *lifetime curve* introduced in Example 7.3. Its use is limited to calculations of the total number of page faults generated by a program, or of its mean fault rate over an entire run, when the memory management scheme belongs to the class of demand-paging fixed-allocation strategies with a specific replacement algorithm (e.g., LRU). Any application of a lifetime curve outside this domain is either impossible or a rough approximation. The latter is the case of our applications of it in several examples in Chapters 7 and 8. As mentioned in Section 9.3.1, the algorithm in Table 9.8

Table 9.15

PAGE REFERENCE STRING DERIVED FROM THE BLOCK
REFERENCE STRING IN TABLE 9.4

(a) Page reference string (reference times are as in Table 9.4)

1 3 4 1 4 1 4 3 1 4 2 4 2 4 2 4 2 4 2 4 2 4 2 4 1 4 1 4 1 2

4 2 4 1 4 1 4 1 2 4 2 4 1 4 1 4 1 2 4 2 4 1 4 1 4 1 2 4 2 4

2 4 2 4 2 1 4 1 4 1 4 1 4 1 4 3 1 1 3 4 1 4 1

(b) String of page reference sets (one set every 25 time units)

(1, 3, 4)(3, 4)(1, 3, 4)(1, 3, 4)(1, 2, 4)(1, 2, 4)(1, 2, 4)(1, 2, 4)(1, 2, 4)(1, 4)(1, 2, 4)

(1, 2, 4)(2, 4)(1, 2, 4)(1, 3, 4)(1, 3, 4)(1, 3, 4)(1, 3, 4)

---

may be slightly modified to yield the LRU lifetime curve of a program in one pass over its reference string.

Given, for example, the block reference string in Table 9.4(a) and the mapping $\pi_1 = (b_1, b_3)$, $\pi_2 = (b_5)$, $\pi_3 = (b_7, b_8)$, $\pi_4 = (b_2, b_4, b_6)$ of the program's eight blocks into the four pages π_1, π_2, π_3, π_4, we obtain the page reference

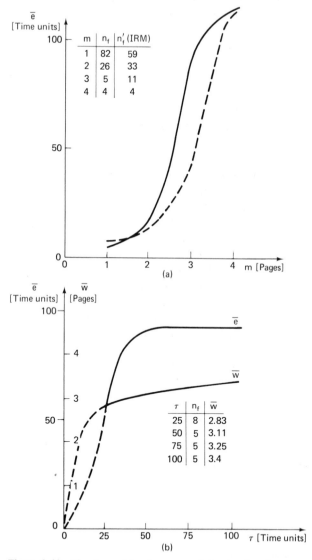

Figure 9.10 Simple models of program behavior for the page reference string in Table 9.15(a): (*a*) LRU lifetime curves, derived from the string (solid line) and predicted by the IRM (broken line); (*b*) time-domain lifetime curve ($\bar{e}$) and working set size characteristic ($\bar{w}$) from the string.

string in Table 9.15(a). From this, we easily derive the solid-line lifetime curve in Fig. 9.10(a). This allows us to calculate the number of page faults generated by the (program, input) pair for a given memory space allotment m, but only if that space remains constant throughout execution and if it is managed according to the LRU algorithm. Note that in applying this algorithm to the page reference string in Table 9.15(a), we have assumed that if the program makes other references which do not appear in the string, they are all to the most recently referenced page. Thus, the string 1 3 4 could in fact be 1 1 1 1 1 3 3 3 4 4 4 4 without making our results erroneous. This assumption is not very realistic. In a string generated at the machine language level, there are frequent alternations of instruction fetches and operand fetches or stores. Thus, the above string is much more likely to be of the type 1 4 1 1 4 3 4 3 4 4 4 3 4. If the alternations are restricted to two pages at a time, as in this string, then only the value of $\bar{e}$ for $m = 1$ in Fig. 9.10(a) is not exact but is higher than the real one, since considering the string in Table 9.15(a) causes the number of page faults generated for $m = 1$ to be underestimated. Note also that the memory partition allotted to the program has been assumed to be initially empty.

Other models of the same type, valid for a working set strategy with constant window size τ, are the curve $\bar{e}(\tau)$, which could be called the *time-domain lifetime curve*, and the *working set size characteristic* $\bar{w}(\tau)$, where $\bar{w}$ is the mean size of the program's working set. Like $\bar{e}(m)$, these curves can be measured or constructed by trace-driven simulation. Figure 9.10(b) shows the two curves derived from the string of page reference sets in Table 9.15(b), corresponding to that of block reference sets in Table 9.4(b) and to the mapping reported above. Note that when the string consists of reference sets instead of references, the algorithm in Table 9.9 must be modified to reflect the fact that the window can advance only by one reference set at a time rather than by one reference. Thus, the window consists of an integral number of sets, and more than one page fault may be generated at every step. If we use a string of reference sets, we obtain curves which only approximate those the pure working set strategy in Table 9.9 would produce operating on the complete reference string. However, most practical implementations of working set strategies do not measure the working set at each reference time but only periodically. If both this period and the window size are integral multiples of the interval corresponding to a reference set, using a string of reference sets does not affect the calculation of the number of page faults and provides a more realistic estimate of the memory space that will actually be requested by the program. Also, the simulation is usually much faster than when it is driven by the complete reference string.

If a model more compact than the reference string but not restricted to only a class of strategies is desired, simplifying assumptions must be made, and the resulting model will therefore represent the program's behavior only approximately. In principle, this is not a problem, since any model of any system is always an approximate representation of it. The problem is the model's adequacy, which can only be judged with respect to some criterion to be specified depending on the modeler's viewpoint and the intended applications of the model.

In program performance evaluation, the basic criterion should be the ability of a model to predict the execution time of a given program. This means that the number of page faults the program will generate running under any given memory management strategy should be predictable. Sometimes, however, there are other criteria worth considering. The modeler may, for instance, be more interested in proving general statements about strategies than in computing the number of page faults produced by a specific program under a specific strategy. In this case, a simple analytic model, whose dynamic behavior bears some resemblance to those of some real programs, is certainly more suitable than a more detailed but mathematically untractable model. The results of program measurement experiments based on the techniques described in Section 9.3.1 should not only be used to calibrate and validate the more detailed models but should also provide inspiration and guidance for the formulation of even the crudest and most generic models.

A popular way of obtaining a concise representation of a complex system's behavior in time is to build a stochastic model of it. This is the normal approach to the modeling of reference strings of programs. In general, stochastic modeling involves defining the states of the system to be modeled and their probabilities or the probabilities of the possible transitions between them. The choice of the states is a crucial one and must be made taking the purposes of the model and the peculiar characteristics of the system into account. The simplest choice is the one which identifies the state of the program at any given instant with the most recently referenced page (or block). In this case, there are as many states as there are pages in the program. If the occurrence of each state is assumed to be statistically independent of those of all other states and of time, we have the *independent reference model* (IRM). Thus, the IRM characterizes the behavior of a program having u pages by the page reference probability distribution $\{p_i\}$, which must obey the relationship

$$\sum_{i=1}^{u} p_i = 1. \tag{9.17}$$

In other words, the IRM's description of a program is equivalent to the program's page or block profile. Table 9.5, which gives the block profiles of the string in Table 9.4(a) and of two substrings of it, shows why the IRM is not an adequate model of program behavior. The IRM is unable to represent the fundamental property of locality, since it reproduces the page usage densities of the program only on a global scale. Note that the IRM coincides with the block profile only if block references are issued at regular intervals. Otherwise, we should also specify for each state the probability of leaving it, which would allow the model to represent variable intervals between consecutive references.

How can a stochastic model like the IRM (and the others which will be described) be used to estimate the performance of the modeled program in a virtual-memory environment? For certain strategies, it is possible to obtain formulas which express the number of page faults, or the mean page fault rate, as a function of $p_1, \ldots, p_u$. For example, the mean page fault rate generated by a program obeying the IRM under LRU with m pages of physical memory space is [*see* Coffman and Denning (1973), p. 272]

$$\bar{f} = \sum_{\text{all } s} D_1^2(s) \prod_{i=1}^{m} \frac{p_{j_i}}{D_i(s)}, \tag{9.18}$$

where $s = (j_1, j_2, \ldots, j_m)$ is a permutation of m page indices taken from $(1, 2, \ldots, u)$ and

$$D_i(s) = 1 - \sum_{k=1}^{m-i+1} p_{j_k} \qquad (i = 1, \ldots, m). \tag{9.19}$$

Applying formula (9.18) to the page reference string in Table 9.15(a) yields the broken-line lifetime curve in Fig. 9.10(a).

If an analytic formula is not available for the stochastic model and the strategy being considered, the model can be used to generate a reference string in real time for what may be called a distribution-driven simulator of the memory hierarchy. For instance, with the IRM, whenever a new page reference is to be processed by the simulator (see step 2 of the algorithms in Tables 9.8 and 9.9), a pseudo-random number is generated and the discrete distribution $\{p_i\}$ used to produce a reference by the technique explained in Example 3.3.

Another model based on the same choice for the program's states as the IRM is the simple Markov model defined by the matrix of page-to-page or block-to-block transition probabilities. These probabilities can be estimated from a reference string. If c_{ik} is the frequency count of the ordered pair (π_i, π_k) in the string, the probability that, after referencing page π_i, the program immediately references π_k may be estimated as

$$p_{ik} = \frac{c_{ik}}{\sum\limits_{k=1}^{u} c_{ik}} \qquad (i, k = 1, \ldots, u). \tag{9.20}$$

Thus, the dynamic behavior of a program is characterized in this model by the pair $(j_1, \{p_{ik}\})$, where j_1 is the index of the first page referenced. The matrices of frequency counts c_{ik} and of transition probabilities p_{ik} derived from the page reference string in Table 9.15(a) are reported in Table 9.16[(a) and (b)]. Note that entries of the c_{ii} and p_{ii} type would be much larger if the string were at the machine language level.

A choice of the program's states which allows the property of locality to be modeled reasonably well is the one based on LRU stack positions rather than on individual pages. If we number the LRU stack positions 1 through u starting from the most recently used page and define the *LRU stack distance* of a reference to page π_i as the position of π_i in the LRU stack at the time the

Table 9.16

MATRICES OF FREQUENCY COUNTS AND TRANSITION
PROBABILITIES FOR TWO MARKOV MODELS OF THE PAGE
REFERENCE STRING IN TABLE 9.15(a)

Characterization in terms of page references

		To page						To page		
		1	2	3	4		1	2	3	4
From page	1	1	4	2	17	1	0.042	0.166	0.084	0.708
	2	1	0	0	17	From page 2	0.055	0	0	0.945
	3	2	0	0	2	3	0.500	0	0	0.500
	4	20	14	2	0	4	0.555	0.389	0.056	0

(a) c_{ik} (b) p_{ik}

Characterization in terms of LRU stack distances

		To distance						To distance		
		1	2	3	4		1	2	3	4
From distance	1	0	1	0	0	1	0	1	0	0
	2	0	41	10	1	From distance 2	0	0.788	0.192	0.020
	3	1	10	6	0	distance 3	0.059	0.588	0.353	0
	4	0	0	1	0	4	0	0	1	0

(c) c_{ik} (d) d_{ik}

reference is issued, we may identify the state of the program with the value of this distance. Note that in the LRU algorithm reported in Table 9.8 the LRU stack distance is the variable denoted by δ. Since the possible distances are $u + 1$ (the first u natural numbers and ∞, which is the distance conventionally assigned to any page never referenced before), the program is characterized as being at any instant in one of $u + 1$ states.

A very popular model based on this characterization is the so-called *simple LRU stack model* (SLRUM). The SLRUM consists of the pair $(s_0, \{d_i\})$, where s_0 is the initial contents of the LRU stack and $\{d_i\}$ $(i = 1, \ldots, u, \infty)$ is the distribution of distance probabilities. Since s_0 is given, all pages are assumed to have been referenced at least once before the beginning of the modeled string. Thus, we have $d_\infty = 0$, and $\{d_i\}$ consists of u probabilities whose sum is 1. As usual, additional information, such as the distributions of the durations of each state, must be supplied if the references in the string from which the model's parameters are estimated were issued at nonuniform intervals. If we ignore this observation, we can model the page reference string in Table 9.15(a) as $[(2, 4, 1, 3), (0.013, 0.818, 0.156, 0.013)]$. Note that the origin of times has been set at the time of the eleventh reference, which is the first reference to page π_2, since the

LRU stack becomes full only at that point. Also, d_1 is very low because of the type of string we are considering. In the actual machine language level strings, d_1 often is the largest of all distance probabilities, and the d_i's are almost always sharply decreasing as i increases.

The SLRUM can adequately represent the locality aspects of program behavior due to its ability to concentrate references over a few pages for extended periods of time without assigning fixed probabilities to those pages. The membership of the current locality is allowed to change, and any new page that joins it is likely to remain in it for a relatively long period. In other words, each page has a time-variant probability of being referenced. This is due to the fact that page identities in the model are ignored. The SLRUM could be viewed as an *independent distance model*, except for the fact that, unlike the IRM, an initial condition (s_0) needs to be specified in order to allow the reference string to be derived from the distance string. This derivation is straightforward. For example, if $s_j = (4, 2, 1, 3)$ and $\delta_{j+1} = 3$, then $i_{j+1} = 1$, that is, the third page in the stack is referenced next, and we have $s_{j+1} = (1, 4, 2, 3)$.

The SLRUM exactly predicts the mean page fault rate of the modeled program running under a fixed-allocation, LRU replacement strategy with m page frames in physical memory:

$$\bar{f} = 1 - \sum_{i=1}^{m} d_i. \tag{9.21}$$

It can also be proved [*see* Coffman and Denning (1973), p. 276] that, given a string generated by a SLRUM with

$$d_1 \geq d_2 \geq \cdots \geq d_n, \tag{9.22}$$

the LRU algorithm is optimum for that string and all $m \geq 1$, in the sense that no replacement algorithm which does not assume foreknowledge of the referencing pattern can generate less page faults than LRU. Thus, we can say that the LRU strategy assumes that programs behave according to the SLRUM, or, equivalently, that the SLRUM is the model underlying the LRU strategy.

Spirn and Denning (1972) found that the SLRUM can also predict the working set size characteristic of a program with good accuracy. Unfortunately, the abrupt locality transitions which characterize the behavior of most programs are not adequately represented by the SLRUM. Since this model can only produce strings with very smooth and slow transitions, it cannot be employed to estimate more sophisticated indices such as the distribution of interfault intervals. In general, the SLRUM should be used with caution because of the fact that the periods of most intense paging activity, under any strategy, are those corresponding to locality transitions, which the SLRUM is unable to properly reproduce.

The characterization of a program's states on which the SLRUM is based can be exploited in more complicated models. For example, a Markov model can be constructed by estimating the probabilities of transition between LRU stack distances. These may be obtained as in (9.20), from the frequency counts of all pairs (δ_i, δ_k) of distances in the distance string. The matrix of these frequency counts for the string in Table 9.15(a), with the first 11 references deleted, is given in Table 9.16(c), and the corresponding transition-probability matrix is given in Table 9.16(d). Note that this model, like the SLRUM, is completely specified only if s_0 is assigned. Thus, it consists of the pair $(s_0, \{d_{ik}\})$, where $\{d_{ik}\}$ $(i, k = 1, \dots, u)$ is the distance transition-probability matrix.

Other choices for the states of a program are possible. For instance, the state might be identified with the current LRU stack, the current reference set, or the current locality. A precise definition of the localities of a program is, of course, a prerequisite to their use in characterizing program behavior, which is certainly an appealing idea. This problem, whose discussion was postponed in Section 9.2.2, will now be dealt with by briefly introducing the definition proposed by Madison and Batson (1976).

At any time instant, the pages in the current locality (whatever its definition is) will tend to occupy the top positions of the LRU stack. Let $\{i_j(t_j)\}$ be a page (or block, or segment) reference string, and let s_j be its LRU stack after the jth reference has been issued (with $s_0 = \mathbf{0}$). Note that even if the intervals between consecutive references in the string are not constant, times t_j can be ignored as long as we assume they are known for any value of the string index j. Their knowledge is required only to determine the duration of each locality in time, not to identify the localities. Let $s_j(k)$ $(k = 1, 2, \dots, u)$ be the contents of the kth position of s_j, and

$$Sh_j = (s_j(1), s_j(2), \dots, s_j(h)) \tag{9.23}$$

be the (nonordered) set of the contents of the h uppermost positions of s_j. Thus, for each stack, there are u sets which are candidates for the role of current locality. These sets are hierarchically related to each other since

$$S1_j \subset S2_j \subset \cdots \subset Su_j. \tag{9.24}$$

Furthermore, each set is characterized by its *age*, which is the number of references the set has been alive. The age of Sh_j is given by $j + 1 - g_j(h)$ if $g_j(h)$ denotes the string index at which the members of Sh_j first appeared in the h uppermost positions of the stack. In other words, the set Sh_j was generated at the $g_j(h)$th reference and did not change membership since then:

$$Sh_{g_j(h)} = Sh_{g_j(h)+1} = \cdots = Sh_j. \tag{9.25}$$

Each stack s_j has a vector g_j associated to it, which contains the *birth dates* of sets Sh_j $(h = 1, \dots, u)$.

Another characteristic of set Sh_j is its level of activity. Our intuitive notion of locality suggests that a page should be part of the current locality if it is referenced together with the other members of this locality. Accordingly, Madison and Batson (1976) define Sh_j to be an *activity set* if all of its members have been referenced at least once since the set was born. The least recently referenced page in Sh_j is $s_j(h)$. Let $r_j(h)$ indicate the value of the string index

Table 9.17

DETECTION OF ACTIVITY SETS AND BOUNDED LOCALITY INTERVALS IN THE FIRST 32 REFERENCES OF THE STRING IN TABLE 9.15(a)

j	1	2	3	4	5	6	7	8	9	10	11	12	13	14	15	16	17	18	19	20	21	22	23	24	25	26	27	28	29	30	31	32
i_j	1	3	4	1	4	1	4	3	1	4	2	4	2	4	2	4	2	4	2	4	2	4	2	4	1	4	1	4	1	2	4	2
s_j	1	3	4	1	4	1	4	3	1	4	2	4	2	4	2	4	2	4	2	4	2	4	2	4	1	4	1	4	1	2	4	2
	0	1	3	4	1	4	1	4	3	1	4	2	4	2	4	2	4	2	4	2	4	2	4	2	4	1	4	1	4	1	2	4
	0	0	1	3	3	3	3	1	4	3	1	1	1	1	1	1	1	1	1	1	1	1	1	1	2	2	2	2	2	4	1	1
	0	0	0	0	0	0	0	0	0	0	3	3	3	3	3	3	3	3	3	3	3	3	3	3	3	3	3	3	3	3	3	3
δ_j	(∞)	(∞)	(∞)	3	2	2	2	3	3	3	(∞)	2	2	2	2	2	2	2	2	2	2	2	2	2	3	2	2	2	2	3	3	2
r_j	1	2	3	4	5	6	7	8	9	10	11	12	13	14	15	16	17	18	19	20	21	22	23	24	25	26	27	28	29	30	31	32
	0	1	2	3	4	⑤	⑥	⑦	⑧	9	10	11	⑫	⑬	⑭	⑮	⑯	⑰	⑱	⑲	⑳	㉑	㉒	㉓	24	25	㉖	㉗	㉘	㉙	30	31
	0	0	1	2	2	2	2	6	7	8	9	9	9	9	9	9	9	9	9	9	9	9	9	9	23	23	23	23	23	28	29	29
	0	0	0	0	0	0	0	0	0	0	8	8	8	8	8	8	8	8	8	8	8	8	8	8	8	8	8	8	8	8	8	8
g_j	1	2	3	4	5	6	7	8	9	10	11	12	13	14	15	16	17	18	19	20	21	22	23	24	25	26	27	28	29	30	31	32
	1	2	3	4	4	4	4	8	9	10	10	11	11	11	11	11	11	11	11	11	11	11	11	11	㉓	㉓	㉓	㉓	㉓	30	31	31
	1	2	3	3	3	3	3	3	3	3	3	11	11	11	11	11	11	11	11	11	11	11	11	11	11	11	11	11	11	11	11	11
	1	2	3	3	3	3	3	3	3	3	3	11	11	11	11	11	11	11	11	11	11	11	11	11	11	11	11	11	11	11	11	11

corresponding to the last reference made to $s_j(h)$. If $r_j(h) > g_j(h)$, Sh_j is an activity set; otherwise it is not. Thus, another vector $\mathbf{r}_j$, containing the string indices of the most recent references to each page in the order which pages have in the stack, will be associated to $\mathbf{s}_j$. A simple comparison between the contents of the corresponding entries of $\cdot\mathbf{r}_j$ and $\mathbf{g}_j$ will allow us to quickly determine all activity sets for any j. Clearly, the above definition of activity set does not exclude the existence of several such sets for each value of j. These sets are hierarchically interrelated both in terms of their memberships, because of (9.23), and in terms of their lifetimes. The *lifetime* of an activity set is equal to its age when it dies. The death of an activity set Sh is caused by a reference whose LRU stack distance is greater than h. The example in Table 9.17 shows that it is very easy to determine when an activity set dies. However, before that example can be analyzed, we must give the rules for the construction and the updating of the vectors $\mathbf{s}_j$, $\mathbf{r}_j$, and $\mathbf{g}_j$. The rules for $\mathbf{s}_j$ have already been presented in Table 9.8 but will be given again for completeness.

Initially, we have

$$s_0 = r_0 = g_0 = 0 . \tag{9.26}$$

To obtain $\mathbf{s}_j$, $\mathbf{r}_j$, $\mathbf{g}_j$ from $\mathbf{s}_{j-1}$, $\mathbf{r}_{j-1}$, $\mathbf{g}_{j-1}$, let the LRU stack distance of the next reference i_j be δ_j, and if i_j is a new page, let us set δ_j equal to $u + 1$ instead of to ∞. Then the following rules are to be applied:

$$
\begin{aligned}
s_j(1) &\leftarrow i_j, \\
s_j(k + 1) &\leftarrow s_{j-1}(k) & (k = 1, \ldots, \delta_j - 1), \\
s_j(k) &\leftarrow s_{j-1}(k) & (k = \delta_j + 1, \ldots, u), \\
r_j(1) &\leftarrow j, \\
r_j(k + 1) &\leftarrow r_{j-1}(k) & (k = 1, \ldots, \delta_j - 1), \\
r_j(k) &\leftarrow r_{j-1}(k) & (k = \delta_j + 1, \ldots, u), \\
g_j(k) &\leftarrow j & (k = 1, \ldots, \delta_j - 1), \\
g_j(k) &\leftarrow g_{j-1}(k) & (k = \delta_j, \ldots, u).
\end{aligned}
\tag{9.27}
$$

Table 9.17 shows the contents of the three vectors $\mathbf{s}_j$, $\mathbf{r}_j$, and $\mathbf{g}_j$ for the first 32 references of the string in Table 9.15(a). The circled entries of $\mathbf{r}_j$ are those greater than the corresponding entries of $\mathbf{g}_j$. Therefore, each one of them identifies an activity set. For example, the fact that the second entry of $\mathbf{r}_6$ is circled means that $S2_6$ is an activity set. Its members are the pages in the first two positions of $\mathbf{s}_6$ (π_1 and π_4). The same activity set is also alive as $S2_7$ for $j = 7$. However, since $\delta_8 = 3 > 2$, the set dies at $j = 8$. Its birth date is given by $g_7(2) = 4$. Thus, its lifetime is $8 - 4 = 4$ references. The end of a string of circled entries of $\mathbf{r}_j$ marks the death of the corresponding activity set. For

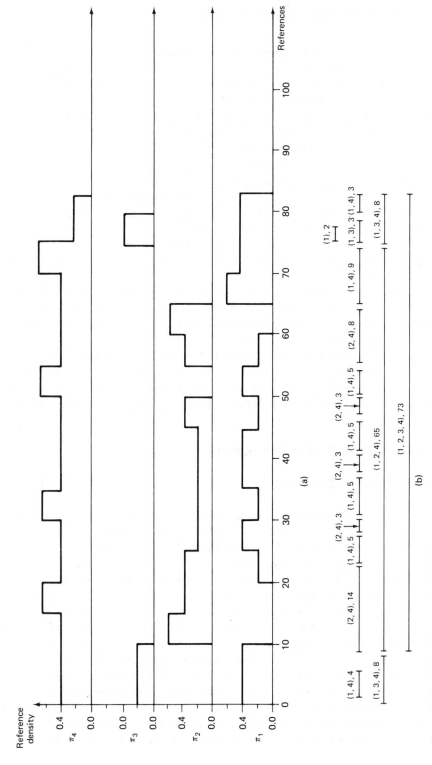

Figure 9.11 Page reference densities (*a*) and bounded locality intervals (*b*) for the page reference string in Table 9.15(*a*).

instance, set $(1, 3, 4)$ is formed at $j = 3$, becomes an activity set at $j = 8$, and dies at $j = 11$, after a lifetime of 8 references. The pair consisting of an activity set and its lifetime, e.g., $[(1, 3, 4), 8]$, is called a *bounded locality interval*.

Figure 9.11 shows the bounded locality intervals which can be found in the string in Table 9.15(a). The reference densities of the four pages in the string, computed over intervals of five references each, are presented in Fig. 9.11(a). Their relationships with the bounded locality intervals displayed in Fig. 9.11(b) are quite evident. Note that the horizontal axes in these diagrams represent numbers of references and not times.

As mentioned above, the hierarchy existing for activity sets holds also for bounded locality intervals. Those with bigger activity sets never have a shorter lifetime. Also the behavior of most programs [*see* Madison and Batson (1976)] seems to be characterized by relatively few long-lived bounded locality intervals and relatively fast transitions between them, during which very many short-lived intervals appear.

The above definition does not identify a single *current locality* but offers us a choice among several precisely defined locality models of program behavior. The existence of several models was informally stated in Section 9.2.2. Table 9.6, for example, presents two such models for our string, and, after mapping blocks into pages, the reader will easily recognize the similarities between them and some particular sequences of bounded locality intervals in Fig. 9.11(b). The various locality models which can be derived from bounded locality intervals differ from each other in their degree of detail and hence in their accuracy and complexity.

9.4   PROGRAM EVALUATION PROBLEMS

9.4.1   Program Selection

A large and rapidly increasing number of applications programs are designed and implemented by computer manufacturers and software houses to be offered to those computer users who find it impossible or less convenient to develop by themselves the programs they need.

Whenever a certain information-processing requirement arises, a computer user is confronted with, among others, the problem of deciding whether the necessary software should be built in-house or procured from some external source. If the procurement alternative is chosen, or seriously considered, then a program selection problem arises, unless only one package is available on the market to fulfill that need. This selection problem also presents itself with increasing frequency for systems packages such as operating systems, operating system modules, translators, and programming and debugging aids, due to the growing number of competitive software products of these types. We have briefly discussed the system aspects of operating system selection in Section 6.3.5. The program performance aspects of operating systems and other packages which are often considered as systems programs (compilers, editors, and so on) do not conceptually differ from those of complex applications programs.

Like the problem of system selection dealt with in Chapter 6, the one of program selection is a multifaceted problem. While performance is an important consideration, reducing the selection of a program to a comparison of performances would be a big mistake. Functional and economical factors are at least as important as, and often more important than, performance considerations. We shall, however, restrict our brief discussion to these considerations.

The selection procedure described in Section 6.2.1 can in principle be applied to the case of software packages. However, a simplified version of it, very similar to that outlined at the end of Section 6.2.1 for system components, seems to be more appropriate for them. In particular, a request for proposals is not usually sent to the vendors, and the data for the validation of the various alternatives are collected by the customer instead of by the vendors. Carrying out the comparison of the performances of the candidate packages in the prospective user's installation offers the advantage of avoiding all sources of variation which would be introduced by the use of a different installation or, even more pronouncedly, by the use of various installations for the various programs. It may be very hard to determine which one of two programs P_1 and P_2 would run more efficiently on system A knowing their execution times t_{1B} and t_{2B} on system B, especially if these times do not drastically differ from each other. And the situation would be even worse, actually much worse, if we knew only times t_{1B} and t_{2C} measured on two different systems B and C. Comparing the performances on the system of the user is also the most convincing way of validating the essential functional requirement that the packages being considered be able to run on that system. Sometimes, there may be obstacles to this comparison. The vendors might be unwilling to install a package before the selection is made and the contract signed, because of security risks or the high costs of modifications or both. However, the prospective customer should insist, especially in the case of new packages which have not been tried in many installations or of programs which have received mixed evaluations from their previous users.

Whether comparison is performed on the customer's system or on another system, there seems to be little doubt about the fact that measurement is the appropriate technique for making it. The only viable alternative might be analytic estimation if formulas or curves were provided by the vendor which allowed one to predict execution times and other indices of interest for a given system, a given configuration, and given input data. These formulas or curves could have been derived from direct measurements, or from analytic approaches like the one described in Example 9.5, or from simulation, or from any combination of these techniques. In all cases, an important problem to be solved by the evaluator of the packages is the one of choosing the input data to be used for their comparison.

No general rules can be given to help one make this choice. If the programs may be executed several times during their evaluation period, the sets of input data should span the typical range of inputs to be submitted by the users of the package that will be selected. Included among these there will be some set representing realistic conditions of *heavy load*, that is, input data which are known or expected to require amounts of execution time or of some system resources substantially larger than the average amounts. For complex programs, determining worst-case input conditions may be extremely difficult or impossible. Accurately estimating the probabilities of occurrence of various input sets may be easy in certain applications and impossible in others. In any case, since the number of instrumented runs of each candidate program will be limited, precedence should be given to those input data sets which, to the best of the investigator's knowledge, could produce critical situations. For instance, in real-time applications, the foremost concern should be with the maximum value of execution time, and the tests should be designed accordingly. The average execution time will probably be more important in batch production applications such as payroll computation, accounting, inventory control, production scheduling, and statistical analysis.

9.4.2   Program Improvement

In program performance evaluation, as in the case of systems, the use of all evaluation techniques is more advanced and widespread for improvement purposes than for any other type of study. The measurement, simulation, and analytic techniques we examined in Sections 9.3.1 and 9.3.2 may be applied both to the diagnosis problem and to the problem of predicting the effects of improvement therapies. Actually, the latter application is less crucial than it is in system performance studies, due to the fact that modifying an applications program is often easier, cheaper, and less risky than modifying a system. Thus, the technique most frequently employed for the assessment of an improved therapy is the direct measurement of the modified program.

As in the case of a system, the performance diagnosis of a program is aimed at discovering the causes of its performance limitations, in other words, its *bottlenecks* or *performance bugs*. Removing a bottleneck will usually increase the performance of the program and reduce its cost. In some studies, the emphasis will be on the performance side and in others on the economical side of the problem. In any case, however, both effects will be obtained if the consumption of system resources is reduced.

How can we detect program performance bottlenecks? In other words, how do we determine where a program spends its execution time? The program profile introduced in Section 9.2.1 is an effective diagnostic tool, certainly more powerful than its system counterpart, the system utilization profile (*see* Sections 2.7.1 and 7.3.3). As described in Example 9.6 below, the program profile, supplemented with time information, tells us exactly where the bottlenecks are. This detection function, as any reasonably experienced programmer knows, cannot generally be left to the program's author to perform if a reliable result is desired. The human mind does not seem to be capable of mastering the level of complexity involved in the dynamics of most programs, even if they belong to the category of nonparallel programs of moderate size.

Given a program profile consisting of the frequency counts c_i ($i = 1, \ldots, n$) of the n executable statements of the program, we can define the *time profile* as the collection of the times spent in the execution of each statement. If t_i denotes the execution time of statement i, its contribution to the total execution time t is $c_i t_i$, and we have

$$t = \sum_{i=1}^{n} c_i t_i. \tag{9.28}$$

A program modification may influence several statements. Their execution times and frequency counts may change even drastically as a result of a single variation, and some statements may have to be added, or displaced. If we consider the simplest possible type of modification, that which only affects one statement, say statement j, we have, from (9.28),

$$\Delta t = c_j \, \Delta t_j, \tag{9.29}$$

since our assumption implies $\Delta c_j = 0$. Note that (9.29) can be easily extended to any group of statements in series.

The time profile allows us to immediately identify the bottlenecks in a program, that is, those statements or groups of statements which contribute the most to the value of t. Concentrating our improvement efforts on these areas of the program is convenient for the following reasons:

a. The high value of t_j may be partially due to wastes caused by careless programming (performance bugs); thus, it may be easier to obtain a certain (negative) Δt_j, or a higher $|\Delta t_j|$ may be achieved with the same amount of effort.
b. Any Δt_j which is obtained is then multiplied by c_j [see (9.29)]; thus, the same or a lesser effort is likely to produce a much more beneficial effect than if it were applied in other areas; this effect obviously grows with c_j.
c. Narrowing the investigation down to only a few statements or a routine at a time generally increases the quality of the results.

Of course, when the change is more radical than those considered above, the simple arguments in a and b, based on (9.29), are not valid anymore, and variations of the frequency counts should also be taken into account. In any case, however, the time profile is extremely useful in the identification of the changes to which a program's execution time is going to be most sensitive. Its use will now be illustrated by an example.

P .455.

Example 9.6 The program in Table 9.1 is to be analyzed in order to determine whether and how its execution time can be decreased. Let its profile, obtained by measurement (or even by simulation or analytic techniques such as those described in Section 9.3.2), consist of the frequency counts given in the same table. This profile looks quite jagged and would be much more so if more realistic input data had been assumed, since this would have caused the loops to be executed many more times. Even with the input data we have chosen, however, three statements (12, 13, and 14), corresponding to little more than 10% of the executable statements, account for 42% of the executions in the profile.

Table 9.1 shows also the time profile of the same (program, input) pair. Statement 12 is the most time-consuming. The program spends about 18% of its time executing it. The function FUN, with its three statements (12, 13, 14), absorbs about 35% of the total execution time. This situation is not surprising. Actually, as noted above, these profiles are less jagged than usual. A very large fraction of the time is normally spent in a very small fraction of the program. Knuth (1971) reports that in the FORTRAN programs of his sample more than half of the time was typically spent in less than 4% of the program. Another area of intense activity is the one between statements 21 and 25, in which the program spends more than 24% of its time. Probably the only other statements whose $c_i t_i$ is sufficiently high to make them worthy of attention are 1, 3, and 9. However, the programmer usually has no jurisdiction over the code of the I/O routines which are invoked by I/O statements such as READ and WRITE and may only influence the time spent in processing I/O requests by changing the way I/O is done by the program. This is a system-dependent and compiler-dependent problem. Only a detailed knowledge of the way I/O operations are handled can allow the programmer to cleverly exploit it with the best possible results. The organization of the files needed by the program and the strategies to access them are the main points to be considered in this area at design time. However, these are often unmodifiable parameters due to system constraints. In the case of the present program, a quick look at the I/O statements convinces us that there is little or nothing that can be done to improve them [except perhaps the packing of more than one entry of vector A(I) per line to be printed in statement 9].

Let us examine function FUN, and especially statement 12, first. The time t_{12} is practically spent establishing the linkage which is required whenever a function is called. The obvious way to reduce the execution time of FUN is to eliminate it and replace every call to it in subroutine RK2 by the equivalent operation, that is, the computation of a reciprocal. This modification is convenient in this program due to the simplicity of function FUN and due to the fact that its name appears only a few times in the program. However, there are many cases in which such change would be inconvenient, either because of the increase it would cause in the space occupied by the program, or because of the demodularization it would bring about, or because of both.

Eliminating FUN also allows us to make some simplification in statements 21 through 25, that is, in the area recognized as the second most active one in the program. Statement 23 can be deleted since it turns out to be identical to statement 22. Without making too big an optimization effort (we could, for example, trade the division in statement 25 with a multiplication if there were a substantial payoff in doing this), the following new statements are obtained:

$$21' \quad T1 = H/X$$

$$22' \quad T2 = H/(X + H2)$$

$$23' \quad -$$

$$24' \quad T4 = H/(X + H)$$

$$25' \quad Y = Y + (T1 + 4.*T2 + T4)/6.$$

Using the same execution times as in Table 9.1, the savings due to these changes can be estimated for the frequency counts given in Table 9.1: 278 out of the total 650 time units would be saved, corresponding to a 42% reduction of the program's execution time. With more realistic input data, the reduction would be even more drastic. The reader might use either of the analytic models developed for this program in Section 9.3.2 to estimate the reduction which would be obtained with a few other sets of input data (*see* Problem 9.16).   ■

If programs are written in a higher-level language and studied for improvement purposes at the level of that language, as has been the case in Example 9.6, the machine that the programmer sees is a higher-level language machine. The internal characteristics of this machine must be well known to the evaluator if a high probability of success and the highest possible payoffs are desired for an improvement study. This means that the investigator should be thoroughly familiar with the inner workings of the compiler, especially if it is an optimizing compiler. An insufficient knowledge may in fact cause changes, which would be very effective, to be overlooked and others, which are only marginally convenient, or even counterproductive, to be chosen. The influence of compilers on program performance is very strong. The use of higher-level languages introduces a filter between the hardware, which ultimately determines the program's execution time, and the programmers, who can no longer optimize their programs directly for that hardware. Thus, a program should be optimized for the hardware-compiler complex. This less direct optimization and the constraints introduced by compilers explain why programs translated from a higher-level language seldom reach the performance they would achieve if they were written by an expert machine language programmer and why certain routines whose execution time is crucial are often written in machine or assembly language.

Sometimes, a space improvement may be sought. This problem arises expecially for programs to which an extremely tight memory space is allocated (for example, the memory-resident part of an operating system or the microprograms to be stored into a small control memory). The problem is encountered also in connection with large data bases, in which data compression techniques or space-saving data structures may be adopted to solve it. To reduce the space occupied by the instructions of a program, one must work on its listing and use ad hoc techniques.

In virtual-memory systems, a very important program performance improvement objective is the one of reducing the fault rate generated by a program. We have seen in Example 7.10 that this reduction generally increases system performance. In Section 9.2.2, we concluded that it always increases program performance and decreases the price of program execution. It was also argued in Section 9.2.2 that the closer a program's behavior is to the one postulated by the memory management strategy implemented by the system, the lower its fault rate is likely to be. Note that this is strictly a program improvement viewpoint, since the strategy is not viewed as a modifiable entity, and only program behavior is supposed to be changeable. We also learned in Section 9.2.2 that strategies usually capitalize on the property of locality. Therefore, one could conclude that improving the locality of a program will certainly increase its performance. This is, in principle, true as we shall see. However, it is also true that each strategy is based on a different definition of locality, or, in other words, on a different model of program behavior. If the improvement technique exploits the available information about the strategy, more successful results will generally be obtained. This philosophy has been called *program tailoring* [*see* Ferrari (1975)], since it advocates improvement methods which tailor the behavior of the program to the one of the model postulated by the given strategy.

How can the dynamic behavior of an existing program be changed so as to approximate a given behavioral model? Redesigning the program might be an acceptable answer in certain special circumstances but only if design methods were available for constructing programs which would match a preassigned behavior. Since this is unfortunately not the case, a technique which is much easier to apply and much cheaper is needed. One such technique is *program restructuring*.

Program restructuring assumes a program's behavior to be characterized by a block reference string (*see* Section 9.2.2). For the technique to be successful, the mean block size must be much smaller than the page size. A good rule of thumb says that it should be between $\frac{1}{3}$ and $\frac{1}{10}$ of the page size. In general, the smaller the blocks, the more effective but also the more expensive the method. Restructuring means determining a new mapping of these blocks into pages to improve the behavior of the program. Note that this mapping takes place at the virtual level and has to do with the allocation of the blocks in the virtual space. In our discussion here, we shall restrict our attention to the case of a static allocation. The program is rearranged only once and then run as if it had been arranged that way by its author. Satisfactory techniques for dynamically assigning blocks to pages have not been developed yet. The (static) mapping we are concerned with does not have anything to do with the (dynamic) mapping of the virtual pages into the physical page frames performed by the memory hierarchy. However, the mechanisms by which the latter is implemented may be profitably taken into account to determine the former.

Different mappings $B \rightarrow \Pi$, where B is the set of blocks and Π the set of pages, transform the same block reference string into different page reference strings, which will generally produce different fault rates. This can be explained by observing that the blocks which are brought into memory when a page is fetched, as well as those which are pushed out when a page is replaced, vary from mapping to mapping. The blocks which are most likely to be useful soon after a certain block is referenced and to be useless as that block ceases to be needed should be grouped together with that block. This statement is still too vague to constitute a satisfactory specification of a restructuring algorithm. We shall describe a few of these algorithms in detail after completing the discussion of a typical restructuring technique.

A number of approaches to program restructuring can conveniently be described as following the four-step procedure which will now be summarized [*see* Ferrari (1974b)].

Step 1. The program to be restructured is subdivided into blocks, whose sizes, as stated above, are sufficiently smaller than the page size. If blocks coincide with relocatable parts of the program (subroutines, functions, proce-dures, data structures such arrays, trees, and so on), restructuring will not entail any reprogramming. However, this is not a necessary requirement but only a convenient criterion for block selection. Having made this selection, an address trace collected from an instrumented run of the program can be easily trans-formed into the corresponding block reference string.

Step 2. A *restructuring algorithm* is applied to the block reference string. The result of this step is a matrix called the *restructuring matrix* $\mathbf{R} = [r_{hk}]$. This matrix may also be viewed as representing a graph, called the *restructuring graph*. An example of such a graph, corresponding to the matrix in Table 9.18(b), is presented in Fig. 9.12. The nodes represent the blocks of the program, each

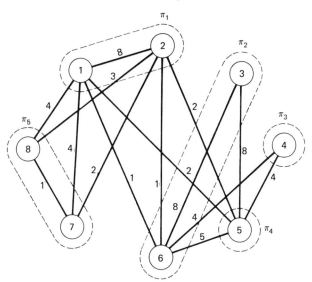

Figure 9.12 Restructuring graph corresponding to the CLRU matrix in Table 9.18(b). The optimum clustering is represented by the groupings indicated by the broken lines.

having a weight equal to the size of the corresponding block. Even though the matrix can be generated by the algorithm as a $u \times u$ square matrix, where u is the total number of blocks, the next step of this procedure usually works on a triangular matrix whose entries are given by $r_{hk} + r_{kh}$. This matrix may be seen as

Table 9.18

RESTRUCTURING MATRICES FOR EXAMPLE 9.7

(a) Nearness matrix [block reference string in Table 9.4(a)]

	2	3	4·	5	6	7	8
1	17	—	—	1	—	2	3
2		—	—	1	—	2	1
3			16	4	4	—	—
4				—	—	—	—
5					30	—	—
6						—	—
7							—

(b) CLRU matrix [string in Table 9.4(a), $m = 2$]

	2	3	4	5	6	7	8
1	8	—	—	2	1	4	4
2		—	—	2	1	2	3
3			—	8	8	—	—
4				4	4	—	—
5					5	—	—
6						—	—
7							1

(c) CWS matrix [string in Table 9.4(b), $\tau = 2$ block reference sets]

	2	3	4	5	6	7	8
1	—	2	2	2	2	1	2
2		2	2	2	2	1	2
3			—	1	1	—	1
4				1	1	—	1
5					—	—	2
6						—	2
7							2

a representation of a nondirected graph such as the one in Fig. 9.12. The labels of the edges in this graph quantify, in a way which depends on the restructuring algorithm used, the desirability that the two corresponding nodes be grouped together into the same page.

Step 3. A *clustering algorithm* is applied to the restructuring graph to solve the following problem: Group the nodes of the graph into clusters so as to maximize the sum of intracluster edge labels under the constraint that the sum of the weights of all nodes in each cluster be not greater than the page size. This is a well-known problem in graph theory. Finding an exact solution to it, that is, an optimal mapping, is not essential to the success of the restructuring procedure. Fast and approximate clustering algorithms have been experimentally found to be so effective as to suggest that the further refinements obtainable by optimum algorithms would probably add very few benefits and much more cost. The complexity of any clustering algorithms grows very rapidly with the number of nodes in the graph. Thus, this number cannot be made as large as the increasing improvements which can be obtained as the block sizes decrease would encourage us to make.

Step 4. The clusters of nodes determined in step 3 specify the block-to-page mapping suggested by the procedure. In this step, the program is rearranged in virtual memory according to this mapping. The size of a cluster will not generally equal the size of a page. Therefore, if the information in the program is to be compacted so as to eliminate some (or all) gaps in the virtual space, another algorithm (possibly also based on **R**) may be applied in this step to determine the best ordering of the pages. If no compaction is made, the page order is of course immaterial.

We shall now describe, as examples, three restructuring algorithms, one of which is strategy-independent and the other two strategy-oriented. Their illustration will be made by discussing the restructuring of the program in Table 9.1.

Example 9.7   The restructuring procedure outlined above will be applied to the program in Table 9.1, assuming that the program is to run under two demand-paging memory management strategies:

a. a fixed-allocation strategy with LRU replacement and allotted space $m = 2$ page frames (briefly, the *LRU strategy*);
b. a variable-allocation working set strategy with window size $\tau = 50$ time units and working set measurement and updating every 25 time units (briefly, the *WS strategy*).

In step 1, the program is to be partitioned into blocks. We select the blocks listed in Table 9.3, which are all relocatable with respect to each other at the source language level. The block reference strings are those in Table 9.4(a) for the LRU strategy (which ignores reference times) and in Table 9.4(b) for the WS strategy. For simplicity, we assume that all blocks have the size of half a page, except block 5, whose size coincides with, or is only slightly smaller than, the page size. Thus, the program will consist of at least five pages, although not all of them will be full.

Step 2 requires a restructuring algorithm to be used in order to obtain the restructuring matrix. A simple, strategy-independent algorithm is the *nearness algorithm* proposed by Hatfield and Gerald (1971). Its result is the *nearness matrix*, which coincides with the transition frequency count matrix introduced in Section 9.3.2 [*see* Table 9.16(a)]. Note, however, that the nearness matrix is drawn from the block (not page) reference string, and its r_{hk} entry is the number of transitions from block h to block k. In other words, the desirability that blocks h and k be grouped together is expressed by $r_{hk} + r_{kh}$, that is, the number of times they follow each other in the block reference string. The triangularized nearness matrix for our string is reported in Table 9.18(a). Note that this matrix is independent of the reference times.

Let us now try to devise other restructuring algorithms by applying the tailoring philosophy. The two strategies we are considering here allow us to determine from the appropriate block reference string the blocks which will be in memory at any given time. We also have to decide what the specific objective of the algorithms will be. Let this be the minimization of the number of page faults in both cases. The program behavior models that the two strategies postulate can both be described as characterized by a minimum probability that the next page to be referenced at any instant is not among those already in memory. The pages already in memory occupy at that instant the first m positions of the LRU stack (if the LRU strategy is used) or are the members of the working set at that time (if the WS strategy is used). In either case, these pages certainly include the blocks which are at the same instant either in the top m positions of the block stack or, respectively, in the working set of blocks. If the block referenced next is already going to be in memory anyway, because its distance in the block stack is not greater than m or because it is in the block working set, the reference is said to be *noncritical*, and nothing is done. If the reference is *critical*, then the mapping should make it noncritical, that is, have the corresponding block ready in memory when it is referenced. To better fit the program's behavior to the model's behavior, the block involved in a critical reference should be grouped with at least one of the blocks already in memory at the time the reference is issued. Because of the conflicts which usually arise, we shall have to choose those groupings which reduce most drastically the number of page faults. To obtain this, we can, for example, increment by 1 the label of each edge connecting the node which represents the critically referenced block to the nodes representing the blocks which are certainly

Table 9.19

CLRU RESTRUCTURING ALGORITHM

Inputs: l = length of the block reference string

u = number of blocks in the program (sizes can be ignored)

m = number of page frames to be allotted to the program

$\{i_j\}$ = block reference string (reference times can be ignored)

Output: $[r_{hk}]$ = the CLRU matrix $(h, k = 1, \ldots, u)$

Algorithm:
1. (Initialize LRU block stack, pointer to current reference, and CLRU matrix.) Set $s_h \leftarrow 0$ for $h = 1, \ldots, u$, $j \leftarrow 0$, $r_{hk} \leftarrow 0$ for $h, k = 1, \ldots, u$.
2. (Move to next reference and to the top of the stack.) Set $j \leftarrow j + 1$, $n \leftarrow 0$.
3. (Search stack for current reference.) Set $n \leftarrow n + 1$. If $n > u$, set $\delta \leftarrow u$ and go to 4. If $s_n = 0$, set $\delta \leftarrow n$ and go to 4. If $s_n = i_j$, set $\delta \leftarrow n$ and go to 4. Otherwise, repeat this step.
4. (Update CLRU matrix.) If $\delta > m$, set $h \leftarrow i_j$, $k \leftarrow s_n$, $r_{hk} \leftarrow r_{hk} + 1$ for $n = 1, \ldots, m$ and for $s_n \neq 0$.
5. (Update stack.) Set $s_h \leftarrow s_{h-1}$ for $h = \delta, \delta - 1, \ldots, 2, s_1 \leftarrow i_j$.
6. (Test termination condition.) If $j < l$, go to 2. Otherwise, stop.

---

going to be in memory at that time. For example, if these blocks are 1, 2, and 7 and the next reference is to block 8, the labels of edges (8, 1), (8, 2), and (8, 7) will be incremented. This is the rationale of a class of restructuring algorithms which are called *critical-set algorithms* [*see* Ferrari (1974a)]. The two algorithms of this class which tailor programs to the two strategies being considered here are detailed in Table 9.19 (the *critical LRU*, or *CLRU*, algorithm) and in Table 9.20 (the *critical working set*, or *CWS*, algorithm). The *CLRU matrix* and the *CWS matrix* produced by these algorithms for our program are given in Tables 9.18(b) and (c), respectively.

Table 9.20

CWS RESTRUCTURING ALGORITHM

Inputs: l = length of the reference string (in number of block reference sets)

   u = number of blocks in the program (sizes can be ignored)

   $\{b_j\}$ = block reference set string (reference sets group blocks referenced during intervals of equal durations)

   l_j = number of blocks in block reference set $b_j = \{b_{jk}\}$ ($j = 1, \ldots, l; k = 1, \ldots, l_j$).

   τ = window size (in number of reference sets)

Output: $[r_{hk}]$ = the CWS matrix ($h, k = 1, \ldots, u$)

Algorithm:
1. (Initialize pointer to current reference set, counters of the blocks in the window, and CWS matrix.) Set $j \leftarrow 0$, $c_i \leftarrow 0$ for $i = 1, \ldots, u$, $r_{hk} \leftarrow 0$ for $h, k = 1, \ldots, u$.
2. (Move to next block reference set.) Set $j \leftarrow j + 1$, $n \leftarrow l_j$, $k \leftarrow 0$.
3. (Move to next reference in reference set and determine whether it is critical.) Set $k \leftarrow k + 1$. If $k > n$, go to 5. Otherwise, set $i \leftarrow b_{jk}$. If $c_i = 0$, go to 4. Otherwise, repeat this step.
4. (Update CWS matrix.) For $h = 1, \ldots, u$, if $c_h \neq 0$, set $r_{ih} \leftarrow r_{ih} + 1$. Go to 3.
5. (Update counters.) For $k = 1, \ldots, n$, set $i \leftarrow b_{jk}$, $c_i \leftarrow c_i + 1$. If $j \leq \tau$, go to 6. Otherwise, set $n \leftarrow l_{j-\tau}$. For $k = 1, \ldots, n$, set $i \leftarrow b_{j-\tau,k}$, $c_i \leftarrow c_i - 1$.
6. (Test termination condition.) If $j < l$, go to 2. Otherwise, stop.

A clustering algorithm, which is independent of the particular restructuring algorithm, is then to be applied to the restructuring graph. In this simple example, it is easy to see that the mappings reported in Table 9.21 are the best ones for the three matrices in Table 9.18 under the given constraints. The broken lines in Fig. 9.12 correspond to the clusters found by working on the CLRU matrix in Table 9.18(b). Note that the mapping determined by the CWS algorithm (*see* Table 9.21) is one of the several optimal clusterings existing for the CWS matrix in Table 9.18(c).

The performance of the restructured program can be estimated by simulation, as described in Section 9.3.2, after having transformed the block reference string into the corresponding page reference string according to the mapping suggested by the restructuring procedure. The results for our three restructured versions of the same program are shown in Table 9.21. The number of page faults generated under the LRU strategy by the

Table 9.21

MAPPINGS SUGGESTED BY THE MATRICES IN TABLE 9.18
AND CORRESPONDING PERFORMANCE INDICES

			Blocks in page	
	Page number	Nearness	CLRU	CWS
Mappings	1	1, 2	1, 2	1, 3
	2	3, 4	3, 6	2, 4
	3	5	4	5
	4	6	5	6
	5	7, 8	7, 8	7, 8
Numbers of page faults generated under LRU with $m = 2$ pages		18	14	31
Numbers of page faults generated under WS strategy with $\tau = 2$ block reference sets		7	7	6
Mean working set size under WS strategy with $\tau = 2$ block reference sets [pages]		2.82	2.82	3.76

version restructured according to the CLRU algorithm is the lowest of the three. This is also the case of the CWS mapping under the WS strategy. Note that, as could have been expected, the CWS algorithm reduces the number of page faults but, at the same time, tends to produce a mean working set size larger than those given by other algorithms. However, unless the nonrestructured program is already quite close to the optimum, the CWS algorithm has also been found to reduce substantially the mean working set size with respect to that of the nonrestructured program. The objective of CWS is not the minimization of this size. In fact, the nearness algorithm and others often produce programs with smaller mean working set sizes. Restructuring algorithms which try to minimize the mean working set size can easily be devised by applying the tailoring philosophy and assuming this size as the performance index.

The two portraits of our program shown in Fig. 9.13 present visually some of the effects of restructuring. The horizontal axes report references instead of times as in Fig. 9.5. The upper portrait is that of the page reference string in Table 9.15(a). The lower portrait represents the string obtained by applying the CLRU algorithm. The two diagrams should help the reader understand why the latter string produces less page faults under the LRU strategy than the former, even though the corresponding program consists of 5 pages instead of 4. ∎

Experiments performed with several programs have shown that, as could be expected, the amount of improvement obtainable by the restructuring procedure described above is related to the quality of the nonrestructured program's behavior. The procedure, even if based on nonoptimum restructuring and cluster-

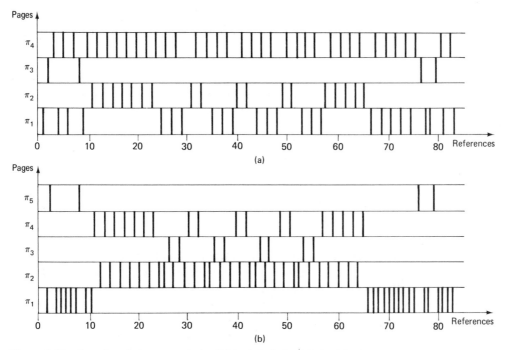

Figure 9.13 Portraits of the program in Table 9.1 derived from (*a*) the page reference string in Table 9.15(a); (*b*) the string obtained from the mapping suggested by the CLRU restructuring algorithm (*see* Table 9.21).

ing algorithms, generally produces bigger improvements for worse programs. Its effectiveness depends on the width of the gap between the behaviors of the given program and of its unknown optimum version. The mapping resulting from the above procedure may often be considered nearly optimum. Improving it further is usually very hard and not sufficiently rewarding.

Even when a dramatic improvement can be obtained due to the poor locality of the initial program, the cost of the restructuring procedure is not justified if the program is to be executed only a few times. All types of improvement studies described in this section should be considered only for programs to be run more times than a certain minimum number. In the case of locality improvement via restructuring, this number depends primarily on the quality of the program, on the specific restructuring algorithm used, and on the choice of the blocks. For all production programs, which constitute a large fraction of the work load in most installations, restructuring is certainly advantageous. Note also that, beyond the break-even point, all of the savings of each run contribute to the total payoff, since the procedure is generally applied only once.

Perhaps the most serious objection which may be raised against the above procedure has to do with the role of the input data. The restructuring algorithm is applied to a block reference string which in fact represents the behavior of a (program, input) pair. If the behavior of the program is very sensitive to the input data, the mapping suggested by the restructuring procedure might produce, with input data different from those used in the instrumented run, a behavior worse than that of the nonrestructured program. However, several experiments have shown that the behavior of programs such as compilers, assemblers, editors, operating systems, and other production programs for which restructuring is most advantageous tends to be remarkably insensitive to the input data, at least from the viewpoint of restructuring efficiency [see, for example, Hatfield and Gerald (1971) and Ferrari (1974b)].

9.4.3 Program Design

Most of the observations made in Section 8.2 on the philosophies of system design and on the role of performance evaluation techniques in them are valid also for program design.

First, it is important to realize that functional considerations, especially those having to do with the correctness of a program being designed, must logically and chronologically precede any performance-related consideration. The program's performance, however, should not be regarded as having secondary importance, nor should it be taken care of only when the program has been designed, implemented, and debugged. In fact, performance specifications should become part of the design specifications, as has always been the case of real-time programs, whose performance requirements are clearly stricter that those of the other types of programs. The specifications should then be taken into account at each step in the design procedure, and a verification that the program's performance satisfies them should be made by applying suitable evaluation techniques. This approach to program design follows the *hierarchical methodology* described in Section 8.2 for system design.

The opposite philosophy, the one of *iterative design*, consists of designing, writing, and debugging a program and finally taking care of its performance by iteratively improving it as described in Section 9.4.2. Evidently, the most important evaluation technique, perhaps the only one, to be employed in iterative design is measurement (*see* Section 9.3.1). For locality improvements, we may adopt that mixture of measurement and modeling techniques which has been called a restructuring procedure. Most of the non-real-time programs today are designed following methods which are closer to the iterative than to the hierarchical philosophy. As in system design, there is a trade-off between the benefits and the costs of iterative improvement efforts. In other words, design costs may be increased to reduce execution costs. The optimum trade-off depends on various factors including the language used (whose choice has a nontrivial influence on the program's performance through the compiler), the cost and ease of measuring and modifying the program, the expected lifetime of the program, and, obviously, the quality of the initial product, which is related to the ability of the designers and of the programmers.

The hierarchical approach proceeds, as described in Sections 8.2 and 8.4, by successive levels of abstraction, which are ideally generated in a top-down fashion. At each level of abstraction, a model of the program is specified, usually in terms of a number of modules and of their interconnections. These modules are to be functionally decomposed into submodules at the next level. The performance requirements of each module are assumed to be defined. For instance, let the maximum execution time be the primary performance index. When we decompose a module whose maximum execution time is known, we have to estimate the maximum execution times of the submodules. From the performance requirements at level i, we ought to be able to derive those at level $i + 1$. Having done this, before proceeding we have to verify that if the submodules satisfy their performance specifications, the performance require-ments of the decomposed module will be satisfied. The success of this procedure, based on estimates, is as good as the accuracy of these estimates. When the lowest level of abstraction is reached, the estimates will generally have to be adjusted, and the changes will ripple up to the top of the tree. Thus, also for performance reasons, the procedure will in most cases be a mixture of top-down and bottom-up approaches.

The verifications to be made when a new level is created as well as during any bottom-up phase of the design require the use of a performance analysis technique. Measurement must be ruled out until the program is totally or at least partially coded and running. Thus, simulation or analytic techniques will be used, as discussed in Section 9.3.2. An illustration of the use of the analytic technique described in Example 9.5 in a very elementary case will now be given.

Example 9.8 The successive D-charts that were obtained in Example 9.5 from the one shown in Fig. 9.9(a) to reduce it to a single rectangular box may be viewed as models of the program in Table 9.1 at different levels of abstraction. A level corresponds to each step in Table 9.11(a). In a top-down procedure, level 0 will correspond to step 6. At that level, we have box X. Let us assume that the maximum execution time of X, TX_{max}, is given. TX_{max} is evidently the maximum execution time of the whole program. X is decomposed into the three boxes A, W, and M when we go from level 0 to level 1. Thus,

$$TX_{max} = TA_{max} + TW_{max} + TM_{max}. \tag{9.30}$$

In this program, it is much easier to estimate TA_{max} and TM_{max} than TW_{max}. Thus, an estimate of TW_{max} will be obtained from (9.30) after having estimated the other two times. If we do this, the condition that the level-0 requirements be satisfied if the level-1 requirements are satisfied will be automatically enforced by our use of (9.30) to specify TW_{max}. Note that, because of the first profile equation in Table 9.12, which expresses the fact that A, W, and M are connected in series, and since we know that $NX = 1$, the execution times of these three boxes every time they are entered coincide with their total execution times, which have just been estimated:

$$ta_{max} = TA_{max}, \qquad tw_{max} = TW_{max}, \qquad tm_{max} = TM_{max}. \tag{9.31}$$

Level 2 is obtained by replacing W with an iteration in which box V appears. Thus, we can write

$$TV_{max} = TW_{max} = nv_{max}(1) \cdot tv_{max}. \tag{9.32}$$

To calculate $tv_{\max}$, the performance requirement at level 2, we must estimate $nv_{\max}(1)$. Our knowledge of the functional aspects of the program being designed should help us here. In this case, $nv(1)$ is the number of significant input cards, and a reasonable upper bound for it should not be too hard to guess. In certain cases, a probabilistic estimation might be more meaningful. The estimated value of $tv_{\max}$ will then have to be broken down into three terms $tr_{\max}$, $tu_{\max}$, and $tt_{\max}$, whose sum should equal $tv_{\max}$. The procedure can be repeated until level 6 [corresponding to step 0 in Table 9.11(a)] is reached. Every time a leaf of the tree is found, the code for it can be written, and its execution time can be calculated or measured with good accuracy. These results should be immediately propagated back toward the root of the tree, and the necessary corrections to the estimates at various levels should be made. For instance, the code of A and M can be written at level 1 and used to calculate $ta_{\max}$ and $tm_{\max}$.   ■

Practical programs will generally be much more complicated than the one discussed in Example 9.8. In the design of large software systems, the number of modules involved may be much larger and their types and interconnections more complex. However, if they are designed according to a structured-programming approach, analytic or simulation techniques, or a mixture of the two, are not too difficult to apply. An ever-present problem is the one of determining the sets of input data which should be used in analyzing the performance of the program. For example, if the primary performance specification is the maximum execution time, we should know or guess which input data set among the possible ones will maximize the execution time.

The use of the hierarchical methodology just described is becoming more popular, mainly for correctness purposes. Incorporating performance verifications in this methodology is possible when indices such as the execution time are chosen. Verifying the referencing behavior during hierarchical design seems to be much more difficult at the present time. However, it is reasonable to expect structured-programming techniques to have a beneficial effect on the locality of programs, due to the criteria according to which modules are decomposed when these techniques are applied.

Insofar as performance-driven program design is concerned, systematic methodologies for the synthesis of programs directly from performance specifications are not available. However, the results of the analysis of many algorithms of practical interest allow programmers to select efficient computational methods and data structures in a number of cases, which are often encountered in program design [see, for example, Knuth (1969)]. Locality-oriented analyses of algorithms have more recently attracted the interest of researchers, and only some results are available. Much more research on the relation between program structure and program behavior is needed.

The conclusion that more research is needed has been drawn several times in this book but probably not so frequently as it should have been. It is perhaps the least controversial statement one can make on the state of many areas of performance evaluation. All of these areas require the thoughtful attention and the creative contributions of our readers.

PROBLEMS

9.1. Repeat the considerations at the beginning of Example 9.1 on the possible definitions of execution time, applying them to a program which runs on an interactive system. List some of the definitions that could be proposed, and discuss their advantages and disadvantages from the viewpoints of system independence, relevance to the user, and measurability.

9.2. The program in Table 9.1 is to be executed on a batch-processing system. The installation's charging formula per job step is

JSPRICE = CPUTIME*CPURATE + ETIME*ERATE + DKOPS*DKRATE
+ CARDS*CRATE + LINES*LPRATE,

where

$$
\begin{aligned}
\text{CPUTIME} &= \text{CPU time consumed in seconds} \\
\text{CPURATE} &= \text{CPU usage price in dollars per second} \\
\text{ETIME} &= (\text{CPUTIME} + (\text{DKOPS} + \text{CARDS} + \text{LINES})*\text{IOTIME})*\text{SPACE} \\
\text{ERATE} &= \text{effective-time price in dollars per } K \text{ byte-second} \\
\text{DKOPS} &= \text{number of disk operations} \\
\text{DKRATE} &= \text{disk I/O price in dollars per disk operation} \\
\text{CARDS} &= \text{number of cards input} \\
\text{CRATE} &= \text{card reader input price in dollars per card} \\
\text{LINES} &= \text{number of lines printed} \\
\text{LPRATE} &= \text{printer output price in dollars per line} \\
\text{IOTIME} &= \text{approximate time in seconds per I/O operation} \\
\text{SPACE} &= \text{memory size occupied in } K \text{ bytes}
\end{aligned}
$$

Considering only the execution job step, determine the relationships between the execution time and the execution price of the program. Assume that the object code and the input data are already stored on disk before the job step begins, and choose (specifying it precisely) the definition of execution time you prefer. To solve this problem, what is the most appropriate characterization of the program in terms of states and the corresponding decomposition of the total execution time?

9.3. Construct a FORTRAN-resource model of the program in Table 9.1, referring to the types of resources listed in Table 6.9. Follow the procedure illustrated in Table 6.11. Construct also a synthetic model of the program as shown in Example 6.3.

9.4. If as the index of program behavior under a given strategy we choose the total number of pages transferred between the primary memory and the paging device, instead of the total number of page faults, is the address trace of the program as defined in Section 9.2.2 a really complete characterization from which that index can be calculated? If your answer is no, state how you would modify it to make it suitable for the calculation of that index.

9.5. Under working set strategies, a page which drops out of the working set may not be immediately pushed out of primary memory. The page frame it occupies is returned to the pool of free frames, but its contents may not be destroyed until the frame is requested by one of the programs in memory. Thus, when a page which dropped out of the working set in the not too remote past is referenced again, there is a chance that it still is in memory. In this case it may be *reclaimed,* and an access to the paging device can be avoided. Is there any way we can take this possibility into account when processing (*see* Table 9.9) a page reference string to compute the number of page faults generated by the program? Can we calculate the exact number of faults in this case? How could we attack the problem probabilistically? What would be the meaning of the number of faults computed by the algorithm in Table 9.9, which ignores the possibility of page reclaims?

9.6. Instrument the program in Table 9.1 so that the times spent in subroutine RK2 and in function FUN may be measured, directly or even indirectly (i.e., calculated from other measured times). Specify in the style of Table 9.7 the changes to be made to the program's text.

9.7. How would you measure the conditional probability of transition from one vertex in the graph model of a program to another vertex? For example, show how you would instrument the program in Table 9.1 so as to measure the probabilities of going from vertex I to vertex II and from V to III in the graph model in Fig. 9.6(*b*).

9.8. Assuming that the references in the string in Table 9.4(a) are issued at regular time intervals, compute the number of block faults that would be generated by the program under the LRU strategy. To obtain in one pass over the string the lifetime curve of the program (for equal-size blocks), the algorithm given in Table 9.8 is to be modified. The memory space m is not known, and the single variable nf is to be replaced by u counters $nf_1, nf_2, \ldots, nf_u$, which accumulate the numbers of faults that would be generated if m were $1, 2, \ldots, u$, respectively. These counters will be incremented or not at each reference being examined depending on the value of δ for that reference. Plot the lifetime curve you have calculated by the modified algorithm.

9.9. Making the same assumption as in Problem 9.8, apply the algorithm in Table 9.9 to the string in Table 9.4(a) to compute the number of block faults and the mean working set size $\bar{w}$ (in number of blocks) that would be generated by the program under the pure working set strategy for $\tau = 2, 3, 4, 5,$ and 6 blocks. Plot diagrams of $\bar{e}$ and $\bar{w}$ versus τ like those in Fig. 9.10(*b*). If you have solved Problem 9.8, compare the performances of the same program under the LRU and working set strategies by considering $\bar{w}$ as an index of memory space demand and plotting $\bar{e}$ versus $m = \bar{w}$ together with the lifetime curve obtained in Problem 9.8. Discuss the discrepancies between the two curves, and state whether you feel these results are atypical (that is, peculiar to this program) or have a more general validity.

9.10. Repeat the calculation of the mean execution time of the program in Table 9.1 based on the probabilistic model described in Example 9.4 for the following values of the branching probabilities:

(a) $p_{hi} = 0.8, p_{lj} = 0.8, p_{ni} = p_{rq} = 0.9$;
(b) $p_{hi} = 0.9, p_{lj} = 0.7, p_{ni} = p_{rq} = 0.9$;
(c) $p_{hi} = 0.9, p_{lj} = 0.8, p_{ni} = p_{rq} = 0.8$.

What inferences about the sensitivity of the mean execution time to these probabilities can you draw from these results? Would you have been able to rank these

probabilities according to their influence on the mean execution time simply by
looking at the program's model in Fig. 9.7(a)?

9.11. Construct a graph model like the one in Example 9.4 [*see* Fig. 9.7(a)] for a program
of your choice, and use it to estimate the mean and variance of the execution time
for given values of the input data. Select reasonable execution times for the various
types of statements in the program. Can you use this model to obtain the program
profile?

9.12. Determine the sensitivity of the execution time of the program in Table 9.1 to the
values of the input data using the model constructed in Example 9.5. You may
proceed graphically, by plotting the function $t = t(\text{IENT, JNT})$, for example, as a
family of curves with parameter JNT in the (t, IENT) plane. Alternatively, you may
choose an analytic approach, defining the sensitivity of t to IENT as given by
$\Delta t / \Delta \text{IENT}$ for constant JNT. Both the sensitivities of t to IENT and to JNT are
likely to be functions of JNT and IENT.

9.13. Eliminate statement 10 (GO TO 10) in the program in Table 9.1, and modify the
D-chart in Fig. 9.9(a) accordingly. Derive the profile equations from the modified
D-chart as described in Example 9.5, and solve them. Compare these solutions and
the formula for the execution time which can be drawn from them with the
corresponding ones in Table 9.13.

9.14. Assume that the program in Table 9.1 is a module (composed of three submodules)
of a large software package being designed. In the final version of the program,
statements 1 and 9 will disappear. The input data will be passed to the called
module, and the results will be returned to the calling modules, as parameters. A
simulator of the package has been built during its design. Depending on the type of
investigation being performed, the simulator needs to know for every call of the
module one or more of the following:

a. how much time is spent in the module;
b. how many I/O operations are performed and to what files;
c. how many times the various submodules (in this case, MAIN, RK2, and FUN) are
called.

How would you represent the module in the simulator?

9.15. Construct a locality model based on the bounded locality intervals reported in Fig.
9.11(b) for the string in Table 9.15(a). Since there is a hierarchy of intervals, you
have to choose those which, in your opinion, most adequately represent the behavior
of the program. Of course, this decision will depend on the objective of the model to
be constructed. For instance, let us assume that the model will have to be used
primarily in the generation of strings for the evaluation of different strategies and
that within each interval the LRU stack model will be applied to the members of the
corresponding activity set to produce the actual sequence of references. Once you
have chosen a stream of intervals, show how you would proceed to build the model
and how you would assign the necessary data to the LRU stack model which is to
simulate the program's behavior inside each interval. Specify in the style of Table
9.8 the algorithm of the string generator, and state how you would validate the

model. Since the model is to represent the behavior of the string in Table 9.15(a), why should it be preferred to the actual string in the particular application described above?

9.16. Estimate the improvement in the execution time of the program in Table 9.1 caused by the modifications described in Example 9.6 when the input data are those reported in Table P9.1. You can use either of the analytic models presented in Section 9.3.2 (*see* Examples 9.4 and 9.5).

Table P9.1
SEQUENCES OF INPUT DATA FOR THE PROGRAM IN TABLE 9.1

JNT	IENT	JNT	IENT	JNT	IENT
2	7	5	3	1	10
4	5	5	4	2	9
12	8	5	5	3	8
9	10	10	6	4	7
	0	10	7	5	6
		10	8		0
		10	9		
		15	10		
			0		

9.17. The program in Table 9.1 is to run in an installation which charges job steps according to the formula reported in Problem 9.2. You have to perform a price improvement study of the program. Describe how you would proceed, what tools you would use to locate economic bottlenecks, and what techniques you would use to estimate the price reductions due to various possible program changes. Rather than trying to generalize first, start by considering specific examples from the program.

9.18. The FIFO replacement algorithm for a fixed-allocation environment replaces, whenever necessary, that page in the program's region of primary memory which has been there for the longest time since it was last fetched from the paging device. Specify the critical FIFO (CFIFO) restructuring algorithm following the conceptual approach illustrated in Example 9.7. Then apply the CFIFO algorithm to the block reference string in Table 9.4(a) with $m = 2$. Cluster the CFIFO matrix with the constraints considered in Example 9.7, and simulate the running of the restructured program, as well as those of its versions restructured according to the nearness, CLRU, and CWS algorithms (*see* Table 9.21), under the FIFO strategy with $m = 2$. Compare the resulting numbers of page faults.

9.19. Does the CWS restructuring algorithm produce lower numbers of page faults than other algorithms, or than no restructuring at all, only when the working set is measured during execution at the same instants it was measured on the string by the CWS algorithm? In other words, should the measurements of the working set during execution be *in-phase*, or synchronous, with the measurements taken by the CWS algorithm, or does this algorithm always work? Devise an experiment to give this question an answer, even if it is limited to the case of a single program. For instance, you may work on the string in Table 9.4(a), assuming regular intervals between consecutive references.

Bibliography

ANDERSON, H. A., JR., AND R. G. SARGENT (1972). A statistical evaluation of the scheduler of an experimental interactive computing system. In: Freiberger (1972), 73–98.

APPLE, C. T. (1965). The program monitor—a device for program performance measurement. *Proc. ACM Nat. Conf.*, 66–75.

ARBUCKLE, R. A. (1966). Computer analysis and thruput evaluation. *Computers and Automation* **15**, 1 (Jan.), 12–15.

ASCHENBRENNER, R. A., AND N. K. NATARAJAN (1971). The Neurotron monitor system. *AFIPS Conf. Proc.* **39** (FJCC), 31–37.

BADEL, M., E. GELENBE, J. LEROUDIER, AND D. POTIER (1975). Adaptive optimization of a time-sharing system's performance. *Proc. IEEE* **63**, 6 (June), 958–965.

BAILLIU, G. R. (1973). A definition, measure and measurement of the activity of an information processing system. Ph.D. Thesis, University of California, Berkeley (Aug.).

BAIRD, G. N., AND L. A. JOHNSON (1974). System for efficient program portability. *AFIPS Conf. Proc.* **43** (NCC), 423–429.

BARD, Y. (1973). Characterization of program paging in a time-sharing environment. *IBM J. Res. Dev.* **17**, 5 (Sept.), 387–393.

BASKETT, F., K. M. CHANDY, R. R. MUNTZ, AND F. G. PALACIOS (1975). Open, closed and mixed networks of queues with different classes of customers. *J. ACM* **22**, 2 (April), 248–260.

530

BEILNER, H. (1973). The method of good balance: A tool for improving computing system performance. *Proc. Computer Science and Statistics: 7th Annual Symp. on the Interface* (Oct.), 110–116.

BEILNER, H., AND G. WALDBAUM (1972). Statistical methodology for calibrating a trace-driven simulator of a batch computer system. In: Freiberger (1972), 423–459.

BEIZER, B. (1970). Analytical techniques for the statistical evaluation of program running time. *AFIPS Conf. Proc.* **37** (FJCC), 519–524.

BELADY, L. A. (1966). A study of replacement algorithms for virtual storage computers. *IBM Sys. J.* **5**, 2, 78–101.

BELADY, L. A., AND C. J. KUEHNER (1969). Dynamic space sharing in computer systems. *Comm. ACM* **12**, 5 (May), 282–288.

BELL, T. E. (1974). Computer performance variability. *AFIPS Conf. Proc.* **43** (NCC), 761–766.

BELL, T. E., B. W. BOEHM, AND R. A. WATSON (1972). Framework and initial phases for computer performance improvement. *AFIPS Conf. Proc.* **41** (FJCC), 1141–1154.

BOYSE, J. W., AND D. R. WARN (1975). A straightforward model for computer performance prediction. *Comp. Surveys* **7**, 2 (June), 73–93.

BRANDWAJN, A., E. GELENBE, J. LENFANT, AND D. POTIER (1973). A model of program and system behavior in virtual memory. IRIA-LABORIA, Rocquencourt, France.

BRINCH HANSEN, P. (1973). *Operating Systems Principles.* Prentice-Hall, Englewood Cliffs, N.J.

BROWNE, J. C., K. M. CHANDY, R. M. BROWN, T. W. KELLER, D. F. TOWSLEY, AND C. W. DIZZLY (1975). Hierarchical techniques for the development of realistic models of complex computer systems. *Proc. IEEE* **63**, 6 (June), 966–975.

BRYAN, G. E. (1967). JOSS—20,000 hours at the console, a statistical summary. *AFIPS Conf. Proc.* **31** (FJCC), 769–777.

BUCHHOLZ, W. (1969). A synthetic job for measuring system performance. *IBM Sys. J.* **8**, 4, 309–318.

BUZEN, J. P. (1971). Analysis of system bottlenecks using a queueing network model. *Proc. ACM-SIGOPS Workshop on System Performance Evaluation*, Harvard University (April), 82–103.

BUZEN, J. P. (1973). Computational algorithms for closed queueing networks with exponential servers. *Comm. ACM* **16**, 9 (Sept.), 527–531.

CAMPBELL, D. J., AND W. J. HEFFNER (1968). Measurement and analysis of large operating systems during system development. *AFIPS Conf. Proc.* **33** (FJCC), 903–914.

CARLSON, G. (1971). Hardware monitoring of a software monitor. *Proc. SUM Users Group 1st Annual Meeting* (Jan.).

CERVENY, R. P., AND K. E. KNIGHT (1973). Performance of minicomputers. *Proc. 2nd Texas Conf. on Computer Systems* (Nov.), 28.1–28.7.

CHAMBERLIN, D. D., S. H. FULLER, AND L. Y. LIU (1973). An analysis of page allocation strategies for multiprogramming systems with virtual memory. *IBM J. Res. Dev.* **17**, 5 (Sept.), 404–412.

CHENG, P. S. (1969). Trace-driven system modeling. *IBM Sys. J.* **8**, 4, 280–289.

CHU, W. W., AND H. OPDERBECK (1972). The page fault frequency replacement algorithm. *AFIPS Conf. Proc.* **41** (FJCC), 597–609.

COCKRUM, J. S., AND D. E. CROCKETT (1971). Interpreting the results of a hardware systems monitor. *AFIPS Conf. Proc.* **38** (SJCC), 23–38.

COFFMAN, E. G., JR. (1969). Analysis of a drum input/output queue under scheduled operation in a paged computer system. *J. ACM* **16**, 1 (Jan.), 73–90.

COFFMAN, E. G., JR., AND P. J. DENNING (1973). *Operating Systems Theory.* Prentice-Hall, Englewood Cliffs, N.J.

CONWAY, R. W. (1963). Some tactical problems in digital simulation. *Management Sci.* **10**, 1 (Oct.), 47–61.

CONWAY, R. W., W. L. MAXWELL, AND L. W. MILLER (1967). *Theory of Scheduling.* Addison-Wesley, Reading, Mass.

COOPERMAN, J. A., H. W. LYNCH, AND W. H. TETZLAFF (1972). SGP—an effective use of performance and usage data. *Computer* **5**,5 (Sept.–Oct.), 20–23.

COURTOIS, P. J. (1971). On the near-decomposability of networks of queues and of stochastic models of multiprogramming computing systems. Rep. CMU-CS-72-111, Computer Science Dept., Carnegie–Mellon University, Pittsburgh (Nov.).

COURTOIS, P. J. (1975). Decomposability, instabilities, and saturation in multiprogramming systems. *Comm. ACM* **18**, 7 (July), 371–376.

DAHL, O., AND K. NYGAARD (1966). SIMULA: An ALGOL-based simulation language. *Comm. ACM* **9**, 9 (Sept.), 671–678.

DEMEIS, W. M., AND N. WEIZER (1969). Measurement and analysis of a demand paging time sharing system. *Proc. ACM Nat. Conf.*, 201–216.

DENISTON, W. R. (1969). SIPE: A TSS/360 software measurement technique. *Proc. ACM Nat. Conf.*, 229–245.

DENNING, P. J. (1968a). The working set model for program behavior. *Comm. ACM* **11**, 5 (May), 323–333.

DENNING, P. J. (1968b). Thrashing: Its causes and prevention. *AFIPS Conf. Proc.* **33** (FJCC), 915–922.

DENNING, P. J. (1970). Virtual memory. *Comp. Surveys* **2**, 3 (Sept.), 153–189.

DENNING, P. J., AND G. S. GRAHAM (1975). Multiprogrammed memory management. *Proc. IEEE* **63**, 6 (June), 924–939.

DEUTSCH, P., AND C. A. GRANT (1971). A flexible measurement tool for software systems. *Information Processing 71* (Proc. IFIP Congress 71). North-Holland, Amsterdam.

DIJKSTRA, E. W. (1968). The structure of THE multiprogramming system. *Comm. ACM* **11**, 5 (May), 341–346.

DIJKSTRA, E. W. (1972). Notes on structured programming. In: O.-J. Dahl, E. W. Dijkstra, and C. A. R. Hoare, *Structured Programming*. Academic Press, London (1972), 1–82.

DRAPER, N. R., AND H. SMITH (1966). *Applied Regression Analysis*. Wiley, New York.

DRUMMOND, M. E., JR. (1973). *Evaluation and Measurement Techniques for Digital Computer Systems*. Prentice-Hall, Englewood Cliffs, N.J.

ERIKSON, W. J. (1966). A pilot study of interactive versus noninteractive debugging. Rept. TM-3296, System Development Corp., Santa Monica, Ca. (Dec.).

ESTRIN, G., D. HOPKINS, B. COGGAN, AND S. D. CROCKER (1967). SNUPER COMPUTER—a computer in instrumentation automaton. *AFIPS Conf. Proc.* **30** (SJCC), 645–656.

FELLER, W. (1968). *An Introduction to Probability Theory and Its Applications*, Vol. I, 3rd ed. Wiley, New York.

FENICHEL, R. R., AND A. J. GROSSMAN (1969). An analytic model of multi-programmed computing. *AFIPS Conf. Proc.* **34** (SJCC), 717–721.

FERRARI, D. (1972). Workload characterization and selection in computer performance measurement. *Computer* **5**, 4 (July-Aug.), 18–24.

FERRARI, D. (1973). Architecture and instrumentation in a modular interactive system. *Computer* **6**, 11 (Nov.), 25–29.

FERRARI, D. (1974a). Improving program locality by strategy-oriented restructuring. *Information Processing 74* (Proc. IFIP Congress 74). North-Holland, Amsterdam, 266–270.

FERRARI, D. (1974b). Improving locality by critical working sets. *Comm. ACM* **17**, 11 (Nov.), 614–620.

FERRARI, D. (1975). Tailoring programs to models of program behavior. *IBM J. Res. Dev.* **19**, 3 (May), 244–251.

FERRARI, D., AND M. LIU (1975). A general-purpose software measurement tool. *Software—Practice and Experience* **5**, 2, 181–192.

FERRARI, D., D. S. LINDSAY, AND P. M. PEAK (1975). Variance reduction techniques in computer system performance measurement. *Proc. Int. Comp. Symp. 75*, North-Holland, Amsterdam, 185–189.

FISHMAN, G. S. (1973). *Concepts and Methods in Discrete Event Digital Simulation*. Wiley, New York.

FLYNN, M. J. (1974). Trends and problems in computer organizations. *Information Processing 74* (Proc. IFIP Congress 74). North-Holland, Amsterdam, 3–10.

FOGEL, M., AND J. WINOGRAD (1972). EINSTEIN: An internal driver in a time-sharing environment. *Operating Systems Rev.* **6**, 3 (Oct.), 6–14.

FOLEY, J. D. (1971). An approach to the optimum design of computer graphics systems. *Comm. ACM* **14**, 6 (June), 380–390.

FREIBERGER, W., ED. (1972). *Statistical Computer Performance Evaluation*. Academic Press, New York.

FUCHS, E., AND P. E. JACKSON (1970). Estimates of distributions of random variables for certain computer communications traffic models. *Comm. ACM* **13**, 12 (Dec.), 752–757.

FULLER, S. H. (1972). An optimal drum scheduling algorithm. *IEEE Trans. on Computers* **C-21**, 11 (Nov.), 1153–1165.

FULLER, S. H., R. J. SWAN, AND W. A. WULF (1973). The instrumentation of C.mmp, a multi-(mini)processor. *Proc. COMPCON 73* (Feb.), 173–176.

GELENBE, E. (1973). The distribution of a program in primary and fast buffer storage. *Comm. ACM* **16**, 7 (July), 431–434.

GIBSON, J. C. (1970). The Gibson mix. IBM Tech. Rept. TR00.2043 (June).

GOEL, A. L., AND Y. LIU (1973). An analysis of ISAM by two-level factorial designs. *Proc. Computer Science and Statistics: 7th Annual Symp. on the Interface* (Oct.), 16–21.

GOLD, M. M. (1967). Methodology for evaluating time-shared computer usage. Ph.D. Thesis, M.I.T., Cambridge, Mass. See also: Time-sharing and batch-processing: An experimental comparison of their values in a problem-solving situation. *Comm. ACM* **12**, 5 (May 1969), 249–259.

GOOD, J., AND B. A. M. MOON (1972). Evaluating computers for the New Zealand universities. *Datamation* **18**, 11 (Nov.), 96–99.

GORDON, G. (1969). *System Simulation.* Prentice-Hall, Englewood Cliffs, N.J.

GORDON, G. (1975). *The Application of GPSS V to Discrete System Simulation.* Prentice-Hall, Englewood Cliffs, N.J.

GORDON, W. J., AND G. F. NEWELL (1967). Closed queueing systems with exponential servers. *Operations Research* **15**, 2 (April), 254–265.

GOSDEN, J. A., AND R. L. SISSON (1962). Standardized comparisons of computer performance. *Information Processing 62* (Proc. IFIP Congress 62). North-Holland, Amsterdam, 57–61.

GRANT, E. E., AND H. SACKMAN (1966). An exploratory investigation of programmer performance under on-line and off-line conditions. Rept. SP-2581, System Development Corp., Santa Monica, Ca. (Sept.).

GREENBAUM, H. J. (1969). A simulator of multiple interactive users to drive a time-shared computer system. Project MAC Tech. Rept. TR-58, M.I.T., Cambridge, Mass. (Jan.).

GRENANDER, U., AND R. F. TSAO (1972). Quantitative methods for evaluating computer system performance—a review and proposals. In: Freiberger (1972), 3–24.

GRUENBERGER, F. (1966). Are small, free-standing computers here to stay? *Datamation* **12**, 4 (April), 67–68.

HATFIELD, D. J., AND J. GERALD (1971). Program restructuring for virtual memory. *IBM Sys. J.* **10**, 3, 168–192.

HELLERMAN, H., AND H. J. SMITH (1970). Throughput analysis of some idealized input, output and compute overlap configurations. *Comp. Surveys* **3**, 2 (June), 111–118.

HELLERMAN, L. (1972). A measure of computational work. *IEEE Trans. on Computers* **C-21**, 5 (May), 439–446.

HENDERSON, G., AND J. RODRIGUEZ-ROSELL (1974). The optimal choice of window sizes for working set dispatching. *Proc. 2nd ACM-SIGMETRICS Symp. on Measurement and Evaluation* (Oct.), 10–33.

HILLEGASS, J. R. (1966). Standardized benchmark problems measure computer performance. *Computers and Automation* **15**, 1 (Jan.), 16–19.

HOLTWICK, G. M. (1971). Designing a commercial performance measurement system. *Proc. ACM-SIGOPS Workshop on System Performance Evaluation*, Harvard University (April), 29–58.

HUGHES, J., AND D. CRONSHAW (1973). On using a hardware monitor as an intelligent peripheral. *Performance Evaluation Rev.* **2**, 4 (Dec.), 3–19.

HUGHES, P. H., AND G. MOE (1973). A structural approach to computer performance analysis. *AFIPS Conf. Proc.* **42** (NCC), 109–120.

HUNT, E., G. DIEHR, AND D. GARNATZ (1971). Who are the users? An analysis of computer use in a university computer center. *AFIPS Conf. Proc.* **38** (SJCC), 231–238.

JACKSON, J. R. (1963). Job shop-like queueing systems. *Management Sci.* **10**, 1, 131–142.

JOSLIN, E. O. (1965). Application benchmarks: The key to meaningful computer evaluations. *Proc. ACM Nat. Conf.*, 27–37.

JOSLIN, E. O. (1968). *Computer Selection.* Addison-Wesley, Reading, Mass.

KARUSH, A. D. (1969). The benchmark method applied to time-sharing systems. Rept. SP-3347, System Development Corp., Santa Monica, Ca. (Aug.).

KARUSH, A. D. (1970). The recording and reduction utility for digital computer systems: Survey and analysis. Rept. SP-3303/000/01, System Development Corp., Santa Monica, Ca. (March).

KERNIGHAN, B. W., AND P. A. HAMILTON (1973). Synthetically generated performance test loads for operating systems. *Proc. 1st ACM-SIGME Symp. on Measurement and Evaluation* (Feb.), 121–126.

KERNIGHAN, B. W., P. J. PLAUGER, AND D. J. PLAUGER (1972). On comparing apples and oranges, or, my machine is better than your machine. *Performance Evaluation Rev.* **1**, 3 (Sept.), 16–20.

KIMBLETON, S. R. (1975). A heuristic approach to computer systems performance improvement. I. A fast performance prediction tool. *AFIPS Conf. Proc.* **44** (NCC), 839–846.

KIVIAT, P. J. (1971). Simulation languages. In: Naylor (1971), 406–436.

KIVIAT, P. J., R. VILLANUEVA, AND H. MARKOWITZ (1969). *The SIMSCRIPT II Programming Language.* Prentice-Hall, Englewood Cliffs, N.J.

KLEINROCK, L. (1968). Certain analytic results for time-shared processors. *Information Processing 68* (Proc. IFIP Congress 68). North-Holland, Amsterdam, 838–845.

KLEINROCK, L. (1975). *Queueing Systems*, Vol. I: Theory. Wiley, New York.

KNIGHT, K. E. (1963). A study of technological innovation: The evolution of digital computers. Ph.D. Thesis, Carnegie Institute of Technology, Pittsburgh (Nov.).

KNIGHT, K. E. (1968). Evolving computer performance, 1962–1967. *Datamation* **14**, 1 (Jan.), 31–35.

KNUTH, D. E. (1968). *The Art of Computer Programming*, Vol. I: Fundamental Algorithms. Addison-Wesley, Reading, Mass.

KNUTH, D. E. (1969). *The Art of Computer Programming*, Vol. II: Seminumerical Algorithms. Addison-Wesley, Reading, Mass.

KNUTH, D. E. (1971). An empirical study of FORTRAN programs. *Software—Practice and Experience* **1**, 105–133.

KOBAYASHI, H. (1974). Application of the diffusion approximation to queueing networks—I: Equilibrium queue distributions. *J. ACM* **21**, 2 (April), 316–328; II: Nonequilibrium distributions and applications to computer modeling. *J. ACM* **21**, 3 (July), 459–469.

KOLENCE, K. W. (1971). A software view of measurement tools. *Datamation* **17**, 1 (Jan. 1), 32–38.

KOLENCE, K. W. (1972). Software physics and computer performance measurement. *Proc. ACM Nat. Conf.*, 1024–1040.

KOLENCE, K. W., AND P. J. KIVIAT (1973). Software unit profiles and Kiviat figures. *Performance Evaluation Rev.* **2**, 3 (Sept.), 2–12.

LASSETER, G. L., T. LO, K. M. CHANDY, AND J. C. BROWNE (1973). Statistical and pattern based models for CPU burst prediction. *Proc. Computer Science and Statistics: 7th Annual Symp. on the Interface* (Oct.), 123–129.

LEWIS, P. A. W., AND P. C. YUE (1972). Statistical analysis of series of events in computer systems. In: Freiberger (1972), 265–280.

LINDSAY, D. S. (1975). A study in operating system performance measurement and modeling. Ph.D. Thesis, University of California, Berkeley (June).

LITTLE, J. D. C. (1961). A proof for the queueing formula $L = \lambda W$. *Operations Research* **9**, 3 (May), 383–387.

LUCAS, H. C., JR. (1971a). Synthetic program specifications for performance evaluation. Research Paper No. 33, Graduate School of Business, Stanford University, Stanford, Ca. (Aug.).

LUCAS, H. C., JR. (1971b). Performance evaluation and monitoring. *Comp. Surveys* **3**, 3 (Sept.), 79–91.

LYNCH, W. C. (1972). Operating system performance. *Comm. ACM* **15**, 7 (July), 579–585.

MACDOUGALL, M. H. (1970). Computer system simulation: An introduction. *Comp. Surveys* **2**, 3 (Sept.), 191–209.

MCKINNEY, J. M. (1969). A survey of analytical time-sharing models. *Comp. Surveys* **1**, 2 (June), 105–116.

MADISON, A. W., AND A. P. BATSON (1976). Characteristics of program localities. *Comm. ACM* **19**, 5 (May), 285–294.

MARTIN, J. (1967). *Design of Real-Time Computer Systems*. Prentice-Hall, Englewood Cliffs, N.J.

MATTSON, R. L., J. GECSEI, D. R. SLUTZ, AND I. L. TRAIGER (1970). Evaluation techniques for storage hierarchies. *IBM Sys. J.* **9**, 2, 78–117.

MORGAN, D. E., AND J. A. CAMPBELL (1973). An answer to a user's plea? *Proc. 1st ACM-SIGME Symp. on Measurement and Evaluation* (Feb.), 112–120.

MUNTZ, R. R. (1975). Analytic modeling of interactive systems. *Proc. IEEE* **63**, 6 (June), 946–953.

NAYLOR, T. (1971). *Computer Simulation Experiments with Models of Economic Systems.* Wiley, New York.

NEWELL, G. F. (1971). *Applications of Queueing Theory.* Chapman & Hall, London, Ch. 6.

NIELSEN, N. R. (1967). The simulation of time-sharing systems. *Comm. ACM* **10**, 7 (July), 397–412.

NIELSEN, N. R. (1971). An analysis of some time-sharing techniques. *Comm. ACM* **14**, 2 (Feb.), 79–90.

NOE, J. D., AND G. J. NUTT (1972). Validation of a trace-driven CDC 6400 simulation. *AFIPS Conf. Proc.* **40** (SJCC), 749–757.

OLIVER, P., G. BAIRD, M. COOK, A. JOHNSON, AND P. HOYT (1974). An experiment in the use of synthetic programs for system benchmarks. *AFIPS Conf. Proc.* **43** (NCC), 431–438.

PARNAS, D. L. (1969). More on simulation languages and design methodology for computer systems. *AFIPS Conf. Proc.* **34** (SJCC), 739–743.

PARNAS, D. L. (1972). On the criteria to be used in decomposing systems into modules. *Comm. ACM* **15**, 12 (Dec.), 1053–1062.

PARNAS, D. L., AND D. P. SIEWIOREK (1975). Use of the concept of transparency in the design of hierarchically structured systems. *Comm. ACM* **18**, 7 (July), 401–408.

PARUPUDI, M., AND J. WINOGRAD (1972). Interactive task behavior in a time-shared environment. *Proc. ACM Nat. Conf.*, 2 (Aug.), 680–692.

PETERSON, T. G. (1974). A comparison of software and hardware monitors. *Performance Evaluation Rev.* **3**, 2 (June), 2–5.

POMEROY, J. W. (1972). A guide to programming tools and techniques. *IBM Sys. J.* **11**, 3, 234–254.

PRIEVE, B. G. (1973). A page partition replacement algorithm. Ph.D. Thesis, University of California, Berkeley (Dec.).

PRITSKER, A. A. (1974). *The GASP IV Simulation Language.* Wiley, New York.

RAICHELSON, E., AND G. COLLINS (1964). A method for comparing the internal operating speeds of computers. *Comm. ACM* **7**, 5 (May), 309–310.

RAMAMOORTHY, C. V. (1965). Discrete Markov analysis of computer programs. *Proc. ACM Nat. Conf.*, 386–392.

RANDELL, B. (1968). Computer and operating system modeling. Draft of a lecture given at the University of Utah, Salt Lake City, Jan. 25.

RECHTSCHAFFEN, R. N. (1972). Queueing simulation using a random number generator. *IBM Sys. J.* **11**, 3, 255–271.

ROEK, D. J., AND W. C. EMERSON (1969). A hardware instrumentation approach to evaluation of a large scale system. *Proc. ACM Nat. Conf.*, 351–367.

ROZWADOWSKI, R. T. (1973). A measure for the quantity of computation. *Proc. 1st ACM-SIGME Symp. on Measurement and Evaluation* (Feb.), 100–111.

RUSSELL, E. C., AND G. ESTRIN (1969). Measurement based automatic analysis of FORTRAN programs. *AFIPS Conf. Proc.* **34** (SJCC), 723–732.

SAAL, H. J., AND L. J. SHUSTEK (1972). Microprogrammed implementation of computer measurement techniques. *Proc. 5th Annual Workshop on Microprogramming* (Sept.).

SACKMAN, H. (1964). Regenerative recording in man-machine digital systems. *Proc. Nat. Winter Convention on Military Electronics* (Feb.), 16.14–16.19

SACKMAN, H. (1968). Time-sharing versus batch processing: The experimental evidence. *AFIPS Conf. Proc.* **32** (SJCC), 1–10.

SALTZER, J. H., AND J. W. GINTELL (1970). The instrumentation of Multics. *Comm. ACM* **13**, 8 (Aug.), 495–500.

SAMMET, J. E. (1969). *Programming Languages: History and Fundamentals.* Prentice-Hall, Englewood Cliffs, N.J.

SAYRE, D. (1969). Is automatic folding of programs efficient enough to displace manual? *Comm. ACM* **12**, 12 (Dec.), 656–660.

SCHATZOFF, M., R. F. TSAO, AND R. WIIG (1967). An experimental comparison of time sharing and batch processing. *Comm. ACM* **10**, 5 (May), 261–265.

SCHERR, A. L. (1967). *An Analysis of Time-Shared Computer Systems.* M.I.T. Press, Cambridge, Mass.

SCHNEIDEWIND, N. F. (1966). Analytic model for the design and selection of electronic digital computers. Ph.D. Thesis, University of Southern California, Los Angeles (Jan.).

SCHULMAN, F. D. (1967). Hardware measurement device for IBM System/360 time sharing evaluation. *Proc. ACM Nat. Conf.*, 103–109.

SCHWETMAN, H. D., AND J. C. BROWNE (1972). An experimental study of computer system performance. *Proc. ACM Nat. Conf.*, 693–703.

SEAMAN, P. H., AND R. C. SOUCY (1969). Simulating operating systems. *IBM Sys. J.* **8**, 4, 264–279.

SEDGEWICK, R., R. STONE, AND J. W. McDONALD (1970). SPY—a program to monitor OS/360. *AFIPS Conf. Proc.* **37** (FJCC), 119–128.

SEKINO, A. (1973). Throughput analysis of multiprogramming virtual memory computer systems. *Proc. 1st ACM-SIGME Symp. on Measurement and Evaluation* (Feb.), 47–53.

SHARPE, W. F. (1969). *The Economics of Computers.* Columbia University Press, New York.

SHERMAN, S., F. BASKETT III, AND J. C. BROWNE (1972). Trace-driven modeling and analysis of CPU scheduling in a multiprogramming system. *Comm. ACM* **15**, 12 (Dec.), 1063–1069.

SHOPE, W. L., K. L. KASHMARAK, J. W. INGHRAM, AND W. F. DECKER (1970). System performance study. *Proc. SHARE* **34**, 1 (Mar.), 439–530.

SMITH, L. B. (1967). A comparison of batch processing and instant turnaround. *Comm. ACM* **10**, 8 (Aug.), 495–500.

SNEDECOR, G. W., AND W. G. COCHRAN (1967). *Statistical Methods*, 6th ed., Iowa State University Press, Ames.

SPIRN, J. R., AND P. J. DENNING (1972). Experiments with program locality. *AFIPS Conf. Proc.* **41** (FJCC), 611–621.

SREENIVASAN, K., AND A. J. KLEINMAN (1974). On the construction of a representative synthetic workload. *Comm. ACM* **17**, 3 (Mar.), 127–133.

STIMLER, S. (1969). *Real-Time Data-Processing Systems*. McGraw-Hill, New York.

STRAUSS, J. C. (1972). A benchmark study. *AFIPS Conf. Proc.* **41** (FJCC), 1225–1233.

STREETER, D. N. (1973). Centralization or dispersion of computing facilities. *IBM Sys. J.* **12**, 3, 283–301.

SVOBODOVA, L. (1973). Online system performance measurements with software and hybrid monitors. *Operating Systems Rev.* **7**, 4 (Oct.), 45–53.

SYMS, G. H. (1974). Benchmarked comparison of terminal support systems for IBM 360 computers. *Performance Evaluation Rev.* **3**, 2 (June), 6–34.

TEICHROEW, D., AND J. F. LUBIN (1966). Computer simulation: Discussion of the technique and comparison of languages. *Comm. ACM* **9**, 10 (Oct.), 723–741.

TIMMRECK, E. M. (1973). Computer selection methodology. *Comp. Surveys* **5**, 4 (Dec.), 199–222.

TRAIGER, I. L., AND R. L. MATTSON (1972). The evaluation and selection of technologies for computer storage systems. IBM Research Rept. RJ 967 (Feb.).

TSAO, R. F., AND B. H. MARGOLIN (1972). A multi-factor paging experiment—II. Statistical methodology. In: Freiberger (1972), 135–158.

TSAO, R. F., L. W. COMEAU, AND B. H. MARGOLIN (1972). A multi-factor paging experiment—I. The experiment and the conclusions. In: Freiberger (1972), 103–134.

WALDBAUM, G. (1973). Evaluating computing system changes by means of regression models. *Proc. 1st ACM-SIGME Symp. on Measurement and Evaluation* (Feb.), 127–135.

WATSON, R. W. (1970). *Timesharing System Design Concepts*. McGraw-Hill, New York.

WILKES, M. V. (1971). Automatic load adjustment in time-sharing systems. *Proc. ACM-SIGOPS Workshop on System Performance Evaluation*, Harvard University (April), 308–320.

WILNER, W. T. (1972). Design of the Burroughs B1700. *AFIPS Conf. Proc.* **41** (FJCC), 489–497.

WOOD, D. C., AND E. H. FORMAN (1971). Throughput measurement using a synthetic job stream. *AFIPS Conf. Proc.* **39** (FJCC), 51–56.

ZURCHER, F. W., AND B. RANDELL (1968). Iterative multi-level modelling—a methodology for computer system design. *Information Processing 68* (Proc. IFIP Congress 68). North-Holland, Amsterdam, 867–871.

Index

541

Critical-set algorithms, 519
Critical working set algorithm, 519
CTSS system, 211, 216, 238, 239, 249
CUE software monitor, 61-64
Current locality, 508
Customization, 399
CWS algorithm, 519
Cycle staggering, 423
Cycle time, 285, 293-294, 420, 423
Cylinders traversed, 63, 64

Dartmouth Time-Sharing System, 325, 331
Data analysis techniques, 82-95
Data block, 460, 461, 466
Data reduction, 28, 80-82
D-chart, 488-494
Debugging, 47, 478
Decomposition:
  of programs into modules, 523-524
  of queuing networks, 163, 202, 434
  of systems into modules, 432, 436
Degradation, 29
Degree of detail:
  of an analytic model, 214
  of a simulator, 108
  of a work-load model, 224
Degree of multiprogramming, 7, 170, 353-354
  control of, 383-385
Degree of overlap, 165
Degree of representativeness, 229
Degrees of freedom:
  of F-distribution, 88
  of sum of squares, 87, 89
  of t-distribution, 59
Demand loading, 69
Demand for service, 179
Density function (see Probability density function)
Density of reference, 468
Departure event, 113
Design:
  of experiments, 66-76, 145-147
  hierarchical (see Hierarchical design)
  initial, 400, 403-424
  iterative (see Iterative design)
  of programs, 522-524
Design methodologies, 400-403
Design parameter space, 402, 431
Design problems, 396-400
Design specifications, 397
Design studies, 17
Design trade-offs, 424-431
Desirable requirements, 279

Detail (see Degree of detail)
Detail-cost trade-off, 108
Deterministic models, 123, 161-162, 163-173
  of programs, 487-500, 504-508
Deterministic simulator, 141
Deterministic work-load models, 164, 225-227, 238-241, 242-245, 246-270
Diagnosis, 334, 336, 341-369
  of programs, 510-513
Difference estimation, 287
Diffusion approximation, 163, 202
Digital Equipment Corporation:
  PDP-8 system, 269
  PDP-10 system, 321
Dijkstra chart, 488-494
Direct access mode, 289
Direct memory access, 422
Discrete distribution generation, 127
Discrete-state Markov process, 173
Discrete-state stochastic process, 57
Discrete-state system, 20
Discrete-time Markov process, 174
Discrete-time stochastic process, 58
Diseconomies of scale, 295
Disk:
  access time, 412
  models, 116
  request rate, 423
  revolution time, 344, 407
  seek time, 27, 63, 97, 361
  service rate, 116, 345
  transfer rate, 116, 407
Display applications, 426
Display console, 425, 431
Display controller, 425, 426, 430, 431
Display interactions, 427
Display macroinstructions, 426, 427
Distance (see Stack distance)
Distinction between hardware and software, 403 (see also Hardware-software trade-offs)
Distributed data base, 449-450
Distributed systems, 295-300
  with centralized control, 449-450
  design of, 425-431, 449-450
  with distributed control, 296-300
  function allocation in, 426, 430-431
  modeling of, 425-430
Distribution-driven simulator, 124, 126, 131

Distribution generation in simulation, 125-128
Distribution model, 36
DMA, 422
DO loop, 488-490
Domain of validity, 137
  of analytic model, 161
  of a simulator, 137
  of a work-load model, 271
Dormant state, 170
Driver, 250, 268
  for a batch system, 268
  for an interactive system, 250-252, 268-269
Drum:
  access time, 406, 412
  request rate, 423
  revolution time, 344, 407, 410
  service rate, 158, 345
  transfer rate, 406, 407, 410, 420
Duration of a measurement session, 73-79
Dynamic statement mix, 249, 462
Dynaprobe 8000/II hardware monitor, 42

Economies of scale, 294-295
Edge effects, 16
Editing commands, 15, 16, 77, 250
Editing script, 77, 322
Effective time, 525
Effects, 83
  of system changes on user communities, 4-5, 222, 232-234, 325, 340
Efficiency (see Performance)
Elapsed time, 33 (see also Benchmarking, Measurement session)
Elementary D-chart, 488, 489
Embedded Markov process, 176
Empirical distribution generation, 127
Empirical model, 85-86
Empirical techniques (see Measurement techniques)
Emulation, 281
End effect, 153
Entropy function, 236
Environment, 4, 221, 222
Equilibrium condition, 171
Equilibrium state probabilities, 175, 199, 204, 211
Equilibrium state probability equations, 184, 204, 211
Equipment cost, 406, 408
  vs. power, 294-297
Equivalence of work loads, 228, 229, 317
Equivalent access time, 414, 420, 421

545

Goodness of fit (*see* Accuracy)
Grand mean, 83
Graphics system, 425-431
Graph models of programs:
in analytic studies, 483-487, 492
in measurement, 474-475
in simulation, 488
Grosch's law, 295, 306

Hand timing, 315, 316
Hardware-firmware-software trade-offs, 450
Hardware-hardware trade-offs, 424, 426, 430
Hardware monitors, 31, 32-44
Hardware-oriented indices, 293-294
Hardware resource utilizations, measurement of, 37-40, 62-63
Hardware-software trade-offs, 403, 424, 426, 430
Head movement time (*see* Seek time)
Head-per-track disk (*see* Drum)
Hierarchical design, 400, 402-403, 431-442
of programs, 522-524
Hierarchically structured system, 433
Hierarchical models, 434
of programs, 488-496, 523-524
Hierarchical simulator, 434-441
Higher-level language machine (*see* FORTRAN machine)
Higher-level language resources, 310-313, 317, 319
High-speed buffer (*see* Cache memory)
Histogram, 36, 48 (*see also* Frequency count)
Historical work-load data, 325
Homogeneous Markov chain, 174
Honeywell:
Series 600 systems, 330
6070 system, 267
Honeywell-Bull G625 system, 321
Hook (*see* Probe)
Horizontal design, 400
Human resources, 290, 291
Hybrid monitor, 31, 46
Hybrid simulator, 444
Hyperexponential distribution, 188
Hyperexponential-service model, 189
Hypoexponential distribution, 189

Hypoexponential-service model, 190
Hypothesis, 11
in diagnosis, 335-339
Hypothesis testing, 87-89
Hypothesis-test-result cycle, 366-367

IBM:
7090 system, 247
System/360 and /370, 34, 46, 247, 248, 302, 304, 315, 321, 366, 479
IC 7000 system, 45
Ideal benchmark characteristics, 319
Idle job, 302
Idle state, 176
Imbalance, 342, 364-365
Implementation of a simulator, 109, 132-134
Improvement, 332-392
to initial design, 401-402
of program performance, 510-522
Improvement methodologies, 334-341
Improvement problems, 332-334
Improvement studies, 17
Inaccuracies (*see* Errors)
Incomplete factorial design, 70
Independence:
statistical, 58, 127, 131, 181
of the system, 224, 232-237, 455, 464
in time series, 58
of the work load, 293-294, 314
Independent distance model, 503
Independent reference model, 500
Independent replications, method of, 76, 240
Indicator, 29
Indices, 11, 13
cost-performance, 304, 306, 426, 431
hardware-oriented, 293-294
of program behavior, 462-472
of program performance, 453-472
work-load independent, 293-294, 314
Infinite-source models, 178
Information-processing power, 293-294, 376
Information-processing requirements, 279, 282-283, 314
Information-processing tasks, 317, 318, 319
Information-processing work, 235-237

Informer software tool, 50-52, 80
Initial conditions, 150-155
Initial system design, 400, 403-424
Input data selection, 509-510
Input data sensitivity, 487 521-522, 527
Input rate, 262
Inside out design, 400
Instabilities, 382
Installation, 4, 5
Installation design, 18
Installation model, 209-212
Installation parameters, 5
Installation selection, 277, 281, 307-313
Instruction block, 460, 461, 466
Instruction execution rate, 13, 24, 246
Instruction mix, 246-248, 294, 319-320
Instruction sets, 248, 320
comparison of, 315, 319-320
suitability of, 320, 321
Instrumentation of a program, 474-478
Instrumentation systems, 46, 64-66
Instruments (*see* Measurement tools)
Interaction:
among factors, 70, 72, 84-89
among instructions, 250
among parameters, 231, 232-233, 235
between terminal users and systems, 13, 41, 427
Interaction cycle, 14
Interaction effect, 84
Interaction point, 122
Interactive driver, 250-252, 268-269
Interactive installation model, 209-212
Interactive mode, 289
vs. batch-processing mode, 290-293
Interactive script, 77
Interactive systems, 8, 449-450
bottlenecks in, 366-367
closed-network model of, 209-212
comparison of, 320-323
initial design of, 410-411, 425-431
M/D/1 model of, 191
M/G/1 model of, 191
M/M/1 model of, 186-187
RR model of, 194-195
saturation point for, 212, 213
terminals supported by, 212
Interarrival time, 179